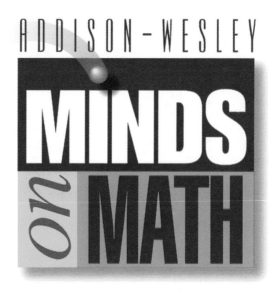

ADDISON-WESLEY MINDS on MATH

▶ *9*

Robert Alexander
Toronto Board of Education
Toronto, Ontario

Brendan Kelly
University of Toronto
Toronto, Ontario

Ron Lancaster
St. Mildred's Lightbourn School
Oakville, Ontario

Paul Atkinson
Waterloo County Board of Education
Kitchener, Ontario

Katie Pallos-Haden
Memorial Composite High School
Stony Plain, Alberta

David DeCoste
Antigonish East High School
Antigonish, Nova Scotia

Fred Crouse
Kings County District School Board
Kentville, Nova Scotia

Jane Forbes
E.C. Drury High School
Milton, Ontario

Addison-Wesley Publishers Limited
Don Mills, Ontario • Reading, Massachusetts • Menlo Park, California
New York • Wokingham, England • Amsterdam • Bonn • Paris
Milan • Madrid • Sydney • Singapore • Tokyo • Seoul • Taipei
Mexico City • San Juan

SENIOR EDITORS
Lesley Haynes
Sarah Mawson

EDITORS
Mei Lin Cheung
Lynne Gulliver
Rajshree Shankar
Anita Smale

RESEARCHER
Louise MacKenzie

DESIGN/ART DIRECTION
ELECTRONIC ASSEMBLY
Pronk&Associates

COVER DESIGN
Pronk&Associates

Acknowledgments appear on pages 533 and 534.

REVIEWERS/CONSULTANTS
Andrew Adler, Ph.D.
University of British Columbia
Vancouver, British Columbia

Lynda E. C. Colgan, Ph.D.
Scarborough Board of Education
Scarborough, Ontario

Liliane Gauthier
Saskatoon Public School Board
Saskatoon, Saskatchewan

Florence Glanfield
Department of Education
Edmonton, Alberta

E. Haines
Beamsville District Secondary School
Beamsville, Ontario

Ivan Johnson
Burnaby South School
Burnaby, British Columbia

Bob Michie
Calgary Board of Education
Calgary, Alberta

Linda Rajotte
Georges P. Vanier Senior Secondary School
Courtenay, British Columbia

Connie A. Shaver
Silver Heights Collegiate
Winnipeg, Manitoba

For their help in the development of the model for this book, the authors and publisher wish to express special thanks to Kim Garner, Michael Grosman, Keith Hall, Wendy Solheim, and their students at Thornhill Secondary School in Thornhill, Ontario, and to Dave Boag, Joyce Finley, Dave Petker, and their students at E.C. Drury High School in Milton, Ontario.

ClarisWorks is a registered trademark of Claris Corporation.
Claris is a registered trademark of Claris Corporation.
Maple is a registered trademark of Waterloo Maple Software.
Microsoft Works is a trademark of Microsoft Corporation.
Microsoft and MS-DOS are registered trademarks of Microsoft Corporation.
The Geometer's Sketchpad is a registered trademark of Key Curriculum Press, Inc.
Windows is a trademark of Microsoft Corporation.
Macintosh is a registered trademark of Apple Computer, Inc.

Canadian Cataloguing in Publication Data

Alexander, Bob, 1941—
    Minds on math 9
Includes index.
ISBN 0-201-56015-1

1. Mathematics — Juvenile literature.
I. Kelly, B. (Brendan), 1943--   . II. Title.

QA107.A54 1994   510   C94-931045-X

ISBN 0-201-56015-1
This book contains recycled product and is acid free.
Printed and bound in Canada.

A B C D E F -- BP -- 99 98 97 96 95 94

CONTENTS

CHAPTER 5: ALGEBRAIC OPERATIONS AND EQUATIONS

CHAPTER 6: RATIO, RATE, AND SIMILARITY

CHAPTER 9: TWO-DIMENSIONAL GEOMETRY

CHAPTER 10: FUNCTIONS

WELCOME TO *MINDS ON MATH 9*

We hope that this book helps you see that mathematics can be useful, interesting, and enjoyable. We wish you every success.

This book is about…

…Problem Solving
Learning to solve problems is the main reason for studying mathematics. You will find that all the parts of this book are designed to help you improve your problem-solving skills.

…Math in the Real World
This book describes many new ways you can use mathematics to understand your everyday world. You'll also learn about how people use mathematics in their careers.

…Calculators and Computers
Technology is a tool you will be using often in your life, and in your study of mathematics. You'll need a scientific calculator to complete some of the activities and exercises in this book. You'll also want to use a computer and some popular software to work with spreadsheets and databases. This book will help you add these tools to the paper and pencil you already use every day.

Take a few moments to read the following pages. They explain how this book is organized and how you will be using it.

CHAPTER CONTENTS

Each chapter begins with a magazine-style Contents. This gives you an idea of what you will be studying and what problems the mathematics can help you solve.

WHAT'S COMING UP?

This is a list of the mathematics topics that are covered in the chapter.

DEPARTMENTS

Most chapters contain five departments. You'll get to know the departments as you use the book. For example, a Quest always offers you an interesting opportunity to build your problem-solving skills — and to discover something new.

START WITH WHAT YOU KNOW

Each chapter begins with Start With What You Know. These questions and activities give you a chance to review so that you can be successful with the new material.

For example, this Start With What You Know describes some recent work by astronomers, biologists, and a mathematician in which they used very large numbers. The questions help you recall what you know about powers and scientific notation.

DEVELOPING THE IDEAS

The mathematics in this book is developed in a variety of ways.
Two or more of these ways are often used in the same lesson.

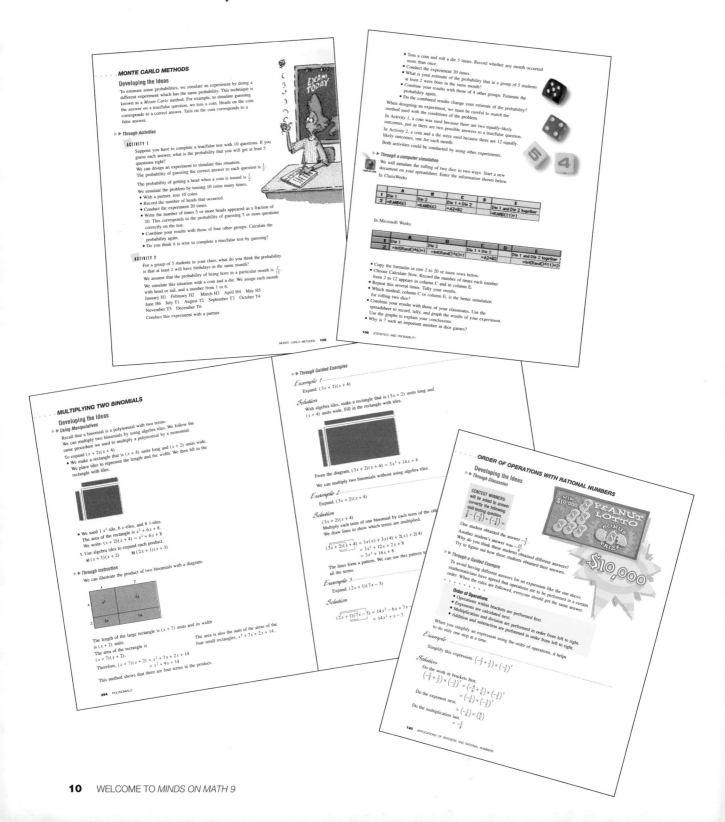

▶▶ Through Activities

I hear and I forget
I see and I remember
I do and I understand

One of the best ways to learn anything new is to become actively involved with it. This is true whether you are learning to play a musical instrument, learning a new sport, or learning to use a computer.

The same is also true of mathematics. When you use this book you will be actively doing mathematics. Many ideas are developed through activities you can do with a partner or in a small group.

▶▶ Using Manipulatives

Some ideas are best understood using concrete materials, called manipulatives. This is an excellent way to develop new ideas in algebra and to help you see the connections between arithmetic and algebra.

▶▶ Through Discussion

New ideas are often introduced through discussion with a partner, in a small group, or as a class.

▶▶ Through Instruction

Some Through Instruction sections help you consolidate the ideas you learned through activities or discussion. In other cases, ideas are easiest to understand when you can read a straightforward explanation of the concepts involved.

▶▶ Through Guided Examples

After you have learned some new ideas through activity or discussion, it helps to see examples showing how to use the ideas. The examples in this book are called guided examples because they usually contain explanations of the steps in the solution.

▶▶ Through a Computer Simulation

Some ideas in probability are developed using computer simulations.

WORKING WITH MATHEMATICS

There are four different kinds of exercises in the lessons in this book.

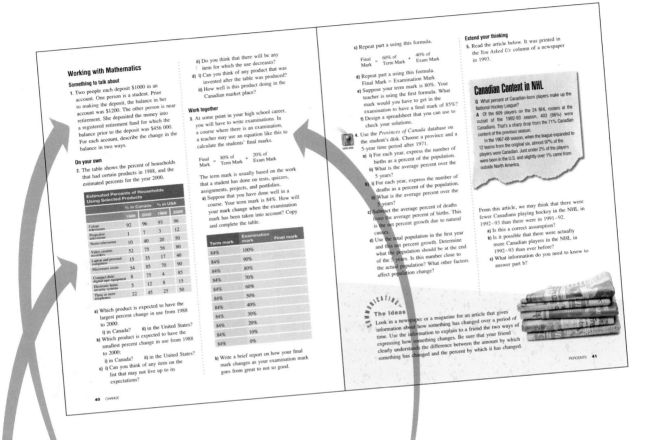

Something to talk about
These exercises will get you talking. They give you and your classmates a chance to check your understanding together before you begin to solve problems on your own.

On your own
Learning anything new requires practice. These exercises let you practise the new skills you have learned.

Work together
You will probably want to complete these exercises with a partner or in a group. Talking with other students helps you learn because you see how they make connections between the new ideas and what they already know. There are two more advantages:

- Other students can sometimes explain new ideas to you in ways that make sense.
- Explaining something you understand to someone else can help you to understand it better.

Technology

The computer is a tool for learning and doing mathematics in ways that weren't possible just a few years ago. Some of the computer exercises give you a chance to work with popular computer applications, such as spreadsheets and Draw programs. The *Minds on Math 9 Student Template Disk* lets you get started right away.

TEMPLATE DISK   DATA DISK

For other computer activities, you'll need to use a computer database. The *Minds on Math 9 Student Data Disk* provides a vast amount of data that you can use to answer questions and to understand and present information.

Using ClarisWorks® or Microsoft Works™ for your applications software will make it easiest for you to do the spreadsheet and Draw computer exercises in this book. You will need one of these programs to use the *Minds on Math 9 Student Template Disk* and the *Minds on Math 9 Student Data Disk*.

Extend your thinking

These exercises are extensions of the ideas in the lesson. Some of these exercises may require you to think about what you have been doing and to apply your thinking to related ideas. Others may be more challenging than the previous exercises.

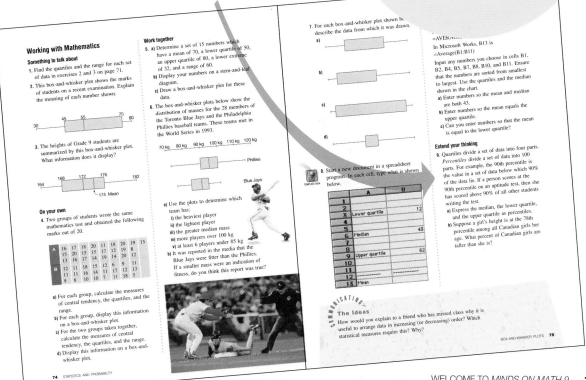

COMMUNICATING THE IDEAS

Communicating your knowledge about a concept or skill can help you learn mathematics. Also, when you learn something interesting or puzzling or exciting, it makes sense to talk about it! In this book you will be asked to communicate your ideas in a variety of ways, such as:

- writing in your journal
- explaining to a friend
- talking on the telephone
- writing a report

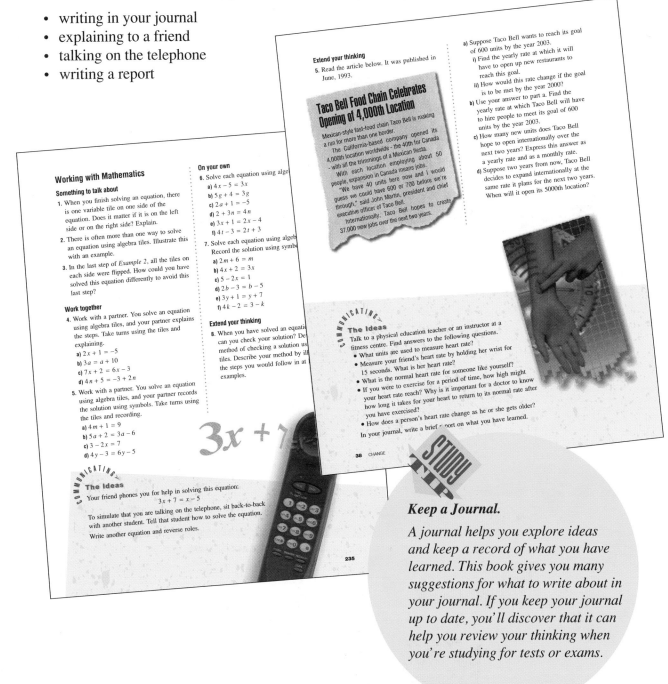

Extend your thinking

5. Read the article below. It was published in June, 1993.

Taco Bell Food Chain Celebrates Opening of 4,000th Location

Mexican-style fast-food chain Taco Bell is making a run for more than one border.

The California-based company opened its 4,000th location worldwide - the 40th for Canada - with all the trimmings of a Mexican fiesta.

With each location employing about 50 people, expansion in Canada means jobs.

"We have 40 units here now and I would guess we could have 600 or 700 before we're through," said John Martin, president and chief executive officer of Taco Bell.

Internationally, Taco Bell hopes to create 37,000 new jobs over the next two years.

a) Suppose Taco Bell wants to reach its goal of 600 units by the year 2003.
   i) Find the yearly rate at which it will have to open up new restaurants to reach this goal.
   ii) How would this rate change if the goal is to be met by the year 2000?
b) Use your answer to part a. Find the yearly rate at which Taco Bell will have to hire people to meet its goal of 600 units by the year 2003.
c) How many new units does Taco Bell hope to open internationally over the next two years? Express this answer as a yearly rate and as a monthly rate.
d) Suppose two years from now, Taco Bell decides to expand internationally at the same rate it plans for the next two years. When will it open its 5000th location?

Working with Mathematics

Something to talk about

1. When you finish solving an equation, there is one variable tile on one side of the equation. Does it matter if it is on the left side or on the right side? Explain.

2. There is often more than one way to solve an equation using algebra tiles. Illustrate this with an example.

3. In the last step of *Example 2*, all the tiles on each side were flipped. How could you have solved this equation differently to avoid this last step?

Work together

4. Work with a partner. You solve an equation using algebra tiles, and your partner explains the steps. Take turns using the tiles and explaining.
   a) $2x + 1 = -5$
   b) $3a = a + 10$
   c) $7x + 2 = 6x - 3$
   d) $4n + 5 = -3 + 2n$

5. Work with a partner. You solve an equation using algebra tiles, and your partner records the solution using symbols. Take turns using the tiles and recording.
   a) $4m + 1 = 9$
   b) $5a + 2 = 3a - 6$
   c) $3 - 2x = 7$
   d) $4y - 3 = 6y - 5$

On your own

6. Solve each equation using algebra
   a) $4x - 5 = 3x$
   b) $5g + 4 = 3g$
   c) $2a + 1 = -5$
   d) $2 + 3n = 4n$
   e) $3x + 1 = 2x - 4$
   f) $4t - 3 = 2t + 3$

7. Solve each equation using algeb Record the solution using symbo
   a) $2m + 6 = m$
   b) $4x + 2 = 3x$
   c) $5 - 2x = 1$
   d) $2b - 3 = b - 5$
   e) $3y + 1 = y + 7$
   f) $4k - 2 = 3 - k$

Extend your thinking

8. When you have solved an equati can you check your solution? De method of checking a solution us tiles. Describe your method by il the steps you would follow in at examples.

COMMUNICATING
The Ideas

Your friend phones you for help in solving this equation:

$$3x + 7 = x - 5$$

To simulate that you are talking on the telephone, sit back-to-back with another student. Tell that student how to solve the equation.

Write another equation and reverse roles.

$3x + 7$

235

COMMUNICATING
The Ideas

Talk to a physical education teacher or an instructor at a fitness centre. Find answers to the following questions.
- What units are used to measure heart rate?
- Measure your friend's heart rate by holding her wrist for 15 seconds. What is her heart rate?
- What is the normal heart rate for someone like yourself?
- If you were to exercise for a period of time, how high might your heart rate reach? Why is it important for a doctor to know how long it takes for your heart to return to its normal rate after you have exercised?
- How does a person's heart rate change as he or she gets older?

In your journal, write a brief report on what you have learned.

38   CHANGE

STUDY TIP

Keep a Journal.

A journal helps you explore ideas and keep a record of what you have learned. This book gives you many suggestions for what to write about in your journal. If you keep your journal up to date, you'll discover that it can help you review your thinking when you're studying for tests or exams.

QUESTS

Most chapters contain two or three Quests. Each Quest is a significant problem for you to solve.

You'll want to approach Quest problems in a thoughtful way. You can use the four-step problem solving plan built into each Quest to help you. As you work, you'll be finding interesting answers to meaningful questions and learning how to be a successful problem solver.

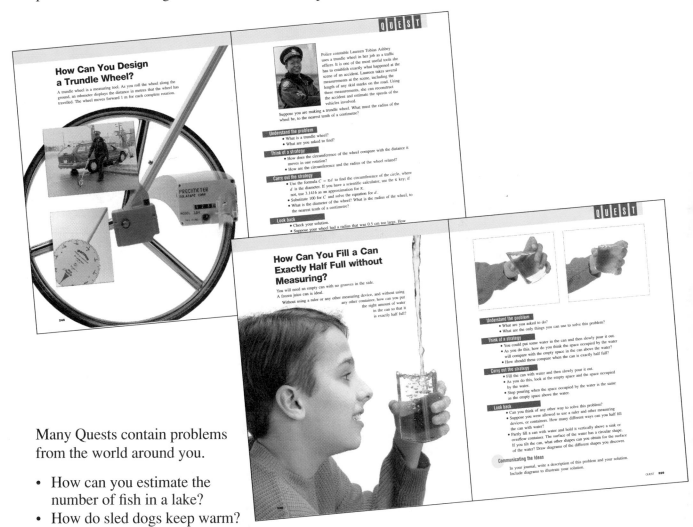

Many Quests contain problems from the world around you.

- How can you estimate the number of fish in a lake?
- How do sled dogs keep warm?
- Is the fuel gauge in a car accurate?

Other Quests involve patterns in arithmetic or geometry.

- What is a shortcut for squaring numbers that end in 5?
- What if you saved 1¢, then 2¢, then 3¢, then 4¢...?

LINKING IDEAS

In the Linking Ideas department, you'll find activities that help you explore connections between mathematics and other subject areas, or between strands in mathematics.

Links with Technology

The computer lets you investigate problems that would be too difficult or involve too much computation to solve with paper and pencil, or even with a calculator. You can also use a computer to explore geometry in a dynamic way that is impossible without a computer.

Other examples of links with technology

- Designing a Lawn Sprinkler System
- Solving Problems with a Spreadsheet
- Investigating Properties of Angles in Triangles

Links with Science

Several linking features show mathematics at work in different fields of science.

Other examples of links with science

- Keeping Ships Afloat
- Fast Food, Safe Food
- How Many Ants Are There?

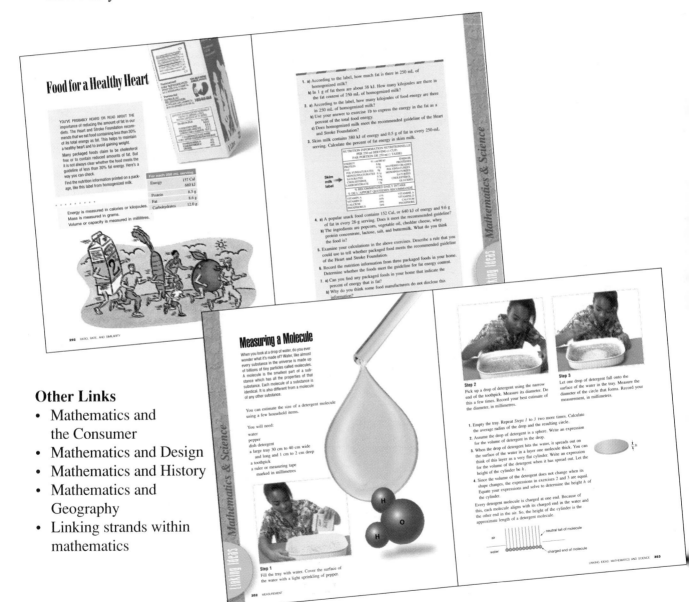

Other Links

- Mathematics and the Consumer
- Mathematics and Design
- Mathematics and History
- Mathematics and Geography
- Linking strands within mathematics

MATHEMATICS FILES

Mathematics Files provide opportunities for you to develop your mathematical understanding. These pages may help you see why many people believe mathematics is a fascinating and even beautiful field of study all on its own, with no need for "uses" or "connections" to make it important.

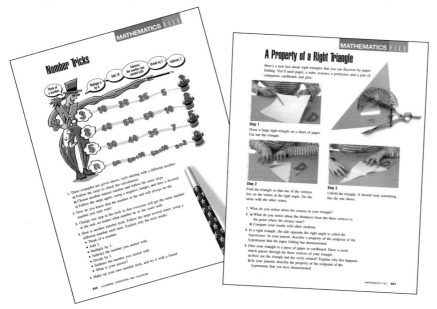

Other examples of Mathematics Files

- Random Numbers
- Some Unusual Transformations
- Naming Very Large and Very Small Numbers
- Extending the Pythagorean Theorem

BOGGLE YOUR MIND

Many problems involving interesting facts and questions occur throughout the text. These give you more opportunities to practise your problem-solving skills. Often the answers you reach will boggle your mind.

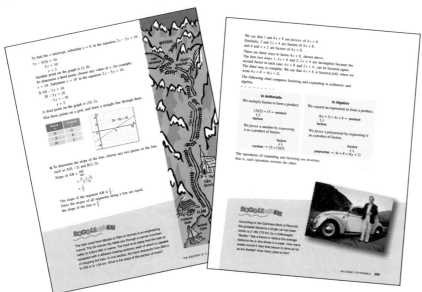

Other Boggle Your Mind topics

- The population density of Bombay
- Canada's annual toxic waste
- Canada's national debt
- Measuring raindrops

MINDS ON MATH

Each chapter ends with a project or investigation that gives you freedom to use and develop mathematics in your own way. You'll need to plan, research, experiment, and make choices and decisions. Probably your project will take a few weeks to complete.

Designing a Scale Model of the Solar System

The Voyager 2 spacecraft was launched in 1977 on a journey of discovery that took over 10 years to complete. Its goal was to travel to the outer planets of our solar system: Jupiter, Saturn, Uranus, and Neptune. The cameras and scientific equipment it carried have provided information about these planets as well as stunning photos like those you see here.

The Apollo 11 spacecraft launched in 1969 reached the moon in only 4 days. Why did it take the Voyager so long to complete its journey? The answer lies in the vast distances which separate the planets. The chart on pages 168 and 169 attempts to illustrate the immensity of remote astronomical objects. Another way to visualize the incredibly large is to design a scale model of the solar system.

ACTIVITY 1
Before you can begin to design your model, you will need to collect some data about the solar system.

The diameter of the sun is about 1.40×10^9 m.

Do some research to find the mean diameter of each planet in our solar system and its distance from the sun, in metres. This information can be found in the *Moon and Planets* database on the student's disk. Express each measurement in scientific notation.

ACTIVITY 2
Obtain a spherical object to represent the sun. Measure and record the diameter of this object. Calculate how many times as small as the diameter of the sun is the diameter of your object. This figure establishes the scale for your model.

ACTIVITY 3
Use the scale established in Activity 2. Calculate the diameters of the objects you would need to represent the planets in your scale model. Think of as many objects as you can with these diameters. As you do this, keep in mind:
- There will probably not be objects with the exact diameters you require. Use other objects whose diameters are approximations of the diameters you require.
- If the diameters of the objects are too small, you may need a larger object to represent the sun. Conversely, if the diameters of the objects are too large, you may need a smaller object for the sun.

ACTIVITY 4
Use the scale established in Activity 2. Calculate the distances from the sun to the objects that represent the planets in your model. Try to visualize where they would be in relation to your sun.

ACTIVITY 5
After the sun, the moon is the celestial body which has the most influence on Earth. The moon has a diameter of about 3.5×10^6 m and is about 3.8×10^8 m from Earth. About how far from Earth would the moon be in your model? How does this compare with the distance from Earth to one of the planets visited by Voyager 2?

ACTIVITY 6
Research to find more information about the Voyager 2 spacecraft, its journey, and the planets it visited. Some questions you may wish to research include:
How was Voyager 2 powered and how was its flight path controlled?
What scientific equipment was on board the craft? How was the information it gathered sent to Earth?
What new information did we learn about the outer planets and their moons?
What happened to the Voyager spacecraft after it reached Neptune in 1989?

ACTIVITY 7
Construct a scale drawing showing the sun and planets as circles. You could use a Draw program that allows you to draw circles with a given radius or diameter. Since the sun is much larger than any of the planets, you might want to show only part of the sun on your drawing.

COMMUNICATING
The Ideas
Write a brief report which summarizes the results of your research and investigations. Include tables and drawings.

Features of Minds on Math

- Each project contains several related activities for you to do over a period of time.
- You can work alone or with a partner.
- The projects are open-ended. This means that there may be more than one answer, or that students doing the same project may get different results.
- You will be asked to write a report or to make a presentation so that you can share your thinking and results with others.

Other topics to explore in Minds on Math

- Determining the availability of large shoes
- Relating the speed of a bicycle to the teeth in the gears
- Counting the number of stars you can see at night

CHANGE

Linking Ideas

Start With What You Know

1. **a)** How has your taste in music changed over the past 5 years?
   b) How has the number of hours per day that you listen to music on the radio changed during those 5 years?

2. **a)** Describe how the price of a case of your favourite soft drink changes from week to week.
   b) How does the price of a litre of gasoline change over the course of a year?

3. Describe how your heart rate changes when you walk up a long flight of stairs or before you write an exam. Why does this happen?

4. Describe how your height has changed since you were born. Were there times when your height changed dramatically? Is your height still changing?

5. **a)** How does the cost of a long-distance phone call change during a week?
   b) When is the best time to make a long-distance phone call?

Mathematics is a useful tool for measuring changes in the world around us. We can look for patterns in the changes and make predictions. We can decide if we should be concerned about the changes. In this chapter you will study many examples of change. You will use the mathematical skills you learned in earlier grades.

Developing the Ideas

▶ ▶ *Through Discussion*

The picture on the right shows a magic square.

When you add the numbers in any row, column or diagonal, the answer is always 15. The number 15 is called the magic sum.

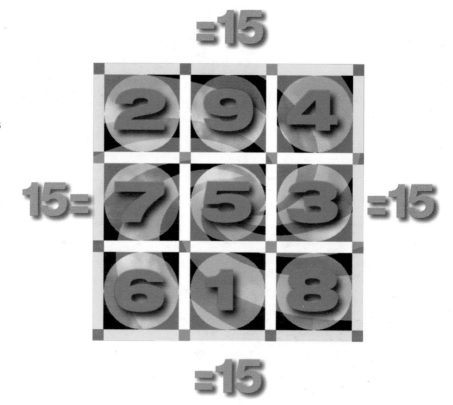

1. **a)** Add 1 to each number in the square. How does the magic sum change?
   b) How would the sum have changed if you had added 2?
   c) What happens if you subtract 1 from each number?

2. **a)** Suppose you want a magic sum of 24. What number should you add to each number in the square? How do you know that the result will be a magic square?
   b) How could you make the magic sum be 0?
   c) Can you arrange for the magic sum to be 16? How?

3. **a)** Multiply each number in the original square by 3. How does the magic sum change?
   b) What happens if you divide each number in the square by 15?

4. Suppose you multiply each number in a magic square by the same number. Will the result be a magic square? How do you know?

5. Suppose you want a magic sum of 150. By what number should you multiply each number in the square above? How do you know that the result will be a magic square?

6. Arrange the numbers from 1 to 16 in a 4 by 4 magic square.

Working with Mathematics

Something to talk about

New Math Gives Superstar Albums Sales Advantage

A recent change in the method for counting sales of multi-album boxed sets means it is now possible for **Pink Floyd** to get a gold record for selling 5,000 units, the late **Elvis Presley** needs 10,000 sales, and the late **Bob Marley** requires 12,500 rings of the cash register.

In fact, both Presley and Marley have already gone platinum, for sales of 20,000 boxes and 25,000 boxes respectively.

In contrast, Toronto's **Barenaked Ladies** had to sell 50,000 copies of their new *Gordon* album to be certified gold and 100,000 for platinum. If they keep going, BNL will reach the rare diamond level of 1 million sales, a figure achieved only by the likes of **Bryan Adams** (twice) and **Alannah Myles** (once).

But the superstar international acts can now reach the top a lot sooner. The new math is thanks to a rule change introduced by the Canadian Recording Industry Association (CRIA), which certifies record sales.

CRIA is now counting each separate CD in a boxed set as a separate album sold, whereas in the past it used a system that required a greater number of units sold. All artists now can win metal and jewel trophies for fewer units sold.

CRIA made the change to bring Canada in line with the counting system of its U.S. counterpart, the Recording Industry Association of America (RIAA).

1. Read the article above. It was printed in December, 1992.
   a) As indicated in the article, there was a change in the way records in Canada are certified as gold, platinum, or diamond. Prior to this change, how many had to be sold before a record was certified: as gold? as platinum? as diamond?
   b) i) What is the major change that occurred in the certification process?
      ii) Why was the change made?
   c) i) How many CDs does Pink Floyd's boxed set contain?
      ii) How many sets would have to be sold for this set to be certified: as gold? as platinum? as diamond?
   d) The statement is made that Bob Marley will need 12 500 rings of the cash register for his boxed set to be certified as gold. How many CDs are in this boxed set?
   e) Most boxed sets use previously released material. Do you feel that this change is unfair towards groups who do not have boxed sets?

Work together

2. In a Letter to the Editor of a local newspaper, the writer complained that the price of gasoline changed from 49.0¢/L to 54.7¢/L just before the start of the July 1 holiday weekend. Suppose you had a car with a 50 L gas tank that was almost empty.
   a) How much would you pay for the gas if you filled up at the lower price? How much would you pay at the higher price?
   b) How much extra would you pay if you filled up at the higher price?

On your own

3. In 1993, the Bank of Canada released the figures below. They show how the number of bank notes in circulation has changed from 1980 to 1993.

	Number of bills in circulation in 1980	Number of bills in circulation in 1993
$2	105 million	205 million
$5	81 million	140 million
$10	128 million	109 million
$20	240 million	350 million
$50	22 million	72 million
$100	27 million	94 million
$1000	326 000	1.8 million

   a) Display this information on a double-bar graph. Describe how the graph illustrates the changes from 1980 to 1993.
   b) Which bank note had the largest change in its number of bills in circulation from 1980 to 1993?
   c) Find the total amounts of paper money in circulation in 1980 and in 1993. By how much did the amount change from 1980 to 1993?

4. Input this information on a spreadsheet. You can use it to produce a magic square with the numbers 2 to 10. To help you, the positions of some of the numbers have been given.

TEMPLATE DISK

	A	B	C	D
1	Magic Squares			=A4+B3+C2
2	7			=A2+B2+C2
3		6		=A3+B3+C3
4			5	=A4+B4+C4
5	=A2+A3+A4	=B2+B3+B4	=C2+C3+C4	=A2+B3+C4

The formula in cell A5 adds the numbers in cells A2, A3, and A4. Similar formulas are used in cells B5 and C5. The formula in cell D2 adds the numbers in cells A2, B2, and C2. Similar formulas are used in cells D3 and D4.
   a) Explain the formulas in cells D1 and D5.
   b) Input the remaining numbers in cells A3, A4, B2, B4, C2, and C3. Rearrange the numbers until you get a magic square.
   c) Design a spreadsheet to produce a 4 by 4 magic square.

Extend your thinking

5. Suppose you used a $100 bill to purchase two tickets for a concert. The total cost of the tickets (taxes included) was $38. List the different ways the cashier could give you change if only bills are used.
   a) How many different ways are there?
   b) Which type of bill occurs most often?
   c) Which type of bill occurs least often?
   d) How would the total number of ways change if the total cost of the tickets was $36 instead of $38?

The Ideas

See what you can find out about magic squares. Use the information to introduce someone else to this interesting topic.

Developing the Ideas

▶ ▶ *Through Instruction*

Many cereal companies package their products to appeal to young children. In each box, there is an item that is part of a collection of similar items. These items are often related to something that is of current interest; movies, cartoon characters, and sports stars.

How many boxes must be purchased to obtain the entire collection? If there are quite a few items in the set, then it seems reasonable that a consumer will have to buy many boxes to complete the set.

There is a method that can be used to calculate the average number of boxes needed to complete a set.

Suppose that there are 4 items in the collection. Also, all the items are distributed randomly and in equal numbers. Each box has only one item.

Then the average number of boxes needed is equal to:

$$4 \times \left(1 + \frac{1}{2} + \frac{1}{3} + \frac{1}{4}\right)$$

The lowest common denominator for the fractions inside the brackets is 12. The steps involved in calculating the answer are given below. Make sure that you understand each step.

$$4 \times \left(\frac{12}{12} + \frac{6}{12} + \frac{4}{12} + \frac{3}{12}\right)$$
$$= 4 \times \left(\frac{25}{12}\right)$$
$$= \frac{100}{12}$$
$$\doteq 8.3$$

This means that if there are 4 items in the set, then, on average, a consumer will have to buy about 8 boxes to collect the entire set.

Another way to add the fractions is to use a common denominator of 24, because $2 \times 3 \times 4 = 24$. Take a few minutes to try this. You will find that the answer is $\frac{200}{24}$, or approximately 8.3. Use this method when you do exercise 3.

It is interesting to see how the average number of boxes needed to complete the set changes when the number of items in the set changes. You will look at this in exercise 3.

Working with Mathematics

Something to talk about

1. a) Is it possible to get a complete set of items by purchasing only 4 boxes? Do you think this is likely to happen? Why?

   b) Is it possible to purchase many boxes and still not get a complete set? Do you think this is likely to happen? Why?

2. If there are 3 items in the set, then the average number of boxes you must purchase is $3 \times \left(1 + \frac{1}{2} + \frac{1}{3}\right)$. If there are 7 items in the set, then the average number of boxes is $7 \times \left(1 + \frac{1}{2} + \frac{1}{3} + \frac{1}{4} + \frac{1}{5} + \frac{1}{6} + \frac{1}{7}\right)$. What is the pattern relating the number in the set, and the number of boxes you need to buy?

Work together

3. Use the formulas in exercise 2. Write the formula for the average number of boxes you must purchase, for each number of items up to 10.

   a) Copy and complete the table. Round your answers to the nearest whole number.

Number of items in the set	Average number of boxes needed
1	
2	
3	
4	8

   b) Graph the average number of boxes against the number of items in the set.

   c) Discuss how the average number of boxes needed to complete the set changes when the number of items in the set increases.

On your own

4. a) Add 1 to the numerator of the fraction $\frac{1}{3}$. How does the size of the fraction change?

   b) Add 1 to the denominator of $\frac{1}{3}$. How does the size of the fraction change?

   c) How does the size of the fraction $\frac{1}{3}$ change when both the numerator and the denominator are increased by 1?

5. Repeat exercise 4 for the fraction $\frac{7}{3}$.

6. Compare your answers to exercises 4 and 5. What do you notice?

Extend your thinking

If a spreadsheet program is available, use it to complete exercise 7.

7. a) Look at the sequence of fractions given below. Determine the pattern that was used to generate the sequence.
   $$\frac{1}{2}, \frac{5}{3}, \frac{11}{8}, \frac{27}{19}, \frac{65}{46}, \ldots$$

   b) Make a sequence of your own that is similar to the one in part a. Use the same pattern, but start with a fraction of your choice. Write the first 10 terms of your sequence.

   c) Convert each fraction in part b to a decimal. As you go from one term to the next, how do the terms change? Compare your findings with other students. Write a brief report on your findings.

   d) Graph the term expressed as a decimal against the number of the term in the sequence.

8. Repeat exercise 7, using the sequence of fractions given below.
   $$\frac{7}{10}, \frac{37}{17}, \frac{88}{54}, \frac{250}{142}, \frac{676}{392}, \ldots$$

The Ideas

Look up the word "fraction" in a dictionary. In your journal, describe the various ways that this word is used. Ask several people to say a sentence that contains the word "fraction." Compare these uses to those you found in the dictionary. Which use is the most common?

How Many Cereal Boxes?

TEMPLATE DISK

On page 27, you discovered that you would need, on average, 8 boxes of cereal before you collected all four items. Let's use the random number feature of the computer to simulate this problem.

Use your spreadsheet program. Set up this table.

	A	B	C	D	E
1	Cereal Box Prize Simulation				
2					
3	Your prize this time is #			Trials	# of boxes
4		=RAND(4)		Trial 1	
5				Trial 2	
6	Results this trial			Trial 3	
7	Prize #1			Trial 4	
8	Prize #2			Trial 5	
9	Prize #3			Trial 6	
10	Prize #4			Trial 7	
11					
12	# of boxes	=SUM(B7..B10)		Average	=AVERAGE(E4..E10)

In ClarisWorks®, the formula in cell B4 will display randomly one of the numbers 1, 2, 3 or 4.
In Microsoft Works™, use =Int(Rand()*4)+1 in cell B4.
The formula in cell B12 adds the numbers in cells B7 to B10.
The formula in cell E12 finds the mean of the numbers in cells E4 to E10.
In Microsoft Works, use =Sum(B7:B10) in cell B12.
Use =Average(E4:E10) in cell E12.

Stegosaurus

Pterosaur

Tyrannosaurus

Triceratops

Step 1   *To buy cereal and see what item you get*

Your spreadsheet has a Calculate Now feature on one of its menus. Select Calculate Now several times and watch the value in cell B4. You should see a number from 1 to 4 displayed each time. Each number represents one of the four possible items.

Step 2   *To tally the results*

Each time you get an item, add 1 to the appropriate number in cells B7, B8, B9, or B10. For example, if you get a 2 when you Calculate Now, change the number in cell B8 to be 1 more than it is currently.

Step 3   *To check for a complete set*

Do you now have at least one of each item? If so, the trial is complete. Select Calculate Now once again. The result is the number of boxes showing in cell B12. Put this number in cell D4. Change the number of items to zero in cells B7 to B10.

Repeat *Steps 1* to *3* six times for a total of 7 trials. Read the number in cell E12. How close is your simulation to the theoretical value of 8.3 boxes?

A Ring Around Earth

Imagine wrapping a steel band around the Equator. How long would the
band be? Suppose you change the position of the band so that it still
wraps around the Equator, but it is 1 m above Earth's surface.
How much extra steel would you need?

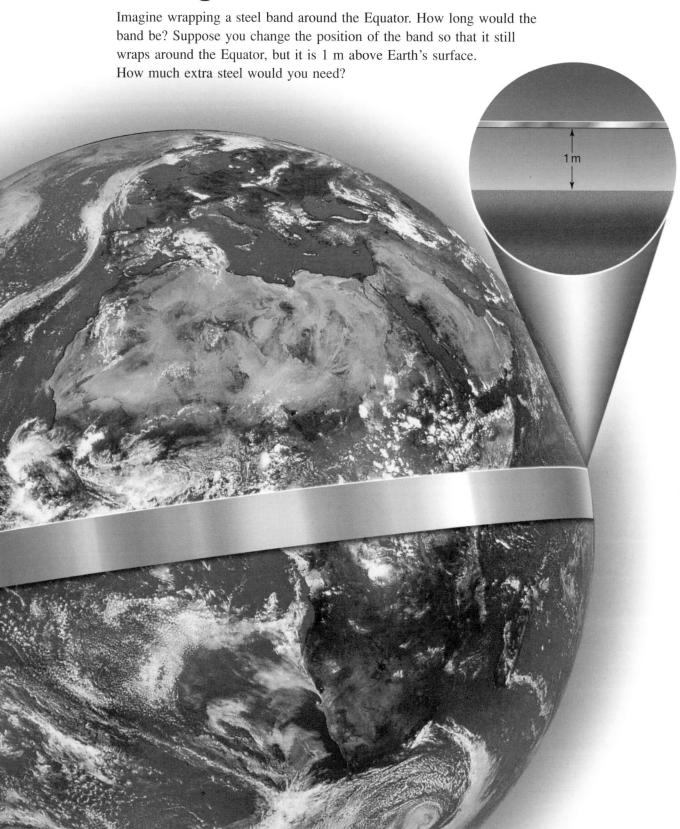

Understand the problem

- What is the Equator?
- Do you think that a much longer steel band will be required when the band is raised 1 m?

Think of a strategy

- Consider a similar problem with a circle that is much smaller than the Equator. For example, use a dinner plate and a piece of rope in place of the steel band.

Carry out the strategy

- You will need several lengths of rope, a metre stick, and a measuring tape.
- Wrap a piece of rope or string around a circular object; for example, a garbage pail, a glass or cup, a pan, a tire, or a big flower pot. Measure the length of this rope. Take another piece of rope. Lay it around the same object so that the rope is always 1 m away from the rim. Measure this piece of rope. Compare this length to the length of the first piece of rope.
- Repeat the process with four different circular objects. What do you notice about your results?
- How does the extra amount of rope that is required for the new position vary as the size of the circle changes?
- Use your observations to predict the difference in lengths of steel bands wrapped around Earth.

DATA DISK

- Find the diameter of Earth by using an encyclopedia or the *Moon and Planets* database on the student's disk. Use this information and the formula: Circumference = π × Diameter. Calculate the circumference of Earth and the circumference 1 m above Earth. Find the extra length needed for the steel band to be 1 m above Earth's surface.

Look back

- Carry out similar investigations for other figures such as a square and a triangle.

Communicating the Ideas

In your journal, write a description of this problem and your solution. Include an explanation of why you think this problem is important.

RATIOS

Developing the Ideas

▶ ▶ *Through Discussion*

- Put 10 black playing cards in one pile and 5 red cards in another pile.
- What is the ratio of black cards to red cards? What is this ratio in simplified form?
- Add 5 black cards and 5 red cards to the corresponding piles. In simplified form, what is the ratio of black cards to red cards?
- How has the ratio changed?

▶ ▶ *Through Instruction*

From the preceding discussion, you should have seen that when you add the same number to both terms of a ratio, the ratio changes. Some people have trouble understanding this idea. Here is an example for you to try out on other people.

Suppose that $1 Can is worth 70¢ U.S. How much would it cost to buy $1 U.S.?

If you were to conduct a poll and ask people this question, chances are that many people would answer, "$1.30."

Here is the reasoning that they used.

The ratio of Canadian currency to American currency is $1 : 0.70$.

By adding 0.30 to each term of the ratio (there is the error!) they derived the ratio $1.30 : 1$.

To answer the question correctly, divide each term of the ratio by 0.70. In this way, the second term of the ratio becomes 1.

That is, $1 : 0.70$ becomes $\frac{1}{0.70} : \frac{0.70}{0.70}$, which is approximately $1.43 : 1$.

This means that when $1 Can is worth 70¢ U.S., it will cost $1.43 Can to buy $1 U.S.

At this rate, to purchase $500 U.S., it will cost $500 \times \$1.43$ Can = $715 Can.

If $1 Can is worth $0.78 U.S., then $1 U.S. will cost $\frac{\$1}{0.78}$ Can, or $1.28 Can.

Working with Mathematics

Something to talk about

1. The city of Saskatoon has a population of approximately 210 000. These residents encounter 190 traffic lights in the city. The general rule of thumb is one traffic light per 1000 residents. The city of Richmond has 125 traffic lights, while Halifax has 98 traffic lights.

    a) What ratio relates the number of traffic lights to the population of the city?

    b) The population of Montreal is 980 000. Use the ratio from part a to estimate the number of traffic lights in Montreal.

    c) Estimate the populations of Richmond and Halifax.

Work together

2. The sign below is familiar to people who travel from Brandon to Portage la Prairie and then to Winnipeg, in Manitoba. At this point on the highway the ratio of the distance to Portage la Prairie to the distance to Winnipeg is 75 : 150, or 1 : 2.

Portage la Prairie 75

Winnipeg 150

    a) As you continue to drive towards Winnipeg, how will this ratio change? Copy and complete the table. Each ratio has been written with a first term of 1. The second term has been rounded to two decimal places.

Distance to Portage la Prairie (km)	Distance to Winnipeg (km)	Distance to Portage la Prairie : distance to Winnipeg
75	150	1 : 2
70	145	1 : 2.07
65	140	1 : 2.15
.	.	
.	.	
.	.	
5	80	
1	76	

    b) How would the ratio change if you were driving away from Winnipeg and Portage la Prairie? Use a table similar to the one in part a. The first row is 75 : 150. The second row is 80 : 155. Continue for 10 rows.

    c) When will the ratio of the distance to Portage la Prairie to the distance to Winnipeg be 1.5 : 1? At this point, are you travelling towards Portage la Prairie or away from it?

On your own

3. **a)** Do you know anyone who is twice as old as you are? How will the ratio of your ages change as you get older?

    b) How is the question in part a related to exercise 2?

Extend your thinking

4. Suppose you are working in Canada for an American company. Each month you receive a cheque for $4350 U.S. When you received your last cheque, $1 Can was worth $0.70 U.S. You were not able to get to the bank that day, so you deposited the cheque the next day. Overnight, the exchange rate changed from 0.70 to 0.71.

    a) Which rate was better for you?

    b) How much difference would it have made to you in cashing your cheque?

COMMUNICATING The Ideas

In your journal, explain why $1.25 Can is not equivalent to $1 U.S., when $1 Can is equivalent to $0.75 U.S.

The Fibonacci Sequence

Have you ever seen this sequence of numbers?
1, 1, 2, 3, 5, 8, 13, 21,...
This sequence is known as the Fibonacci sequence.
Many connections have been made between
this sequence, and nature and art.

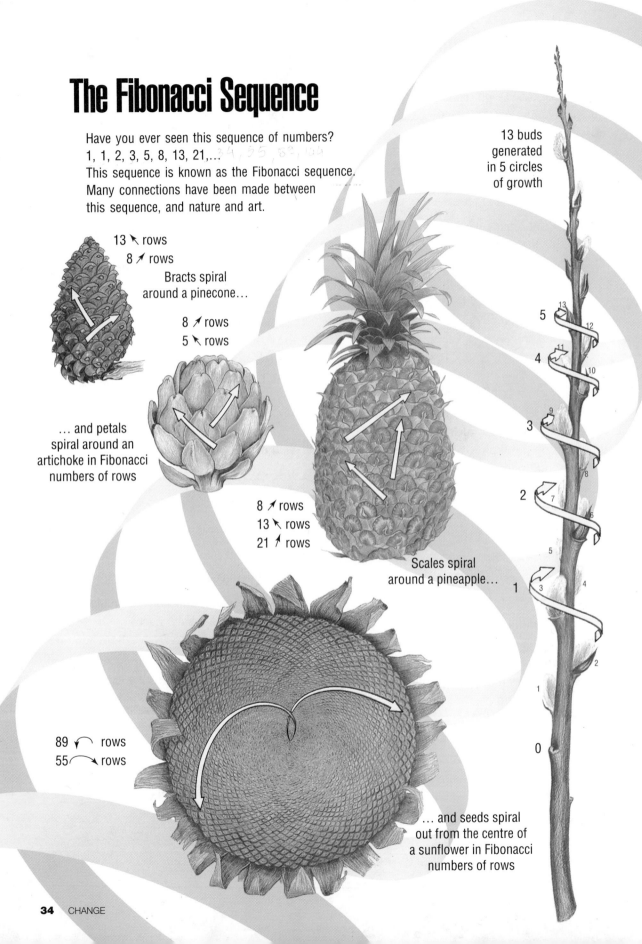

13 ↖ rows
8 ↗ rows
Bracts spiral
around a pinecone…

8 ↗ rows
5 ↖ rows

… and petals
spiral around an
artichoke in Fibonacci
numbers of rows

8 ↗ rows
13 ↖ rows
21 ↗ rows

13 buds
generated
in 5 circles
of growth

Scales spiral
around a pineapple…

89 ↶ rows
55 ↷ rows

… and seeds spiral
out from the centre of
a sunflower in Fibonacci
numbers of rows

1. **a)** How is the third term in the sequence obtained from the first two terms?
   b) How is the fourth term obtained from the second and third terms?
   c) Write a general rule for obtaining each term beyond the second term.

2. Find the next 7 terms in this sequence.

3. The width of a rectangle is 8 cm and its length is 13 cm.
   a) Write the ratio of the length to the width so that the second term of the ratio is 1. Include as many decimal places as your calculator allows.
   b) Repeat this procedure for the ten rectangles listed below. Copy and complete the table.
   c) How are the widths and lengths related to the Fibonacci sequence?
   d) How does the ratio of the length to the width change as you move down the table?

Width of rectangle (cm)	Length of rectangle (cm)	Length : width
3	5	1.667 5:3
5	8	
8	13	1.625 : 1
13	21	
21	34	
34	55	
55	89	
89	144	
144	233	
233	377	

In 438 B.C., the ancient Greeks completed their masterpiece of architecture. It was dedicated to the goddess *Athena Parthenos*. This temple, called the *Parthenon*, was designed so that its width-to-height ratio was a special number called the *golden ratio*.

4. Measure the width and the height of this picture of the Parthenon. Calculate its width-to-height ratio.

5. Artists often use a golden rectangle for their paintings. A rectangle is *golden* if the ratio of the length to the width is approximately 1.618 : 1. Measure the sides of a filing card, a paperback novel, and a window. Are any of these a golden rectangle? Try other rectangles. See how many golden rectangles you can find.

6. Are any of the rectangles in exercise 3 golden?

Developing the Ideas

▶ ▶ *Through Discussion*

Read the article below. It was printed in the
You Asked Us column of a newspaper in May, 1993.

Costs of foreign mail

Q Who pays for delivery of international mail,
such as letters sent to Greece from Canada? Is
it borne by the Greek postal system or by
Canada Post?

A When a country's postal system receives
more mail than it delivers to another, it is
reimbursed for the difference.

With Greece, under the Postal Union dues
system this amounts to almost $4 a kilogram.
Canada Post delivers about 48,000 kg of mail a
year from Greece and sends about 30,000 kg.
The Greek postal system would compensate
Canada Post for the 18,000 kg difference.

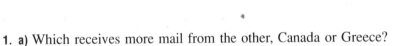

1. **a)** Which receives more mail from the other, Canada or Greece?
   b) How much more mail does that country receive?
   c) By how much is that country reimbursed?

It is interesting to see how the reimbursement changes if the amount of
mail that we exchange begins to rise. Let's suppose that the amount of
mail that Greece sends to us increases at the rate of 1000 kg per year.
At the same time the amount of mail that we send to Greece increases
at the rate of 4000 kg per year.

2. With a partner, investigate how the money exchanged between
   Canada and Greece would change over the next 10 years if the
   increases occurred. Show the results in a table. Draw a graph to
   illustrate these results.

Working with Mathematics

Something to talk about

1. Suppose you and your family are travelling along the TransCanada Highway. In the middle of nowhere, when your speed is 100 km/h, a car travelling in the same direction passes you. It is travelling at 120 km/h. Suppose both cars continue to travel at the same speeds. How will the distance between the cars change over the next few hours?

Work together

2. In 1993, the city of Winnipeg received 180 969 telephone calls for help on its 911 emergency line.
   a) About how many phone calls per day were made on the 911 line?
   b) How many phone calls is this per month?
   c) Suppose the emergency line continues to receive calls at this rate. How long, after the beginning of 1993, will it take before the number of emergency calls reaches 1 000 000?

3. Estimate how many phone calls your home receives in one week.
   a) Use this information to estimate the average number of calls that your family receives per day. Compare this estimate with your partner's estimate.
   b) Suppose your household continues to receive calls at this rate. How long would it take to reach the 1 000 000 mark?
   c) How long would it take for your partner's household to reach the 1 000 000 mark?

On your own

4. In 1993, newspapers across Canada reported that the population of the world was estimated to be 5.57 billion. The world's population had increased by 93 million people from the year before.
   a) What was the population of the world in 1992?

   Suppose the population of the world continues to grow at the rate of 93 million per year.
   b) How will it change over the next 5 years?
   c) Do you think that the population will continue to grow at that rate?

Extend your thinking

5. Read the article below. It was published in June, 1993.

Taco Bell Food Chain Celebrates Opening of 4,000th Location

Mexican-style fast-food chain Taco Bell is making a run for more than one border.

The California-based company opened its 4,000th location worldwide - the 40th for Canada - with all the trimmings of a Mexican fiesta.

With each location employing about 50 people, expansion in Canada means jobs.

"We have 40 units here now and I would guess we could have 600 or 700 before we're through," said John Martin, president and chief executive officer of Taco Bell.

Internationally, Taco Bell hopes to create 37,000 new jobs over the next two years.

a) Suppose Taco Bell wants to reach its goal of 600 units by the year 2003.

　i) Find the yearly rate at which it will have to open up new restaurants to reach this goal.

　ii) How would this rate change if the goal is to be met by the year 2000?

b) Use your answer to part a. Find the yearly rate at which Taco Bell will have to hire people to meet its goal of 600 units by the year 2003.

c) How many new units does Taco Bell hope to open internationally over the next two years? Express this answer as a yearly rate and as a monthly rate.

d) Suppose two years from now, Taco Bell decides to expand internationally at the same rate it plans for the next two years. When will it open its 5000th location?

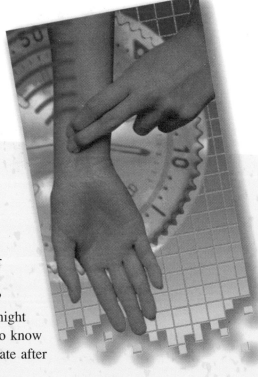

COMMUNICATING
The Ideas

Talk to a physical education teacher or an instructor at a fitness centre. Find answers to the following questions.

• What units are used to measure heart rate?
• Measure your friend's heart rate by holding her wrist for 15 seconds. What is her heart rate?
• What is the normal heart rate for someone like yourself?
• If you were to exercise for a period of time, how high might your heart rate reach? Why is it important for a doctor to know how long it takes for your heart to return to its normal rate after you have exercised?
• How does a person's heart rate change as he or she gets older?

In your journal, write a brief report on what you have learned.

Developing the Ideas

▷▶ *Through Discussion*

Like many other provinces in Canada, British Columbia has changed a great deal over the past few years. In fact, in 1993, its population boomed, with record increases in new arrivals from overseas and other provinces. The table gives specific details about the changes that occurred in Vancouver between 1986 and 1991.

First language	1986	1991
English	1 043 015	1 151 975
Chinese	76 115	130 680
Punjabi	20 830	38 255
German	35 175	34 765
French	17 715	20 585
Italian	17 170	17 775
Tagalog (Filipino)	6755	14 025
Dutch	10 685	10 740
Japanese	9470	10 340

What can we learn from the table?
We shall look at how the populations of some groups changed in 5 years.

1. Consider the group whose first language is Punjabi.
   a) Did the population increase or decrease?
   b) By how much did the population change?
   c) Write the change as a fraction of the 1986 population.
   d) Write this fraction as a percent to the nearest whole number.

2. Repeat exercise 1 for the group whose first language is English.

3. Which group, English or Punjabi, had the greater increase in number?

4. Which group, English or Punjabi, had the greater percent increase?

The exercises above illustrate two ways to measure change. One way is to calculate the increase (or decrease) by using subtraction. The second way is to divide the increase (or decrease) by the original number and then express the result as a percent.

Working with Mathematics

Something to talk about

1. Two people each deposit $1000 in an account. One person is a student. Prior to making the deposit, the balance in her account was $1200. The other person is near retirement. She deposited the money into a registered retirement fund for which the balance prior to the deposit was $456 000. For each account, describe the change in the balance in two ways.

On your own

2. The table shows the percent of households that had certain products in 1988, and the estimated percents for the year 2000.

Estimated Percents of Households Using Selected Products				
	% in Canada		% in USA	
	1988	2000	1988	2000
Colour televisions	92	96	93	96
Projection televisions	1	7	3	12
Stereo televisions	10	40	20	50
Video cassette recorders	52	75	56	80
Laptop and personal computers	15	35	17	40
Microwave ovens	54	85	70	90
Compact disk/ digital tape equipment	8	75	4	85
Electronic home security systems	5	12	8	15
Three or more telephones	22	45	25	50

a) Which product is expected to have the largest percent change in use from 1988 to 2000:
   i) in Canada? ii) in the United States?
b) Which product is expected to have the smallest percent change in use from 1988 to 2000:
   i) in Canada? ii) in the United States?
c) i) Can you think of any item on the list that may not live up to its expectations?
   ii) Do you think that there will be any item for which the use decreases?
d) i) Can you think of any product that was invented after the table was produced?
   ii) How well is this product doing in the Canadian market place?

Work together

3. At some point in your high school career, you will have to write examinations. In a course where there is an examination, a teacher may use an equation like this to calculate the students' final marks.

$$\text{Final Mark} = 80\% \text{ of Term Mark} + 20\% \text{ of Exam Mark}$$

The term mark is usually based on the work that a student has done on tests, quizzes, assignments, projects, and portfolios.

a) Suppose that you have done well in a course. Your term mark is 84%. How will your mark change when the examination mark has been taken into account? Copy and complete the table.

Term mark	Examination mark	Final mark
84%	100%	
84%	90%	
84%	80%	
84%	70%	
84%	60%	
84%	50%	
84%	40%	
84%	30%	
84%	20%	
84%	10%	
84%	0%	

b) Write a brief report on how your final mark changes as your examination mark goes from great to not so good.

c) Repeat part a using this formula.

$$\text{Final Mark} = 60\% \text{ of Term Mark} + 40\% \text{ of Exam Mark}$$

d) Repeat part a using this formula.
Final Mark = Examination Mark

e) Suppose your term mark is 80%. Your teacher is using the first formula. What mark would you have to get in the examination to have a final mark of 85%?

f) Design a spreadsheet that you can use to check your solutions.

DATA DISK

4. Use the *Provinces of Canada* database on the student's disk. Choose a province and a 5-year time period after 1971.

a) i) For each year, express the number of births as a percent of the population.
   ii) What is the average percent over the 5 years?

b) i) For each year, express the number of deaths as a percent of the population.
   ii) What is the average percent over the 5 years?

c) Subtract the average percent of deaths from the average percent of births. This is the net percent growth due to natural causes.

d) Use the total population in the first year and this net percent growth. Determine what the population should be at the end of the 5 years. Is this number close to the actual population? What other factors affect population change?

Extend your thinking

5. Read the article below. It was printed in the *You Asked Us* column of a newspaper in 1993.

Canadian Content in NHL

Q What percent of Canadian-born players make up the National Hockey League?

A Of the 609 players on the 24 NHL rosters at the outset of the 1992-93 season, 403 (66%) were Canadians. That's a sharp drop from the 71% Canadian content of the previous season.

In the 1967-68 season, when the league expanded to 12 teams from the original six, almost 97% of the players were Canadian. Just under 2% of the players were born in the U.S. and slightly over 1% came from outside North America.

From this article, we may think that there were fewer Canadians playing hockey in the NHL in 1992–93 than there were in 1991–92.

a) Is this a correct assumption?

b) Is it possible that there were actually more Canadian players in the NHL in 1992–93 than ever before?

c) What information do you need to know to answer part b?

COMMUNICATING

The Ideas

Look in a newspaper or a magazine for an article that gives information about how something has changed over a period of time. Use the information to explain to a friend the two ways of expressing how something changes. Be sure that your friend clearly understands the difference between the amount by which something has changed and the percent by which it has changed.

The Cost of Natural Gas

DID YOU KNOW THAT ONE CUBIC METRE OF NATURAL GAS HAS LESS ENERGY VALUE AT higher elevations (when it is expanded) than it does at lower elevations (when it is compressed)?

Before 1991 this fact was not taken into account. This meant that some consumers were overpaying while others were not paying enough. To create a fairer system, Union Gas changed the way it charged its customers for the natural gas that they had used. This change occurred in December 1991 and other natural gas companies in Canada made similar changes at about the same time.

At sea level, a sealed balloon with a diameter of 20 cm contains about 4200 cm³ of gas.

If this balloon were taken to the top of Mount Everest, it would expand to a diameter of 29 cm. Its volume would be about 3 times as great, 12 600 cm³.

Union Gas split the area that it serves into 11 zones. It assigned each zone a number. The average altitude above sea level of an area was used to designate its zone.

Zone	Zone number	Zone	Zone number
1	1.009 73	7	0.986 28
2	1.005 66	8	0.982 03
3	0.999 20	9	0.980 33
4	0.997 49	10	0.975 23
5	0.993 08	11	0.971 83
6	0.990 02		

The money that a consumer owes is calculated as shown below. By reading a meter, a person from the gas company determines the total amount of natural gas that was used.

Cost for consumer = amount of gas used (m^3) × zone number × rate ($\$/m^3$)

The rate is the cost in dollars for 1 m^3 of gas.

1. Calculate the cost for each gas consumption.
   a) 1000 m^3 was used in zone 2 and the rate is $0.18/m^3$.
   b) 1000 m^3 was used in zone 9 and the rate is $0.18/m^3$.
   c) Which zone has the lowest average altitude above sea level? Which zone has the highest?

The rate card below is typical of the kind used by natural gas companies all across Canada.

GENERAL SERVICE RATE

Monthly fixed charge		$7.50
and		
First	1 400 m^3 consumed per month	19.3999¢ per m^3
Next	4 600 m^3 consumed per month	16.1416¢ per m^3
Next	124 000 m^3 consumed per month	14.9178¢ per m^3
Next	270 000 m^3 consumed per month	14.0333¢ per m^3
All over	400 000 m^3 consumed per month	13.9128¢ per m^3

2. Calculate the bill a consumer would get for each gas consumption.
   a) 1000 m^3 of gas was used in zone 3.
   b) 120 000 m^3 of gas was used in zone 9.

Developing the Ideas

▶ ▶ *Through Discussion*

Are you familiar with the wind-chill factor? On a cold day the wind can make it feel colder than the temperature indicated on the thermometer.

A table like the one below is often used by the media for weather reports. The wind-chill equivalent temperature is the temperature you would feel at a wind speed of 8 km/h. For example, when the temperature is −5°C and the wind speed is 30 km/h, the wind-chill equivalent temperature is −18°C. This means that it would feel like −18°C in a wind speed of 8 km/h.

Wind-Chill Equivalent Temperature						
Temperature (°C)	Wind speed (km/h)					
	10	20	30	40	50	60
5	4	−2	−5	−7	−8	−9
0	−2	−8	−11	−14	−16	−17
−5	−7	−14	−18	−21	−23	−24
−10	−12	−20	−25	−28	−30	−32
−15	−18	−26	−32	−35	−38	−39
−20	−23	−32	−38	−42	−45	−47
−25	−28	−39	−45	−49	−52	−54
−30	−33	−45	−52	−56	−60	−62
−35	−39	−51	−59	−64	−67	−69
−40	−44	−57	−65	−71	−74	−77

Temperature, −5°C
Wind speed, 30 km/h
Feels like −18°C

Several years ago, in an area of northern Canada, there was a day when the temperature was 5°C in the morning. The temperature changed dramatically throughout the day. It dropped at a rate of about 5°C per hour. Eventually, the temperature was −40°C! The wind speed was about 10 km/h throughout the day.

1. Use the table.

   a) How did the wind-chill equivalent temperature change throughout the day?

   b) Did it drop at the rate of about 5°C per hour? If not, how did it change?

Working with Mathematics

Something to talk about

1. **a)** Do you remember the rules for multiplying integers? If you have forgotten, here is an interesting way to develop the rules. Start with a product you know, like $4 \times 4 = 16$. Change the second number by subtracting 1, then calculate the new product.

$$4 \times 4 = 16$$
$$4 \times 3 = 12$$
$$4 \times 2 = 8$$
$$4 \times 1 = 4$$
$$4 \times 0 = 0$$
$$4 \times -1 = ?$$

The product decreases by 4 with each step. Continuing the pattern, what should the product be in the last line? Based on this answer, what is the rule for multiplying a positive number and a negative number?

b) What do you think will happen if you continue, but now subtract 1 from the first number? Can you see that you will eventually have two negative numbers multiplied together? Try it and see what happens.

$$3 \times -1 =$$
$$2 \times -1 =$$
$$1 \times -1 =$$
$$0 \times -1 =$$
$$-1 \times -1 =$$

c) What is the rule for multiplying two negative numbers?

Work together

2. **a)** When the temperature drops, how do its measurements on the Celsius scale and Fahrenheit scale compare? To find out, copy and complete the table below.

Temperature (°C)	Temperature (°F)
30	
25	
20	
15	
10	
5	
0	
−5	
−10	
−15	
−20	
−25	
−30	

To convert a temperature from degrees Celsius to degrees Fahrenheit: multiply the Celsius temperature by 9, divide the answer by 5, and add 32.

b) As you move from the top row to the bottom row, how does the difference between consecutive numbers in the two columns change ?

c) Use your answer to part b to predict what the numbers in the two columns would be if they were continued for 5 more rows.

d) Extend the two columns by completing 5 more rows. Was your answer to part c correct?

e) Plot a graph of temperature in degrees Fahrenheit against temperature in degrees Celsius.

On your own

3. Recall the cold day in northern Canada discussed at the beginning of this section.
   a) Suppose the wind speed had been 60 km/h. How would the wind-chill equivalent temperature have changed throughout the day?
   b) Suppose the wind speed had increased by 10 km/h per hour and at the start of the day the wind speed was 10 km/h. How would the wind-chill equivalent temperature have changed throughout the day ?

Extend your thinking

4. The values of wind-chill equivalent temperature in the table were calculated by using a formula. In the formula, W represents the wind-chill equivalent temperature, S represents the wind speed in kilometres per hour, and T represents the temperature in degrees Celsius.

$$W = 33 - \frac{(10 - 0.28 \times S + \sqrt{28 \times S}) \times (33 - T)}{22.727}$$

Use this formula to check three of the values for wind-chill equivalent temperature in the table on page 44.

5. Exposed flesh freezes when the wind-chill equivalent temperature is approximately −30°C.
   a) Use the table on page 44 to estimate some approximate combinations of wind speed and temperature that result in a wind-chill equivalent temperature of −30°C.
   b) Draw a graph that shows the combinations of temperature and wind speed that cause exposed flesh to freeze.

COMMUNICATING

The Ideas

In your journal, write a few sentences about what the world would be like without integers. Respond to these questions.
Without integers:
- What changes would have to be made to thermometers?
- How could we describe a situation where something decreases in size?
- What changes would occur in how we score in golf?

The Celsius temperature scale is based on the freezing and boiling points of water. When Anders Celsius first proposed this scale in 1742, he chose 100° to represent the freezing point and 0° to represent the boiling point. What if this scale had not been reversed? What do you think it would be like to use this scale?

MEASUREMENT

Developing the Ideas
▶ ▶ *Through Discussion*

As noted in the article below, in January 1992, The Toronto Star and The Financial Post newspapers became smaller.

Papers Shrink Pages

Post, Star to use smaller formats

You could forgive the publishers of The Financial Post and The Toronto Star if scenes from the 1989 comedy movie *Honey, I Shrunk The Kids* have lately been flashing through their minds.

The Post is set to shrink its traditional broadsheet weekly edition into the 50% smaller tabloid format—measuring about 30 cm wide by 38 cm deep—it uses for its weekday papers.

By contrast, The Star is expecting to make "huge" savings on its newsprint bill by trimming its pages to about 32 cm by 56 cm from their present 34 cm by 59 cm.

"There may be a small increase in the number of pages, but we're looking at probably over $10 million a year in savings."

Discuss the following questions

1. How did the dimensions of each paper change?

2. How did the area of one page of each newspaper change? Find the percent decrease in the area.

3. During the week, The Toronto Star is often about 90 pages long. About 500 000 papers are sold per day. Calculate the area of newsprint that was saved daily by making the change.

4. Is there a newspaper in your area of the country that has made some changes that are similar to those made by The Financial Post and The Toronto Star?

Arrange for some of your classmates to bring the following items into your mathematics class: kitchen scales, several different newspapers, and a large pair of scissors.

- Weigh each newspaper.
- Record the mass of each newspaper.
- Cut each newspaper in half length-wise and then width-wise.

1. By what percent have the length and width been reduced?

2. By what percent has the area been reduced?

- Weigh each "reduced" newspaper. Compare each new mass with the original mass.

3. By what percent has the mass of each newspaper been reduced?

Working with Mathematics

Something to talk about

1. Have you ever bought chocolate milk in a 500-mL container? Would you notice a difference if the container held 501 mL? If you live in Quebec you might not notice the change in volume, but you would notice a change in price. As indicated in the article below, which was printed in October 1991, there is a tax difference between the two sizes. The dairies made a change to save consumers paying a tax on their purchases.

   a) Do you think that the dairies had to change their containers to accommodate the extra 1 mL?

   b) Can you think of any other products that may have been changed (or could be changed) to save consumers from paying tax on them?

TAX/ *Quebec dairies have made a major minor change that shields their product from the tax man*

Milking the Rules to the Smallest Drop

Call it the one-millilitre solution.

With a little help from the Quebec government, the province's dairies have found a way to avoid provincial and federal sales taxes on some single-serving containers of chocolate milk.

That is because in designing the GST, Ottawa determined that single-serving containers of flavoured milk—including chocolate milk—would be taxed, while larger sizes would be exempt as basic groceries. And Revenue Canada decided 500 mL was a reasonable cutoff.

The dairies have started to sell chocolate milk in containers holding 501 mL of milk, instead of the standard 500 mL. By doing so, they avoid the 7% GST and the 8.56% Quebec provincial sales tax.

Work together

2. a) Suppose you were to fold this net to form a cube. How many times on the cube would arrows be pointing towards each other across an edge?

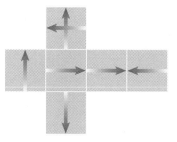

   b) Suppose all the dimensions of the net in part a were doubled. How would the surface area and the volume of the cube change?

   c) Make up a puzzle of your own that is similar to the one in part a. Which is easier: making up this type of puzzle or finding the answer?

If a spreadsheet program is available, use it to complete exercise 3.

3. Cut a piece of paper 26 cm by 20 cm. Remove a 1-cm square from each corner. Fold up the edges to make an open box.

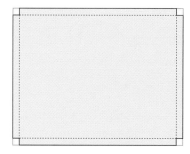

The width of the paper is 20 cm. 1 cm is removed from each end. So, the width of the open box is 18 cm. Similarly, the length of the box is 24 cm. The height is 1 cm. The volume of the box is
24 cm $\times$ 18 cm $\times$ 1 cm = 432 cm^3.
Suppose you were to change the size of the cut-out square. How do you think the volume would change? Would it be bigger or smaller?

If the length of the cut-out square is 2 cm, then the dimensions of the open box will be 22 cm by 16 cm by 2 cm. The volume is 22 cm × 16 cm × 2 cm = 704 cm³, which is much greater than the first volume. So, what do you think? If we increase the size of the cut-out square, will the volume increase too?

a) Copy and complete the table. Write a brief report on how the volume of the open box changes as the length of the cut-out square increases from 1 cm to 9 cm.

Length of the cut-out square (cm)	Length of the box (cm)	Width of the box (cm)	Height of the box (cm)	Volume of the box (cm³)
1				
2				
3				
4				
5				
6				
7				
8				
9				

b) i) Is it possible for the length of the cut-out square to be less than 1 cm?

ii) Is it possible for it to be more than 9 cm?

iii) What is the volume of the open box for each case?

c) i) Draw a graph of the volume of the open box against the length of the cut-out square.

ii) What environmentally-related problem could be addressed by using this graph?

Extend your thinking

4. Refer to exercise 3.

a) Repeat the investigation starting with a square piece of paper. Use your graph to determine the size of square to be removed from the corners to maximize the volume.

b) Repeat part a using other sizes of squares.

c) For each square, compare the size of square cut out for maximum volume with the size of the original square. Describe any patterns that you see. Write a report of your findings.

COMMUNICATING

The Ideas

Look through a magazine. Estimate the percent of space that is devoted to advertizing. How do you think this percent may change throughout the year? Would this percent be different in a magazine that appealed to a different age group? In your journal, write a report to summarize your comments.

In January 1994, Canada's national debt was $500 billion. With this amount of money, one media report said, the TransCanada highway from Vancouver to Ottawa could be "paved" in both directions with $100 bills. Find the dimensions of a $100 bill and the width of the highway. Use these values to calculate the distance from Vancouver to Ottawa. Was the media report correct?

Review

1. Consider the arrangement of numbers below.

4	512	16
128	32	8
64	2	256

Pick any row. Multiply the three numbers in this row. Repeat for the other two rows, then for the three columns and the two diagonals. What do you notice about your answers? How is this square related to the magic square on page 24?

2. Mathematics enables us to predict the year in which a comet, not seen in our lifetime, will reappear. In 1682, Sir Edmund Halley saw the comet that now bears his name. He learned that a major comet had also been sighted in the years 1380, 1456, 1531, and 1607. Halley guessed that these sightings were of the same comet. He successfully predicted the year when it would return.
    a) In what year do you think the comet was next seen?
    b) The last time Halley's comet appeared was in 1986. In what year might you next see the comet?

3. The average heartbeat pumps 50 mL of blood through the heart. Suppose a teenager has 4.75 L of blood.
    a) How many heartbeats are needed to pump this blood once through the heart?
    b) Suppose a heart beats 72 times per minute. How long will it take to pump the blood once through the heart?

4. Find the cost of purchasing $350 U.S. if $1 Can is worth each amount.
    a) 72¢ U.S.
    b) 80¢ U.S.
    c) 83¢ U.S.
    d) 74.5¢ U.S.

5. Sarah's brother Evan was born on her third birthday.
    a) Find the ratio of their ages when Sarah is 6, and every 3 years after, until Evan is 18.
    b) What is the ratio of their ages when Sarah is each age?
       i) 33 years   ii) 63 years   iii) 93 years

6. Sacha purchased some ski equipment. Here is the list of prices.

Skis	$275
Boots	$180
Bindings	$145
Clothing	$165

    a) Suppose the boots and bindings are on sale at a 20% discount. What was the total cost for all the items?
    b) Suppose the clothing was on sale at a 35% discount. What was the total cost for all the items?
    c) Suppose Sacha bought the items at the listed prices. She paid 8% provincial sales tax and 7% GST. What was the total cost?
    d) Suppose the skis were on sale for $195. What percent reduction is this?

7. A used car has a "For sale" sign, and a price of $8999 on the windshield. The dealer wants to sell it quickly so she adds a "15% off this price" to the sign.
    a) What will the car cost at the lower price?
    b) The purchaser will have to pay provincial sales tax of 8%. What is the total cost of the car?

8. Some integers can be written as the sum of two or more consecutive integers; for example, $+7 = (+3) + (+4)$. Write each integer as the sum of consecutive integers.
    a) -11 b) 18   c) -14
    d) -17 e) 21   f) 20

Rounding Prices

The CD Café opened for business in 1993 in Ontario. It was one of the first music stores in Canada to allow a customer to listen to a CD before deciding whether or not to buy it.

Trevor Poczynek is the owner and manager. He created a casual and relaxed atmosphere in which customers can sip on coffee, pop, or tea while they listen to CDs of their choice.

When Trevor was planning his store, he decided that he did not want to be bothered with making change. He chose his retail prices carefully so that the after-tax price was always a multiple of 25¢. The multiples that he decided to use are: $18.25, $19.50, $20.50, $22.75, $24.00, and $25.25.

ACTIVITY 1

In Ontario there are two taxes that consumers pay on most things that they buy. There is an 8% provincial sales tax (PST) and a 7% federal goods and services tax (GST). These taxes are applied separately. In effect, there is a 15% sales tax on purchases that are taxable. How should Trevor price each CD so that its after-tax price is one of the multiples of 25¢?

ACTIVITY 2

Suppose that Trevor decides to open a store in Alberta. Here, there is no provincial sales tax and the GST is 7%. Trevor wants to use the same after-tax prices that he uses in Ontario.
What changes should he make in his retail prices?

ACTIVITY 3

Trevor has set his prices on single purchases so that the only change he needs is quarters.
What happens if someone buys two or more CDs?
What happens if these CDs have different retail prices?
In these cases, is it possible for the after-tax price *not* to be a multiple of 25¢?

The article below was printed in July, 1993. There is a trend throughout the United States not to give change when the amount is small.

Pennies From Hell: Businesses Starting to Keep the Change

In trendy Georgetown, Rocklands Barbecue Restaurant programs its cash register to round off to $5.70 a check that would normally total $5.66.

More than 1,000 Winn-Dixie, Kroger and other supermarkets offer customers the option of raising their tabs to the next dollar, with the extra pennies and other small change designated for charity.

And uncounted bars, restaurants and other retail establishments across the land are ignoring register exactitude, preferring to allow 1 to 4 cents a transaction—occasionally more—simply to go uncollected.

Opposition to Small Change

Americans have become impatient with transactions involving small change, especially pennies. Increasingly, they eliminate the one-cent coin, so prominent in popular imagination and idiom—penny pincher, penny arcade, "a penny saved is a penny earned"—from daily life.

ACTIVITY 4

Keep track of purchases made by you, your family, and your friends over a period of time. Investigate how many times the total amount is rounded up or down or not at all. Assume that the rounding is done to the nearest multiple of 10¢. What do you think of this idea?

Do you think that this idea would be accepted by most people?

ACTIVITY 5

How many stores do you know where there is a container of pennies that is used when a customer does not have the exact money?

Do you think this is costly for stores that do this?

COMMUNICATING The Ideas

Write a brief report that summarizes the results of your investigations.

WHAT'S COMING UP?

DEPARTMENTS

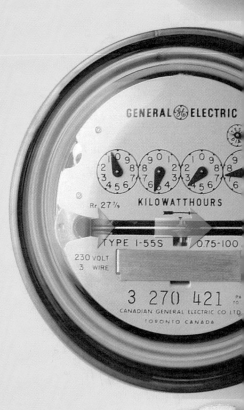

Linking Ideas

Mathematics Files

Quests

Minds on Math

Start With What You Know

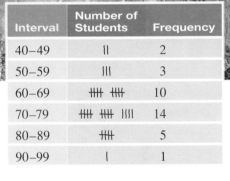

Miscellaneous
15%

Industrial
4%

Railway
7%

Lightning
43%

Resident
12%

Recreation
19%

**Causes of Ontario
Forest Fires**

ONTARIO WILDFIRES BURN HUNDREDS OF thousands of hectares of forest each year. The Ministry of Natural Resources keeps records of the causes of the fires. In this way it can target the right groups for fire-prevention education.

Interval	Number of Students	Frequency
40–49	II	2
50–59	III	3
60–69	IIII IIII	10
70–79	IIII IIII IIII	14
80–89	IIII	5
90–99	I	1

1. What percent of Ontario's forest fires are caused by lightning?

2. There were 2560 fires last year. How many were caused by people using the forests for recreation?

3. How could this information be displayed using another type of graph?

Two ways to show the marks of a mathematics test are shown on the right.

4. What percent of students scored above 79?

5. In which interval is the median mark?

6. What percent of students had marks below 60?

7. The pass mark is 50. How many students failed the test?

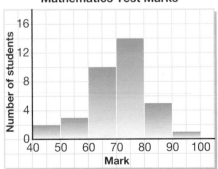

Mathematics Test Marks

Number of students (vertical axis: 0, 4, 8, 12, 16)
Mark (horizontal axis: 40, 50, 60, 70, 80, 90, 100)

St. John's, Newfoundland, is renowned for its fog. However, as this graph shows, it has its share of rain and snow, too.

8. What appears to be the rainy season in St. John's?

9. In which month did the rainfall equal the snowfall?

10. Explain the difference between:
    a) a pictograph and a bar graph
    b) a broken-line graph and a continuous-line graph
    c) a bar graph and a histogram

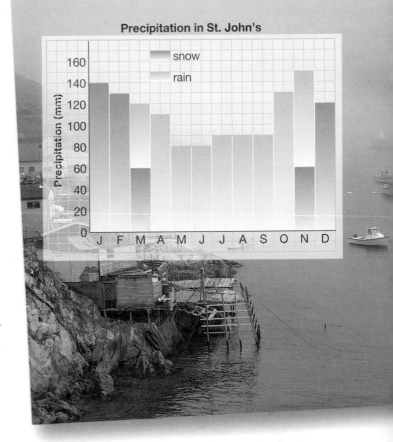

Precipitation in St. John's

Suppose you and your friend are deciding who should pay for a movie you want to rent.

You shuffle a deck of cards. You say you will pay if you pick a card which is 6 or less (ace counts as 1). You pick a card.

11. Who is more likely to pay for the movie?

In front of you are 3 paper bags. They contain red and purple "jaw-breakers." Without looking at the candies, you pick one from a bag.

12. From which bag are you most likely to pick a red candy?

13. Suppose you picked a red candy from that bag. Another candy is picked from the same bag. What are the chances that it is also red?

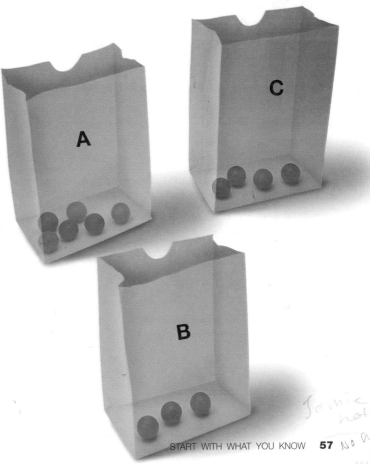

The pointer on this circle is spun.

14. What is the probability that the pointer will stop on the blue region?

COLLECTING DATA

Developing the Ideas
▶ ▶ *Through Instruction*

The first part of this chapter deals with statistics.

We need to understand statistics because advertisers, the media, and governments use statistics to influence our decisions.

How do researchers determine:
- the most popular television program?
- the percent of families in which more than one language is spoken?
- the average income of high-school graduates?
- the clothing preferences of teenagers?

There are two ways to obtain the information needed to answer questions like these. We could collect data directly, or use reference books and computer databases.

Data are collected directly by:

- Telephone Surveys

Most opinion polls are conducted this way. They are used to determine trends or opinions across the province or country.

- Personal Interviews

These are usually conducted in shopping malls. They are used by a company that wants to know what the public feels about one of its products. People are approached and asked one or more questions. These people may evaluate the taste, the smell, or the look of a product. They may have to compare similar products. A market research company will design the survey, analyze the data, and report to the company.

- Mail-in Questionnaires

These are found in newspapers and magazines. They may be received in the mail from government agencies or advertisers. A bank may send surveys to some of its customers to find out how satisfied they are with the services at their local branches.

12- 18075

Statistics Canada / **Statistique Canada**

CANADIAN RESIDENT QUESTIONNAIRE FOR SAME DAY AUTOMOBILE TRAVEL BETWEEN THE U.S. AND CANADA

QUESTIONNAIRE DESTINÉ AUX AUTOMOBILISTES DU MÊME VOYAGES ENTRE LES ÉTATS-UNIS ET LE CANADA POUR D RÉSIDENTS DU CANADA

Welcome!
In a given year, more than 60 million international automobile trips of less than 24 hours are taken by both U.S. and Canadian residents. This voluntary sample survey measures the level of same day international travel — an economic and cultural characteristic of hundreds of communities on both sides of the border.

Please take the time to tell us about this same day trip. The survey is conducted under the authority of the Statistics Act (R.S.C. 1985, c S19) and your answers will be kept confidential. Your cooperation is essential and appreciated. Please print.

Bienvenue!
Au cours d'une année, il y a plus de 60 millions de voyages internationaux de moins de vingt-quatre heures effectués par des résidents américains Cette enquête-échantillonnage volontaire vise à déterminer les caractè voyages internationaux du même jour – une caractéristique culturelle et é pour des centaines de localités des deux côtés de la frontière.
Veuillez prendre le temps de nous renseigner sur ce voyage d'un mê L'enquête est menée selon les dispositions de la Loi sur la statistique (L.R. ch. S19) et vos réponses seront tenues confidentielles. Votre collaboration es tielle et appréciée. Écrire en lettres moulées s.v.p.

1. Where do you live? / Où habitez-vous? Country: / Pays: 1 ☐ Canada 2 ☐ United States / États-Unis 3 ☐ Other / Autres

City/Town: / Cité/Ville:

Province:

Postal Code: / Code postal:

2. On this trip, where and when did you enter Canada? / Lors de ce voyage, où et quand êtes-vous entré(e) au Canada?   Canadian border crossing – Endroit (Poste-frontière)

Definition of TRAVELLING PARTY Includes yourself and only those for whom you feel comfortable reporting spending. / **La définition D'UN GROUPE** Nous vous demandons d'inclure vous-même et seulement les personnes pour qui vous ne voyez pas d'inconvénient à ra dépenses.

3. On this trip, how many people, including yourself, were in the travelling party? / Lors de ce voyage, combien de personnes, y compris vous-même, comptait votre groupe?

4. What was the main destination on this trip? / Quelle était votre destination principale lors de ce voyage?   City/Town: / Cité/Ville:

State: / État:

5. What was the TOTAL SPENDING (including cash or credit transactions) on this trip for all persons reported in Question 3? Estimates are appreciated or if no spending occurred, please check the appropriate box. / Quelles étaient LES DÉPENSES TOTALES (incluant les transactions au comptant ou à crédit) au cours de ce voyage pour toutes les personnes déclarées à la question 3? Des estimations sont satisfaisantes ou s'il n'y a pas eu de dépenses, veuillez cocher la boîte appropriée.

6 ☐ Spending / Dépense $ .00
or – ou
7 ☐ No Spending / Aucune dépense

6. What was the MAIN reason for this trip? / Quelle était la raison PRINCIPALE de ce voyage?
1 ☐ Commuting to work / Navette travail/domicile
2 ☐ Business / Affaires
3 ☐ Pleasure (including shopping or entertainment) / Agrément (y compris magasinage ou divertissements)
4 ☐ Visit friends or relatives / Visite à des amis ou des parents
5 ☐ Other (specify) / Autre (précisez)

THANK YOU. Please drop this card in any mail box in Canada. / MERCI. Veuillez déposer cette carte dans n'importe quelle boîte postale au Canada.

8-2200-338: 1990-08-13 STC/ECT-250-02797 SQC/ECT-250-02797

Can

Here is a sample from a survey given to people who return to Canada after a trip to the U.S. One reason for the survey is to find out how much money people spend outside Canada.

- Observations or Experiments

Information is found by testing or measuring. For example, the most popular chocolate bar in Canada is Crispy Crunch. Neilson Cadbury produces over 600 bars per minute. Each bar has a declared mass of 50 g. To check this, 125 samples are taken each day. The wrappers are removed and each bar is weighed.

What are the advantages and disadvantages of each method of collecting data directly?

We can find data in:
- encyclopedias and almanacs
- Statistics Canada publications
- library materials
- newspaper files
- computer databases (including the disk that accompanies this text)

We rely on other people who have collected the data directly, and published them in a source we can reference.

What are the advantages and disadvantages of collecting data from reference books and computer databases?

Working with Mathematics

Something to talk about

1. Have you ever participated in a survey? Tell your classmates about it.

2. Suppose a question on a survey asked, "How many are in your family?". What else might you need to know before you could respond?

3. Suppose you wanted to determine students' opinions of the food in the school cafeteria. What questions would you include in a personal interview survey?

4. Suppose you were estimating the percent of Canadian families with two parents who work outside the home. What are the advantages and disadvantages of obtaining the data:
   a) directly?
   b) from reference books?

On your own

5. To answer each question:
   i) Would you seek the data from a reference book? If so, what source?
   ii) Or, would you collect the data directly? If so, how would you collect them?
   a) What fraction of Canadians are under 18 years of age?
   b) What fraction of students in your class have jobs during the school year?
   c) What is the world record for the women's high jump?
   d) How much would it cost to buy $100 in U.S. funds?
   e) What percent of the meals eaten by Canadian teenagers are not eaten at home?
   f) What percent of the cars on the road have personalized licence plates?
   g) How many telephone calls does the average person make in one year?
   h) How many television stations can be received in your community?
   i) What percent of the Canadian population was born in Canada?

Work together

6. With three other students, select one of the following activities. Decide how to collect the data, then collect them. Discuss your results with the rest of the class. Keep the data you collected for future use.

If you choose Activity 1, you could use a word processor to construct your survey form.

Record your results in a database or a spreadsheet program. For example, if your survey contains 5 questions, create a database with these fields: Student's name, Question 1, Question 2, and so on.

If the possible responses to each question are labelled A, B, C, D, and E, enter these on the database. You can then sort the database using these as the sort criteria.

ACTIVITY 1

Conduct a survey of students in your class or school to determine:
a) their favourite songs in the current "top ten"
b) their favourite "junk foods"
c) their ideal dream vacations
d) what they would do if they won $1 000 000 in a lottery

ACTIVITY 2

Conduct experiments to determine:
a) the temperature of a cup of very hot water, taken every 30 s, for several minutes
b) the percent of times a total of seven occurs when two dice are rolled
c) the percent of times a thumbtack lands point up when tossed
d) the percent of times two heads occur when five coins are tossed

ACTIVITY 3

Use direct observation to determine:

a) the number of cars of each make in the school parking lot

b) the most popular colour of sweatshirt worn by students

c) the choice of beverage by students in the cafeteria during lunch

d) the number of students and teachers who watch a sports game at the school this week

ACTIVITY 4

Use reference materials to determine:

a) the Consumer Price Index for the last 10 years

b) the quantities of wheat exported by Canada during the last 10 years

c) the percent by volume of various gases in our atmosphere

d) the populations of the 10 largest countries in the world

e) the unemployment rates for various age groups in your province

DATA DISK

7. Use the *Land Use* database on the student's disk. Determine the change in the amount of forest/woodland in South American countries from 1974 to 1989. How does this compare with North American countries?

Extend your thinking

8. Develop a method for collecting data on the number of students with part-time jobs. The data should include the types of jobs, the numbers of hours worked, the rates of pay, and how the money is spent. How would you present the results to your classmates?

COMMUNICATING

The Ideas

In your journal, describe a data collection method you've observed. Why do you think this method was used? Compare the method with others that might have been used.

BOGGLE YOUR MIND

The Thousand Islands in the St. Lawrence River is one of the most picturesque regions in Canada. In 1985, when the last count was made, there were 1149 islands in the region. What if you were given the job of counting the islands? How do you think you could do this?

PRESENTING DATA

Developing the Ideas

After data have been collected, the information must be organized. This is important especially if you are dealing with large amounts of data. The presentation of the data should illustrate significant features and identify trends. In previous grades you learned how to draw and interpret different types of data graphs. Some of these are included in *Start With What You Know*; others are in the exercises that follow.

▶▶ *Through Instruction*

A bag of Cadbury's Mini Eggs has a label that reads 43 g. Every hour, 10 bags are taken from the production line and weighed. Here are some of the results.

Time	Mass of bag in grams
7:00	44.8, 44.9, 44.8, 44.7, 43.5, 44.9, 43.1, 44.8, 43.3, 45.0
8:00	43.6, 43.7, 43.2, 43.6, 43.1, 43.1, 43.2, 43.2, 43.6, 44.8
9:00	43.3, 43.4, 43.1, 43.3, 44.0, 45.0, 43.2, 43.2, 43.2, 45.2

One of the most useful ways to present these data is with a *stem-and-leaf diagram*. In this example the whole number part of each mass forms the stem, and the decimal part forms the leaf.

The whole number parts of the masses are 43, 44, and 45. A line is drawn to the right of these values. The leaves from the first column of data, namely 8, 6, and 3, are entered opposite the appropriate stem.

```
43. 63
44. 8
45.
```

When the next two columns of numbers are entered, the stem-and-leaf diagram looks like this:

```
43. 637421
44. 898
45.
```

When all of the numbers have been entered, the result is:

```
43. 6374216351112222362
44. 89870988
45. 002
```

On occasion, a more refined stem-and-leaf diagram may be an advantage. We split each stem into two parts, and arrange the numbers in order. The first part represents masses with decimal parts of 0, 1, 2, 3, or 4. The second part represents decimal parts of 5, 6, 7, 8, or 9.

43.	11112222223334
43.	56667
44.	0
44.	7888899
45.	002

Each line of the stem-and-leaf diagram is known as an *interval*. It represents an interval of numbers in the set of data.

When you have a lot of data, input them on a spreadsheet or database program in a computer, or in the data memory of a graphing calculator. The computer can sort the data. You can create a stem-and-leaf diagram more easily from sorted data.

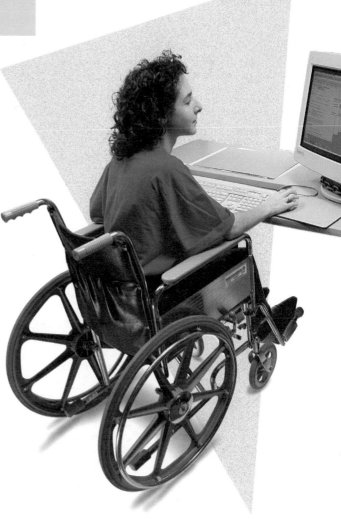

▶ ▶ *Through Discussion*

The Canadian Health and Disability Survey defines the disabled as those people who have trouble performing one or more of 17 activities. These include walking up stairs, lifting packages, reading newsprint (with glasses if usually worn), and hearing a normal conversation between two people. The disabled also include a person with a mental handicap, or with a long-term physical condition or health problem.

1. In the 15–34 age group, what percent of disabled men are employed?
2. In the 35–54 age group, what percent of disabled women are employed?
3. In which group is the greatest percent of people employed?
4. In which group is the least percent of people employed?
5. a) How does the percent of disabled people employed change as the people get older?
   b) Why do you think this happens?

Percent of disabled and non disabled populations employed, by age, 1991

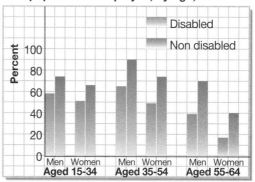

Working with Mathematics

Something to talk about

1. Suppose the marks (out of 100) on a mathematics test for your class ranged from 38 to 92. You are to show these marks on a stem-and-leaf diagram.
   a) What would you use:
      i) as the stems?
      ii) as the leaves?
   b) What would the length of the interval be?

2. What numbers are represented by this stem-and-leaf diagram?

```
10 | 79
11 | 2234
11 | 57789
12 | 0134
```

3. Name the type of graph you would use to display each set of data. Explain your choice.
   a) how a teenager spends her money:

entertainment	25%
sports equipment	40%
clothes	25%
miscellaneous	10%

   b) the value of the Canadian dollar relative to the U.S. dollar, the Japanese yen, the German mark, the French franc, the Dutch guilder, the Mexican peso, and the British pound
   c) the times the sun sets in Saskatoon at the end of each month throughout the year
   d) the favourite compact disk of the students in your school
   e) the stopping distances of a car travelling at various speeds
   f) the number of Grade 9 students in each province in Canada

On your own

4. A local radio station, CHFI, divides each hour of broadcast time as shown in the circle graph.

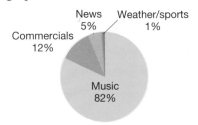

One Hour of Radio Time

   a) What percent of each hour is devoted to news?
   b) How many minutes each hour are devoted to commercials?

5. The bar graph shows the energy used for different activities. Energy is measured in kilojoules per minute.

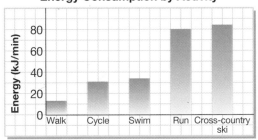

   a) Which activity burns up energy nearly three times as fast as walking?
   b) Suppose you cycled for 30 min. How much energy would you use?
   c) Suppose you want to burn up 2200 kJ of energy from a chocolate milkshake. For how long would you have to run ?

6. A recent census shows how the approximately 28 000 000 people living in Canada are divided among various age groups.

Age group (years)	0–14	15–34	35–54	Over 55
Percent of population	21%	32%	37%	10%

a) Display this information on a circle graph.
b) Display this information on a histogram.
c) Which graph do you think is more useful? Why?
d) How many Canadians are under 35 years of age?
e) How many Canadians are over 14 years of age?

Work together

7. There is an international standard for the size of golf balls. They must have a minimum diameter of 42.7 mm. A ball that has a diameter more than 0.3 mm smaller than this is marked "seconds." Randomly-selected golf balls are passed through a ring gauge to check their diameters. Measurements of 30 randomly-selected golf balls yielded these diameters in millimetres:

42.3	42.7	42.7	42.4	43.1	42.2
42.5	42.5	43.0	42.9	42.3	42.6
42.9	42.3	42.5	42.8	42.8	42.3
42.5	42.7	42.7	42.5	42.6	43.1
42.1	42.6	42.5	43.1	42.7	42.6

a) Construct a stem-and-leaf diagram to display these measurements.
b) What percent of these balls must be declared as "seconds"?
c) Construct a graph to represent these measurements.
d) Does it appear that about the same number of undersize golf balls are produced as oversize golf balls?

8. Use the *World Health and Education* database on the student's disk. Select 40 countries. The fertility rate of a country is the average number of children born to a woman in that country.

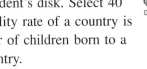

DATA DISK

a) Sort the countries by the Fertility rate 1980 field. Draw a stem-and-leaf diagram to represent these data.
b) Sort the countries by the Fertility rate 1990 field. Draw a stem-and-leaf diagram to represent these data.
c) Compare the two diagrams. Describe and explain any differences.

9. The tables show the percent of the disabled and the non disabled populations who are employed, and the education they received.

EMPLOYMENT RATE OF DISABLED PEOPLE		Elementary or no education	Post secondary education
Aged 15–34	Men	33%	78%
	Women	28%	69%
Aged 35–64	Men	42%	70%
	Women	18%	52%

EMPLOYMENT RATE OF NON DISABLED PEOPLE		Elementary or no education	Post secondary education
Aged 15–34	Men	71%	88%
	Women	38%	77%
Aged 35–64	Men	82%	93%
	Women	39%	68%

a) Draw a double-bar graph to illustrate the data for disabled people, and the data for non disabled people.
b) "The better educated a person is, the more likely he or she is to be employed." From your graphs, is this statement true?
c) What other conclusions can you draw from these graphs?

10. The chart shows the stopping distances for speeds from 20 km/h to 130 km/h on dry, clean, level pavement. This information is used in drivers' education courses. A stopping distance is the sum of the driver reaction distance and the braking distance. Many factors affect stopping distance: road conditions, the incline of the road, tire conditions, and so on.

Speed (km/h)	Average stopping distance (nearest metre)
20	8
30	12
40	17
50	23
60	31
70	41
80	52
90	66
100	81
110	99
120	120
130	143

a) What is meant by "driver reaction distance"?

b) What is meant by "braking distance"?

c) Draw a continuous-line graph to illustrate these data.

d) What is the stopping distance for a speed of:
   i) 65 km/h?   ii) 95 km/h?

e) How does a wet road affect stopping distance?

11. Record the heights of the students in your class.
   a) Construct a stem-and-leaf diagram for these heights using an interval of:
      i) 10 cm   ii) 5 cm
   b) Draw a histogram to display these data.
   c) Why would it be inappropriate to draw a bar graph of these data?

Extend your thinking

12. A school's Grade 9 students obtained these marks (out of 100) on an English examination.

55 66 64 98 56 69 68 62 52 69 65 63 51 90 69

68 32 66 72 44 80 61 84 74 66 79 61 89 78 63

66 59 75 53 69 23 92 78 73 67 38 65 67 41 75

63 71 57 77 66 56 63 73 24 56 76 71 61 51 46

84 55 63 68 86 65 69 66 60 62 68 82 73 65 76

79 88 44

a) Organize and display these data in three different ways.

b) Which method of presentation is most effective, and why?

c) Enter the data in a spreadsheet. Experiment with various charts to present the data in different ways.

COMMUNICATING The Ideas

In the preceding section you worked with a group of students to collect data for one of four activities. Work with the same students to organize the data you collected. Present your results to the rest of the students in your class.

If you used a spreadsheet to record your data, you can use the program to do calculations with the data, and report the results. Use the word processor to write up your report, and the Draw program to produce illustrations, charts, and graphs.

Electricity Use

We have many labour-saving appliances and entertainment equipment in our homes. These use electricity as do some heating and cooling systems. If we pay attention to our use of electricity, we should be able to save money and resources.

You can see how an appliance uses energy. Locate the electricity meter in your home. Observe the speed of the turning dial. Have someone in your home turn on the stove or clothes dryer. Watch what happens to the speed of the dial.

Energy is measured in watts (W) or kilowatts (kW). Energy use is measured in kilowatt-hours. For any appliance, energy use is the product of energy and the time for which the appliance is in use (kWh).

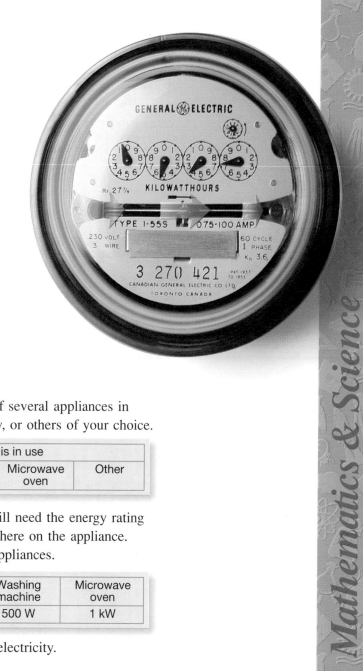

Set up a chart to record data on the energy use of several appliances in your home. Consider the appliances shown below, or others of your choice.

Date	Time in hours for which each appliance is in use				
	Clothes dryer	Television	Washing machine	Microwave oven	Other

Fill in the chart every day for one month. You will need the energy rating for each appliance. This should be shown somewhere on the appliance. Here are the average ratings for some common appliances.

Appliance	Clothes dryer	Television	Washing machine	Microwave oven
Energy rating	5 kW	80 W	500 W	1 kW

From your hydro bill, find the cost of 1 kWh of electricity.

1. For each appliance:
   a) Calculate the total time in hours that it is in use.
   b) Calculate the energy use in kilowatt-hours.
   c) Calculate the cost of running it for the month.

2. Construct a graph that illustrates the cost of running each appliance.

3. Comment on the graph. Can you think of ways in which your household could reduce its electricity use? Contact your local utility office for information.

MEASURES OF CENTRAL TENDENCY

Developing the Ideas

▶ ▶ *Through Discussion*

Here are the pay scales for Winnipeg fire fighters and police constables.

. ● ● ● ● ● ● ● ● ●

Class of constable	Pay	Level of fire fighter	Pay
4th	$24 908	Trainee	$27 274
3rd	$28 756	1st	$29 562
2nd	$38 324	4th	$38 662
1st	$47 918	Senior	$47 658

Who earns more, police constables or fire fighters?

From the data given, it appears that fire fighters earn more.
- Would all police constables earn less than all fire fighters?
- Would some fire fighters earn less than some police constables?
- What single number best represents the income of all members of each occupation? What further information would you need to calculate this number?

Recall that there are three commonly used averages:

● ● ● ● ● ● ● ●

The *mean* of a set of numbers is the average of the numbers: that is, the sum of all the numbers divided by the number of numbers.

● ● ● ● ● ● ● ●

The *median* of a set of numbers is the middle number when the numbers are arranged in order. If there is an even number of numbers, the median is the mean of the two middle numbers.

● ● ● ● ● ● ● ●

The *mode* of a set of numbers is the most frequently occurring number. There may be more than one mode, or there may be no mode.

The mean, the median, and the mode are *measures of central tendency*. They tend to be located somewhere in the "centre" of the data. They give us information about the data. Often, large amounts of data are summarized by stating the values of the mean, the median, and the mode. The mode is seldom used as an average because it ignores all values except the most frequent.

Example 1 ....

The annual incomes for the people who work at the Beta Metal Works are shown below.

1 Manager: $80 000	3 Mechanics: $35 000
1 Supervisor: $45 000	5 Labourers: $25 000

a) Determine the mean, the median, and the mode for the payroll.

b) Which measure could be used to make the salaries look:

  i) high?   **ii)** low?

c) Which measure most fairly represents the average income?

d) Suppose the manager's salary were changed to $150 000. What changes would that make to the answers in part a?

Solution

a) The mean salary, in dollars, is given by:

$$\frac{80\ 000 + 45\ 000 + (3 \times 35\ 000) + (5 \times 25\ 000)}{10} = \frac{355\ 000}{10}$$
$$= 35\ 500$$

For the median, arrange the salaries in order:

80 000, 45 000, 35 000, 35 000, 35 000, 25 000, 25 000, 25 000, 25 000, 25 000

Since there is an even number of salaries, the median is the mean of the fifth and sixth values.

$$\frac{35\ 000 + 25\ 000}{2} = \frac{60\ 000}{2}$$
$$= 30\ 000$$

The mode is the salary that occurs most often, $25 000.
The mean is $35 500, the median is $30 000, and the mode is $25 000.

b) i) To make the salaries look high, the mean value of $35 500 would be chosen as being representative.

ii) To make the salaries look low, the mode value of $25 000 would be chosen as being representative.

c) Only 2 of the 10 employees earn more that the mean value of $35 500. Therefore, as a representative value, it is too high. Since every employee earns at least the mode value of $25 000, as a representative value, this is too low. The median value of $30 000 probably best represents the average income.

d) If the manager's salary is increased to $150 000, the total payroll increases by $70 000. The mean increases by $\frac{\$70\ 000}{10}$, or $7000, to $42 500. The median does not change. It is not affected by large changes in extreme values. The mode does not change either.

$80 000

$45 000

$35 000

$25 000

Example 2..

The number of tonnes of household garbage taken to a municipal landfill site each day of a month is shown below. The landfill site is closed on weekends.

304	312	285	328	316	309	315	293
340	314	299	281	323	309	324	313
307	296	342	321	284	317	298	

a) What are the mean and median masses of household garbage taken to the landfill site?

b) The landfill site can accommodate 500 000 t of garbage before it is full. When must a new site be found?

c) Suppose reducing, reusing, and recycling result in a 15% reduction in household garbage each year. How much longer would the municipality be able to use the landfill site?

Solution

a) The mean $= \dfrac{\text{sum of all the garbage}}{\text{number of days}}$

$= \dfrac{304 + 312 + 285 + \cdots + 284 + 317 + 298}{23}$

$= \dfrac{7130}{23}$

$= 310$

The mean mass is 310 t.

To find the median, we create a stem-and-leaf diagram. We arrange the leaves in numerical order.

```
28 | 1 4 5
29 | 3 6 8 9
30 | 4 7 9 9
31 | 2 3 4 5 6 7
32 | 1 3 4 8
33 |
34 | 0 2
```

The median is the middle value. There are 23 values. The median is the twelfth value from either 281 or 342. The median mass is 312 t.

b) Since the landfill site is closed on weekends, the 7130 t of garbage were collected in approximately one month.
In one year, approximately 12×7130 t, or 85 560 t are collected.
Since the capacity of the site is 500 000 t, a new site must be found in $\dfrac{500\ 000}{85\ 560}$ years, or approximately 6 years after this site is first used.

c) Suppose the amount of garbage collected in 1 year is reduced by 15%. The annual amount collected would then be 85% of 85 560, which is $0.85 \times 85\ 560 = 72\ 726$. A new site would have to be found in $\dfrac{500\ 000}{72\ 726}$ years, or approximately 7 years. A 15% reduction would enable the landfill site to be used for an additional year.

Working with Mathematics

Something to talk about

1. Which measure of central tendency is most suitable to describe each average? Why?
   a) the average volume of water used by a Canadian household in one day
   b) the average number of pages in a newspaper
   c) the average mark of a student on a test
   d) the average rainfall in Quebec city
   e) the average time you spend on homework each night
   f) the average size of shoes sold by a store

On your own

2. State the mean, median, and mode for the data in this stem-and-leaf diagram.

   ```
   2 | 3 3 5 7 8
   3 | 0 1 2 2 5 7
   4 | 0 1 1 2 6 8 9
   5 | 1 4 4 6 8 9
   ```

3. State the mean and the median for each set of data.
   a) 15, 18, 16, 21, 18, 14, 12, 19, 11, 16
   b) 1, 2, 2, 3, 4, 3, 4, 4, 4, 4, 4, 4, 5
   c) 9, 12, 7, 5, 18, 15, 5, 11

4. In one year, a person bought 3 CDs at $18.99, 5 CDs at $14.99, and 1 CD at $10.99. Find the mean and the median for the amounts spent.

5. The mean of the numbers 8, 12, 13, 14, and x is 13. What is the value of x?

6. Use the *Olympic Summer Games* database on the student's disk. Choose an event. Extract the winning time (or distance) for each year. Use the sorting capabilities of the program to help you create a stem-and-leaf diagram to represent these results. From the diagram, determine the mean and median times (or distances).

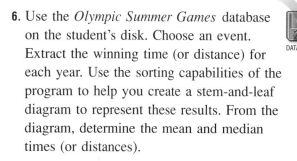
DATA DISK

Work together

7. For the numbers 40, 42, 43, 44, 45, 46, 47, 48, 49, 50, and 52, find the effect on the mean and the median if:
   a) each number is increased by 5
   b) each number is doubled
   c) the smallest number is increased by 2 and the largest number is decreased by 2

8. The table shows the annual incomes of people who work for a CBC network current affairs show.

POSITION	SALARY ($)
1 executive producer	76 000
1 senior producer	65 000
2 hosts	63 000
4 producers	55 000
2 associate producers	44 500
4 researchers	33 000

   a) Find the measures of central tendency for these salaries.
   b) Which measure of central tendency most fairly represents the pay structure? Give reasons for your answer.

Extend your thinking

9. Determine 7 numbers that have a mean of:
   a) 12 and a median of 13
   b) 62 and a median of 65
   c) 8, a median of 10, and a mode of 5
   d) 15, a median of 12, and a mode of 15

COMMUNICATING

The Ideas

Use a dictionary to find the meaning(s) of the word "median." In your journal, explain how the meaning in statistics is similar to the meanings in other uses, such as median of a highway.

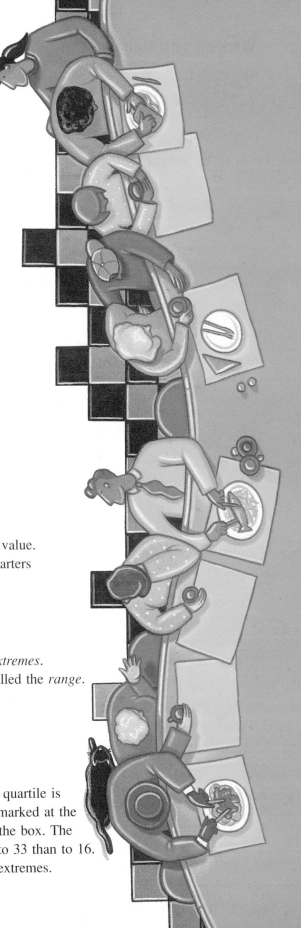

BOX-AND-WHISKER PLOTS

Developing the Ideas

▶ ▶ *Through Instruction*

We display data on a graph or a chart. How do we display the measures of central tendency? Are there other numbers that can be used to represent data? Can we display these numbers as well?

In the last section we learned that the *median* is the value that is located at the half-way point when the data are arranged in increasing order.

There are other values that are useful to know. The value that is located at the one-quarter point is called the *lower quartile*. The value that is located at the three-quarters point is called the *upper quartile*.

Suppose, for 11 days, the manager of a local coffee shop counted the numbers of people eating lunch. Here are the numbers:

9, 16, 37, 28, 32, 18, 30, 21, 40, 33, 12

We will find the median and the quartiles for these data. To do this, we arrange the data in increasing order.

9   12   16   18   21   28   30   32   33   37   40

Since there are 11 values, the half-way point is the sixth value. The one-quarter point is the third value, and the three-quarters point is the ninth value.

The median is 28.
The lower quartile is 16.
The upper quartile is 33.

The least and greatest values in the data are called the *extremes*. The difference between the extremes, 40 − 9 = 31, is called the *range*.

We use a *box-and-whisker plot* to display these data.

The box and the whiskers are drawn to scale. The lower quartile is marked at the left end of the box. The upper quartile is marked at the right end. The median is shown as a vertical line inside the box. The median is closer to the upper quartile since 28 is closer to 33 than to 16. We draw line segments from the ends of the box to the extremes.

Example ....

Example 2 on page 70 listed the tonnes of household garbage taken to a landfill. Use the stem-and-leaf diagram in the solution of that example to draw a box-and-whisker plot to display these data.

Solution

The stem-and-leaf diagram is shown at the right.
There are 23 values.
The median is the value at the half-way point, 312.
The lower quartile is the value at the one-quarter point:
it is the sixth value, 298.
The upper quartile is the value at the three-quarters point:
it is the eighteenth value, 321.
The extremes are 281 and 342.

28	1 4 5
29	3 6 8 9
30	4 7 9 9
31	2 3 4 5 6 7
32	1 3 4 8
33	
34	0 2

We use these values to draw the box-and-whisker plot.

```
        298      312   321
281  ┌────────┬──────┐              342
 ├───┤        │      ├──────────────┤
     └────────┴──────┘
```

The mean can also be marked on the box-and-whisker plot.
Draw a vertical line to scale at the appropriate location.

For the landfill site data, recall that the mean is 310.

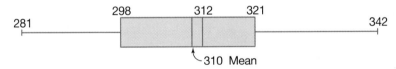

```
        298      312  321
281  ┌────────┬─┬──┐               342
 ├───┤        │ │  ├───────────────┤
     └────────┴─┴──┘
              └ 310 Mean
```

When you are working with a lot of data, you could input them in a spreadsheet or a database program and use the Sort feature. This makes it easier to create a stem-and-leaf diagram or a box-and-whisker plot.

Recall that to find the median when there is an even number of values, we arrange the data in order and find the mean of the two middle values. Similarly, to find the quartiles when there is an even number of values in the first and second halves of the ordered data, we find the mean of the two middle values in each half.

Working with Mathematics

Something to talk about

1. Find the quartiles and the range for each set of data in exercises 2 and 3 on page 71.

2. This box-and-whisker plot shows the marks of students on a recent examination. Explain the meaning of each number shown.

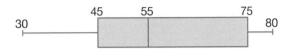

3. The heights of Grade 9 students are summarized by this box-and-whisker plot. What information does it display?

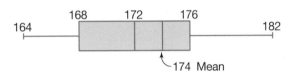

On your own

4. Two groups of students wrote the same mathematics test and obtained the following marks out of 20.

A	16	17	18	20	11	18	20	19	15
	15	20	15	15	17	12	19	8	
	13	16	17	14	19	14	20	12	
B	12	11	18	15	12	6	9	11	
	11	11	16	14	11	17	12	13	
	9	8	10	10	7	11	18	5	

a) For each group, calculate the measures of central tendency, the quartiles, and the range.

b) For each group, display this information on a box-and-whisker plot.

c) For the two groups taken together, calculate the measures of central tendency, the quartiles, and the range.

d) Display this information on a box-and-whisker plot.

Work together

5. a) Determine a set of 15 numbers which have a mean of 70, a lower quartile of 50, an upper quartile of 80, a lower extreme of 32, and a range of 60.

   b) Display your numbers on a stem-and-leaf diagram.

   c) Draw a box-and-whisker plot for these data.

6. The box-and-whisker plots below show the distribution of masses for the 28 members of the Toronto Blue Jays and the Philadelphia Phillies baseball teams. These teams met in the World Series in 1993.

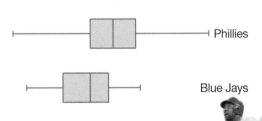

a) Use the plots to determine which team has:
   i) the heaviest player
   ii) the lightest player
   iii) the greater median mass
   iv) more players over 100 kg
   v) at least 6 players under 85 kg

b) It was reported in the media that the Blue Jays were fitter than the Phillies. If a smaller mass were an indication of fitness, do you think this report was true?

7. For each box-and-whisker plot shown below, describe the data from which it was drawn.

a)

b)

c)

d)

TEMPLATE DISK

8. Start a new document in a spreadsheet program. In each cell, type what is shown below.

	A	B
1		
2		
3	Lower quartile	12
4		
5		
6	Median	43
7		
8		
9	Upper quartile	62
10		
11		
12	----------	----------
13	Mean	

In cell B13, type a formula to calculate the mean of the numbers in cells B1 to B11.

In ClarisWorks, B13 is
=AVERAGE(B1..B11)

In Microsoft Works, B13 is
=Average(B1:B11)

Input any numbers you choose in cells B1, B2, B4, B5, B7, B8, B10, and B11. Ensure that the numbers are sorted from smallest to largest. Use the quartiles and the median shown in the chart.

a) Enter numbers so the mean and median are both 43.

b) Enter numbers so the mean equals the upper quartile.

c) Can you enter numbers so that the mean is equal to the lower quartile?

Extend your thinking

9. Quartiles divide a set of data into four parts. *Percentiles* divide a set of data into 100 parts. For example, the 90th percentile is the value in a set of data below which 90% of the data lie. If a person scores at the 90th percentile on an aptitude test, then she has scored above 90% of all other students writing the test.

a) Express the median, the lower quartile, and the upper quartile as percentiles.

b) Suppose a girl's height is at the 78th percentile among all Canadian girls her age. What percent of Canadian girls are taller than she is?

COMMUNICATING

The Ideas

How would you explain to a friend who has missed class why it is useful to arrange data in increasing (or decreasing) order? Which statistical measures require this? Why?

Unemployment Rates in Two Canadian Provinces

DATA DISK

Use the *Provinces of Canada* database on the student's disk. Each entry in the database provides data for one province for one year. Make a copy of the database, leaving the original for other people to use. Focus on the number of unemployed and the number of people in the labour force.

The unemployment rate is the percent of the labour force who are not employed.

1. Choose two provinces. For one year in each province:
   a) Identify the number of employed people and the number in the labour force.
   b) How many people are unemployed?
   c) Write the number of unemployed as a fraction of the labour force.
   d) Write the fraction as a percent. This is the unemployment rate for that year.

The computer will calculate the unemployment rate using this expression:

$$100 \left(1 - \frac{\text{number of employed persons}}{\text{number in labour force}} \right)$$

2. Create a new field. Define it as a calculated field by using the above expression. Name the field, Unemployment Rate.

   Note: Some database programs do not have calculated fields. If this is the case, create the field and use your calculator to determine the unemployment rate for each field. Enter the data by hand.

3. Select all the records for one of your two chosen provinces. Sort these records by the Unemployment Rate field.

4. Use the sorted list to draw a box-and-whisker plot of unemployment rate for this province.

5. Repeat exercises 3 and 4 for the second province. Draw the box-and-whisker plot against the same number line you used for the first province. In this way, you can compare the data.

6. Use the program to draw a double-bar graph. Plot Years along the x-axis and Rate along the y-axis. Use a different colour for each province.

7. The box-and-whisker plots and the double-bar graph both represent sorted data. The plots are sorts by unemployment rates; the graph is a sort by years. Interpret the plots and graph, and make comparisons between the provinces.

Mathematics & Technology

Linking Ideas

The Poggendorf Effect

Answer this question without using a ruler or drawing a line.
If line *l* were extended, where do you think it would cross the line AB?

Copy this diagram. Just look at the diagram on your copy and mark the point on AB with an X. Make your decision quickly without experimenting.

The diagram is an optical illusion. Most people tend to place their X too high on AB. Place a ruler along *l*. See how close your X is to the correct location.

This is known as the *Poggendorf effect*. To measure the magnitude or size of the effect, we measure the distance in millimetres from X to the correct location for *l* to cross AB.

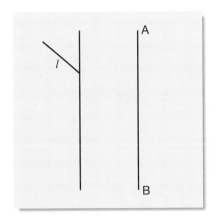

Does the magnitude of the Poggendorf effect depend on:
a) the distance between the vertical lines?
b) the angle at which *l* meets the first vertical line?
c) whether *l* slopes up to the right or down to the left?

Conduct a survey to find answers to these questions. Organize your data by using the methods you have learned in this chapter.
Write a report of your findings. What do you think is the cause of the Poggendorf effect?

a)

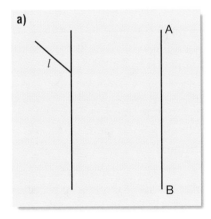

b) **c)**

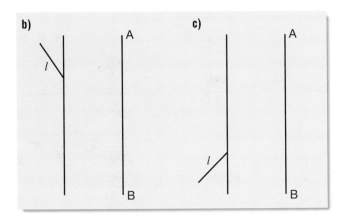

SAMPLES AND POPULATIONS

Developing the Ideas

▶ ▶ *Through Discussion*

In Activity 1 on page 60, students were surveyed to determine their preferences or opinions on a number of items.

- How were the students selected for the survey?

- Were some students, who could have been asked, left out of the survey? Why?

- How does the number of students surveyed compare with the number who could have been surveyed?

In these activities, a *sample* of students was consulted. That is, only a small number of those who could have been asked were included in the survey. All of those who could have been asked make up the *population*.

Sampling is useful to gain information about a very large body by observing or testing only a portion of it.

- When you sip a spoonful of soup to test how hot a bowl of soup is, you are sampling. Based on the temperature of the soup in your spoon, you decide if it is too hot to eat. In this case, the bowl of soup is the population.

- When you listen to one song on a CD before buying it, you are sampling the music on the CD. All the songs on the CD make up the population.

Various companies use sampling to survey the Canadian population.

- Gallup is a company that publishes monthly opinion surveys to identify trends in Canada. For a national survey, Gallup interviews 1000 people in Canada. This sample represents the population of 18 000 000 people in Canada who are 18 years and older.

- A. C. Nielsen is a company that monitors the TV viewing habits of Canadians. The company installs monitoring devices on TV sets in 1500 Canadian households. This sample represents the population of nearly 10 500 000 TV viewing households in Canada.

- The Society of Composers, Authors, and Music Publishers of Canada (SOCAN) is an organization that samples, in one year, about two weeks of air time on every Canadian radio station. SOCAN uses these data to decide how much royalty should be paid to each recording artist whose songs are played on the radio.

For each company named above, discuss these questions:

- What method of collecting data is used?

- What fraction of the population is chosen as the sample?

- Why is the entire population not surveyed?

If a sample is to represent a population, we must be sure that:

- the sample accurately reflects the population. Suppose 10 students in Canada are asked about their favourite TV programs and 7 of them pick the same program. We cannot say that 70% of all students in Canada prefer that program. The sample does not reflect the population.

- all members of the population have an equal chance of being selected; that is, it is a *random sample*.

Suppose only students in your class are asked about their favourite TV programs. Since students in other classes and grades have not been asked, the sample is not a random sample.

If the sample is selected at random then it accurately reflects the population, and conclusions about the population are likely to be valid.

▷ ▶ *Through a Guided Example*

Example ....

A Vancouver company is hired by a sports magazine to find out which teams Canadians think will meet in the World Series later in the year. To collect the data, the company considers sampling Canadians in one of the following ways.

a) Poll a random sample of 1000 people in British Columbia.

b) Put an advertisement in all major newspapers asking people to tell their preferences.

c) Send 100 questionnaires to all major businesses to be completed by anyone selected at random.

Describe the main weakness of each method.

Solution

a) Preferences in sports are often regional. A sample of people in British Columbia is not likely to be representative of the opinions of all Canadians.

b) Generally, only ardent baseball fans would take the trouble to respond to this advertisement. The sample will not be random.

c) This sample tends to exclude groups such as students, farmers, homemakers, and senior citizens. Therefore, it is not a random sample.

Working with Mathematics

Something to talk about

1. Explain why each sample may not provide accurate information about its population.
   a) A survey of your classmates is used to estimate the average age of students in your school.
   b) A survey of senior citizens is used to determine the music that is best liked by Canadians.
   c) To determine the proportion of domestic cars to foreign cars purchased by Canadians, a person records the numbers of domestic cars and foreign cars in the parking lot of the General Motors Assembly Plant in Oshawa, Ontario.
   d) To determine which movie is best liked by teenagers, 12 of your closest friends are interviewed.
   e) To estimate how many Canadians want the legal drinking age raised, a radio station runs an open-line talk show titled "Should we lower the drinking age?" and tallies the number of callers who are in favour and against.

2. For each case in exercise 1, describe how data might be collected to obtain valid information about each issue.

3. When a sample is used to find out about a population, some people think that the predictions are not valid. They do not believe that a well-constructed sample can provide data that are accurate. These people say that the information would be more accurate if the entire population was surveyed. Do you support this argument?

On your own

4. For each situation, explain why data are collected from a sample and not the population.
   a) The quality of flash bulbs
   b) The number of families who eat at least one meal together as a family per week
   c) The purity of processed food
   d) The strength of aluminum extension ladders
   e) The cost of ski equipment
   f) The percent of the population with each blood type

Work together

5. How would you collect data to find the following information? Give reasons for your answers.
   a) The popularity of a TV program
   b) The most popular breakfast cereal
   c) The average number of compact disks owned by high-school students
   d) The average number of people in one car in rush hour
   e) The most popular recording artist or group
   f) The average weekly fast-food budget for a teenager

6. For *one* of the following statements, decide what kind of sample you need. Work in a group of three or four to collect the data.
   a) The average age and height of the students in your class
   b) The average number of people in one car in rush hour
   c) The average amount spent on lunch in the school's cafeteria
   d) The most popular musical group
   e) The average time spent waiting in line in the cafeteria
   f) The average weekly earnings of students with part-time jobs
   g) The average number of letters in English words

7. For each study described, answer these questions.
   i) What is the population about which the information is sought?
   ii) How is the sample chosen?
   iii) Is it a random sample?

a) To assess the opinions of Canadians regarding the team who will win the Stanley Cup, researchers conducted telephone surveys of 10 000 people selected randomly from the Calgary telephone book.

b) To assess the support of the Canadian people for a tax on the wealthy, a researcher tallied the number of callers for and against this tax on the Money Matters TV phone-in show.

c) To estimate the annual income of the typical Canadian, researchers interviewed 5000 pedestrians randomly encountered on the streets of several Canadian cities.

d) To determine what legal drinking age is preferred by Canadian teenagers, researchers interviewed 8000 randomly-selected high-school students from across Canada.

8. For this exercise, work in groups of three or four. Your group has to determine whether most people prefer Coke or Pepsi or another soft drink. To do this, each member of the group should survey 5 to 10 teens and 5 to 10 adults. Try to ensure that the same people are not surveyed by two or more members of your group. Record the name and drink preference (Coke, Pepsi, or other) of each person you survey.

  a) After you have collected your data, prepare a brief report on the preferences of the teens and the adults.

  b) Combine the data from all group members.

    i) Tally the responses for each preference (Coke, Pepsi, or other).

    ii) Graph these data without regard for the age of those surveyed.

    iii) Graph these data showing how many teens and how many adults expressed each preference.

    iv) Name the soft drink which most teenagers preferred.

    v) Name the soft drink which most adults preferred.

    vi) Indicate whether age is a factor in soft drink preferences.

  c) i) Do the conclusions of your combined report agree with the conclusions of your individual reports? Discuss any differences.

    ii) Do you feel more confident in the conclusions of the combined report? Why?

  d) Try a blind taste test with 5 people who expressed a preference for either Coke or Pepsi.

    i) How many people were able to identify their favourite drinks while blindfolded? Express this number as a fraction of the total number surveyed.

    ii) Do people really know what they like?

Extend your thinking

9. The written material that accompanied the first CD players available in stores included a reference to "sampling" or "over-sampling." The quality of the machine was determined by how much over-sampling it did: 4 times, 8 times, 16 times. Contact a manufacturer of CD players to find out what this means.

The Ideas

In your journal, briefly describe the advantages of using a sample to collect data from a population. What must you remember when you work with samples?

Sampling and TV Ratings

How do television stations know which programs are the most popular? Why is this information important?

For the week of April 5–11, 1993, the top 5 programs in North America are shown.

RANK	PROGRAM	RATING POINT	SHARE	VIEWERS
1	NCAA Championship	22.2	34	32.9
2	Home Improvement	19.3	30	31.3
3	Roseanne	18.7	30	28.6
4	20/20	16.9	30	24.4
5	Seinfeld	16.2	27	23.1

One *Rating point* represents 931 000 households.
The *Share* is the percent of sets in use.
The *Viewers* is the number of viewers in millions.

Suppose 20% of households in Saint John watched a particular show. We can be sure, 15 times out of 20, that between 18.6% and 21.4% of the population with TV sets has watched the program.

There are more that 10 000 000 TV sets in Canada. The favourite programs are determined by using a random sample of viewers. Every home containing one or more TV sets has an equally-likely chance of being selected.

The A. C. Nielsen company monitors the TV viewing habits of Canadians. Since 1990, "people meters" have been used in 1500 households. Each meter records the television programs that are watched. A television set is connected to a small computer device, which in turn is connected to a special telephone line. Information about which station is watched, and by how many people, is stored at one-minute intervals throughout the day and night. A central computer retrieves these data daily, by using the special telephone line.

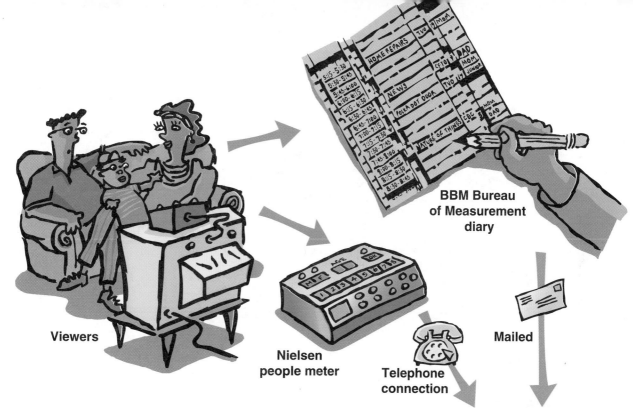

Viewers

Nielsen people meter

Telephone connection

Mailed

BBM Bureau of Measurement diary

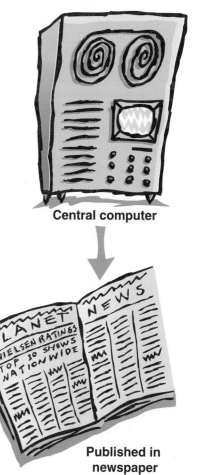

Central computer

The BBM Bureau of Measurement samples differently. It mails diaries to 60 000 homes each week. About 33 000 diaries are returned. There is one diary for each TV set in the home. When a person in the home watches TV, he or she records the name of the program every 15 min. Also recorded is the number of people watching the program.

The Nielsen ratings are frequently reported in the newspaper, as shown on the preceding page. These ratings rank the popularities of the shows by listing the numbers of people who watch them. Television ratings do not pass judgment on the quality of the program.

1. In the paragraph following the chart on the previous page, why do you think the phrase "15 times out of 20" is included?

2. What percent of TV sets in Canada have a "people meter"?

3. How many households in North America watched each program listed on the preceding page?

4. How many more viewers watched the NCAA championship than Seinfeld?

5. How many TV sets in Canada were tuned to Roseanne?

6. Why do the numbers in the Share column not add to 100%?

7. Check a newspaper to find the ratings for last week. How do they compare with the ratings above?

8. Why do you think the research companies have developed such sophisticated methods to determine viewer preferences?

Published in newspaper

Developing the Ideas

▶ ▶ *Through Discussion*

The cartoon illustrates that when we read or hear a statement involving statistics (especially a sensational one), we should think carefully about it. In this case, we must consider which groups of people are included in the 25 million.

From time to time, people may misinterpret statistics. In some cases, these misuses are by accident or lack of knowledge. In other cases, the misuse is deliberate and intentionally misleading.

A news commentator introduces a story with the statement: "32% of high-school students drop out."
Upon hearing this, you should ask questions like these:
- What is meant by "drop out"?
- Is the statement true for students in your school?
- If a student moves to another school, is he or she a "dropout"?
- If a student leaves school to take a job, is he or she a "dropout"?

What other questions could we ask?
Why would the commentator make such a statement?

Read the excerpt from a real-estate newspaper.
How is it misleading?

REAL-ESTATE SALES SOAR THIS SEPTEMBER

The slump in the real-estate market may be over. Sales of houses in September jumped by 18% over August, which is a traditionally slow month for real estate. Sales in September last year were 35% higher than the same month this year.

The heading states that the sales had "soared." The first sentence says that the real-estate slump may be over. This September's sales were 18% more than August's sales. However, last year's September sales were 35% higher than this September's. Also, since August is said to be a slow month for sales, we would expect September sales to be higher. A more accurate heading might be "Real-Estate Sales Improve in September."

In the previous section, we discussed the uses of sampling to survey a population. The sample must be random and must accurately reflect the population.

Sometimes data are collected in a way that may appear to be valid, but which in fact introduces a bias. In such a case, the biased sample has characteristics which are not typical of the population. Here is an example.

Ann Landers, an advice columnist, once asked readers, "If you had to do it over again, would you have children?"

Almost 10 000 letters from parents poured in and about 70% of these answered no. These letters typically expressed parents' anger at their children's behaviour and often reflected resentment.

Later, a scientific survey was conducted, using random sampling. It revealed that about 90% of the respondents answered yes to the same question.

Discuss these questions.
- In what ways might the people who wrote the letters to Ann Landers differ from the typical reader of her column?
- Do you think that a parent who would respond yes would be as likely to send a letter?
- Would you consider those who responded to be a random sample of parents?
- Is it reasonable to conclude that 70% of parents wish they didn't have children?

Here is another example.
Do you feel that the information presented in the newspaper report reflects an accurate use of statistics?
Discuss these questions.
- Are Dr. Cole's patients representative of the general population?
- Is the headline accurate?

A graph can be used to persuade people to believe claims that are untrue. You will see exercises relating to this on the next page.

Working with Mathematics

Something to talk about

1. Explain why each graph is misleading.

   a) **Winter Resort Industry Takes Off**

   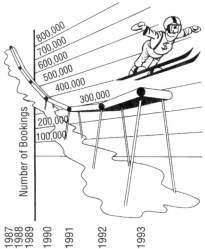

   b) **Unemployment (Annual Average)**

   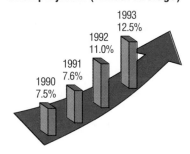

2. Explain how each statement is misleading.

   a) A cure for the common cold has been found. In a recent test, 300 people with a cold took a new drug. After only five days, their colds were gone.

   b) In a recent year, the "help wanted" advertisements filled a column in most newspapers. There were nearly 1 500 000 unemployed people. This shows that the unemployed are not interested in working.

3. Some of these statements are misleading. Which ones do you think they are? Explain why they are misleading.

   a) Last year approximately 55% of skiing injuries were suffered by people who had taken skiing lessons. This suggests that it may be better not to take lessons.

   b) Saskatchewan, one of three Prairie provinces which grows wheat for export, produced almost half of all the wheat shipped to other countries.

   c) Too many car accidents occur when young drivers are at the wheel. To prevent these accidents, the age at which a person can get a driver's licence should be raised.

   d) In 1991, 1775 drivers and 102 cyclists were killed in traffic accidents. This shows that it is safer to ride a bike than to drive a car.

On your own

4. As a teenage driver, you are applying for insurance. You make a case for cheaper insurance rates for people under 25 years of age based on these figures from Statistics Canada. How do you think the insurance company will respond?

PEOPLE KILLED IN CAR ACCIDENTS		
Age Group	Number	Percent
Under 25	1258	34.15
25 and over	2426	65.85

5. A company sells ice skates, in-line skates, and hockey equipment. The table shows the annual sales for several years.

   a) Draw an honest graph to represent the data.

   b) Draw a graph on which the annual sales do not appear to change very much.

   c) Draw a graph that exaggerates the increase in sales.

YEAR	SALES ($)
1988	105 923
1989	98 263
1990	143 829
1991	149 066
1992	177 062

Work together

6. **a)** Interview 10 people. Record their yes/no responses to the question: "Do you believe that the number of days in a school year should be increased?"

   b) Interview 10 people (not included in your first survey). Record their yes/no responses to the question: "Statistics indicate that students in countries where the school year is longer receive a better education and obtain better paying jobs. Would you support increasing the length of the school year?"

   c) Compare the results of the two surveys. Explain the difference (if any) in the results.

   d) How can the wording of a question in a survey affect the results?

7. Choose an issue on which you would like to survey the opinions of other students. Write the question in two significantly different ways. Interview 10 students using one wording of the question and 10 students using the other wording. Compare the results of the two surveys.

8. Comment on the reasoning in this sentence. As few accidents happen in the early morning, very few of these as a result of fog, and fewer still as a result of travelling faster than 150 km/h, it would be best to travel at high speeds on a foggy morning.

9. For each population in exercise 6, on page 80, describe how you would select a sample and collect data to obtain the valid, unbiased information.

10. Use the *Billboard Number One Hits* database on the student's disk. Consider this statement. "The oldies were better. Elvis and the Beatles are much better performers than any of the number one artists of the 90s."

    a) Use the database to support this statement.

    b) Use the database to argue against this statement.

    In each case, use a graph to illustrate your arguments.

Extend your thinking

11. At the beginning of the school year, the dance committee of the Students' Council set a goal to increase the attendance of Grade 9 students at the six dances held during the year. At the end of the school year, the number of Grade 9 students who attended each dance is as follows:

Dance #	1	2	3	4	5	6
Attendance	125	110	140	135	160	150

    a) Do you think the committee met its goal?

    b) What statistics would you use to support your answer?

    c) The chairperson of the dance committee plans to run for Student Council president for the next year. She want to use her "success" on the committee to enhance her chances of being elected. Draw a graph that uses these data, but is misleading to the students.

The Ideas

The British statesman, Benjamin Disraeli, is reported to have said, "There are three kinds of lies: lies, damned lies, and statistics." What do you think he meant by the statement?

How Many People in the Crowd?

After the Blue Jays won their second World Series in October, 1993, it was widely reported that 1 000 000 people celebrated along Yonge Street in Toronto. How was this number determined?

Understand the problem

- The media often report attendance statistics for rock concerts or sports events. How are these numbers obtained?
- Do you think that the numbers in the media reports are accurate? Would it be easy to determine the exact number of people who celebrated along Yonge Street?
- Would it be easy to estimate the number of people?

Think of a strategy

- Have a group of friends stand close together. How could you use the space occupied by your friends to estimate how many people would fill a space twice as large?
- How could you use your group to estimate how many people would fill 100 m^2?

Carry out the strategy

- Have 8 or 10 of your friends stand close together, as if they were in a crowd on a street. Make a rectangle with rope (or draw a rectangle with chalk if you are outside) to enclose your friends. Measure the length and width of the rectangle.
- Calculate the area of the rectangle. Count the number of students inside the rectangle. How many students are there per square metre of your rectangle?
- Use this number to estimate how many people could fit in an area of 100 m^2.
- The crowd filled Yonge Street from Front Street to Dupont Street. This is a distance of 1.3 km. Along this stretch, Yonge Street is approximately 18 m wide. Calculate the area of this stretch of Yonge Street.
- Use your estimate, and the area of Yonge Street to calculate the size of the crowd.

Look back

- Do you think your estimate could be improved by your repeating the experiment with several different-sized groups of students, or by doing the calculations at an actual event?
- Would your estimate change if the crowd were all children or all adults?
- At a political rally, why would the organizers be tempted to exaggerate the number of people or the opposition to underestimate the number?
- In what other situations would it be useful to be able to estimate the size of the crowd?

Communicating the Ideas

In your journal, write an account of this problem and your conclusions. Include an explanation of how to estimate the size of a crowd and what you can do to ensure that your estimate is reasonably accurate.

• • • • • MAKING PREDICTIONS

Developing the Ideas

▶ ▶ *Through Instruction*

One of the principal uses of statistics is in making predictions.

- By determining the blood types of a sample of Canadians, the Red Cross attempts to predict the number of people with type AB blood who will attend the next clinic.
- By testing a sample of flashlight batteries, a technician can estimate the life of the batteries.
- By sampling the garbage at a landfill site, an engineer can determine how much of the garbage could have been recycled.
- By comparing the frequency of letters in a secret code with the frequency of letters in the English language, we can "crack" secret codes.
- By studying samples of voter opinions, analysts attempt to predict who will be elected in a general election.

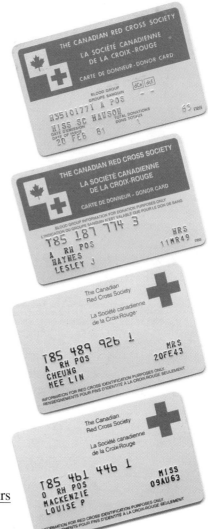

There is no guarantee that any prediction will come true. However, based on what has been learned from the sample, a good guess can be made. The accuracy of the prediction depends on the sample being truly representative of the population, that is, it must be a random sample.

When a question is asked on a survey, or an experiment is performed, the answer or result is known as an *outcome*.

Recall that the *relative frequency* of an outcome is a measure of how often that outcome occurs, relative to the total number of outcomes.

$$\text{Relative frequency of an outcome} = \frac{\text{Number of times the outcome occurs}}{\text{Total number of outcomes}}$$

▶ ▶ *Through an Activity*

When a paper cup is tossed it can land in one of three ways: on its top, on its side, or on its bottom.

a) With a partner, toss a paper cup 40 times. Record the frequency of each outcome — top, side, or bottom.

b) Calculate the relative frequency of each outcome.

c) Combine your results with those of 9 other students. Determine the relative frequency of each outcome for these combined results.

d) Use these results to predict how many times the cup would land on its bottom if it were tossed 400 times.

Example ··

A die has these faces.

The die was rolled 100 times.
The frequency of each outcome is shown on the graph.

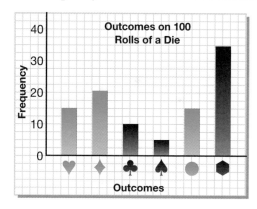

a) Find the relative frequency of each outcome.

i)

ii)

iii)

b) Do you think it is a fair die? Give reasons for your answer.

c) Suppose the die were rolled 250 times. The faces showed in the same
proportions as indicated by the graph. About how many times would
each of these outcomes occur?

   i) a heart   **ii)** a diamond   **iii)** a spade or a circle

Solution

a) From the graph, we read the number of times each outcome occurred.
The total number of outcomes is 100.

   i) The heart showed 15 times.
   The relative frequency of a heart is $\frac{15}{100}$, or 0.15.

   ii) The circle showed 15 times.
   The relative frequency of a circle is $\frac{15}{100}$, or 0.15.

   iii) The club showed 10 times.
   The relative frequency of a club is $\frac{10}{100}$, or 0.10.

b) It does not appear to be a fair die. A hexagon is more likely to occur than any of the other outcomes. A spade is least likely to occur. If the die were fair, each of the faces would turn up approximately the same number of times.

c) We write each relative frequency as a percent. We assume that each outcome occurs the same percent of the time for 250 rolls as it did for 100 rolls.

  i) For 250 rolls of the die, a heart would occur approximately

$$15\% \text{ of } 250 \text{ times} = 0.15 \times 250$$
$$= 37.5$$

  An outcome cannot appear 0.5 times. So we approximate the answer to 37 or 38 times.

  ii) The relative frequency of a diamond is $\frac{21}{100}$, or 0.21.

  For 250 rolls of the die, a diamond would occur approximately
$$21\% \text{ of } 250 \text{ times} = 0.21 \times 250$$
$$= 52.5$$

  We approximate this to 52 or 53 times.

  iii) On 100 rolls, a spade occurred 5 times and a circle occurred 15 times. We add these numbers to get the number of times the outcome "a spade or a circle" occurs.

  The relative frequency of the outcome "a spade or a circle" is $\frac{20}{100}$, or 0.20.

  For 250 rolls of the die, a spade or a circle would occur approximately
$$20\% \text{ of } 250 \text{ times} = 0.20 \times 250$$
$$= 50$$

▶ ▶ *Through a computer simulation*

TEMPLATE DISK

Most computers have functions or commands which generate random numbers. These can be used to represent the toss of a coin or the roll of a die. You can access the random-number generator through the spreadsheet program. The computer can "toss" a coin and "roll" a die instead of you!

Start a new spreadsheet. In cell A1,
in ClarisWorks, type =RAND(2)
in Microsoft Works, type =Int(Rand()*2)+1

Choose the Calculate Now option many times. The numbers 1 and 2 are displayed randomly in cell A1. Assume that each time a 1 shows that represents a coin landing heads. Each time a 2 shows that represents a coin landing tails.

To do many tosses at once, copy the formula in cell A1 into many cells below or to the right. Recalculate, and count the heads (1) and the tails (2).

To get the computer to "roll" a die, replace the 2 in the formula with a 6.

You can also generate random numbers using other programs such as Maple®, Basic, and LOGO.

Working with Mathematics

Something to talk about

1. a) By the end of the second week of the 1993 baseball season, John Olerud had 20 hits out of 50 times at bat. Calculate his batting average.

   b) In his next game, John had 1 hit out of 4 times at bat. Calculate his batting average after this game.

   c) By the final month of the season, John had 175 hits out of 458 times at bat. Calculate his batting average.

   d) John had 1 hit out of his next 3 times at bat. What did this make his average?

   e) To predict John's chances of getting a hit, is it better to use his batting average at the start of the season, or near the end of it? Why?

On your own

2. The owner of a craft shop decided to make and sell wooden letters used for signs and crafts. She intends to make a total of 500 letters. She needs to know how many of each letter to make. In a sample paragraph of 301 letters, Jane found there were these numbers of letters — a: 29; e: 39 ; n: 20; and s: 15. How many of each of these letters should she make?

3. A computer simulated the roll of a die 7200 times. The frequency of each outcome is shown in the table.

   a) What is the relative frequency of each outcome?

   b) Do you think it is a fair die? Explain your answer.

Outcome	1	2	3	4	5	6
Frequency	1175	1225	1142	1168	1273	1217

4. A computer simulated the roll of a pair of dice 5350 times. A pair of 6s occurred 140 times. What was the relative frequency of a pair of 6s?

5. A dental survey of 360 students at a local high school revealed that 135 of them had two or more cavities. The total school enrolment is 1656. About how many students would you expect to have two or more cavities?

6. The table shows the blood types of a random sample of residents in an isolated northern community. Estimate the number of residents with each blood type in a population of 1850.

Blood type	O	A	B	AB
Number of residents	75	59	14	8

Work together

7. a) Toss two coins 30 times. Record the number of times they show each outcome.
   i) two heads
   ii) two tails
   iii) one head, one tail

   b) Calculate the relative frequency of each outcome.

   c) Combine your results with those of other students. Find the relative frequency of each outcome again.

   d) Suppose two coins were tossed 5000 times. About how many times would they show each outcome?

8. When a thumbtack is tossed, there are two outcomes: point up and point down.

   a) Work with a partner. Decide how many times you should toss a thumbtack before you can calculate the relative frequency of each outcome. Toss the thumbtack and do the calculations.

   b) Suppose 10 000 thumbtacks were tossed. How many do you predict would land point up?

   c) Combine your data with several other groups. Determine the relative frequency of each outcome.

   d) Do the combined results cause you to change your answer to part b?

9. When a cylinder is tossed, there are two outcomes: it can land on an end or on its side. From a broom handle, cut cylinders 1 cm, 2 cm, 3 cm, and 4 cm long.

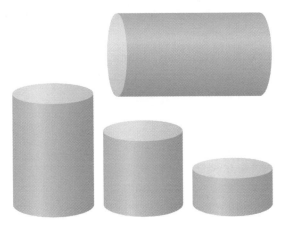

   a) Toss each cylinder 50 times. Record the outcomes.

   b) For each cylinder, calculate the relative frequency of its landing on an end.

   c) How does the length of the cylinder affect how it lands?

10. a) Roll two dice 25 times. Record the total showing on the dice.

    b) Combine your results with those of three other groups.

    c) Suppose two dice were rolled 750 times. Based on your results, how many times would you expect the dice to show each outcome?

       i) a sum of 7

       ii) a sum of 11

       iii) a product of 12

Extend your thinking

11. Decode each secret message.

    a) Npafsdxgb jrnjsrno ao igr dgcgrrgh, lad sc X rnspy igr dgpsy?

    b) Hxde odsdxodxfo yga fsb iggv cgod gi den jngjvn cgod gi den dxcn, lad bgd svv gi den jngjvn svv gi den dxcn.

12. Type a message in your word processor. Use the Replace (or Change) command to replace each a with 1, e with 2, i with 3, o with 4, u with 5, and y with 6. Then replace 6 consonants with vowels. Don't forget what you changed. Then replace 6 more consonants with the ones you have just deleted, and so on. When you have changed all the letters, print your message. Give it to a friend to decode.

The Ideas

Suppose you are the vice-president of an entertainment company that specializes in promoting music concerts. It is your responsibility to conduct surveys to determine which musical groups to book for future concerts. Suppose a decision you made concerning a particular band turned out to be a bad one; that is, very few people came to the concert. How would you explain the "mistake"?

Developing the Ideas
▶ ▶ *Through Instruction*

Every ticket sold in a raffle is assumed to have an equal chance of winning.

A large number of tickets are sold and the person with the winning ticket wins the prize.

If 10 000 tickets are sold, there are 10 000 outcomes on the drawing of a single ticket.

Since one outcome is just as likely to occur as any other outcome, we say the outcomes are *equally likely*.

If you buy a ticket, there is one chance in 10 000 that you will win.

If you buy 5 tickets, and 10 000 in total are sold, there are 5 chances in 10 000 that you will win.

We say that there are 5 winning outcomes, or 5 outcomes that are favourable to your winning.

When we talk about the chances of winning, recall that we use the word *probability*. We can express probability as a fraction.

We say: the probability of winning with 5 tickets out of 10 000 is $\dfrac{5}{10\ 000}$.

We write: $\text{P(Winning)} = \dfrac{5}{10\ 000}$

For an experiment where the outcomes are equally likely, the probability of an event A is given by $\text{P(A)} = \dfrac{\text{Number of outcomes favourable to A}}{\text{Total number of outcomes}}$

For the raffle, the outcomes are the different tickets that can be drawn. The event is the result that the ticket drawn will be yours.

Probability and relative frequency are closely linked. To see how, consider the spinner shown. There are three equally-likely outcomes: landing on blue; landing on red; and landing on yellow. The probability that the spinner lands on blue is $P(\text{blue}) = \frac{1}{3}$

This does not mean that if you spin the spinner 3 times it will land on blue once. Nor does it mean that if you spin the spinner 30 times it will land on blue 10 times. It means that if you spin the spinner many times, the fraction of times it lands on blue will get closer and closer to $\frac{1}{3}$.

▶ ▶ *Through a Guided Example*

Example ....

Use the graph to calculate the probability of each event. For each event, the name of a student is picked at random.

a) A is the event that the student picked has a birthday in January.

b) B is the event that the student picked has a birthday in October, November, or December.

c) C is the event that the student was not born in February.

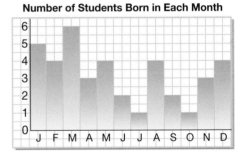

Number of Students Born in Each Month

Solution

From the graph, the total number of students in the class is 39. The outcomes are equally likely.

a) Five students were born in January.
$$P(A) = \frac{5}{39}$$

b) A total of $1 + 3 + 4 = 8$ students were born in the last three months of the year.
$$P(B) = \frac{8}{39}$$

c) Four students were born in February.
So, $39 - 4 = 35$ were not born in February.
$$P(C) = \frac{35}{39}$$

Working with Mathematics

Something to talk about

1. In the SCRABBLE game, 100 tiles have the letters of the alphabet, as shown below.

DISTRIBUTION OF TILES					
A–9	F–2	K–1	P–2	U–4	Z–1
B–2	G–3	L–4	Q–1	V–2	Blank–2
C–2	H–2	M–2	R–6	W–2	
D–4	I–9	N–6	S–4	X–1	
E–12	J–1	O–8	T–6	Y–2	

Suppose you put your hand into a full bag of tiles. What is the probability of selecting each tile?

a) B **b)** E **c)** S

2. The diagram shows a jar of pistachio nuts the same size and shape. You put your hand in the jar and do not look at the nuts. What is the probability of each nut being selected?
a) natural
b) green
c) pink
d) not natural
e) either natural or pink
f) neither natural nor pink

3. For each experiment:
i) List the outcomes.
ii) State whether the outcomes are equally likely.
   a) Without looking, a golf ball is drawn from a bag containing one pink ball, one yellow ball, and one orange ball.
   b) A quarter and a nickel are tossed.
   c) Without looking, a marble is taken from a bag containing 2 purple marbles, 3 green marbles, and 5 red marbles.
   d) A circle is divided into 8 equal sectors. Each letter A to H is printed in a sector. A spinner connected to the centre of the circle is spun.

On your own

4. Some board games use a tetrahedral die. It has 4 numbered faces. A die has each set of numbers below on its faces. Calculate the probability of rolling each die so that it lands with the 4-face down.
a) 2, 4, 6, 8
b) 1, 4, 4, 7
c) 1, 3, 5, 7

5. The table lists the numbers of loaves of bread on a store shelf by their "use-by" dates.

Date	Oct 24	Oct 25	Oct 26	Oct 27	Oct 28
Number	3	12	17	24	21

Suppose that today is October 26. Calculate the probability that a loaf selected at random:
a) will be out of date
b) will be 2 days beyond its "use-by" date
c) will be 2 days ahead of its "use-by" date
d) should be eaten today

Work together

6. The words ENVIRONMENTAL AWARENESS are spelled out with Scrabble tiles. These tiles are put in a bag. What is the probability of each outcome for a tile drawn at random from the bag?

a) a vowel   **b)** a consonant

c) one of the first ten letters of the alphabet

7. To win the card game "In-Between", the third card dealt must lie between the first two cards dealt. What is the probability of winning for each pair of first cards listed?

a) a 2 and a 6   **b)** a 5 and a queen

c) a 7 and an 8   **d)** a jack and a king

8. Our calendar repeats itself every 400 years. There are 4800 months during this period. The table shows how often the 13th day of the month occurred on each day of the week.

a) Triskaidekaphobia is the fear of Friday the 13th! Find the probability that the 13th day of the month will fall on a Friday.

b) Is this probability greater than, less than, or equal to the probability of its falling on any other day of the week?

c) What is the probability that the first day of the month falls on a Sunday?

Day of the week	S	M	T	W	T	F	S
How often the 13th day occurs	687	685	685	687	684	688	684

Extend your thinking

9. Life insurance companies use statistics to calculate the premiums for their policies. The table shows how many of 100 000 people at age 10 are still living at ages 30, 50, 70, and 90.

Age (years)	10	30	50	70	90
Number of people living	100 000	95 144	83 443	46 774	2220

a) What is the probability that a 10-year-old child will live to each age?

  i) 50   **ii)** 70   **iii)** 50 but not 70

b) What is the probability that a 30-year-old person will live to age 90?

c) Why do you think life-insurance premiums are greater for older people?

COMMUNICATING The Ideas

A student says that the probability of his passing the next mathematics test is 0.5 because there are only two possible outcomes, pass or fail. Do you agree? In your journal, explain your answer.

BOGGLE YOUR **MIND**

It is estimated that by the time the average child reaches the age of 13, he or she will have heard the word "no" 13 000 times. Do you think this is a reasonable estimate? How do you think a person would make such an estimate?

Random Numbers

A list of digits, selected so that each of the digits from 0 to 9 has an equal chance of being selected, is called a list of *random numbers*. We can use random numbers to estimate probabilities. There are several ways to generate random numbers.

Spinners

Divide a large cardboard circle into 10 equal sectors. Label the sectors from 0 to 9. To make a spinner, straighten out one end of a paper clip. Hold the folded end with a pencil point at the centre of the circle. Spin the paper clip about the pencil. Write down the number it lands on. Spin again. In this way you generate a list of random numbers.

Telephone directory

Turn to any white page of a telephone directory. Without looking, put a pencil point on a number on the page. Ignore the first three digits in the number. They designate the exchange and are often repeated. Consider the last four digits of the number your pencil lands on. These digits are four random numbers. Continue down the page listing the last four digits for as many random numbers as you need.

Table of random numbers

Mathematics texts and reference books contain pages of random numbers. These numbers are generated by a computer that has been programmed to produce random numbers. Some scientific calculators can generate random numbers.

- Can you think of other ways to generate random numbers?
- Why is it important that every number has an equal chance of being selected?
- What are the advantages and disadvantages of each method?

Use random numbers to complete these exercises.

1. Estimate the probability that exactly 2 digits out of 4 randomly-chosen digits are even. To do this, count how many of twenty 4-digit numbers have exactly 2 even digits. Combine your results with those of 4 other students. Write the number you found as a fraction of 100.

2. Use the result of exercise 1 to estimate the probability that a family of 4 children has exactly 2 girls and 2 boys.

3. Estimate the probability that a family of 8 children has exactly 5 boys.

4. Estimate the probability that at least 2 of the 3 digits on a licence plate are the same.

Sharing a Birthday

In a group of 30 people, what is the probability that two people have the same birthday?

Understand the problem

- In a group of 30 people, is it possible that no two people have the same birthday?
- Is it possible that every person in the group has the same birthday? How probable is it?
- If you were in a group of 30 people, would you be surprised if there were two people who had the same birthday?

Think of a strategy

- How could you conduct a study to answer the question above?
- Is it sufficient to consider two or three groups of 30 people?
- How could you get your classmates to help with the study?

Carry out the strategy

- Find a group of 30 different people. Ask each student in the class to do the same. You could use family members and friends, books from the "Who's Who" series, or choose groups of 30 people at random from an encyclopedia. If you have access to a computer bulletin board, leave a message asking people to respond with their first names and birthdays.
- For each group of 30 people, record whether two people have the same birthday. Pool your results with those of your classmates. Calculate the probability that in a group of 30 people, two people have the same birthday.

Look back

- The probability that, in a group of 30 people, two people have the same birthday is about 71%. How does this value compare with your value? If your value is different, give reasons why.
- Use your results for groups of 30 people to find the probability that, in a group of 60 people, two people have the same birthday.

Communicating the Ideas

Write a description of this problem in your journal. Include reasons why your answer might have been different from the value given above.

THE PROBABILITY OF COMPOUND EVENTS

Developing the Ideas

▶ ▶ *Through Discussion*

There is a coin-tossing game for two people (player A
and player B) in which a coin is tossed twice.

Player A wins if a head appears on at least one of the two tosses.
What is the probability that player A wins?

Legend has it that two 17th century mathematicians,
Roberval and Fermat, discussed this game.

Roberval argued this way:
There are 3 possible outcomes.

First toss	Second toss	Result
H	No second toss because game ends	A wins
T	H	A wins
T	T	B wins

A wins on 2 out of 3 outcomes.
The probability that A wins is $\frac{2}{3}$.

Fermat argued this way:
There are 4 possible outcomes.

First toss	Second toss	Result
H	H	A wins
H	T	A wins
T	H	A wins
T	T	B wins

A wins on 3 out of 4 outcomes.
The probability that A wins is $\frac{3}{4}$.

Who was right, Roberval or Fermat?

ACTIVITY 1

We know that the probability of an event is very close to the relative frequency of the event if the experiment is conducted a large number of times.

If we toss a coin many times we can get an idea of the probability of at least one head in every two tosses. In this way we can test the reasoning of Roberval and of Fermat.

It does not matter whether we toss the coins one after the other, or together. So, we can simulate the game by tossing two coins at the same time.

Work with a classmate. Select two different coins, such as a nickel and a quarter. Toss the coins 50 times. Tally the outcomes in a table like this:

Two heads	A head and a tail	Two tails	Number of tosses

- Calculate the relative frequency of the outcome a head and a tail.
- What do you think the probability of that outcome is?
- Combine your data with that of three other groups. Calculate the probability of the outcome a head and a tail.
- Whose argument, Roberval's or Fermat's, is better supported by these results?

Each event of this experiment is the combined outcomes of tossing a nickel and tossing a quarter. This result is called a *compound event* because it consists of two single events.

We can show the possible outcomes with a *tree diagram*.

There are 4 outcomes: H H, H T, T H, T T.

There are 3 events: two heads, two tails, a head and a tail.

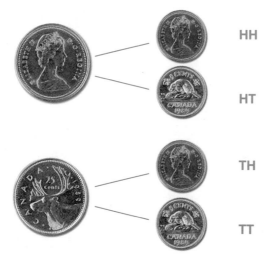

ACTIVITY 2

With a partner, toss a coin and roll a die.

1. How many different outcomes are there for one toss of the coin?

2. How many different outcomes are there for one roll of the die?

A tree diagram can represent the outcomes of this experiment. Each branch of the tree shows one combined outcome of tossing a coin and rolling a die.

3. How many branches should the tree diagram have?

4. Draw the tree diagram. Label each branch with the combined outcomes.

5. Use the tree diagram to calculate the probability of each compound event:
  a) a tail and a four
  b) a head and an even number
  c) a tail and a number greater than two
  d) a head and a prime number

▶ ▶ *Through Instruction*

From your tree diagram, you should have found that:
The probability of a head and an even number, P(H and E), is $\frac{3}{12}$, or $\frac{1}{4}$.

The probability of a head, P(H), is $\frac{6}{12}$, or $\frac{1}{2}$.

The probability of an even number, P(E), is $\frac{6}{12}$, or $\frac{1}{2}$.

Notice how these fractions are related.

The probability of a head and an even number, $P(H \text{ and } E) = P(H) \times P(E)$
$$= \frac{1}{2} \times \frac{1}{2}$$
$$= \frac{1}{4}$$

Similarly, from your tree diagram:

The probability of a tail and a number greater than 2, P(T and > 2), is $\frac{4}{12}$, or $\frac{1}{3}$.

The probability of a tail, P(T), is $\frac{6}{12}$, or $\frac{1}{2}$.

The probability of a number greater than 2, P(> 2), is $\frac{8}{12}$, or $\frac{2}{3}$.

We can write $P(T \text{ and } > 2) = P(T) \times P(> 2)$
$$= \frac{1}{2} \times \frac{2}{3}$$
$$= \frac{1}{3}$$

These activities illustrate the following rule:

• • • • • • • • • •

> If P(A) is the probability of event A, and P(B) is the probability of event B, then the probability of the compound event A and B is P(A and B). $P(A \text{ and } B) = P(A) \times P(B)$

Working with Mathematics

Something to talk about

1. Explain what is meant by a *compound event*. Give an example.

2. **a)** What is the probability of obtaining a head and a tail on the toss of a nickel and a dime?

   b) Does the probability change if the two coins are both nickels?

   c) Does the probability change if a single coin is tossed once, and then tossed again?

On your own

3. Two dice are rolled. What is the probability of each event?

   a) The numbers total 8.

   b) The numbers total 12.

   c) Both dice display the same number.

   d) The sum of the numbers is greater than 10.

   e) The sum of the numbers is not 8.

4. Assume it is equally likely that a child be born a boy or a girl.

   a) Draw a tree diagram to show the possible outcomes for a family of 2 children.

   b) What is the probability that both children will be girls?

5. **a)** Extend the tree diagram in exercise 4. Show the possible outcomes for a family of 4 children.

   b) What is the probability that all the children will be boys?

Work together

6. To answer exercise 3, you could use a grid showing all possible outcomes when two dice are rolled. Suppose one die is red and the other is green. To show the outcome green 3 and red 5, circle the dot at the point (3, 5). Copy this grid.

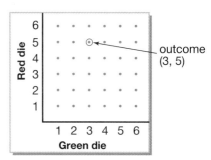

   a) Circle all the outcomes for which both dice show the same number. Write the probability for rolling a double.

   b) Circle all the outcomes for which the sum of the numbers is 7. Write the probability of obtaining 7 on the roll of two dice.

   c) Repeat part b for the sum of the numbers being 9.

   d) Is there a pattern in the points which correspond to outcomes with the same total? Explain your answer.

Extend your thinking

7. In basketball, a player given a one-and-one foul shot is given a second shot only if the first is successful. The player can score 0, 1, or 2 points in this situation. The player shoots with 75% accuracy. Find the probability that she will score:

   a) 0 points   **b)** 1 point   **c)** 2 points

The Ideas

In your journal, describe some limitations of a grid for listing the outcomes of an experiment. Describe some limitations of a tree diagram for listing the outcomes of an experiment.

MONTE CARLO METHODS

Developing the Ideas

To estimate some probabilities, we simulate an experiment by doing a different experiment which has the same probability. This technique is known as a *Monte Carlo* method. For example, to simulate guessing the answer on a true/false question, we toss a coin. Heads on the coin corresponds to a correct answer. Tails on the coin corresponds to a false answer.

▶ ▶ *Through Activities*

ACTIVITY 1

Suppose you have to complete a true/false test with 10 questions. If you guess each answer, what is the probability that you will get at least 5 questions right?

We can design an experiment to simulate this situation.

The probability of guessing the correct answer to each question is $\frac{1}{2}$.

The probability of getting a head when a coin is tossed is $\frac{1}{2}$.

We simulate the problem by tossing 10 coins many times.

- With a partner, toss 10 coins.
- Record the number of heads that occurred.
- Conduct the experiment 20 times.
- Write the number of times 5 or more heads appeared as a fraction of 20. This corresponds to the probability of guessing 5 or more questions correctly on the test.
- Combine your results with those of four other groups. Calculate the probability again.
- Do you think it is wise to complete a true/false test by guessing?

ACTIVITY 2

For a group of 5 students in your class, what do you think the probability is that at least 2 will have birthdays in the same month?

We assume that the probability of being born in a particular month is $\frac{1}{12}$.

We simulate this situation with a coin and a die. We assign each month with head or tail, and a number from 1 to 6.

January H1   February H2   March H3   April H4   May H5
June H6   July T1   August T2   September T3   October T4
November T5   December T6

Conduct this experiment with a partner.

- Toss a coin and roll a die 5 times. Record whether any month occurred more than once.
- Conduct the experiment 20 times.
- What is your estimate of the probability that in a group of 5 students at least 2 were born in the same month?
- Combine your results with those of 4 other groups. Estimate the probability again.
- Do the combined results change your estimate of the probability?

When designing an experiment, we must be careful to match the method used with the conditions of the problem.

In Activity 1, a coin was used because there are two equally-likely outcomes, just as there are two possible answers to a true/false question.

In Activity 2, a coin and a die were used because there are 12 equally-likely outcomes, one for each month.

Both activities could be conducted by using other experiments.

TEMPLATE DISK

▶ ▶ *Through a computer simulation*

We will simulate the rolling of two dice in two ways. Start a new document on your spreadsheet. Enter the information shown below.

In ClarisWorks

	A	B	C	D	E
1	Die 1	Die 2	Die 1 + Die 2		Die 1 and Die 2 together
2	=RAND(6)	=RAND(6)	=A2+B2		=RAND(11)+1

In Microsoft Works

	A	B	C	D	E
1	Die 1	Die 2	Die 1 + Die 2		Die 1 and Die 2 together
2	=Int(Rand()*6)+1	=Int(Rand()*6)+1	=A2+B2		=Int(Rand()*11)+2

- Copy the formulas in row 2 to 20 or more rows below.
- Choose Calculate Now. Record the number of times each number from 2 to 12 appears in column C and in column E.
- Repeat this several times. Tally your results.
- Which method, column C or column E, is the better simulation for rolling two dice?
- Combine your results with those of your classmates. Use the spreadsheet to record, tally, and graph the results of your experiment. Use the graphs to explain your conclusions.
- Why is 7 such an important number in dice games?

Working with Mathematics

Something to talk about

1. A multiple-choice test has 10 questions. Each question has 4 answers. Explain how this spinner could be used to estimate the probability of guessing at least 3 correct answers.

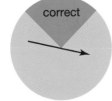

2. a) Explain what is meant by *simulation*.
   b) Why do we use a simulation to calculate a probability?
   c) Why do we expect the results of a simulation to provide a good estimate of the probability?

3. To simulate each event, would you use one or more of: a coin, a die, a spinner, or some other object?
   a) The birth of a girl
   b) The selection of a month of the year
   c) The correct answer to a multiple-choice question which has four choices
   d) The selection of an even number

4. Describe a simulation you could conduct to estimate each probability.
   a) The probability that in a family of 4 children there are exactly 3 boys
   b) The probability that you will guess correctly more than 5 answers on an 8-question true/false test

On your own

5. A student guesses each answer for an 8-question true/false quiz. Design an experiment to estimate the probability that the student will get exactly 5 answers correct.

6. A student guesses each answer for a 10-question multiple-choice test. For each question there are 3 possible answers. Design an experiment to estimate the probability that a student will guess at least 7 answers correctly.

Work together

7. According to a news report, one in every six railroad cars is defective. Design an experiment to estimate the probability that a 7-car train contains 2 or more defective cars. What is the probability that the train has no defective cars?

8. A batter is hitting 0.500; that is, she gets a hit 50% of the times she comes to bat. Design an experiment to estimate the probability that she will get at least 3 hits in her next 5 times at bat.

9. The first traffic light the school bus reaches each morning is green for 25 s, yellow for 10 s and red for 25 s out of every minute. Design a simulation to estimate the probability that the light, when first seen by the driver, will be green at least 3 times in a week.

Extend your thinking

10. A survey indicates that 75% of all consumers prefer Brand A cola to Brand B cola. A sample of 10 consumers is chosen. What is the probability that 8 or more of them prefer Brand A?

The Ideas

Only 4 of the 6 students who volunteered to organize the spring dance are needed to put up the decorations. In your journal, explain how Monte Carlo methods could be used to select the students.

Games of Chance

Games of chance have been played for thousands of years. Dice have been found in the tombs of ancient Greeks and Egyptians. However, it was not until the 16th and 17th centuries that mathematicians studied games of chance.

Chevalier de Méré was a professional gambler and amateur mathematician. He had many questions about dice probabilities. He turned to the mathematician, Blaise Pascal, for answers. Pascal, with his associate, Pierre de Fermat, began a study of games of chance.

One of de Méré's questions was,

"What is the probability of rolling two dice and *not* getting a 1 or a 6?"

Pascal answered,

"For each die, the probability is $\frac{4}{6}$, or $\frac{2}{3}$.

For both dice, the probability is $\frac{2}{3} \times \frac{2}{3}$, or $\frac{4}{9}$."

With this information, de Méré offered the equivalent of this gamble.

Bet $1. Roll two dice. If 1 or 6 do NOT show, you win $2.

De Méré knew that for every 9 people who played the game, about 4 would win. That meant that he would take in $9 and pay out $8. He could expect to win about $1 every time 9 people played. Now that you know this, would you spend $1 to play this game?

For each game of chance:

a) Determine whether you can expect to win or lose if you play the game many times.

b) Decide whether you are willing to play the game.

c) Explain your decision.

1. Bet $1. Toss a coin. If it shows a head, you win $2.

2. Bet $1. Draw a card from a well-shuffled deck. If it shows a spade, you win $5.

3. Bet $1. Draw a card from a well-shuffled deck. If it shows an ace, you win $10.

4. Bet $1. Toss two coins. If they show heads, you win $3.

Blaise Pascal

Review

1. Conduct a survey of students in your class to determine:
   a) their favourite song in the "top 10"
   b) the average shoe size
   c) the average time spent on homework each week

2. Draw a graph to display each set of data you collected in exercise 1. In each case, could more than one type of graph be drawn? What are the advantages of the graph you drew?

3. Suppose you want to determine the stopping distances for a car travelling at different speeds. Would you collect data directly, or from reference materials? Explain your answer.

4. In one year, Canada produced 24 million tonnes of wheat. Look at the graph below. How much wheat was produced in each of the three Prairie provinces that year?

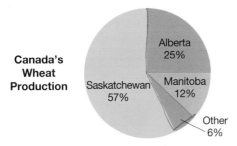

Canada's Wheat Production
Alberta 25%
Saskatchewan 57%
Manitoba 12%
Other 6%

5. A school's basketball team sponsored a "Thanksgiving Turkey Shoot" to raise money. Each student paid $1.00 to shoot 25 foul shots. The student with the best score was awarded a prize. Here are the scores for the Grade 9 students who participated.

12	18	21	8	16	11	14	4
9	8	13	17	23	7	12	5
14	12	6	13	18	17	22	

   a) Draw a stem-and-leaf diagram to display these data.
   b) Find the mean and the median scores.
   c) Determine the range and the quartiles.
   d) Draw a box-and-whisker plot.
   e) Display these data graphically.

6. Which measure of central tendency is most suitable to describe each average? Why?
   a) the average time a teenager spends watching TV each week
   b) the average price of gasoline in a certain area

7. Use a calculator which has Memory Add and Memory Recall keys. Clear the memory. Enter any number and add it to the memory. Repeat for 7 different numbers. Clear the display (but not the memory). Display the memory and divide by 8. Add the result to the memory. Clear the display. Display the memory and divide by 9. Explain what happened. Make it happen again, and again.

8. The mean mark for a student's seven mathematics tests is 68. However, the correction of an error in marking in the latest test raises the student's mark for that test by 14. Calculate the new mean.

9. In the first section of this chapter, you worked with a group to collect data. Work with the same students to determine the measures of central tendency for your data. Is it possible to determine the mean, the median, and the mode for your data? Why or why not?

10. A student's earnings from her part-time job for the past four weeks are: $18.00, $25.00, $23.00, and $22.00. How much must the student earn this week so that her mean earnings will be $23.00 a week for the 5-week period?

11. In each situation, why would data be collected from a sample and not from the population?
    a) to find the average age of drivers when they get their drivers' licences
    b) to find the number of hours a high-efficiency light bulb will burn
    c) to find the average volume of milk in a 4 L bag

12. How would you collect data to find the following information? Give reasons for your answers.
    a) the most popular sports car sold in Canada
    b) the average distance students walk to school
    c) the average cost of a compact disk
    d) the most popular brand of athletic shoe
    e) the average number of words in an English sentence

13. Bell Canada used this graph in its financial report in 1989 to show how money paid to shareholders had grown from 1985. How is this graph misleading?

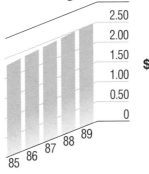

14. Are the following statements correct interpretations of the data in the table?

Age of skier (in years)	Percent of skiing accidents
under 10	10
10 – 19	61
20 – 29	19
30 – 39	5
40 – 49	3
over 50	2

Teenagers are more likely to have skiing accidents than persons in other age groups. People over 50 years of age are the best skiers.

15. At the annual meeting of a large company, the president used a graph to display the company's profit over the past 5 years.

Year	Profit
1990	$540 000
1991	$590 000
1992	$670 000
1993	$720 000
1994	$770 000

Draw a graph that the president could use to represent:
a) the profit in an honest way
b) a very small increase in profit each year
c) a large increase in profit each year

16. A computer simulates the tossing of 3 coins 6000 times. The frequency of each outcome is shown in the table.

Outcome	3 heads	2 heads, 1 tail	1 head, 2 tails	3 tails
Frequency	725	2175	2325	775

a) What is the relative frequency of each outcome? Give the answers to three decimal places.
b) Suppose 3 coins were tossed 100 times.
   i) About how many times would you expect 2 heads and 1 tail to occur?
   ii) Suppose 2 heads and 1 tail occurred 52 times. Are the coins fair? Explain your answer.

17. A regular die is rolled. What is the probability of its showing each number?
   a) 5
   b) an odd number
   c) a prime number
   d) a number less than 3
   e) a one-digit number
   f) a two-digit number

18. A true/false test has 5 questions. Suppose all the questions are answered by guessing.
    a) Draw a tree diagram to show the possible combinations of answers.
    b) What is the probability of guessing all answers correctly?

19. What is the probability of *not* obtaining a total of 7 on the roll of two dice?

20. A bag contains 3 red balls and 5 green balls. Find the probability of drawing 2 green balls in succession:
    a) if the first ball is replaced before drawing the second ball
    b) if the first ball is not replaced before drawing the second ball

21. A bag contains Canadian and American quarters. One coin is selected at random. Then a second coin is selected at random. The first coin is replaced before the second coin is drawn. Find the probability of selecting two Canadian quarters if the bag contains each set of coins.
    a) 4 American quarters and 6 Canadian quarters
    b) 5 American quarters and 4 Canadian quarters
    c) 8 American quarters and 12 Canadian quarters

22. Repeat exercise 21 for the situation where the first coin is not replaced before the second coin is selected.

23. Suppose you were to design an experiment to simulate each event listed. Would you use one or more of: a coin, a spinner, a die, or some other object?
    a) The selection of a single-digit number
    b) The correct answer to a multiple-choice question that has three choices
    c) The correct answer to a true/false question

24. Describe a simulation you could conduct to estimate each probability.
    a) The probability that 3 people born in April are all born on an even-numbered day
    b) The probability that the last two digits in a randomly-selected telephone number are both even

25. A family has 4 children. Design an experiment to estimate the probability that there are 2 girls and 2 boys.

26. A student guesses each answer for an 8-question multiple-choice test. Each question offers 6 possible answers. Conduct a simulation to estimate the probability of the student's guessing at least 2 correct answers.

27. Each question of a 10-question multiple-choice test has 4 possible answers. Design an experiment to estimate the probability that a student will guess at least 6 questions correctly.

BOGGLE YOUR MIND

A single CD-ROM disk, less than 13 cm across, can contain the names, addresses, and telephone numbers of all the people in Canada, with room to spare. What if the telephone company stopped printing a separate telephone directory for each community, and produced a single CD-ROM disk for the entire country? Do you think this would be a good idea? Why?

Determining the Availability of Large Shoes

Read this letter. In it, Joan Hardwick makes many strong statements. In this project, you will conduct studies that will either support or refute her statements.

Discuss Joan's comments with your friends. What is the general feeling about what she says? Is there anyone you know who has large feet and has trouble finding shoes?
Are the prices of shoes in the U.S. very much lower than in Canada?
Record your answers to these questions and compare them to your findings from the project.

Before beginning Activity 1, read through the entire project. As a group, make a list of the measurements and information you have to find. By developing a plan, you can minimize the number of times you have to collect data.

Have large feet, will travel south

Referring to Brenda West's letter Extra-large shoppers get a break in the U.S. Very true, we have three sons, 6-foot-4, 6-foot-5 and 6-foot-7, with big feet requiring size 12 to a size 14, depending on the make. Try and find them in Canada? Where? We do shop in Factory Outlet, Kitchener, but you are either there when the shipment comes in or you take what they have.

We try to get down to Michigan a couple of times a year. Why? Pic-Way. Walk in, try and decide what style you prefer and try them on, they carry up to size 13 for women, and size 16 for men.

It's time store owners and clothing/shoe manufacturers realize that this generation is bigger and taller. The last trip to the U.S. we bought six pairs of shoes for $99 (U.S.) but even with the exchange, gas (definitely cheaper) and motel/meals (considerably cheaper), we still felt we saved.

Canadian manufacturers smarten up, size 9 for men and size 7 for women went out years ago.

Joan Hardwick
Kincardine

ACTIVITY 1

The letter does not say how old the sons are. Since Joan is buying their shoes, we'll assume they are in their teens. Find as many people in this age group as you can. Ask them for, or measure, their heights. Analyze the data. Are Joan's sons unusually tall?

ACTIVITY 2

Find the shoe size of each person whose height you recorded. Plot a graph of shoe size against height. Is there a relationship between a person's shoe size and her or his height? If there is, describe it. Are you surprised that the shoe sizes of Joan's sons range from 12 to 14?

ACTIVITY 3

Find a shoe store in your area that sells, but does not specialize in, shoes for people with large feet. Ask an employee how quickly the large sizes sell out. Is there any basis for Joan's comment that, "You are either there when they come in or you take what they have."?

ACTIVITY 4

Joan implies that the stores in the U.S. cater much better to people with large feet. Try and find someone who will be visiting the U.S. in the near future. Ask that person to check a few shoe stores. If this person determines that Joan has a valid claim, give some reasons why the stores south of the border are able to carry a greater range of sizes.

ACTIVITY 5

Joan writes that, "This generation is bigger and taller." Conduct a statistical study to determine if her claim is valid.

ACTIVITY 6

Joan says that, compared to Canada, the costs of shoes, gasoline, accommodations, and meals are lower in the States.

Ask the person who helped you with *Activity 4* to bring back specific names of shoes along with their prices.

For each pair of shoes, try to find the cost of an identical pair in a store in Canada.

Convert the American prices to Canadian currency and compare the prices.

Conduct a similar comparison for the costs of gasoline, accommodation, and meals.

Are all these items cheaper in the States?

ACTIVITY 7

In her final comment, Joan advises Canadian manufacturers to "smarten up; size 9 for men and size 7 for women went out years ago."

Conduct a statistical study to determine the average shoe sizes for men and women in Canada.

Compare your findings with Joan's comments.

ACTIVITY 8

Find shoes in a wide range of sizes for men and women.

Try to determine a relationship between shoe size and:
• the outside length of the shoe
• the inside length of the shoe

If you do find a relationship, measure the length of your foot. Use this length to determine accurately your shoe size.

APPLICATIONS OF INTEGERS AND

WHAT'S COMING UP?

DEPARTMENTS

RATIONAL NUMBERS

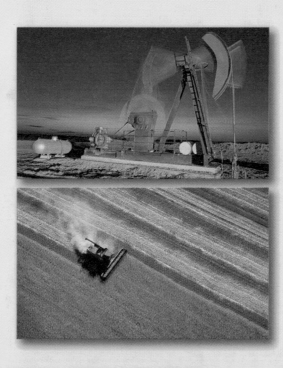

Start With What You Know

Use the numbers in the pictures on these pages to answer the following questions.

1. Explain the meaning of each type of number. Then find as many examples of each as you can.

   a) multiples of 5   b) perfect squares

   c) fractions   d) integers

   e) powers of 2   f) consecutive numbers

   g) prime numbers

2. Several pictures contain numbers that are factors of 30. Find as many of these numbers as you can.

3. Find a picture containing two numbers whose product is in another picture.

4. Find a picture containing a number whose square root is in another picture.

5. There is only one two-digit number whose square root is equal to the sum of its digits. This number appears in one of the pictures. What is the number?

6. Find a picture containing a number whose reciprocal is in another picture.

7. Find a number that is the number of degrees in a right angle.

8. Some of the numbers in the pictures are exact, and others are rounded. Find the numbers that you think have been rounded. Why do you think each one has been rounded?

North York

Welcome to the City with heart

North York

Population 560,000

No Parking On City Streets
2AM To 6AM From Dec.1st To Mar.31st

Buying a souvenir hat? Make sure you choose the correct size.

Imperial							
6⅝	6¾	6⅞	7	7⅛	7¼	7⅜	7½

Continental							
54	55	56	57	58	59	60	61

Jasper Tramway, Alberta, Canada
Visited by over 150 000 people every year.
From the 2500m observation deck, you have a
breathtaking view of the majestic Rocky Mountains.
#SL-64-526   16/08/94

Dear Gita:
    Having a great vacation!
Today we took this cable car
ride. It was pretty exciting.
In less than 10 minutes we
went up 973 metres to the
top. The view was amazing.
We're staying in Jasper
2 more days before driving
to Edmonton. My cousin
promised she'll take me
to the West Edmonton
Mall. See you in 3 weeks,
                        Julie

Gita Azarshahi
81 ½ Coronation Avenue
Halifax, Nova Scotia
B3N 2M5

Developing the Ideas

▶ ▶ *Through Instruction*

Each year, Statistics Canada estimates the number of Canadians who move from one province to another. The results (rounded to the nearest thousand) for recent years are shown in the population table. Some of the numbers in the table are positive and others are negative. All the numbers in the table are integers.

Where Canadians Move Within Canada
(thousands of persons)

YEARS	YT	NWT	BC	Alta	Sask	Man	Ont	Que	NB	NS	PEI	Nfld
1976-81	−1	−4	123	186	−10	−42	−58	−156	−10	−7	−1	−19
1981-86	−3	0	7	−32	−3	−3	122	−81	0	7	1	−15
1986-91	1	−4	139	−41	−66	−36	72	−40	−5	−2	−1	−16
1992	1	−1	41	−1	−8	−7	−3	−15	−2	−2	1	−4

A positive number shows that more Canadians moved into that province than out of that province. For example, from 1976 to 1981, about 186 000 more Canadians moved into Alberta than out of Alberta. The *net gain* in population was 186 000.

A negative number shows that more Canadians moved out of that province than into that province. For example, from 1976 to 1981, about 58 000 more Canadians moved out of Ontario than into Ontario. The *net loss* in population was 58 000.

We say that the *net change* in population from 1976 to 1981 was +186 000 for Alberta and −58 000 for Ontario.

Adding Integers

To determine the net change in Ontario's population from 1976 to 1992, add the integers in the Ontario column.

Think: $(-58) + (+122) + (+72) + (-3)$
Write: $-58 + 122 + 72 - 3$

You can add integers in any order.

$$-58 + 122 + 72 - 3 = 122 + 72 - 58 - 3$$
$$= 194 - 61$$
$$= 133$$

From 1976 to 1992, about 133 000 more Canadians moved into Ontario than out of Ontario.

Subtracting Integers

From 1981 to 1986, the net change in British Columbia's population was $+7000$.
From 1986 to 1991, the net change increased to $+139\ 000$.
The net change increased by 132 000.

Write this subtraction statement: $(+139) - (+7) = +132$
Compare with this addition statement: $(+139) + (-7) = +132$

From 1981 to 1986, the net change in Manitoba's population was -3000.
From 1986 to 1991, the net change decreased to $-36\ 000$.
The net change decreased by 33 000.

Write this subtraction statement: $(-36) - (-3) = -33$
Compare with this addition statement: $(-36) + (+3) = -33$

These examples suggest that adding the opposite of an integer gives the same result as subtracting the integer.

• • • • • • • • •

To subtract an integer, add its opposite.

Multiplying Integers

From 1981 to 1986, the net change in population in each of Manitoba, Saskatchewan, and Yukon was -3000.
What was the total net change?
To calculate the total net change, you can multiply -3000 by 3.

To multiply integers, we must define what we mean by products such as these:
$$(+3)(+3) \qquad (+3)(-3) \qquad (-3)(+3) \qquad (-3)(-3)$$

Since $+3$ can be written as 3, we know that $(+3)(+3) = 9$.

Recall that multiplication means repeated addition.
For example, $3 \times (-3)$ means $(-3) + (-3) + (-3)$.
Therefore, $(+3) \times (-3) = -9$

What does $(-3)(+3)$ mean?
It does not make sense to say that it means to add negative three 3s.

Since we would like integers to behave as much as possible like whole numbers, we will agree that you can multiply two integers in any order.

Then, $(-3) \times (+3) = (+3) \times (-3)$; that is, $(-3) \times (+3) = -9$

What does $(-3)(-3)$ mean?

We will agree that number patterns we find for positive integers can be extended to negative integers.

According to the number patterns on page 45 in Chapter 1, we should define $(-3)(-3)$ to be equal to $+9$.

- - - - - - - - -

Definitions: $(+3)(+3) = 9$ ◄ The product of two integers with the same signs is positive.
$(-3)(-3) = 9$
$(+3)(-3) = -9$ ◄ The product of two integers with different signs is negative.
$(-3)(+3) = -9$

The total net change is $(-3000)(3) = -9000$.

From 1981 to 1986, 9000 more Canadians moved out of Manitoba, Saskatchewan, and Yukon than moved in.

Dividing Integers

From 1986 to 1991, the net change in Quebec's population was $-40\ 000$.

What was the mean net change each year?

To answer this question, you divide $-40\ 000$ by 5.

To divide integers, we must define what we mean by quotients such as these:

$$\frac{+40}{+5} \qquad \frac{+40}{-5} \qquad \frac{-40}{+5} \qquad \frac{-40}{-5}$$

Division is the inverse of multiplication.

This means that we can obtain division facts from multiplication facts.

For example, since $5 \times 8 = 40$, then $\frac{40}{5} = 8$

Similarly, since $(+5)(-8) = -40$, then $\frac{-40}{+5} = -8$

Since $(-5)(+8) = -40$, then $\frac{-40}{-5} = +8$

Since $(-5)(-8) = +40$, then $\frac{+40}{-5} = -8$

The definitions for division are similar to those for multiplication.

- - - - - - - - -

Definitions: $\frac{+40}{+5} = 8$ ◄ The quotient of two integers with the same signs is positive.

$\frac{-40}{-5} = 8$

$\frac{-40}{+5} = -8$ ◄ The quotient of two integers with different signs is negative.

$\frac{+40}{-5} = -8$

The mean net change in Quebec's population each year was $\frac{-40\ 000}{+5} = -8000$.

On average, from 1981 to 1986, 8000 more Canadians moved out of Quebec each year than moved in.

Working with Mathematics

Something to talk about

1. All the numbers in the population table on page 118 are integers. None of these numbers is an integer:
$\frac{2}{3}$ 6.5 $-3\frac{1}{2}$ -4.07 $-\frac{5}{4}$

   a) Which of these numbers are integers?
   72   -2.35 -19
   $\frac{1}{2}$ $2\frac{3}{4}$ 893 -5662

   b) How would you describe an integer?

2. To calculate the numbers in the table, Statistics Canada used this formula:

Net change in population	=	Number of Canadians moving in	−	Number of Canadians moving out

   Use this formula to explain why some of the numbers in the table are negative and others are positive.

Work together

3. Add.
   a) $(-6) + (+2)$
   b) $(+8) + (-5)$
   c) $(-3) + (-4)$
   d) $(-2) + (-5) + (+6)$
   e) $(+9) + (-3) + (-7)$
   f) $(-1) + (+5) + (-8)$

4. Read each expression as a sum of integers. Then simplify the expression.
   a) $5 + 9 - 7$ b) $-3 + 8 - 1$
   c) $2 - 6 - 3 + 1$ d) $-1 - 2 + 9$
   e) $5 - 3 - 7 + 12$ f) $-8 + 4 - 10 - 2$

5. Create a question like those in exercise 4. Your partner calculates the answer and explains why it is correct. Take turns creating questions, calculating, and explaining.

6. Subtract.
   a) $(+4) - (+6)$ b) $(-8) - (+4)$
   c) $(+6) - (-1)$ d) $(-3) - (-2)$
   e) $0 - (+3)$ f) $(+3) - (-9)$

7. Create a question like those in exercise 6. Your partner calculates the answer and explains why it is correct. Take turns creating questions, calculating, and explaining.

8. Copy and complete the chart. Add 3 when moving to the right. Subtract 2 when moving up. What patterns do you notice on the diagonals? Explain why the patterns occur.

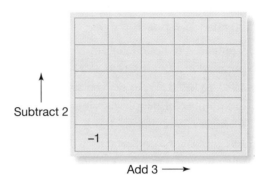

9. Multiply.
   a) $(-5)(+6)$ b) $(+7)(-3)$
   c) $(-5)(-4)$ d) $(-2)(+3)(-4)$
   e) $(+3)(+4)(-5)$ f) $(-1)(-2)(-3)(-4)$

10. Create a question like those in exercise 9. Your partner calculates the answer and explains why it is correct. Take turns creating questions, calculating, and explaining.

11. By comparing the answers in exercises 9 and 10, what appears to be true for:
    a) the product of an even number of negative integers?
    b) the product of an odd number of negative integers?

12. Divide.
    a) $\frac{-24}{4}$ b) $\frac{-35}{-7}$ c) $\frac{45}{-15}$

13. Create a question like those in exercise 12. Your partner calculates the answer and explains why it is correct. Take turns creating questions, calculating, and explaining. In each question, the answer must be an integer.

14. Find out how to use your calculator to do operations with integers. Write some sample questions and describe the keying sequence you would use to find each answer.

15. a) From 1981 to 1986, which provinces had more Canadians moving in than moving out? What was the net change in population for each province?
    b) From 1981 to 1986, which provinces had more Canadians moving out than moving in? What was the net change in population for each province?

16. a) Compare the net change in Nova Scotia's population from 1976 to 1981 and from 1981 to 1986. What do you know about the number of people moving into and out of Nova Scotia during those years?
    b) Integers such as −7 and 7, which differ only in sign, are called *opposites*. Find other examples of opposites in a column in the table. What do they tell you about the people moving into and out of that province?
    c) What is the sum of an integer and its opposite?

17. Determine the net change in population for each province from 1976 to 1992.

18. Add the integers in each row of the population table. Explain the results.

19. Draw a graph showing the net change in population for each province in 1992.

20. Only one province has all positive net changes in population from 1976 to 1992.
    a) Which province is this?
    b) Why do you think more Canadians are moving into this province than leaving it?

21. a) Which provinces have all negative net changes in population from 1976 to 1992?
    b) Why do you think more Canadians are leaving these provinces than moving into them?

22. Why do you think so many Canadians moved into Alberta from 1976 to 1981 and then out of Alberta after 1981?

23. Here is another situation in which you can use integers to describe change. Use the *Land Use* database from the student's disk. Create a table showing the increase or decrease in Forest/Woodland area for the time periods and countries shown below. What trends do you see in the data?

Country	1974–79	1979–84	1984–89
Canada			
USA			
Brazil			
China			
Norway			
Australia			

Extend your thinking

24. List all the ways the integer 12 can be expressed as:
    a) a product of 3 positive integers
    b) a product of 3 integers

COMMUNICATING

The Ideas

A student was overheard saying "two negatives make a positive."
a) What did the student mean by this?
b) Are there any examples where "two negatives make a negative"?
c) Are there any examples where "two negatives sometimes make a positive and sometimes make a negative"?

Record your ideas in your journal.

Atoms and Integers

All matter is made of *atoms*. An atom consists of a *nucleus* surrounded by *electrons*. The nucleus is composed of *protons* and *neutrons*. Protons and electrons have electrical charges which are represented using integers. A proton is positively charged, with a charge of $+1$. An electron is negatively charged, with a charge of -1. A neutron has no charge.

Atom

Electrons

Nucleus
(Protons and
Neutrons)

Normally, an atom is electrically neutral, with equal numbers of protons and electrons. This means the number of positive charges is equal to the number of negative charges. For example, a neutral oxygen atom has 8 protons and 8 electrons. You can calculate the charge on the atom with the addition statement: $(+8) + (-8)$. Since $+8$ and -8 are opposites, the overall charge is 0.

About 100 types of atoms, called the elements, exist. Each element is identified by its name and chemical formula. The elements are arranged in rows and columns on the *periodic table*. In each box on the table, there are four pieces of information. The atomic number is the number of protons a neutral atom has. Since the atom is neutral, this is also the number of electrons. The first column of the periodic table is shown on the right.

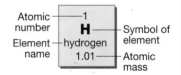

Atomic number — 1 · H — Symbol of element · Element name — hydrogen · 1.01 — Atomic mass

When different elements form compounds during chemical reactions, electrons can be transferred from the atoms of one element to those of the other. An atom which has gained or lost electrons is said to be *charged*, and is called an *ion*. For example, an oxygen atom usually gains 2 electrons in a chemical reaction. The number of protons does not change. So, each oxygen ion will have 8 protons and 10 electrons. You can calculate the charge on the ion with the addition statement: $(+8) + (-10) = -2$. The oxygen ion has an overall charge of -2.

1. Use a periodic table. Four elements are listed below, along with a description of how each element usually acts during a chemical reaction.

  a) State the number of protons and the number of electrons in a neutral atom of each element.

  b) Determine the number of protons and the number of electrons in an ion of each element. State the ion's overall charge.

  i) Fluorine; gains 1 electron
  ii) Magnesium; loses 2 electrons
  iii) Aluminum; loses 3 electrons
  iv) Nitrogen; gains 3 electrons

| 3 |
| Li |
| lithium |
| 6.9 |

| 11 |
| Na |
| sodium |
| 23.0 |

| 19 |
| K |
| potassium |
| 39.1 |

| 37 |
| Rb |
| rubidium |
| 85.5 |

| 55 |
| Cs |
| cesium |
| 132.9 |

| 87 |
| Fr |
| francium |
| (223) |

Mathematics & Science

Linking Ideas

Why Is the Product of Two Negative Numbers Positive?

If you have been wondering why the product of two negative numbers is positive, you are not alone. When mathematicians began working with negative numbers, they also had difficulties understanding this.

For example, if you start with a negative number such as -3, and do something "negative" to it, such as multiplying it by -2, then why is the answer the positive number $+6$?

The method of extending patterns was used on page 45 in Chapter 1. Several other ideas are given on the following page to help you answer this question.

Understand the problem

- What are you asked to do?

Think of some strategies

- Some situations are described here. Answer the questions to help you understand why the product of −3 and −2 should be +6.

Carry out the strategies

Using Gains and Losses
- A person spends $3 per week on lotteries, but never wins.
- Two weeks ago, how did the amount of money the person had compare with the amount he or she has now?
- What does $(-3)(-2)$ represent in this context?

Travelling on a Number Line
- Suppose the integers on a number line are 1 cm apart. A toy car is travelling to the left along the number line at 3 cm/s.
- Two seconds ago, how did the position of the car compare with its present position?
- What does $(-3)(-2)$ represent in this context?

Using Good People and Bad People
- In a certain town, all people are identified as good or bad.
- Suppose there are two families each containing three bad people. What will the effect be on the town if these two families leave the town?
- What does $(-3)(-2)$ represent in this context?

Eliminating Possibilities
- During the 18th century, the great Swiss mathematician Leonhard Euler argued that $(-1)(-1)$ had to be equal to either +1 or −1. Since $(+1)(-1) = -1$, he said that $(-1)(-1)$ could not also equal −1, and so it must be equal to +1.
- Using this reasoning, why does $(-3)(-2) = +6$?

Look back

- Which of the above ideas (including the method of extending patterns) do you think is the best one for explaining why the product of two negative numbers is positive?

Communicating the Ideas

Choose one of the ideas. In your journal, use the idea to explain why the product of two negative numbers is positive.

RATIONAL NUMBERS

Developing the Ideas

▶▶▶ *Through Discussion*

A person who owns stocks in a company is a part owner of that company. The stock market report in the pages of a newspaper shows how the value of the stocks changes.

THIS WEEK ON THE TORONTO STOCK EXCHANGE

Stock	Vol	Bid or High	Ask or Low	Last Price	Chge	Last 52 wks High	Low
Aber Res J	520040	$5	430	445	−.45	5 3/4	136
BCE Inc	3315553	$44 3/8	43	44 1/8	−1 3/8	47 3/8	40 3/4
Disys Corp	4000	290	250	250	−50	350	115
Irwin Toy Nv	425	$5 1/2	5 3/8	5 3/8	−1/8	6 5/8	485
Macmillan G J	34500	20	20	20		35	2
Mitel Corp	4000683	$7 1/4	475	6 7/8	+1.92	7 1/4	1.65
Petromet R J	168700	$5 1/2	5 1/4	5 3/8	+1/8	5 5/8	45
Shelter O&G J	882022	85	54	83	+29	85	6

The change in the value of a stock is listed in the **Chge** column. These numbers are repeated below.

$$-.45 \qquad -1\tfrac{3}{8} \qquad -50 \qquad -\tfrac{1}{8} \qquad 0 \qquad +1.92 \qquad +\tfrac{1}{8} \qquad +29$$

These numbers are all examples of rational numbers. Although they are written in different forms in the stock report, they can all be written as fractions with numerators and denominators as integers. For example:

$$-.45 = -\frac{45}{100}, \text{ or } \frac{-45}{100} \qquad -1\tfrac{3}{8} = -\frac{11}{8}, \text{ or } \frac{-11}{8}$$

1. Write each number in the **Chge** column as a fraction with numerator and denominator as integers.

2. Make a number line showing numbers from −2 to +2. Locate some of the numbers in the stock report on your number line. If you drew a number line showing numbers beyond 2 and beyond −2, do you think that it would be possible to locate every number in the stock report on it?

⋯⋯⋯⋯

> Any number that can be written in the form $\frac{m}{n}$, where m and n are integers and $n \neq 0$, is called a *rational number*.

You can represent any rational number on a number line.
You can write any rational number as a decimal by dividing the numerator by the denominator.

Working with Mathematics

Something to talk about

1. State the rational number for each letter on the number line.

   a)

   b)

   c)

2. Which rational number is greater?

   a) $\dfrac{1}{4}, -\dfrac{3}{4}$ b) $-\dfrac{1}{4}, -\dfrac{3}{4}$ c) $\dfrac{3}{2}, -\dfrac{5}{2}$

   d) $\dfrac{1}{2}, \dfrac{2}{3}$ e) $\dfrac{1}{2}, -\dfrac{2}{3}$ f) $-\dfrac{1}{2}, -1\dfrac{1}{4}$

3. Which of these statements are true? Which are false? Explain your answers.

   a) Every natural number is an integer.

   b) Every integer is a natural number.

   c) All integers are rational numbers.

   d) Some rational numbers are integers.

Work together

4. List in order from least to greatest.

   a) $-\dfrac{1}{5}, -\dfrac{3}{5}, -\dfrac{2}{5}$ b) $\dfrac{5}{8}, -\dfrac{1}{2}, \dfrac{1}{4}$

   c) $1\dfrac{2}{5}, \dfrac{3}{7}, -\dfrac{2}{9}$ d) $-\dfrac{1}{4}, \dfrac{1}{4}, -\dfrac{1}{2}$

   e) $-\dfrac{5}{6}, \dfrac{2}{3}, -\dfrac{1}{2}$ f) $-\dfrac{3}{2}, -\dfrac{5}{4}, \dfrac{1}{3}$

5. Express each rational number as a decimal.

   a) $\dfrac{-3}{-10}$ b) $\dfrac{+5}{-6}$ c) $\dfrac{-12}{+5}$

   d) $\dfrac{+3}{-8}$ e) $\dfrac{4}{-9}$ f) $\dfrac{-8}{-15}$

6. Reduce to lowest terms.

   a) $\dfrac{+9}{-12}$ b) $\dfrac{-15}{+6}$ c) $\dfrac{-10}{-45}$ d) $\dfrac{8}{-18}$

On your own

7. The second last column in the stock report lists the highest value of each stock during the previous 52 weeks.

   a) Write each number in this column as a fraction, with numerator and denominator as integers.

   b) Write each number in this column as a decimal.

Extend your thinking

8. a) Here is the paper-and-pencil calculation for expressing $\dfrac{22}{7}$ as a decimal:
   The last three remainders appeared earlier in the calculation. What does this tell you about the rest of the digits in the quotient? Explain your answer.

   b) Suppose you express any rational number in decimal form by paper-and-pencil calculation. Explain why you will eventually get a zero remainder or a remainder that appeared earlier in the calculation.

   c) Do you think that it is possible to have a number in decimal form that never repeats? Would this be a rational number? Explain your answer.

COMMUNICATING

The Ideas

During the next two days, make a note of the numbers you use in your daily activities outside school. When do you use the numbers? What kinds of numbers do you use? In your journal, illustrate your answers to both questions with specific examples.

The Introduction of Zero

0-Nothing or Something

WHAT KIND OF A NUMBER IS 0? IS IT A DIGIT OR isn't it? 1, 2, 3, 4, 5, 6, 7, 8, and 9 are all digits that can be instantly understood. But how about 0? It is usually regarded as 'nothing' and at other times it is definitely 'something'. $3 + 0 = 3$, for example, as does $3 - 0$. Here, 0 is 'nothing' added or subtracted. But when 0 follows another number, as in 30, it suddenly multiplies that number by 10, so it is clearly 'something'. And in a number such as 40 000, the string of 'nothings' multiplies the 4 ten thousand times. No wonder that a French writer of the 15th century called 0 *un chiffre donnant umbre et encombre*, 'a figure causing confusion and difficulty'.

From *The Guinness Book of Numbers*

People gathered on the steps to the Ganges River in Varanasi, India.

Mayan stone carvings illuminated at night in Rio Lacantun, Mexico.

The Mohammed Ali Mosque in Cairo, Egypt.

Mayan A.D. 200-600   **Hindu** A.D. 600   **Arabic** A.D. 1000

Zero as a placeholder

In our place-value system, the meaning of each digit in a number, such as 4023, depends on the place where it is written. The 0 is called a placeholder. In this case, it indicates that there are no hundreds.

The idea of using a special symbol as a placeholder was introduced in India many centuries ago. This idea was adapted by many other civilizations. It is one of the greatest practical ideas of all time. Some examples of the placeholder symbols used by ancient civilizations are shown above.

Zero as a number

The idea of using 0 as a number probably originated about A.D. 800 when the Hindus used positive and negative numbers to represent credits and debits. They needed a special number for no credit and no debit. This number was gradually picked up by the Arabs, and eventually reached Spain. But mathematicians regarded this number with suspicion, and 0 was not completely accepted and used as a number in the western world until after 1500.

Properties of zero

Because 0 is a number, you can calculate with it.
- When 0 is added to or subtracted from any number, that number does not change.
  $5 + 0 = 5$ $7 - 0 = 7$
- When any number is multiplied by 0, the product is 0.
  $3 \times 0 = 0$
- There is a restriction involving division.
  Recall that $6 \div 2 = 3$ because $3 \times 2 = 6$.
  But if you try to find a meaning for $6 \div 0$, you would have to find a number that gives 6 when it is multiplied by 0. Since this is impossible, we say that division by 0 is undefined. Although you cannot divide by 0, you can divide 0 by any number other than 0.
  $0 \div 5 = 0$ because $0 \times 5 = 0$

1. Simplify, if possible.
   a) $17 + 0$ b) $4 - 0$ c) $259 + 0$ d) $23 - 0$
   e) 9×0 f) 0×25 g) $0 \div 2$ h) $5 \div 0$

2. Refer to the quotation on page 128. If the 0 in 30 is 'something', what is it? If the 0s in 40 000 are 'something', what are they?

Mathematics & History

Linking Ideas

Developing the Ideas

▶▶ *Through Discussion*

You know how to add and subtract integers. Integers are rational numbers. Do you think that you could add and subtract rational numbers using the same methods as those for adding and subtracting integers?

SUMS OF RATIONAL NUMBERS	
Sums of Integers	
$(+3) + (-2)$	$(+3.5) + (-2.1)$
$(-5) + (+1)$	$(-5.6) + (+1.3)$
$(-4) + (-3)$	$(-4.8) + (-3.5)$

Look at the box above.

1. For each sum of integers on the left, there is a sum on the right. In what way is the sum on the right similar to the one on the left? In what way is it different?

2. Add each pair of integers on the left. Use the result to help you add the rational numbers on the right.

DIFFERENCES OF RATIONAL NUMBERS	
Differences of Integers	
$(+3) - (-2)$	$(+3.5) - (-2.1)$
$(-2) - (+7)$	$(-2.6) - (+7.3)$
$(-6) - (-1)$	$(-6.8) - (-1.5)$

Look at the box above.

3. For each difference of integers on the left, there is a difference on the right. In what way is the difference on the right similar to the one on the left? In what way is it different?

4. Subtract each pair of integers on the left. Use the result to help you subtract the rational numbers on the right.

The methods of adding and subtracting rational numbers are the same as those of adding and subtracting integers. If the numbers are in fractional form, the methods of adding and subtracting fractions apply.

Example 1 ....

Subtract. $\left(-\frac{3}{2}\right) - \left(-\frac{5}{6}\right)$

Solution

$$\left(-\frac{3}{2}\right) - \left(-\frac{5}{6}\right) = -\frac{3}{2} + \frac{5}{6} \qquad \text{Subtract by adding the opposite.}$$

$$= -\frac{3}{2} \times \frac{3}{3} + \frac{5}{6} \qquad \text{Obtaining a common denominator}$$

$$= -\frac{9}{6} + \frac{5}{6}$$

$$= \frac{-9 + 5}{6} \qquad \text{Combining the numerators}$$

$$= -\frac{4}{6} \text{ or } -\frac{2}{3}$$

Example 2 ....

Add. $\frac{3}{4} + \left(\frac{2}{-3}\right)$

Solution

$$\frac{3}{4} + \left(\frac{2}{-3}\right) = \frac{3}{4} + \left(-\frac{2}{3}\right)$$

$$= \frac{3}{4} \times \frac{3}{3} - \frac{2}{3} \times \frac{4}{4} \qquad \text{Obtaining a common denominator}$$

$$= \frac{9}{12} - \frac{8}{12}$$

$$= \frac{9 - 8}{12} \qquad \text{Combining the numerators}$$

$$= \frac{1}{12}$$

BOGGLE the MIND

According to the *Guinness Book of Records*, Mexico City has the largest taxi fleet in the world, with 60 000 taxis. The city has a population of about 20 200 000. London, England, has 16 600 taxis and a population of about 6 400 000. In which city do you think it would be easier to get a taxi?

Working with Mathematics

Something to talk about

1. Add or subtract, as indicated.
   a) $(+3.5) + (-2.5)$ b) $(+3.5) + (-4.5)$
   c) $(+3.5) - (+4.5)$ d) $(+3.5) - (-1.5)$
   e) $(+3.5) - (+2.5)$ f) $(+3.5) + (-0.5)$

2. Add or subtract, as indicated.
   a) $\left(+\frac{1}{5}\right) + \left(-\frac{3}{5}\right)$ b) $\left(-\frac{1}{6}\right) + \left(-\frac{5}{6}\right)$
   c) $\left(+\frac{1}{8}\right) + \left(-\frac{3}{8}\right)$ d) $\left(-\frac{5}{4}\right) - \left(-\frac{3}{4}\right)$
   e) $\left(+\frac{3}{10}\right) - \left(-\frac{4}{10}\right)$ f) $\left(-\frac{1}{2}\right) + \left(+\frac{3}{4}\right)$

3. A student has a chequing account at a local bank. Here are some entries from her statement for one month:

Date	Item	Debit	Credit	Balance
JAN 10 94				55.40
JAN 14 94	CHQ	69.20		13.80 DR
JAN 15 94	DEP		100.00	86.20

   a) How much money was in the account on January 10?
   b) What happened on January 14? Why do the letters 'DR' appear beside the balance? Check that the balance on this day is correct.
   c) What happened the next day? Check that the balance on this day is correct.

Work together

4. Add. Explain to your partner how you got the answer.
   a) $(+3.5) + (-4.2)$ b) $(-1.7) + (-1.3)$
   c) $(-2.4) + (+6.1)$ d) $\frac{3}{4} + \left(-\frac{1}{4}\right)$
   e) $\left(-\frac{5}{4}\right) + \left(-\frac{1}{2}\right)$ f) $-\frac{3}{2} + \frac{2}{5}$

5. Subtract. Explain to your partner how you got the answer.
   a) $(+4.5) - (-0.5)$ b) $(-3.1) - (-1.4)$
   c) $(+6.2) - (+8.7)$ d) $\frac{1}{2} - \left(-\frac{1}{4}\right)$
   e) $\frac{1}{3} - \frac{1}{2}$ f) $\left(-\frac{3}{4}\right) - \left(-\frac{5}{2}\right)$

6. Using rational numbers, write a number sentence for each question.
   a) Juan dives from a 26.7-m ledge on the cliffs in Acapulco, Mexico. The water is 3.6 m deep. What is the change in height from the ledge to the bottom of the sea?

   b) The temperature in St. John's is 6.5°C. In Corner Brook it is 8.0°C colder. What is the temperature in Corner Brook?
   c) In 1990, the Canadian national debt was $407.1 billion. In 1991, the debt increased by $36.2 billion. What was the total debt in 1991?

7. Copy each chart. Add the numbers in each row and each column. Find the sum of the numbers in each chart in two different ways.
   a)

+5	−6	+2	
−4	+12	−8	
+7	−6	−10	

   b)

−5.2	−8.9	+2.6	
−6.0	+3.3	+9.4	
+8.5	−5.7	+15.1	

8. Here is a pattern of integers in three rows. Assume that the pattern continues in both directions.

Row 1	...	−8	−5	−2	1	4	7	...
Row 2	...	−7	−4	−1	2	5	8	...
Row 3	...	−6	−3	0	3	6	9	...

a) Describe the pattern.

b) What are the next five integers in row 2?

c) In which row will each of these integers appear?

  i) 36   ii) 62   iii) 100

  iv) −24   v) −47   vi) −64

9. a) Use a spreadsheet to explore the pattern in exercise 8. Your challenge is to recreate the rows by entering only 1 number and using formulas to display the rest. Begin by entering −8 in cell A1. Enter a formula in cell B1 which can be copied to other cells in the first row and will cause the computer to display −5, −2, 1, and so on. Enter a formula in cell A2 to display −7 using the value in cell A1. Copy the formula to the other cells in the second row. Finally, develop a formula to express the values in the third row using those in the second row. Use your completed spreadsheet to check your answers to exercise 8b.

b) Develop a method for extending the patterns in your spreadsheet to the left. Use the extended spreadsheet to check your answers to exercise 8c.

c) What happens if you change the initial value you entered?

10. Use the *World Health and Education* database on the student's disk. The numbers in the birth rate and death rate data fields are rational numbers. A birth rate of 19.8 means 19.8 children were born for every 1000 people in the country. You know that 0.8 of a child cannot be born. The 19.8 is the numerator of a reduced fraction, such as $\frac{198}{10\ 000}$ or $\frac{1980}{100\ 000}$. The rates are all based on 1000 so that they can be compared.

a) For each country, the birth rates are given for two time periods. Find a country in which the birth rate increased, one in which it decreased, and one in which it did not change. Calculate each change and explain the result in terms of what you know about rational numbers.

b) Use the population data and the death rate to calculate the approximate number of deaths in 1970 for your selected countries.

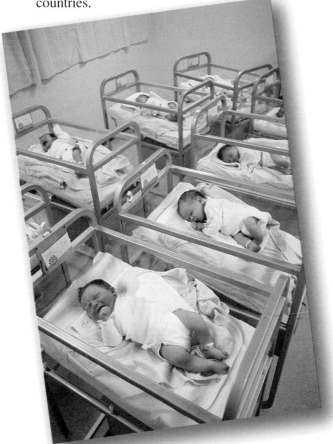

On your own

11. Add or subtract, as indicated.
    a) $(+2.3) + (-8.3)$ b) $(-4.1) + (-3.1)$
    c) $(-2.8) - (-1.2)$ d) $(-6.3) - (+3.3)$
    e) $2.9 - (-3.9)$ f) $(-4.6) + (-2.6)$

12. Add or subtract, as indicated.
    a) $\left(-\frac{7}{5}\right) + \left(+\frac{2}{5}\right)$ b) $\left(+\frac{3}{8}\right) + \left(-\frac{1}{2}\right)$
    c) $\left(-\frac{1}{5}\right) - \left(-\frac{7}{10}\right)$ d) $\left(+\frac{2}{3}\right) + \left(-\frac{11}{12}\right)$
    e) $\left(-\frac{7}{5}\right) + \left(-\frac{7}{15}\right)$ f) $\left(-\frac{4}{9}\right) - \left(-\frac{5}{18}\right)$

13. Add or subtract, as indicated.
    a) $\left(-\frac{4}{3}\right) + \left(-\frac{7}{6}\right)$ b) $\left(-\frac{6}{7}\right) + \left(-\frac{1}{2}\right)$
    c) $\left(-\frac{2}{5}\right) - \left(+\frac{3}{10}\right)$ d) $\left(+\frac{7}{6}\right) + \left(-\frac{3}{4}\right)$
    e) $\left(+\frac{3}{8}\right) - \left(-\frac{7}{6}\right)$ f) $\left(-\frac{5}{6}\right) - \left(+\frac{5}{9}\right)$

14. Add or subtract, as indicated.
    a) $\frac{2}{3} - \frac{5}{6}$ b) $-\frac{3}{2} + \frac{5}{4}$
    c) $-\frac{1}{8} - \frac{1}{4}$ d) $\frac{7}{5} - \frac{9}{10}$
    e) $\frac{5}{6} - \frac{2}{9}$ f) $-\frac{7}{12} - \frac{5}{8}$

15. On a certain day, the temperature at Canmore, Alberta is −4.5°C. It is 2.5°C colder at Banff. What is the temperature at Banff?

Extend your thinking

16. Two friends left work together and had supper at G.T.'s. Shortly after they placed their orders, a third friend joined them. She quickly ordered a meal too. The total bill (without taxes) for these three people was $18.55.

a) i) What time did each person arrive at the restaurant?
   ii) How many answers are there to this question?
b) i) What do you think of this idea?
   ii) Do you think that it was easy for the employees to get used to?

COMMUNICATING

The Ideas

Find a way to use your calculator to add or subtract rational numbers given in fractional form. In your journal, write a description of your method with some examples. Compare your method with a partner's method.

Local Time Around the World

The time of day changes 1 h for every 15° difference in longitude. When it is noon in London, England (0° longitude), it is midnight at 180° longitude. A place on this line is 12 h ahead of London.

The times at different places in the world are usually compared with the time in London.

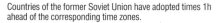

Standard time difference in hours between London, England, and other cities			
Athens	+2	Mexico City	–6
Bangkok	+7	Moscow	+3
Beijing	+8	Ottawa	–5
Brasilia	–3	Rome	+1
Canberra	+10	Santiago	–4
Dublin	0	St. John's	–3.5
Halifax	–4	Washington	–5
Jakarta	+7	Wellington	+12
Jerusalem	+2	Vancouver	–8

Countries of the former Soviet Union have adopted times 1 h ahead of the corresponding time zones.

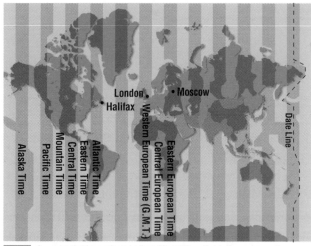

Countries that have adopted a time different from that in the corresponding time zone

Halifax −4 means that Halifax is 4 h behind London.
Moscow +3 means that Moscow is 3 h ahead of London.
Hence, Moscow is 3 h − (−4 h) = 7 h ahead of Halifax.

1. It is 8 a.m. in London. State the local time in each city.
   a) Ottawa   **b)** Mexico City   **c)** Jerusalem   **d)** Canberra

2. It is 8 a.m. in St. John's. State the local time in each city.
   a) Halifax   **b)** Vancouver   **c)** Jakarta   **d)** Beijing

3. It is noon in Jakarta. State the local time in each city.
   a) Bangkok   **b)** Athens   **c)** Wellington   **d)** Halifax

4. The scenes of an earthquake in Chile are sent via television satellite from Santiago at 4 p.m. At what local time is the transmission received in each city below?
   a) London   **b)** Ottawa   **c)** St. John's   **d)** Mexico City
   e) Moscow   **f)** Vancouver   **g)** Brasilia   **h)** Wellington

5. a) From the table, find examples of cities which are 12 h apart. Locate these cities on a globe. What do you notice about their locations?
   b) i) Which two cities in the table have the greatest difference in times?
      ii) What is the difference in times at these cities?
     iii) Locate these cities on a globe. Explain why the difference in times is so great.

**London
England**

**Halifax
Nova Scotia**

**Moscow
Russia**

MULTIPLYING AND DIVIDING RATIONAL NUMBERS

Developing the Ideas

▶ ▶ *Through Discussion*

You know how to multiply and divide integers. Integers are rational numbers. Do you think that you could multiply and divide rational numbers using the same methods as those of multiplying and dividing integers?

PRODUCTS OF RATIONAL NUMBERS		
Products of Integers		
(+3)(−2)	(+3.5)(−2)	(+3)(−2.5)
(−4)(+5)	(−4.2)(+5)	(−4)(+5.1)
(−5)(−2)	(−5.5)(−2)	(−5)(−2.2)

Look at the box above.

1. For each product of integers on the left, there are two products on the right.
    a) In what ways are these products similar to the one on the left?
    b) In what ways are they different?

2. Multiply each pair of integers on the left. Use the result to help you multiply the rational numbers on the right.

QUOTIENTS OF RATIONAL NUMBERS		
Quotients of Integers		
$\frac{-10}{+5}$	$\frac{-9}{+5}$	$\frac{-10.5}{+5}$
$\frac{+8}{-2}$	$\frac{+7}{-2}$	$\frac{+7.6}{-2}$
$\frac{-6}{-3}$	$\frac{-6.3}{-3}$	$\frac{-6}{-4}$

Look at the box above.

3. For each quotient of integers on the left, there are two quotients on the right.
    a) In what ways are these quotients similar to the one on the left?
    b) In what ways are they different?

4. Divide each pair of integers on the left. Use the result to help you divide the rational numbers on the right.

The methods of multiplying and dividing rational numbers are the same as those of multiplying and dividing integers.

- The product or quotient of two rational numbers with the same signs is positive.
- The product or quotient of two rational numbers with different signs is negative.

If the rational numbers are in fractional form, the methods of multiplying and dividing fractions apply.

Example ....

Divide. $\dfrac{3}{2} \div \left(-\dfrac{4}{3}\right)$

Solution

$$\dfrac{3}{2} \div \left(-\dfrac{4}{3}\right) = \dfrac{3}{2} \times \left(-\dfrac{3}{4}\right) \quad \text{— Divide by multiplying by the reciprocal.}$$

$$= -\dfrac{3 \times 3}{2 \times 4} \quad \text{— The product is negative.}$$

$$= -\dfrac{9}{8} \quad \text{— Multiplying the numerators and multiplying the denominators}$$

Here is an alternative solution.

$$\dfrac{3}{2} \div \left(-\dfrac{4}{3}\right) = \dfrac{\frac{3}{2}}{\frac{-4}{3}} \times 1 \quad \text{— Expressing as a fraction and multiplying by 1}$$

The common denominator of the fractions is 6. So, write the 1 as $\dfrac{6}{6}$.

$$= \dfrac{\frac{3}{2}}{\frac{-4}{3}} \times \dfrac{6}{6}$$

$$= \dfrac{\frac{3}{2} \times \cancel{6}^3}{\frac{-4}{3} \times \cancel{6}^2} \quad \text{— Cancelling common factors before multiplying}$$

$$= -\dfrac{9}{8}$$

BOGGLE YOUR MIND

Cinram is Canada's largest manufacturer of compact disks. The company has the capacity to produce 200 000 compact disks every day. What if Cinram was to operate to full capacity for a month? How much space would be needed to store the disks produced?

Working with Mathematics

Something to talk about

Estimate to answer exercises 1 to 4. Then use a calculator to check your answers.

1. Suppose you multiply each rational number below by -2.5. Which will give a product greater than 10?

   a) -5.5 b) $+7.2$ c) -4.1
   d) -3.2 e) -8 f) $+200$

2. Which of these products is closest to -36?

   a) $(-3.5) \times (+9.5)$
   b) $(-14.7) \times (-1.9)$
   c) $(+5.9) \times (-6.2)$

3. Suppose you divide each rational number below by $-\frac{1}{2}$. Which will give a quotient less than 1?

   a) $\frac{2}{3}$ b) -5 c) $-\frac{3}{4}$
   d) -0.6 e) $+0.45$ f) -0.01

4. Suppose -24 is divided by each rational number below. Which will give a quotient greater than -24?

   a) 6 b) -3.8 c) 0.75
   d) -4.8 e) $-\frac{1}{2}$ f) 0.01

5. In 4 h, the effect of the tide at a sea port changed the water level by -4.8 m. What was the average hourly change in water level?

Work together

6. Multiply. Explain to your partner how you got the answer.

   a) $(+4.3) \times (-2)$ b) $(-1.5) \times (-3.2)$
   c) $(-0.25) \times (+8.4)$ d) $\frac{3}{8} \times \left(-\frac{2}{3}\right)$
   e) $\left(-\frac{4}{3}\right) \times \frac{1}{6}$ f) $\left(-\frac{1}{2}\right) \times \left(-\frac{3}{2}\right)$

7. Divide. Explain to your partner how you got the answer.

   a) $(-2.4) \div 2$ b) $36 \div (-1.5)$
   c) $(-18.7) \div (-6.8)$ d) $\frac{2}{3} \div \left(-\frac{1}{6}\right)$
   e) $\left(-\frac{1}{2}\right) \div \frac{4}{3}$ f) $\left(-\frac{1}{3}\right) \div \left(-\frac{3}{2}\right)$

8. Using rational numbers, write a number sentence for each question.

   a) A diver descends at a rate of 12.4 m/min. What is her depth after 2.5 min?
   b) The temperature drops 10.5°C over a 6-h period. What is the average temperature change per hour, to the nearest tenth of a degree?
   c) The temperature drops about 2.5°C for every 500 m increase in altitude. What is the approximate change in temperature for an altitude increase of 3000 m?

On your own

9. Multiply or divide, as indicated.

   a) $(+4.2) \times (-2)$ b) $(-3.1) \times 10$
   c) $(-12.5) \div (+5)$ d) $18.6 \div (-10)$
   e) $(-4.8) \times 9$ f) $(-10) \div (-2.5)$
   g) $(+23.5) \div (-0.5)$ h) $(-9.6) \times (-1.5)$
   i) $(-5.2) \div (+0.3)$ j) $7.5 \times (-8.1)$

10. Multiply or divide, as indicated.

a) $\left(-\frac{4}{5}\right) \times \left(-\frac{3}{2}\right)$ 　　 b) $\left(-\frac{1}{3}\right) \times \frac{5}{2}$

c) $\frac{2}{3} \div \left(-\frac{4}{5}\right)$ 　　 d) $\frac{7}{9} \times \left(-\frac{3}{5}\right)$

e) $\left(-\frac{3}{8}\right) \div \left(-\frac{5}{4}\right)$ 　　 f) $\left(-\frac{2}{5}\right) \div \left(-\frac{8}{3}\right)$

g) $\left(-\frac{3}{10}\right) \times \left(-\frac{4}{9}\right)$ 　　 h) $\frac{9}{2} \times \left(-\frac{4}{3}\right)$

i) $\left(-\frac{3}{4}\right)^{2}$ 　　 j) $\frac{7}{4} \div \left(-\frac{1}{6}\right)$

TEMPLATE DISK

11. You can use positive and negative rational numbers on a spreadsheet to observe some patterns. Set up a spreadsheet as shown below.

	A	B	C	D	E
1		Add 2	Add -2	Multiply by 2	Multiply by -2
2		=A2+2	=A2-2	=A2*2	=A2*-2
3	=A2+1	=A3+2	=A3-2	=A3*2	=A3*-2

a) Explain each formula in row 3. Copy the formulas in row 3 for 15 rows down.

b) Enter any rational number expressed in decimal form in cell A2. Look at columns B and C. Describe the difference between numbers in the same row. Explain the difference.

c) Look at columns D and E. Compare the patterns in these two columns. Describe the effect of multiplying a rational number by a negative number.

Extend your thinking

12. Choose a rational number in the form $\frac{m}{n}$, where m and n are positive integers, and $n \neq 1$. Reduce both the numerator and the denominator by 1, to form a different rational number. Is the second rational number equal to, greater than, or less than the first one? Does your answer depend on whether $m = n$, $m < n$, or $m > n$?

COMMUNICATING

The Ideas

A rule for subtracting rational numbers is "add the opposite."

A rule for dividing rational numbers is "multiply by the reciprocal."

In your journal, describe how these rules are similar. Illustrate your answer with examples.

One of the largest postage stamps in the world was issued in 1962 by the Soviet Union. It measures 15.1 cm by 7.0 cm. The smallest postage stamp was issued in 1863 by Columbia. It measures 0.8 cm by 0.95 cm. How many of these small stamps would fit on one large one?

ORDER OF OPERATIONS WITH RATIONAL NUMBERS

Developing the Ideas

▶ ▶ *Through Discussion*

CONTEST WINNERS will be asked to answer correctly the following skill-testing question.
$$\frac{1}{8} - \left(-\frac{1}{2}\right) \div \left(-\frac{1}{4}\right) =$$

One student obtained the answer $-\frac{5}{2}$.

Another student's answer was $-\frac{15}{8}$.

Why do you think these students obtained different answers?

Try to figure out how these students obtained their answers.

▶ ▶ *Through a Guided Example*

To avoid having different answers for an expression like the one above, mathematicians have agreed that operations are to be performed in a certain order. When the rules are followed, everyone should get the same answer.

• • • • • • • • •

Order of Operations
- Operations within brackets are performed first.
- Exponents are calculated next.
- Multiplication and division are performed in order from left to right.
- Addition and subtraction are performed in order from left to right.

When you simplify an expression using the order of operations, it helps to do only one step at a time.

Example

Simplify this expression. $\left(-\frac{2}{3} + \frac{1}{2}\right) \times \left(-\frac{3}{2}\right)^2$

Solution

Do the work in brackets first.
$$\left(-\frac{2}{3} + \frac{1}{2}\right) \times \left(-\frac{3}{2}\right)^2 = \left(-\frac{4}{6} + \frac{3}{6}\right) \times \left(-\frac{3}{2}\right)^2$$
$$= \left(-\frac{1}{6}\right) \times \left(-\frac{3}{2}\right)^2$$

Do the exponent next.
$$= \left(-\frac{1}{6}\right) \times \left(\frac{9}{4}\right)$$

Do the multiplication last.
$$= -\frac{3}{8}$$

Working with Mathematics

Something to talk about

1. Simplify each expression. Describe each step of the process.

a) $(+4) + (-3)(-2)$

b) $(-5)(-4) \div (-2)$

c) $(-18) \div (+3) + (-11)$

d) $(-6) + (-12) \div (+4)$

e) $\dfrac{-20}{5} + \dfrac{12}{-2}$ f) $\dfrac{10}{-2} - \dfrac{8}{-4}$

g) $\dfrac{1}{4} - 2$ h) $\dfrac{1}{4} - \dfrac{1}{2} \times \dfrac{3}{2}$

On your own

2. Simplify each expression.

a) $(+11) - (+9) \div (-3)$

b) $(-21) \div (+7)(-5)$

c) $(-2)(+5) + (-3)(-8)$

d) $-7 - (-3)^2$

e) $(2 - 6) \times 5$

f) $2 - 6 \times 5$

g) $(1 - 3)^2 + (2 - 3)^2$

h) $(-1)^2 - (-3)^2$

3. Simplify each expression.

a) $3(-2 + 6) - 5(4 - 1)$

b) $-2(-4 + 3) + 3(-1 - 5)$

c) $5(2 - 6)(2 - 6)$

d) $(-3 + 4)(8 - 10) - (7 - 9)(4 - 1)$

e) $\dfrac{-36}{-9} + \dfrac{48}{-6}$ f) $\dfrac{28}{-4} - \dfrac{-24}{8}$

g) $\dfrac{-2 + 5}{7 - 1}$ h) $\dfrac{4 - 3(-2)}{-3 - (-1)}$

4. Simplify each expression.

a) $\dfrac{1}{2} - \dfrac{1}{4} \times \dfrac{1}{2}$ b) $\left(\dfrac{1}{2} - \dfrac{1}{4}\right) \times \dfrac{1}{2}$

c) $\dfrac{3}{4} \times \dfrac{1}{2} - \dfrac{3}{4}$ d) $\dfrac{3}{4} \times \left(\dfrac{1}{2} - \dfrac{3}{4}\right)$

e) $\dfrac{1}{2} \times \left(-\dfrac{2}{3}\right)^2$ f) $\left(\dfrac{1}{2} \times \dfrac{-2}{3}\right)^2$

g) $\left(\dfrac{1}{3} - \dfrac{1}{2}\right) \times \left(-\dfrac{1}{3}\right)^2$ h) $\dfrac{1}{3} - \dfrac{1}{2}\left(-\dfrac{1}{3}\right)^2$

Work together

5. Use brackets with the expression $5 - 3 \times 4 + 6$ so that it simplifies to each number.

a) 14   b) 20   c) -25

d) -13 e) -1

6. Use brackets with each expression so that it simplifies to the answer given.

a) $1 - 3 \times 5 - 7$; answer -7

b) $2 \times 2 - 2 \times 2$; answer -4

c) $5 + 5 \times 5 + 5$; answer 100

Extend your thinking

7. Here is an expression without brackets:
$\dfrac{1}{2} - \dfrac{1}{3} \times \dfrac{1}{2} - \dfrac{1}{3}$

a) Simplify the expression.

b) By inserting one pair of brackets, how many different answers can you get?

c) By inserting two pairs of brackets, can you get an answer that is different from any of the previous ones?

COMMUNICATING

The Ideas

Why is it necessary to have rules for the order of operations? Write an explanation in your journal. Include some examples to illustrate your explanation.

Averaging Coordinates

On a coordinate grid, two points determine a line segment. Suppose you find the mean of the two x-coordinates and the two y-coordinates. Use these numbers as the coordinates of a point. How is this point related to the line segment you started with?

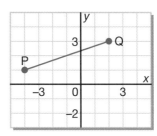

Understand the problem

- What is a line segment?
- How would you determine the mean of the x-coordinates and the mean of the y-coordinates?

Think of a strategy

- Start with PQ and then investigate other line segments.

Carry out the strategy

- Plot the line segment PQ on grid paper. Determine the mean of the x-coordinates and the mean of the y-coordinates.
- Plot the point which has these numbers as its coordinates. How does this point appear to be related to the line segment PQ?
- Repeat for other line segments. Include some horizontal and vertical line segments. Include some sloping up to the right and some sloping down to the right. Use points in all four quadrants as endpoints for your segments.

Look back

- If you know the coordinates of the endpoints of a line segment, how can you determine the coordinates of its midpoint?
- Investigate a similar problem for triangles. For example, start with a triangle such as $\triangle ABC$ with A(1, 8), B(−1, 2), and C(3, 2). Find the mean of the three x-coordinates and the three y-coordinates, and plot the corresponding point. How is this point related to $\triangle ABC$? It may help you to plot the midpoints of the three sides of the triangle.
- Repeat for other triangles, including right triangles and obtuse triangles.

Communicating the Ideas

In your journal, write a description of the problems you investigated, and your results.

SLOPE OF A LINE SEGMENT

Developing the Ideas
▷ ▷ Through an Activity

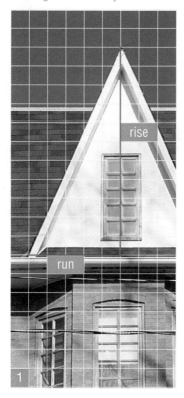
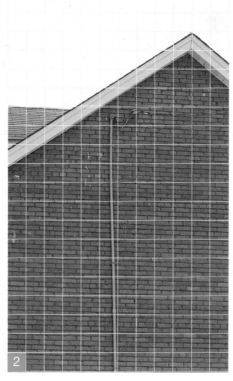

1. **a)** Which house has the steepest roof?
   b) Which has the roof which is the least steep?
   c) List the houses in order of steepness.

2. The first diagram shows what is meant by the *rise*
   and the *run* of a roof.
   a) Use the grid to determine the rise and the run of each roof.
   Copy and complete this table.

House	rise	run	$\frac{rise}{run}$
1			
2			
3			

   b) Use your calculator to divide the rise by the run.
   Write the results in the fourth column.
   c) Compare the numbers in the fourth column with your
   answers to exercise 1. What do you notice?

Each number in the fourth column is called the *slope* of the
corresponding roof. We determine slope using this formula: slope $= \dfrac{\text{rise}}{\text{run}}$

Since the rise and the run are obtained by measuring, the slope of a roof is usually represented by a rational number. Other examples of slope are shown in these photographs.

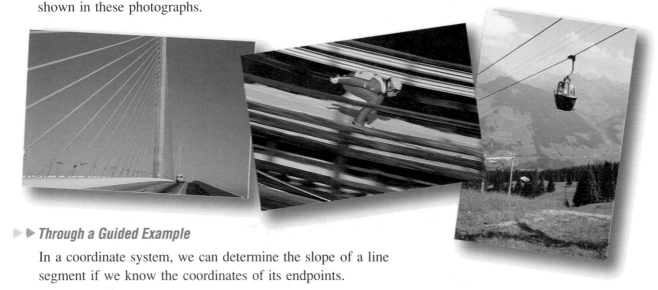

▶▶ *Through a Guided Example*

In a coordinate system, we can determine the slope of a line segment if we know the coordinates of its endpoints.

Example ....

Determine the slope of each line segment in the diagram.

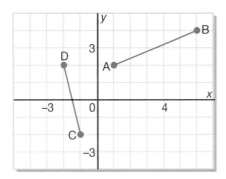

Solution

The coordinates of the endpoints of AB are A(1, 2) and B(6, 4).
Subtract the coordinates in the same order.
The rise from A to B is $4 - 2 = 2$
The run from A to B is $6 - 1 = 5$
Slope of AB $= \frac{2}{5}$, or 0.4

The coordinates of the endpoints of CD are C(−1, −2) and D(−2, 2).
The rise from C to D is $2 - (-2) = 4$
The run from C to D is $-2 - (-1) = -1$
Slope of CD $= \frac{4}{-1}$, or −4

Since we usually work with points whose coordinates are rational numbers, the slopes we obtain are often rational numbers.

Working with Mathematics

Something to talk about

1. What is the slope of the ramp below?

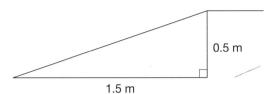

0.5 m

1.5 m

2. What can you say about the slope of a line segment that is:
   a) parallel to the *x*-axis?
   b) parallel to the *y*-axis?

Work together

3. The graph represents the side view of a ski tow. Each section of the tow is approximated by a line segment.

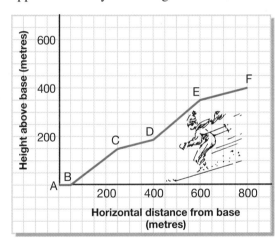

Height above base (metres)

600

400

200

E

F

C

D

B

A

200   400   600   800

Horizontal distance from base (metres)

   a) List the coordinates of points A, B, C, D, E, and F.
   b) Determine the slopes of the segments.
   c) Which segment is the steepest? Which is the least steep?

On your own

4. Determine the slope of each line segment.

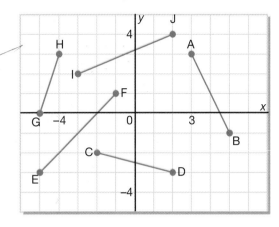

5. Determine the slope of the line segment joining each pair of points.
   a) A(−4, 1), B(3, 5)
   b) C(−3, −2), D(5, −1)
   c) E(2, 3), F(−3, 3)
   d) G(7, 3), H(−2, −4)
   e) J(−3, 6), K(8, −4)
   f) L(−1, 5), M(6, −3)
   g) N(2, 7), P(−5, −5)
   h) Q(−1.5, 6.5), R(8.5, −3.5)

6. a) Graph the quadrilateral with vertices A(4, −5.5), B(2, 4), C(−6, 9.5), D(−4, 0).
   b) Compare the slopes of:
      i) AB and CD   ii) BC and AD
   c) What kind of quadrilateral is this?

Extend your thinking

7. Does every line segment on a coordinate grid have a slope? If your answer is yes, explain your answer. If your answer is no, draw a diagram showing a line segment that does not have a slope.

COMMUNICATING

The Ideas

Look up the word "slope" in the dictionary. Is more than one meaning given? Do any of the meanings given in the dictionary resemble the mathematical meaning? Record your ideas in your journal.

Identifying Transformations

In earlier grades you encountered transformations like these:

Rotation	Reflection	Translation
	R	Я	R
R		R

The title of this book is shown on the first line below. Identify the transformation that was used to produce each image below the title.

MINDS ON MATH

Understand the problem
- What are you asked to do?

Think of a strategy
- Use a tracing.

Carry out the strategy
- Trace the title on a slip of paper and try to arrange the paper so that the tracing fits each image.
- Try tracing individual words or letters.

Look back
- Are there any other ways in which you could get different images?

Communicating the Ideas

In your journal, write a description of this problem and your solution.

Scott Kim's Inversions

Scott Kim is known for his unusual designs made of words which are meant to be seen as well as read. Here are five examples of his work. If you study these examples closely, you will see how he has created each desired effect.

1. Find examples of reflections, translations, rotations, and dilations in these designs.

2. How many times does the word "infinity" appear in the design at the lower right?

3. a) Which designs have rotational symmetry?
   b) Which designs have line symmetry?

4. a) Which designs would look the same in a mirror?
   b) Which designs look the same when you turn them upside down?

5. Scott Kim calls these designs *inversions*. Look up this word in the dictionary. Why do you think he chose this word for his designs?

Developing the Ideas

▶ ▶ *Through Instruction*

Whenever the shape, size, or position of a figure is changed, we say that it has undergone a *transformation*. Some common transformations are illustrated below.

Translation

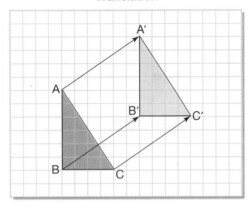

Rotation

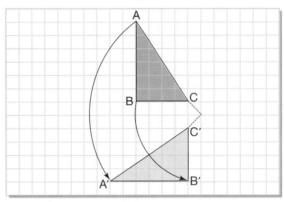

Reflection

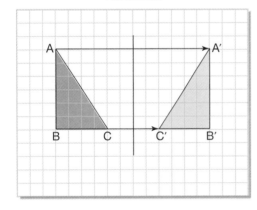

Dilation

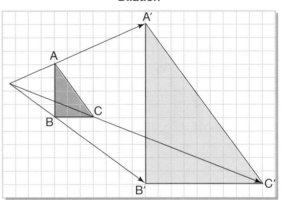

In each diagram above, corresponding points on the two triangles are related.

You say:	You write:
A maps onto A′	A → A′
B maps onto B′	B → B′
C maps onto C′	C → C′

A′, B′, and C′ are the *images* of A, B, and C.

We often work with transformations using a coordinate grid. The coordinates of the vertices of the figures we transform are usually rational numbers.

You can use a *mapping rule* such as $(x,y) \rightarrow (x+5, y-2)$ to determine the image of any point with coordinates (x,y). A mapping rule tells you what to do to the coordinates of a point to determine the coordinates of its image. This mapping rule tells you to add 5 to the x-coordinate and to subtract 2 from the y-coordinate.

....

This trapezoid has vertices A(−1, −1), B(1, −1), C(1, 3), and D(−1, 1). Suppose you apply the mapping rule $(x,y) \rightarrow (x+5, y-2)$ to this trapezoid.

a) Draw a diagram to show the image of the trapezoid.

b) Describe what happened to the trapezoid.

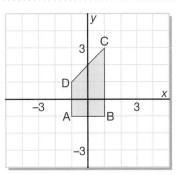

Solution

a) Make a table. Determine the image of each vertex to complete the table. Add 5 to each x-coordinate and subtract 2 from each y-coordinate.

For example,

A(−1, −1) → A′(−1 + 5, −1 − 2), or A′(4, −3)

POINT (x, y)	IMAGE $(x + 5, y - 2)$
A(−1, −1)	A′(4, −3)
B(1, −1)	B′(6, −3)
C(1, 3)	C′(6, 1)
D(−1, 1)	D′(4, −1)

The image of the trapezoid is shown below.

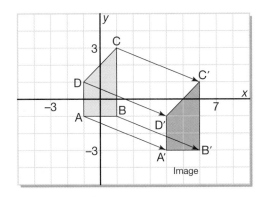

Image

b) The trapezoid moved 5 units to the right and 2 units down.

For most of the following exercises, it will be sufficient for you to determine the images of the vertices. When you need to use extra points you will be told to do so.

Working with Mathematics

Work together

1. Many mapping rules are listed below. Each mapping rule represents a transformation. Draw a separate diagram to show the image of the trapezoid ABCD after each transformation has been applied to it. Describe what happened to the trapezoid in each case.

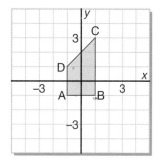

a) $(x,y) \rightarrow (x,-y)$ **b)** $(x,y) \rightarrow (-x,y)$

c) $(x,y) \rightarrow (3x,y)$ **d)** $(x,y) \rightarrow (-y,x)$

e) $(x,y) \rightarrow (3,y)$ **f)** $(x,y) \rightarrow (x,-2)$

g) $(x,y) \rightarrow (-2,4)$ **h)** $(x,y) \rightarrow (y,x)$

i) $(x,y) \rightarrow (x-3,y+2)$

j) $(x,y) \rightarrow (2x+1,y)$

k) $(x,y) \rightarrow (x+y,y)$

l) $(x,y) \rightarrow (x,x+y)$

m) $(x,y) \rightarrow (2x,2y)$

n) $(x,y) \rightarrow (0.5x,0.5y)$

o) $(x,y) \rightarrow (x,-2y)$

p) $(x,y) \rightarrow (-x,-y)$

q) $(x,y) \rightarrow (x+4,-y+1)$

r) $(x,y) \rightarrow (6-x,y)$

s) $(x,y) \rightarrow (x+y,x-y)$

t) $(x,y) \rightarrow (2x-y+3,x+2y-4)$

2. Diagrams of a translation, a reflection, a rotation, and a dilation are shown on page 148. Compare the results of exercise 1 with these diagrams.

  a) Which mapping rules in exercise 1:

    i) represent translations?

    ii) represent reflections?

    iii) represent rotations?

    iv) represent dilations?

  b) Which mapping rules in exercise 1 appear to represent combinations of the four transformations?

  c) Which mapping rules in exercise 1 appear to represent none of the four transformations or combinations of them?

3. Here is another mapping rule:

$$(x,y) \rightarrow \left(\frac{x^2 - y^2}{8}, \frac{xy}{4}\right)$$

Draw a diagram to show what happens to the triangle with vertices P(0, 4), Q(4, 4), and R(4, 0) when this mapping rule is applied to it. You will need to apply the mapping rule to more than just the three vertices. Use the lattice points on the boundary and the three lattice points inside the triangle.

Extend your thinking

4. Look at your diagrams in exercise 1. Compare the image figure with the original trapezoid ABCD. On some of these diagrams, the line segments on the image have the same length as the corresponding line segments on the original trapezoid. A transformation that preserves length is called an *isometry*. Which of the transformations in exercise 1 appear to be isometries?

The Ideas

A student asked the teacher, "Will a reflection in the *y*-axis followed by a reflection in the *x*-axis produce the same result as a reflection in the *x*-axis followed by a reflection in the *y*-axis?". The teacher turned the question back to the class. How would you answer this question?

Transformations and Grids

This diagram shows a grid made from squares, an original figure, and some images of that figure. The original figure is red. Each image can be obtained by applying one or more transformations to the original figure.

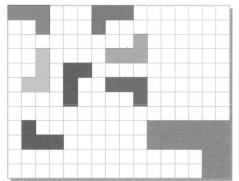

1. Identify a transformation or a sequence of transformations that relate the original figure to each image.

   The grid does not have to be square. Here is a grid made from isosceles triangles. You can create some interesting patterns when you transform a figure on a grid like this.

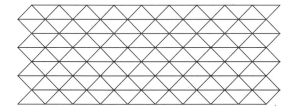

2. Use a Draw program for this activity. Construct a figure you can Duplicate and drag into position many times to create a grid. Experiment with different figures until you find one that will tessellate; that is, form a grid with no gaps.

   Draw an original figure in the upper left corner of your grid by filling parts of the grid with colours or patterns. Create a variety of images of your figure by applying different transformations to it.

   Print your diagram and exchange it with a friend. Challenge your friend to identify the transformations you used.

Mathematics & Technology

Linking Ideas

Some Unusual Transformations

These diagrams show the images of a figure after six different transformations were applied.

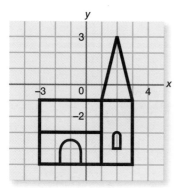

Original figure

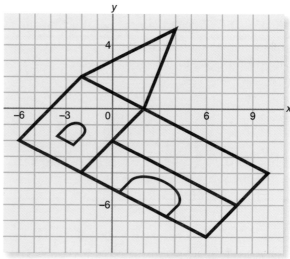

Image 1

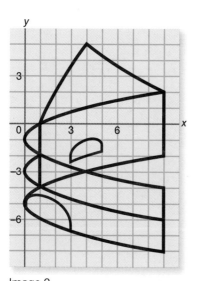

Image 2

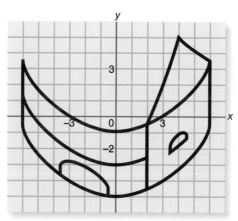

Image 3

1. The mapping rules for the six transformations are given below, but not in the correct order. Choose some points on the original figure and use the mapping rules to determine the coordinates of their images. Compare with the diagrams to determine the mapping rule for each image. Use other points as a check.

a) $(x,y) \rightarrow (-x - 1, 4y - 2)$

b) $(x,y) \rightarrow (2x, 0.5x^2 + y)$

c) $(x,y) \rightarrow \left(\dfrac{x^2 - y^2}{4}, \dfrac{xy}{2}\right)$

d) $\left(\dfrac{20x}{x^2 + y^2 + 1}, \dfrac{20y}{x^2 + y^2 + 1}\right)$

e) $(x,y) \rightarrow (x^2, x + y)$

f) $(x,y) \rightarrow (-2x + y + 5, x + y)$

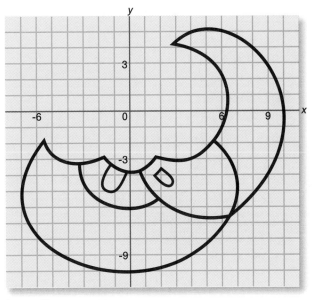

Image 5

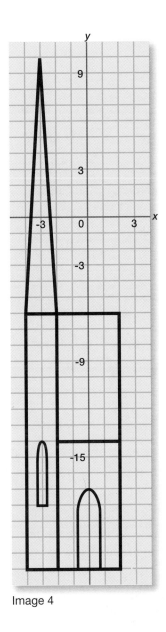

Image 4

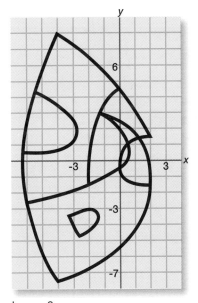

Image 6

2. Compare the images with the mapping rules. How can you tell from the mapping rules when all straight lines on a figure are transformed into straight lines on the image?

3. On two of the images, parts of the figure overlap. Use the mapping rules to explain why this occurs with these transformations.

Review

1. Add or subtract, as indicated.
   a) $(-5) + (-3)$
   b) $(-6) + (+9)$
   c) $(-19) + (+11)$
   d) $(+7) - (+4)$
   e) $(-9) - (-2)$
   f) $(-5) - (+5)$
   g) $(+2) + (-7) + (-4)$
   h) $(-43) - (-17) + (-26)$

2. Copy and complete the chart. Subtract 4 when moving to the right. Add 7 when moving up. What patterns do you notice on the diagonals? Explain why the patterns occur.

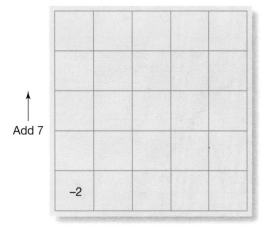

Add 7

−2

Subtract 4 ⟶

3. Multiply or divide, as indicated.
   a) $(-7)(+8)$
   b) $(-6)(-9)$
   c) $(-12)(-6)$
   d) $(+3)(-14)$
   e) $\dfrac{-16}{4}$
   f) $\dfrac{-63}{-7}$
   g) $\dfrac{81}{-3}$
   h) $\dfrac{121}{-11}$

4. Check that the arithmetic in each row is correct. Predict the next three rows in each pattern. Check that your prediction is correct. Then describe each pattern in words.
   a) $1 = 1 \times 1$
      $1 + 3 = 2 \times 2$
      $1 + 3 + 5 = 3 \times 3$
   b) $2 = 1 \times 2$
      $2 + 4 = 2 \times 3$
      $2 + 4 + 6 = 3 \times 4$

5. Which rational number is greater?
   a) $\dfrac{8}{6}, \dfrac{2}{3}$
   b) $\dfrac{-7}{10}, \dfrac{-16}{10}$
   c) $\dfrac{7}{5}, \dfrac{12}{5}$
   d) $\dfrac{-8}{28}, \dfrac{-3}{7}$
   e) $\dfrac{-27}{24}, \dfrac{-10}{8}$
   f) $\dfrac{52}{16}, \dfrac{11}{4}$

6. Express each rational number as a decimal.
   a) $\dfrac{5}{8}$
   b) $\dfrac{-4}{9}$
   c) $\dfrac{8}{-11}$
   d) $\dfrac{13}{11}$

7. Add or subtract, as indicated.
   a) $\left(-\dfrac{2}{3}\right) + \left(-\dfrac{1}{4}\right)$
   b) $\left(-\dfrac{3}{8}\right) - \dfrac{3}{4}$
   c) $\dfrac{9}{4} + \left(-\dfrac{7}{3}\right)$
   d) $\left(-\dfrac{20}{6}\right) - \left(-\dfrac{13}{3}\right)$
   e) $\dfrac{5}{7} - \dfrac{3}{2}$
   f) $\left(-\dfrac{25}{2}\right) + \dfrac{13}{5}$
   g) $(-1.7) + (-3.1)$
   h) $23.9 - (-15.6)$
   i) $14.2 + (-27.3)$
   j) $(-7.9) + 8.4$

8. Multiply or divide, as indicated.
   a) $\left(-\dfrac{18}{7}\right) \times \left(-\dfrac{21}{9}\right)$
   b) $\dfrac{3}{28} \div \left(-\dfrac{9}{7}\right)$
   c) $\left(-\dfrac{72}{7}\right) \div \left(-\dfrac{12}{49}\right)$
   d) $\dfrac{9}{48} \div \left(-\dfrac{6}{16}\right)$
   e) $\left(-\dfrac{33}{4}\right) \times \dfrac{7}{22}$
   f) $\left(-\dfrac{75}{3}\right) \div \left(-\dfrac{15}{4}\right)$
   g) $(-0.2) \times 0.6$
   h) $(-3.6) \div (-4)$
   i) $(-1.21) \div 1.1$
   j) $1.3 \times (-0.5)$
   k) $(-17.9) \times (-1.4)$
   l) $(-10.8) \div (-0.9)$

9. The chart below lists the amount of time it would take 4 different animals to travel 100 m at top speed. How many times as fast as each of the other animals is the lion?

Animal	Time to travel 100 m
Lion	4.5 s
Giraffe	5.6 s
Giant tortoise	22 min
Snail	2 h 40 min

10. Simplify each expression.

a) $(+13) - (-4) \div (-2)$

b) $(-42) \div 3 - (-7)$

c) $-3(5 + 6) + 2 \times 8$

d) $(-6)^2 - (2 + 3)^2$

e) $\frac{2}{3} \times \frac{5}{8} - \frac{1}{2}$

f) $\frac{7}{4} - \left(\frac{-5}{6}\right)^2$

g) $\frac{2}{3} \div \frac{5}{6} + \left(-\frac{1}{4}\right)$

11. Use brackets with each expression so that it simplifies to the answer given.

a) $9 - 4 \times 2 - 3$; answer 13

b) $3 \times 8 + 6 \div 2$; answer 33

c) $7 + 6 \times 6 - 7$; answer 1

12. Calculate the slope of each line segment.

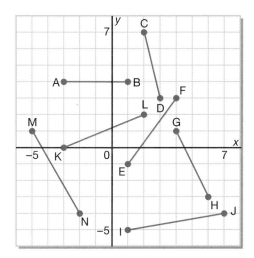

13. The coordinates of the vertices of four triangles are given. Graph the triangles and find the slope of each side.

a) A(5, −1), B(0, 4), C(−2, −5)

b) R(−3, 4), S(6, 7), T(2, −3)

c) L(4, −2), M(−4, 8), N(4, 8)

d) E(−2, −1), F(−1, −6), G(5, 6)

14. An original figure is shown below in red. Identify the transformation that was used to produce each image below the original.

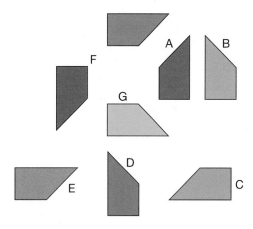

15. △PQR is shown below. Graph △PQR and its image under each mapping rule.

a) $(x, y) \rightarrow (x + 3, y - 4)$

b) $(x, y) \rightarrow (-x, y)$

c) $(x, y) \rightarrow (-y, -x)$

d) $(x, y) \rightarrow (-x + 4, y)$

e) $(x, y) \rightarrow (3x, 3y)$

f) $(x, y) \rightarrow (2x - 3, 2y + 1)$

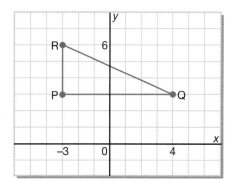

16. What transformation is represented by each mapping rule?

a) $(x, y) \rightarrow (2x, 2y)$

b) $(x, y) \rightarrow (x - 2, y + 7)$

c) $(x, y) \rightarrow (x, -y)$

d) $(x, y) \rightarrow (-y, -x)$

e) $(x, y) \rightarrow (x + 3, y + 1)$

f) $(x, y) \rightarrow (-x, y)$

Graphing Population Shifts

An article entitled *Harvests of Ruin* was printed in Canadian Geographic in 1992. It described the decline of Saskatchewan's rural way of life. This graph appeared in the article.

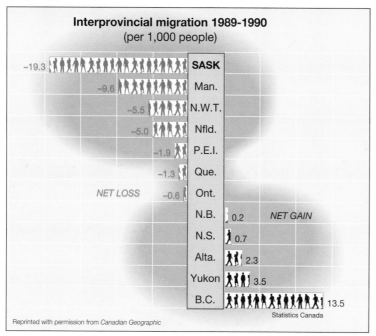

Interprovincial migration 1989-1990
(per 1,000 people)

−19.3	SASK
−9.6	Man.
−5.5	N.W.T.
−5.0	Nfld.
−1.9	P.E.I.
−1.3	Que.
−0.6	Ont.
N.B.	0.2
N.S.	0.7
Alta.	2.3
Yukon	3.5
B.C.	13.5

NET LOSS

NET GAIN

Statistics Canada

Reprinted with permission from *Canadian Geographic*

The title of the graph, "Interprovincial migration", means the net change in the number of Canadians who move from one province to another.

ACTIVITY 1

Compare this graph with the graph you drew in exercise 19 on page 122. List the ways in which the two graphs are different.

ACTIVITY 2

Use the last row of the table on page 118 and the populations in the table below. Calculate the interprovincial migration per 1000 people for each province in 1992.

POPULATION, 1992 (thousands of persons)			
YK	30	Ont	10 278
NWT	58	Que	6969
BC	3373	NB	926
Alta	2582	NS	904
Sask	990	PEI	132
Man	1096	Nfld	568

ACTIVITY 3

Use your results from *Activity 2* to construct a graph, like the one on the facing page, for 1992.

Compare your graph with the one on the facing page. Why are the provinces showing the greatest net loss and net gain not the same in both graphs?

Compare your graph with the graph you drew in exercise 19 on page 122. In what ways are the two graphs similar? In what ways are they different?

ACTIVITY 4

From an almanac or some other source, determine the most recent figures you can for interprovincial migrations. Determine also the populations of the provinces.

Use your data to draw two graphs.
• a graph like the one you drew in exercise 19 on page 122 showing the net changes in population
• a graph like the one on page 156 showing the changes per 1000 people

If you have access to a computer with a spreadsheet program, use it to do the calculations and to construct the graphs in this project.

WHAT'S COMING UP?

DEPARTMENTS

Linking Ideas

Mathematics Files

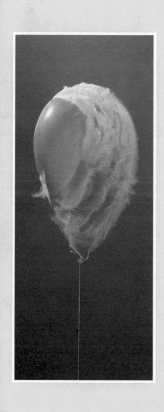

Quests

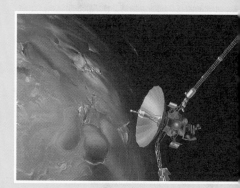

Minds on Math

Start With What You Know

ASTRONOMERS JACQUELINE HEWITT and John Tonry are trying to determine the age of the universe. Scientists can measure many things with great precision, but not the age of the universe. It may be as old as 20 000 000 000 years, as young as 10 000 000 000 years, or somewhere in between.

In 1985 the world population reached 5 billion. According to United Nations projections, if current growth rates continue, the population will reach 694 billion by the year 2150. Although no one knows how many people Earth can support, scientists agree that a population of 694 billion is too great. Studies conducted by biologists Anne Ehrlich, Paul Ehrlich, and others, suggest that the maximum sustainable population may be about 16 billion.

About 15 years ago, Erno Rubik invented an intriguing puzzle. The goal is to rotate the puzzle pieces until each face of the cube is one solid colour. Although a Rubik's cube can be jumbled in approximately 43 million million million different ways, some people can solve the puzzle in seconds.

1. Two estimates for the age of the universe are given on page 160. How would you read each number?

2. Three population figures are given on page 160. How would you write these numbers in decimal form?

3. How would you write each number below in decimal form?
   a) 10^8
   b) 9.2×10^8
   c) 920×10^8
   d) $10^3 \times 10^8$

4. One of the numbers in exercise 3 is written in scientific notation. Which one is it? Write the large numbers in the captions on these pages in scientific notation.

5. Only one of these names for large numbers is correct. Which one do you think it is?

   gazillion   zillion   trillion

Forming Expressions with 1, 4, 8, and 9

Using the digits 1, 4, 8, and 9, can you write an expression for each whole number from 1 to 100?

Understand the problem

Study the examples on the right.
Discuss these questions with a partner.
- Does each digit have to be used?
- Do the digits have to be in numerical order?
- What mathematical symbols can you use?
- Can you use 2-digit numbers?

$$6 = 4 + 9 - 8 + 1$$
$$35 = 9(4 - 1) + 8$$
$$40 = 4 \times 8 - 1 + 9$$
$$54 = 18 + 4 \times 9$$

Think of a strategy

- Study the patterns formed by the operations in each example above.
- Use these patterns and other patterns like them to help you create your expressions.

Carry out the strategy

- In the first example, $4 + 9 - 8 + 1$ was used. In this expression there are two additions and one subtraction: ■ + ■ − ■ + ■

  Think of the shaded boxes as places to write the digits. Write the digits in this pattern in as many different ways as you can.
- Think of other patterns similar to the one above. For each pattern, write the digits in as many different ways as you can.
- Repeat these steps using the patterns in the other examples.

  ■(■ − ■) + ■   ■ × ■ − ■ + ■
  ■■ + ■ × ■

Look back

- Can you think of any other patterns for the operations? Each pattern you come up with gives you another opportunity to get more numbers.
- Did you think to use powers in your expressions?

Communicating the Ideas

Write a description of this problem in your journal.
Include a list of the numbers from 1 to 100.
As you obtain an expression, write it beside the appropriate number.

Plan to work on this problem for a few minutes each day. In a few days you will probably have expressions for most of the numbers from 1 to 100.

Developing the Ideas

▶ ▶ *Through an Activity*

Work in a group.

You will need a telephone book, a ruler, a measuring tape, and a calculator.

Estimating the number of telephone numbers

1. How many telephone numbers do you think there are in your telephone book? Don't try to calculate the number — just look through the book and estimate roughly how many telephone numbers you think it contains.

2. Discuss with your partner how you could determine approximately how many telephone numbers there are in your telephone book. Carry out your ideas. What answer do you get? Do you think the actual number is more or less than this?

Estimating the number of telephones

3. **a)** Do you think the number of telephones in the region served by your telephone book would be more than or less than the number of telephone numbers? Give reasons for your answer.

   b) About how many telephones do you think there might be in the region served by your telephone book?

Estimating the number of telephone books

4. About how many telephone books do you think were printed for your community?

5. If all these telephone books were stacked one on top of another, about how high would the pile be?

6. **a)** About how many telephone books would you need to cover the floor of your classroom?

   b) If all the telephone books were to be stored in your empty classroom, how many layers would there be?

   c) How high would the stacks of telephone books be? How does this compare with the height of your classroom?

Estimating the number of trees used to produce the books

7. **a)** Measure or estimate the mass of 1 telephone book.

   b) What is the approximate mass of all the telephone books printed for your community?

   c) It takes about 17 trees to produce 1 t of newsprint. Suppose none of the paper in the telephone books was made from recycled material. About how many trees would have been used to produce the telephone books for your community?

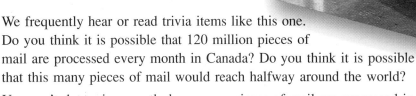

Canada Post Delivers!
Canada Post processes an average of 120 million pieces of mail every month. If all the mail processed in one month were placed in a line, it would reach more than halfway around the world.

We frequently hear or read trivia items like this one. Do you think it is possible that 120 million pieces of mail are processed every month in Canada? Do you think it is possible that this many pieces of mail would reach halfway around the world?

You can't determine exactly how many pieces of mail are processed in Canada in one month. But you can estimate the answer based on some common knowledge and some reasonable assumptions.

1. Check the amount of mail processed.

   a) Compare the number of items processed with the population of Canada. On average, about how many pieces of mail would every person in Canada have to send to total 120 million in one month?

   b) Do you think this is reasonable?

   c) If your answer to part b was no, then how many pieces of mail do you think would be processed in Canada in one month?

Common knowledge:
Population of Canada

Reasonable assumption:
Average number of pieces of mail sent per person in one month

Some populations useful for estimation:

	10 000 000 000	World	5.3 billion
1 billion	1 000 000 000		
	100 000 000	United States	250 million
	10 000 000	Canada	28.9 million
1 million	1 000 000	Vancouver	1.6 million
	100 000		
	10 000	Football stadium	60 000
1 thousand	1 000	High school	1000
	100	Family reunion	100
	10		
	1		

Items of many different sizes are sent in the mail. So, no one knows exactly how far 120 million pieces of mail would reach if they were placed in a line. But you can use some common knowledge and some reasonable assumptions to check the statement that the mail would reach halfway around the world.

2. Check the distance the mail would reach.

a) About how long do you think an average envelope is?

b) If all the envelopes were this long, how far would 120 million pieces of mail reach?

c) How does this compare with the distance around the world shown below?

d) Do you think that the statement about the distance the mail would reach is reasonable?

e) If your answer to part d was no, then how would you describe the distance that 120 million pieces of mail would reach?

Reasonable assumption:
Average size of an envelope

Common knowledge:
Distance around the world at the Equator

Some distances useful for estimation:

1 trillion	1 000 000 000 000
	100 000 000 000
	10 000 000 000
1 billion	1 000 000 000
	100 000 000
	10 000 000
1 million	1 000 000
	100 000
	10 000
1 thousand	1 000
	100
	10
	1

Distance to sun	150 000 000 000 m
Distance to moon	376 000 000 m
Earth circumference	40 000 000 m
Distance across Canada	5 500 000 m
Length of a football field	100 m
Height of a door	2 m

Working with Mathematics

Something to talk about

1. Use common knowledge and some reasonable assumptions. Can you choose the number that is closest to the answer to each question? Use the information on pages 164 and 165. How could you determine if your answer is reasonable? Where could you find the information?

   a) What is the population of Halifax?
   32 050
   320 500
   3 205 000

   b) What is the total area of Canada?
   9 970 000 km²
   99 700 000 km²
   997 000 000 km²

   c) What is the top speed of a peregrine falcon?
   3.5 km/h
   35 km/h
   350 km/h

   d) How many people were granted Canadian citizenship in 1990?
   1040
   104 000
   104 000 000

   e) What is the population of China?
   11 500 000
   115 000 000
   1 150 000 000

   f) How many compact disks were sold in Canada in 1992?
   2 600 000
   26 000 000
   260 000 000

   g) What was the total value of all the goods and services produced in Canada in 1991?
   $68 000 000
   $680 000 000
   $680 000 000 000

   h) What is the total length of the Canada-U.S. border, including the part between Yukon and Alaska?
   8890 km
   88 900 km
   889 000 km

   i) How high is the world's highest waterfall?
   80.7 m
   807 m
   8070 m

   j) How many households in Canada have at least one telephone?
   99 000
   990 000
   9 900 000

2. On July 20, 1990, a statement about blue boxes appeared in three different editions of The Toronto Star newspaper:
   - 200 million Ontario households have blue boxes for recycling bottles and cans.
   - 200 000 Ontario households have blue boxes for recycling bottles and cans.
   - 2 million Ontario households have blue boxes for recycling bottles and cans.

   Which number do you think is correct? Give a reason for your answer.

Work together

Estimate each number. Include some calculations when you need them.

3. About how many times will your heart beat in your lifetime?

4. About how many hours of television have you watched in your lifetime?

5. About how far do you walk in a day?

6. About how many words do you speak in a day? in a week? in a month? in a year?

On your own

7. In keyboarding, a character refers to a letter, space, or punctuation mark. Estimate how many characters you think an average novel would contain. What assumptions are you making?

8. **a)** Refine your estimate in exercise 7 using a word processing program. Input 100 characters. Copy these and paste them 9 times to make 1000 characters. Copy the 1000 characters and paste to make 10 000. How many pages of print does this represent? Refine your original estimate based on this information.

   b) How many characters can you input in 5 min? If you were to keep inputting at this rate, about how long would it take you to input a novel?

Extend your thinking

9. In two different ways, these magazine excerpts express the rate at which the tropical rainforests are disappearing.

   > The tropical rainforests are disappearing at 30 ha per minute.
   >
   > *E Magazine*

   > The tropical rainforests are disappearing at 3.7 million ha per year.
   >
   > *Scientific American*

   a) The symbol 'ha' is the metric symbol for a unit of area called a hectare. Do you need to know what a hectare is to determine if the two rates are the same? If so, find out this information.

   b) Carry out calculations to compare the two rates. Try to think of an explanation for any difference in the rates.

   c) How do you think scientists estimate the rate of disappearance of the tropical rainforests?

COMMUNICATING The Ideas

About how many hours will you spend eating in your lifetime? Include with your final answer an explanation of the assumptions you made.

Developing the Ideas

▷ ▶ *Through Discussion*

All measurements in this chart are approximate.
They are expressed in metres.

$10^{26} = 100\ 000\ 000\ 000\ 000\ 000\ 000\ 000\ 000$	Diameter of the universe
$10^{25} = 10\ 000\ 000\ 000\ 000\ 000\ 000\ 000\ 000$	Diameter of the Great Wall of galaxies
$10^{24} = 1\ 000\ 000\ 000\ 000\ 000\ 000\ 000\ 000$	
$10^{23} = 100\ 000\ 000\ 000\ 000\ 000\ 000\ 000$	Diameter of the Virgo Cluster of galaxies
$10^{22} = 10\ 000\ 000\ 000\ 000\ 000\ 000\ 000$	Diameter of the Local Group of galaxies
$10^{21} = 1\ 000\ 000\ 000\ 000\ 000\ 000\ 000$	Diameter of the Milky Way galaxy
$10^{20} = 100\ 000\ 000\ 000\ 000\ 000\ 000$	
$10^{19} = 10\ 000\ 000\ 000\ 000\ 000\ 000$	Diameter of the Tarantula Nebula
$10^{18} = 1\ 000\ 000\ 000\ 000\ 000\ 000$	
$10^{17} = 100\ 000\ 000\ 000\ 000\ 000$	Diameter of the Crab Nebula
$10^{16} = 10\ 000\ 000\ 000\ 000\ 000$	
$10^{15} = 1\ 000\ 000\ 000\ 000\ 000$	
$10^{14} = 100\ 000\ 000\ 000\ 000$	
$10^{13} = 10\ 000\ 000\ 000\ 000$	Diameter of the solar system
1 trillion $10^{12} = 1\ 000\ 000\ 000\ 000$	Diameter of the largest star
$10^{11} = 100\ 000\ 000\ 000$	
$10^{10} = 10\ 000\ 000\ 000$	
1 billion $10^{9} = 1\ 000\ 000\ 000$	Diameter of the sun
$10^{8} = 100\ 000\ 000$	Diameter of Jupiter
$10^{7} = 10\ 000\ 000$	Diameter of Earth
1 million $10^{6} = 1\ 000\ 000$	
$10^{5} = 100\ 000$	
$10^{4} = 10\ 000$	Height of the highest mountain
1 thousand $10^{3} = 1\ 000$	
$10^{2} = 100$	Height of the tallest tree
$10^{1} = 10$	Height of the tallest dinosaur
$10^{0} = 1$	Height of a child

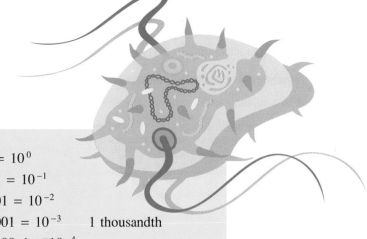

Height of a child	$1 = 10^0$	
	$0.1 = 10^{-1}$	
Width of a calculator key	$0.01 = 10^{-2}$	
Diameter of a grain of sugar	$0.001 = 10^{-3}$	1 thousandth
Diameter of a pollen grain	$0.000\ 1 = 10^{-4}$	
Diameter of a white blood cell	$0.000\ 01 = 10^{-5}$	
Diameter of a bacterium	$0.000\ 001 = 10^{-6}$	1 millionth
Diameter of a virus	$0.000\ 000\ 1 = 10^{-7}$	
Diameter of a protein molecule	$0.000\ 000\ 01 = 10^{-8}$	
	$0.000\ 000\ 001 = 10^{-9}$	1 billionth
Diameter of a carbon atom	$0.000\ 000\ 000\ 1 = 10^{-10}$	
	$0.000\ 000\ 000\ 01 = 10^{-11}$	
	$0.000\ 000\ 000\ 001 = 10^{-12}$	1 trillionth
	$0.000\ 000\ 000\ 000\ 1 = 10^{-13}$	
Diameter of the nucleus of a uranium atom	$0.000\ 000\ 000\ 000\ 01 = 10^{-14}$	
Diameter of the nucleus of a carbon atom		
Diameter of a proton	$0.000\ 000\ 000\ 000\ 001 = 10^{-15}$	
	$0.000\ 000\ 000\ 000\ 000\ 1 = 10^{-16}$	
Diameter of a quark	$0.000\ 000\ 000\ 000\ 000\ 01 = 10^{-17}$	
Diameter of an electron	$0.000\ 000\ 000\ 000\ 000\ 001 = 10^{-18}$	

Work with a partner. Use the information in the chart on these two pages to answer the question below.

1. The approximate dimensions of seven objects on the chart are included among the numbers below. Which objects do you think they are?

14 million metres	10 millionths of a metre
1.4 billion metres	10 billionths of a metre
14 billion metres	1 billionth of a metre
900 billion metres	100 trillionths of a metre
90 trillion metres	1 trillionth of a metre
90 thousand trillion metres	one ten-trillionth of a metre

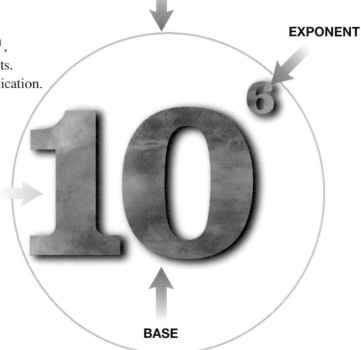

POWER

EXPONENT

BASE

Powers with positive exponents

Look at the chart on page 168.
The numbers written like this: 10^9, 10^{10}, 10^{11},
are examples of powers with positive exponents.
We define powers in terms of repeated multiplication.

· · · · · · · · · ·

A power such as 10^6 is defined as
$10 \times 10 \times 10 \times 10 \times 10 \times 10$.
The exponent 6 tells you how many
10s are multiplied together.

1. What does each power mean? Evaluate each power.

　　a) 10^3　　　　　**b)** 10^7

　　c) 10^1　　　　　**d)** 2^2

　　e) 3^4　　　　　**f)** 1.5^3

　　g) $(-5)^3$　　　　**h)** $(-2)^8$

2. How would you write each expression as a power?

　　a) $2 \times 2 \times 2 \times 2 \times 2 \times 2$

　　b) $7 \times 7 \times 7 \times 7 \times 7 \times 7 \times 7 \times 7 \times 7$

　　c) $(-1) \times (-1) \times (-1) \times (-1) \times (-1)$

3. The definition above applies to only two of the powers below.
Which powers are they? Why doesn't the definition apply
to the other powers?

　　a) 2^0　　　　　**b)** 10^{-1}

　　c) $10^{0.5}$　　　　**d)** 3^{225}

　　e) 0^5　　　　　**f)** 5^{-3}

Powers with an exponent of 0

The definition above does not apply to a power
such as 10^0. It is not possible to multiply zero
10s together. We need a different definition for
a power with an exponent of 0.

4. Use the chart on pages 168 and 169. Try to
think of a reason why 10^0 is equal to 1.

Powers with negative exponents

Look at the chart on page 169. The numbers written like this: 10^{-2}, 10^{-3}, 10^{-4}, are examples of powers with negative exponents.

Our definition does not apply to a power with a negative exponent. For example, in 10^{-2}, it is not possible to multiply -2 10s together. We need a different definition for a power with a negative exponent. The clue to this definition lies in the patterns in the chart on pages 168 and 169.

$$10^4 \quad = 10\ 000 \quad = 10 \times 10 \times 10 \times 10$$
$$10^3 \quad = 1000 \quad = 10 \times 10 \times 10$$
$$10^2 \quad = 100 \quad = 10 \times 10$$
$$10^1 \quad = 10 \quad = 10$$

Reducing each exponent by 1 ...

$$10^0 \quad = 1 \quad = 1$$
$$10^{-1} \quad = \frac{1}{10} \quad = \frac{1}{10}$$

$$10^{-2} \quad = \frac{1}{100} \quad = \frac{1}{10 \times 10}, \text{ or } \frac{1}{10^2}$$

$$10^{-3} \quad = \frac{1}{1000} \quad = \frac{1}{10 \times 10 \times 10}, \text{ or } \frac{1}{10^3}$$

$$10^{-4} \quad = \frac{1}{10\ 000} \quad = \frac{1}{10 \times 10 \times 10 \times 10}, \text{ or } \frac{1}{10^4}$$

... divides each answer by 10

These patterns suggest that we should define powers with negative exponents in terms of fractions.

• • • • • • • • •

A power such as 10^{-5} is defined as the reciprocal of 10^5.
$$10^{-5} = \frac{1}{10^5}$$

5. What does each power mean? Evaluate each power.
   a) 10^{-3} **b)** 10^{-1} **c)** 10^{-9} **d)** 2^{-1}
   e) 5^{-2} **f)** 2.5^{-1} **g)** $(-2)^{-1}$ **h)** $(-1)^{-3}$

6. How would you write each expression as a power?
   a) $\frac{1}{2} \times \frac{1}{2} \times \frac{1}{2} \times \frac{1}{2}$ **b)** $\frac{1}{3 \times 3 \times 3 \times 3 \times 3}$ **c)** $\frac{1}{7} \times \frac{1}{7} \times \frac{1}{7}$

The total assets of the Bank of Canada are approximately $27.29 billion. What if this money was shared equally among all the people of Canada? What would be the value of your share?

Working with Mathematics

Something to talk about

1. What does the word "reciprocal" mean?

2. Express each product as a power.
    a) $2 \times 2 \times 2 \times 2 \times 2$
    b) $3 \times 3 \times 3 \times 3$
    c) $(-2) \times (-2) \times (-2) \times (-2)$
    d) $\frac{1}{2} \times \frac{1}{2} \times \frac{1}{2}$

3. Express each number as a power of 2.
    a) 2   b) 4   c) 8   d) 16
    e) $\frac{1}{2}$ f) $\frac{1}{4}$ g) $\frac{1}{8}$ h) $\frac{1}{16}$

Work together

4. Evaluate each power.
    a) 10^2 b) 10^{-2} c) $(-10)^2$
    d) $(-10)^{-2}$ e) 4^3 f) 4^{-3}
    g) $(-4)^3$ h) $(-4)^{-3}$ i) 5^1
    j) 1^5 k) 5^0 l) 0^5

5. a) Try calculating large powers of 2 with your calculator.
    b) What does the calculator do if the number is too large to be displayed? What is the largest power you can calculate before the next power is too large to be displayed?
    c) What does the calculator do if the number is too large to be calculated? What is the largest power you can calculate?

6. Simplify each expression.
    a) $3^2 + 4^2$ b) $(3 + 4)^2$ c) $3^2 + 4$
    d) $3 + 4^2$ e) $2^3 + 2^3$ f) $3^2 + 3^2$
    g) $2^2 + 3^3$ h) $2^3 + 3^2$ i) $2^0 + 2^2$
    j) $3^4 - 3^0$ k) $(2 + 3)^0$ l) $2^0 + 3^0$
    m) $2^0 + 2^{-1}$ n) $2^{-1} - 2^{-2}$ o) $(2 + 2)^{-1}$

7. Write the digits 1, 2, 3, 4, 5, 6 in these spaces $\blacksquare^{\blacksquare} + \blacksquare^{\blacksquare} + \blacksquare^{\blacksquare}$ to form:
    a) the greatest possible sum
    b) the least possible sum

On your own

8. What does each power mean? Evaluate each power.
    a) 5^2 b) 5^{-2} c) $(-5)^2$ d) $(-5)^{-2}$
    e) 2^5 f) 2^{-5} g) $(-2)^5$ h) $(-2)^{-5}$

9. Which is the greater number in each pair?
    a) $2^3, 2^4$ b) $2^{-3}, 2^{-4}$ c) $2^3, 3^3$
    d) $2^{-3}, 3^{-3}$ e) $2^3, 3^2$ f) $2^{-3}, 3^{-2}$
    g) $3^4, 4^3$ h) $3^{-4}, 4^{-3}$ i) $3^{22}, 3^{25}$

10. Continue working on the Quest on page 162. You can also use powers in your expressions. For example, if you need an expression for 88, you can write $89 - 1^4$. In this expression, the pattern is: $\blacksquare\blacksquare - \blacksquare^{\blacksquare}$
    a) Use this pattern. Write the digits 1, 4, 8, and 9 in as many ways as you can.
    b) Think of other patterns using powers. For each pattern, write the digits in different ways. Can you get all the numbers from 1 to 100 now?

Extend your thinking

11. Two students were discussing how to write the largest number using the digits 1, 4, 8, and 9 and no other symbols.
    Nigel: "The largest number I can make is 98^{41}."
    Saidah: "I think that 41^{98} is larger."
    a) Do you think Saidah was correct? Explain your reasoning.
    b) Using the four digits, write a number that is larger than Saidah's. Explain how you know that your number is larger.

COMMUNICATING

The Ideas

Look at the powers in the exercises. Some bases are positive and some are negative. Some answers are positive and some are negative. If a power is given, how can you tell if the number it represents is positive or negative? Share your thoughts with a partner.

How Big is One Billion?

The exercises below will help you visualize how big a number one billion is. Work with a partner.

Estimating one million seconds

1. How many days, months, or years do you think it would take to equal one million seconds? Don't try to calculate this. Just think about one million seconds and estimate how long you think they are.

2. Use your calculator to calculate how many seconds there are in:
   a) one hour   **b)** one day   **c)** one year

3. Have you reached one million yet? How many days does it take to equal one million seconds?

Estimating one billion seconds

4. How many days, months, or years do you think equal one billion seconds?

5. Calculate approximately how many years equal one billion seconds.

6. Use a ruler to draw a line segment 10 cm long. Make this a number line by marking the left end 0 and the right end 1 000 000 000. Where would you put the number 1 000 000 on this number line?

7. Read the caption describing the photograph below. Is Loring's claim reasonable? Include some calculations to support your answer.

CBC Radio's Barbara Smith wipes away tears as newsreader Rex Loring signs off after 35 years with the network. Loring has delivered World Report for more than 20 years, and claims to have spoken 7 billion on-air words.

The National Debt Clock

The Vancouver Board of Trade has been maintaining a debt clock since 1990. It shows the Canadian national debt and the amount by which this debt is increasing every minute. When this photograph was taken in early 1994, the debt was about to reach half a trillion dollars.

How big was the national debt one year after the photograph was taken?

CANADA'S FEDERAL DEBT
LA DETTE FEDERALE DU CANADA

BILLIONS MILLIONS THOUSANDS MILLES

$499,519,037,702

THE FEDERAL DEBT   LA DETTE FEDERALE

CHANGE PER MINUTE
VARIATION PAR MINUTE $85,600

VANCOUVER BOARD OF TRADE

NEON PRODUCTS LTD.

Understand the problem

- What are you asked to do?
- Do you think it is possible to give an exact answer to this question? Explain your answer.

Think of a strategy

- The second number in the photograph tells you how fast the Canadian national debt was growing each minute in early 1994.
- You can use this information to calculate how it changed in one year. What assumption are you making when you do this?

Carry out the strategy

- Calculate the number of minutes in one year.
- The national debt increases by $85 600 each minute. How much did it increase in one year?
- What was the national debt one year after the photograph was taken?

Look back

- What numbers do you think would appear on the sign today?
- The population of Canada in early 1994 was about 28.9 million. What if the national debt were divided equally among all Canadians? What would be each person's share? This number is the national debt per capita.

Communicating the Ideas

In your journal, write a description of this problem and your solution.

DATA DISK

The chart lists the national debts of eight different countries in 1988. For ease of comparison, each number is given in U.S. dollars. Use the *Land Use* or *World Health and Education* database from the student's disk to determine the population of each country. Based on this population, calculate the national debt per capita in each country.

Country	National Debt (U.S. $)
Argentina	12 290 000 000
Australia	48 740 000 000
Canada	231 990 000 000
Italy	775 050 000 000
Malawi	1 250 000 000
Malaysia	32 790 000 000
United States	2 097 000 000 000
Uruguay	1 930 000 000

Developing the Ideas

▶ ▶ *Through Discussion*

Powers are defined in terms of repeated multiplication. Do you think powers would have some special properties when they are multiplied or divided?

Multiplying powers

1. **a)** What does 10^3 mean? What does 10^4 mean?
   b) What does $10^3 \times 10^4$ mean? How many 10s are multiplied together?
   c) Using the result of part b, write $10^3 \times 10^4$ as a power of 10.

2. **a)** What does $10^2 \times 10^6$ mean? How many 10s are multiplied together?
   b) Write $10^2 \times 10^6$ as a power of 10.

3. Based on the above results, state a rule that you could use to multiply two powers of 10. Explain why your rule is correct. Could you use your rule to multiply more than two powers of 10?

4. Can you use your rule to multiply powers of 2? Make up some examples to test your prediction.

5. Can you use your rule to multiply any powers? Illustrate your answer with some examples.

6. In the above examples, the exponents are positive. Do you think that your rule would still apply if one or both of the exponents are 0 or negative? Make up some examples to test your prediction.

Dividing powers

7. **a)** What does 10^6 mean? What does 10^4 mean?
   b) What does $10^6 \div 10^4$ mean? Write this expression as a fraction and simplify it. How many 10s are multiplied together in the answer?
   c) Using the result of part b, write $10^6 \div 10^4$ as a power of 10.
   d) How would you write $10^4 \div 10^6$ as a power of 10?

8. **a)** What does $10^7 \div 10^3$ mean? How many 10s are multiplied together in the answer?
   b) Write $10^7 \div 10^3$ as a power of 10.
   c) How would you write $10^3 \div 10^7$ as a power of 10?

9. Based on the above results, state a rule that you could use to divide two powers of 10. Explain why your rule is correct.

10. Can you use your rule to divide two powers of 2? Make up some examples to test your prediction.

11. Can you use your rule to divide any two powers with the same base? Illustrate your answer with some examples.

12. In the above examples, the exponents are positive. Do you think that your rule would still apply if one or both of the exponents are 0 or negative? Make up some examples to test your prediction.

Powers of powers

Expressions such as $(10^4)^2$ and $(10^3)^5$ are powers in which the base is also a power. These are called *powers of powers*.

13. a) What does $(10^4)^2$ mean? How many 10s are multiplied together?
   b) Write $(10^4)^2$ as a power of 10.
   c) How would you write $(10^2)^4$ as a power of 10?
     Explain your answer.

14. a) What does $(10^3)^5$ mean? How many 10s are multiplied together?
   b) Write $(10^3)^5$ as a power of 10.
   c) How would you write $(10^5)^3$ as a power of 10?
     Explain your answer.

15. Based on the above results, state a rule that you could use to determine a power of a power of 10. Explain why your rule is correct.

16. Can you use your rule to determine a power of a power of 2? Make up some examples to test your prediction.

17. Can you use your rule to determine a power of any power? Illustrate your answer with some examples.

18. In the above examples, the exponents are positive. Do you think that your rule would still apply if one or both of the exponents are 0 or negative? Make up some examples to test your prediction.

On average, the human eye blinks once every 5 s. At this rate, about how many blinks would there be in your classroom during one math class?

◗ ◗ *Through Instruction*

In the preceding discussion, you used the definitions of powers to discover some properties of operations with powers. Now we will explain these properties.

Multiplying powers with positive exponents

Since n^3 means $n \times n \times n$ and n^4 means $n \times n \times n \times n$, we know that

$$n^3 \times n^4 = n \times n \times n \times n \times n \times n \times n$$
$$= n^7$$

Observe that the powers n^3 and n^4 have the same base. We can obtain the product $n^3 \times n^4$ by adding the exponents:

$$n^3 \times n^4 = n^{3+4}$$
$$= n^7$$

1. Do you think we would get similar results if the exponents were different from 3 and 4? What kinds of numbers can the exponents be?

2. Do you think we would get similar results with a different base?

- - - - - - - - - -

> To multiply powers with the same base, keep the base and add the exponents:
> $$n^a \times n^b = n^{a+b}$$

Dividing powers with positive exponents

Since n^5 means $n \times n \times n \times n \times n$ and n^3 means $n \times n \times n$, we know that

$$n^5 \div n^3 = \frac{n \times n \times n \times n \times n}{n \times n \times n}$$
$$= n^2$$

Observe that the powers n^5 and n^3 have the same base. We can obtain the quotient $n^5 \div n^3$ by subtracting the exponents:

$$n^5 \div n^3 = n^{5-3}$$
$$= n^2$$

In the above example, the exponent in the numerator is greater than the exponent in the denominator. Suppose the exponent in the numerator is less than the exponent in the denominator.

$$n^3 \div n^5 = \frac{n \times n \times n}{n \times n \times n \times n \times n}$$
$$= \frac{1}{n \times n}$$
$$= \frac{1}{n^2}$$
$$= n^{-2}$$

Here, too, we can obtain the quotient $n^3 \div n^5$ by subtracting the exponents:

$$n^3 \div n^5 = n^{3-5}$$
$$= n^{-2}$$

3. Do you think we would get similar results if the exponents were different from 5 and 3? What kinds of numbers can the exponents be?

4. Do you think we would get similar results with a different base?

• • • • • • • •

> To divide powers with the same base, keep the base and subtract the exponents:
> $$n^a \div n^b = n^{a-b} \qquad n \neq 0$$

5. In the conclusion above, why is it stated that $n \neq 0$?

Powers of powers with positive exponents

Since n^3 means $n \times n \times n$ and $(n^3)^4$ means $n^3 \times n^3 \times n^3 \times n^3$ we know that

$$(n^3)^4 = n \times n \times n \times n \times n \times n \times n \times n \times n \times n \times n \times n$$
$$= n^{12}$$

Observe that you can obtain the power of a power $(n^3)^4$ by multiplying the exponents:

$$(n^3)^4 = n^{3 \times 4}$$
$$= n^{12}$$

6. Do you think we would get similar results if the exponents were different from 3 and 4? What kinds of numbers can the exponents be?

7. Do you think we would get similar results with a different base?

• • • • • • • • •

> To determine a power of a power, multiply the exponents:
> $$(n^a)^b = n^{ab}$$

BOGGLE YOUR MIND

A blue whale consumes 1.5 million calories every day. How many days would it take an average human to consume this many calories?

Working with Mathematics

Something to talk about

Look at the chart on pages 168 and 169. Then answer these questions.

1. a) About how many times as high as the tallest tree is the highest mountain?

  b) About how many times as great as the diameter of Earth is the diameter of the sun?

  c) About how many times as large as the diameter of its nucleus is the diameter of a carbon atom?

2. Every object in the universe has a place on this chart. Suppose you know the positions of two objects on the chart. Describe how you would compare their sizes.

3. What do exercises 1 and 2 have to do with multiplying and dividing powers?

Work together

4. Write each expression as a power.

  a) $10^3 \times 10^2$ **b)** $10^8 \times 10^5$

  c) $10^{12} \times 10^4$ **d)** $10^6 \div 10^2$

  e) $10^7 \div 10^2$ **f)** $(10^3)^4$

  g) $(-4)^{12} \times (-4)^5$ **h)** $3^3 \times 3^8$

  i) $7.2^5 \times 7.2^7$ **j)** $(-5)^3 \div (-5)^5$

  k) $1.2^6 \div 1.2^3$ **l)** $(9^4)^2$

5. In the chart on page 168, the largest number name is 1 trillion. To name larger numbers, we often combine number names. For example, the diameter of the Crab Nebula is approximately 95 000 000 000 000 000 m.

We think: 95 000 000 000 000 000 m

  95 million billion m

Therefore, the number 10^{15}, or 1 000 000 000 000 000 is named one million billion. We also use this system for number names such as these:

100 000

one hundred thousand

  a) Use this system to name each number.
   i) 100 000
   ii) 100 000 000
   iii) 100 000 000 000
   iv) 1 000 000
   v) 1 000 000 000
   vi) 1 000 000 000 000

  b) Write each number in decimal form.
   i) one thousand billion
   ii) one million million

  c) The diameter of the Tarantula Nebula is approximately 8 600 000 000 000 000 000 m. Write this distance using the above system.

  d) How is this system of naming large numbers related to multiplying powers with the same base?

On your own

6. Write each product as a power.

  a) $10^4 \times 10^5$ **b)** $10^8 \times 10$

  c) $10^4 \times 10^6$ **d)** $10^{11} \times 10^3$

  e) $10^6 \times 10^2$ **f)** $10^2 \times 10^7$

  g) $10^3 \times 10^5$ **h)** $10^3 \times 10^5 \times 10^7$

  i) $10^8 \times 10 \times 10^2$ **j)** $10^4 \times 10^2 \times 10^9$

7. Write each expression as a power.

  a) $10^{10} \div 10^3$ **b)** $10^{11} \div 10^6$

  c) $\dfrac{10^9}{10^2}$ **d)** $\dfrac{10^{12}}{10^8}$

  e) $10^5 \div 10^3$ **f)** $10^7 \div 10^4$

8. Write each expression as a power.

  a) $(10^3)^4$ **b)** $(10^2)^3$

  c) $(2^5)^5$ **d)** $[(-3.5)^4]^2$

9. Write each expression as a power.

   a) $3^3 \times 3^2$ b) $9^4 \div 9^2$
   c) $(-8)^7 \div (-8)^4$ d) $(-2)^4 \times (-2)^3$
   e) $5^4 \div 5$ f) $(2^2)^3$
   g) $4^3 \div 4^5$ h) $7^5 \div 7^3$
   i) $11^4 \times 11^3$ j) $5.2^{10} \div 5.2^3$
   k) $(-3)^{11} \div (-3)^6$ l) $\dfrac{8.3^9}{8.3^2}$

10. Write each expression as a power.

   a) $\dfrac{10^5 \times 10^2}{10^3}$ b) $\dfrac{2^7 \times 2^3}{2^4}$
   c) $\dfrac{3^{12}}{3 \times 3^6}$ d) $\dfrac{(-5)^9 \times (-5)}{(-5)^4}$
   e) $\dfrac{6^7 \times 6^{11}}{6^8 \times 6^2}$ f) $\dfrac{(-1)^{10}}{(-1)^5 \times (-1)}$

11. Astronomers estimate that there are about
    10^{11} galaxies in the universe. They also
    estimate that each galaxy contains about
    10^{11} stars. About how many stars are there
    in the universe?

Extend your thinking

12. Here is a magic square like the one on
    page 24.

8	1	6
3	5	7
4	9	2

   a) What is the magic sum for this magic
      square?
   b) Change this magic square so that the
      product of the numbers in any row,
      column, or diagonal is the same. What
      is the magic product for your square?

13. Write these numbers in order from least to
    greatest:
    2^{5555} 3^{4444} 4^{3333} 5^{2222}

COMMUNICATING

The Ideas

To *multiply* two powers with the same base you *add* the exponents.

For example, to multiply $10^2 \times 10^4$, you add $2 + 4$, and write 10^6.

What are some other examples in mathematics where you carry out
one operation by performing a different operation? In your journal, list
your ideas, with examples.

Powers of 2

Use only the table of powers of 2 to answer the exercises below it.

$2^{25} = 33\ 554\ 432$ $2^8 = 256$ $2^{-9} = 0.001\ 953\ 125$
$2^{24} = 16\ 777\ 216$ $2^7 = 128$ $2^{-10} = 0.000\ 976\ 562\ 5$
$2^{23} = 8\ 388\ 608$ $2^6 = 64$ $2^{-11} = 0.000\ 488\ 281\ 25$
$2^{22} = 4\ 194\ 304$ $2^5 = 32$ $2^{-12} = 0.000\ 244\ 140\ 625$
$2^{21} = 2\ 097\ 152$ $2^4 = 16$ $2^{-13} = 0.000\ 122\ 070\ 312\ 5$
$2^{20} = 1\ 048\ 576$ $2^3 = 8$ $2^{-14} = 0.000\ 061\ 035\ 156\ 25$
$2^{19} = 524\ 288$ $2^2 = 4$ $2^{-15} = 0.000\ 030\ 517\ 578\ 125$
$2^{18} = 262\ 144$ $2^1 = 2$ $2^{-16} = 0.000\ 015\ 258\ 789\ 062\ 5$
$2^{17} = 131\ 072$ $2^0 = 1$ $2^{-17} = 0.000\ 007\ 629\ 394\ 531\ 25$
$2^{16} = 65\ 536$ $2^{-1} = 0.5$ $2^{-18} = 0.000\ 003\ 814\ 697\ 265\ 625$
$2^{15} = 32\ 768$ $2^{-2} = 0.25$ $2^{-19} = 0.000\ 001\ 907\ 348\ 632\ 812\ 5$
$2^{14} = 16\ 384$ $2^{-3} = 0.125$ $2^{-20} = 0.000\ 000\ 953\ 674\ 316\ 406\ 25$
$2^{13} = 8192$ $2^{-4} = 0.062\ 5$ $2^{-21} = 0.000\ 000\ 476\ 837\ 158\ 203\ 125$
$2^{12} = 4096$ $2^{-5} = 0.031\ 25$ $2^{-22} = 0.000\ 000\ 238\ 418\ 579\ 101\ 562\ 5$
$2^{11} = 2048$ $2^{-6} = 0.015\ 625$ $2^{-23} = 0.000\ 000\ 119\ 209\ 289\ 550\ 781\ 25$
$2^{10} = 1024$ $2^{-7} = 0.007\ 812\ 5$ $2^{-24} = 0.000\ 000\ 059\ 604\ 644\ 775\ 390\ 625$
$2^9 = 512$ $2^{-8} = 0.003\ 906\ 25$ $2^{-25} = 0.000\ 000\ 029\ 802\ 322\ 387\ 695\ 312\ 5$

1. Determine each answer without doing the arithmetic.
   a) 4096×256 **b)** $256 \times 128 \times 64$ **c)** $65\ 536 \div 2048$
   d) $\dfrac{262\ 144 \times 8192 \times 512}{16\ 384 \times 64}$ **e)** 64^3 **f)** 4^{10}

2. Computer monitors combine different shades of red, green, and blue colours to display pictures. Each dot on the screen has a shade of red, a shade of green, and a shade of blue. On some high-quality monitors there are 256 possible shades of each colour. How many different colours can these monitors display?

3. a) Find as many patterns as you can in the final digits of the powers of 2.
   b) Explain why the patterns occur.

4. Determine each answer without doing the arithmetic.
   a) 0.125×0.0625 **b)** $131\ 072 \times 0.007\ 812\ 5$
   c) $256 \times 0.003\ 906\ 25$ **d)** $0.015\ 625 \div 0.0625$
   e) $16\ 384 \div 0.031\ 25$ **f)** $0.003\ 906\ 25 \div 4096$
   g) 0.25^5 **h)** 0.125^4

5. a) Create a table of powers of 4.
   b) Create a table of powers of 8.
   c) Create a table of powers of 16.

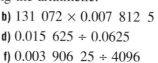

Half-life on a Spreadsheet

IN APRIL 1986, THERE WAS AN ACCIDENT AT A NUCLEAR POWER PLANT IN CHERNOBYL.
The atmosphere was contaminated with radioactive material including iodine-131.
This substance has a half-life of about 8 days. This means that every 8 days, half of
the iodine decays to a form that is not radioactive.

What if 100 g of iodine-131 were released?
How long would it take for less than 1 g
to remain?

You can develop a simple spreadsheet
model to analyze this situation.
Set up your spreadsheet as shown and
answer the questions below.

TEMPLATE DISK

	A	B
1	Radioactive decay	
2		
3	Remaining iodine-131	Time units in days
4		0
5	=A4*0.5	=B4+8

1. **a)** What does each formula in cells A5 and B5 tell the computer to do?
   b) Enter 100 in cell A4 to indicate that 100 g is the mass of iodine-131
      released. What values does the computer display in cells A5 and
      B5?

2. Copy the formulas in cells A5 and B5 to the next 20 cells below.
   Some of the cells in column A may display answers in scientific
   notation, such as 7.62939453125e−6. To avoid this, you can widen
   column A and change its format to display numbers as fixed decimals
   to 10 places. Use your spreadsheet to determine how many days it
   would take for the iodine-131 to decay to less than 1 g.

3. In how many days will 1000 g of iodine-131 decay to less than 1 g?
   Change the spreadsheet to answer this question.

4. In cell C5 enter the formula =A5/1000. This tells the computer to
   calculate and display the quotient of the amount of iodine-131 left after
   1 time unit and the initial amount. Copy this formula to all the rows in
   column C. What pattern do you notice?

Mathematics & Technology

Linking Ideas

SCIENTIFIC NOTATION

Developing the Ideas

▶ ▶ *Through Discussion*

You've used scientific notation to express very large numbers more simply. Now that you've had some practice using negative powers of 10, you can also express very small numbers in scientific notation.

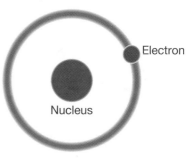

Diagram of a hydrogen atom

. . . .

> To write a number in scientific notation, write it as the product of:
> - a number greater than -10 and less than -1 or greater than 1 and less than 10 and
> - a power of 10

Scientists tell us that there are about 120 000 000 000 stars in our galaxy, the Milky Way. The zeros in this number are place holders to show the position of the decimal point. When a decimal point occurs at the end of the number, as in this case, we don't usually show it. To express the number of stars in our galaxy using scientific notation, you write:

$$120\ 000\ 000\ 000 = 1.2 \times 100\ 000\ 000\ 000$$
$$= 1.2 \times 10^{11}$$

The number of stars in our galaxy is about 1.2×10^{11}.

Hydrogen is the most abundant element in the universe. The mass of a hydrogen atom is about 0.000 000 000 000 000 000 000 001 67 g. As before, the zeros are place holders to show the position of the decimal point. To express the mass of a hydrogen atom using scientific notation, you write:

$$0.000\ 000\ 000\ 000\ 000\ 000\ 000\ 001\ 67 = 1.67 \times 0.000\ 000\ 000\ 000\ 000\ 000\ 000\ 000\ 001$$
$$= 1.67 \times 10^{-24}$$

The mass of a hydrogen atom is about 1.67×10^{-24} g.

Work with a partner to answer the questions below. To help you, use the two examples above.

1. When writing a very large number in scientific notation, how can you tell which power of 10 to use? Illustrate your answer with examples.

2. When writing a very small number in scientific notation, how can you tell which power of 10 to use? Illustrate your answer with examples.

3. Do you think that every number can be written in scientific notation? Explain your answer.

4. Can you think of any reason for writing numbers such as 880 and 0.025 in scientific notation?

▶▶ *Through a Guided Example*

Example ....

The mass of Earth is about 6.0×10^{24} kg.

a) The mass of the sun is about 3.3×10^5 times as great as the mass of Earth. What is the mass of the sun?

b) The mass of the sun is about 2.7×10^7 times as great as the mass of the moon. What is the mass of the moon?

Solution

a) Use a scientific calculator to multiply 3.3×10^5 by 6.0×10^{24}.
   $(3.3 \times 10^5) \times (6.0 \times 10^{24}) = 1.98 \times 10^{30}$
   The mass of the sun is approximately 2.0×10^{30} kg.

b) The mass of the moon is about 2.7×10^7 times as small as the mass of the sun.
   Thus, divide 1.98×10^{30} by 2.7×10^7.
   $$\frac{1.98 \times 10^{30}}{2.7 \times 10^7} \doteq 7.33 \times 10^{22}$$
   The mass of the moon is approximately 7.3×10^{22} kg.

185

Working with Mathematics

Work together

1. What numbers complete this table?

Item	Decimal	Scientific Notation
a) Temperature of the sun's interior	1 300 000 °C	
b) Thickness of a plastic film	0.000 01 m	
c) Mass of electron		9.2×10^{-28} g
d) Number of galaxies in the universe		1.2×10^{11}
e) Estimated age of Earth	4 500 000 000 years	
f) Diameter of a hydrogen atom	0.000 000 005 cm	
g) Land area of Earth		1.5×10^{8} km^2

2. Express each number in these news items in scientific notation.

a) A new fingerprinting method uses gold particles to bind to the proteins every finger leaves behind. The amount of protein is tiny—only one billionth of a gram per print. The gold particles are about two thousandths of a millimetre in diameter.

b) The information on a compact disk is permanently encoded in the form of tiny pits made by a laser beam. There are as many as 8.2 billion pits on a compact disk, each measuring approximately 5 millionths of a metre across.

3. The smallest hole ever made in solid material is so small that 4 000 000 of them side by side are needed to make a line 1 cm long. Calculate how many of these holes could be made in a square with each side length.

a) 1 cm   **b)** 1 m   **c)** 1 mm

4. It has been estimated that if the average mass of an automobile were reduced from 1500 kg to 1000 kg, Canada would save about 2.9×10^{7} L of gasoline each day.

a) How much gasoline would Canada save in 1 year?

b) Make a reasonable estimate of the number of automobiles in Canada. Based on your estimate, about how much gasoline would be saved per vehicle in 1 year?

c) About how much is the gasoline in part b worth?

On your own

5. Write in scientific notation.

a) 4300   **b)** 430 000
c) 0.0043   **d)** 0.000 043
e) 37 500   **f)** 3 750 000
g) 0.0375   **h)** 0.000 000 375
i) −845   **j)** 0.006 11
k) −0.000 098 6   **l)** 0.000 000 708 2
m) 1000   **n)** −3 210 000
o) 0.0001   **p)** −0.000 000 1

6. Use the *Moon and Planets* database from the student's disk to find the information you need to answer each question.

DATA DISK

a) The nearest star is about 2.7×10^{5} times as far from the sun as Earth is. How far is the nearest star from the sun?

b) The mass of the heaviest known star, *Eta Carinae*, is about 6.23×10^{8} times as great as the mass of Mars. What is the mass of *Eta Carinae*?

c) The diameter of the largest known star, *Betelgeux*, is about 1.35×10^4 times as great as the diameter of Uranus. What is the diameter of *Betelgeux*?

7. The paragraph below appeared in *Discover* magazine in January 1992. Write the paragraph in your notebook. Replace each asterisk with a number chosen from the list. Write the numbers in a form that is appropriate for a paragraph in a magazine.

1.1×10^4	1.3×10^7	2.0×10^3
5.5×10^3	6.5×10^7	8.0×10^2

All manner of objects came to light in 1991, and they span the ages, from a *-year old crater that could mark the impact site of a dinosaur-killing asteroid to what could be a solar system now being born. Between these two extremes, in order of age, are: a jawbone, picked out of the dirt in Namibia, belonging to a *-year old creature that could be a common ancestor of both modern apes and humans; live bacteria, culled from the intestinal remains of a mastodon that had been buried in a peat bog for the past * years; the world's oldest wine stain, found in a *-year old jar; a preserved Bronze Age man of * B.C., who melted out of an Alpine glacier; and the first catacombs ever found in the United States, built by the Mogollon people * years ago in what is now Arizona.

8. In chemistry, each element is assigned a number, called its atomic mass. That number of grams of the element contains 6.02×10^{23} atoms. The atomic mass of gold is 197.0.
   a) How many atoms are in 197.0 g of gold?
   b) How many atoms are in 1 g of gold?
   c) How many atoms are in a 31.1 g gold coin?

COMMUNICATING
The Ideas

Two numbers are written in scientific notation. How can you tell which is the greater number? In your journal, write an explanation and illustrate it with some examples.

9. Every atom contains negatively charged particles called electrons and positively charged particles called protons. Each electron has a mass of 9.11×10^{-28} g and each proton has a mass of 1.67×10^{-24} g.
   a) A hydrogen atom contains one electron and one proton. What is the mass of a hydrogen atom?
   b) How many times as heavy as an electron is a proton?

Extend your thinking

10. A unit for measuring astronomical distances is the *light-year*. One light year is the distance light travels in one year. In 1986, astronomers discovered a chain of galaxies which stretches one billion light-years from one end to the other. It is one of the largest structures ever found in the universe.
    a) The speed of light is 3×10^8 m/s. Calculate one light-year, in metres.
    b) Suppose the units on pages 168 and 169 had been light-years instead of metres. What change would there be in the numbers?

11. A unit for measuring atomic distances is the *angstrom*, Å. One angstrom is 10^{-10} m. Suppose the units on pages 168 and 169 had been angstroms instead of metres. What change would there be in the numbers?

Naming Very Large and Very Small Numbers

Large number names

thousand	10^3	undecillion	10^{36}	
million	10^6	duodecillion	10^{39}	
billion	10^9	tredicillion	10^{42}	
trillion	10^{12}	quattuordecillion	10^{45}	
quadrillion	10^{15}	quindecillion	10^{48}	
quintillion	10^{18}	sexdecillion	10^{51}	
sextillion	10^{21}	septendecillion	10^{54}	
septillion	10^{24}	octodecillion	10^{57}	
octillion	10^{27}	novemdecillion	10^{60}	
nonillion	10^{30}	vigintillion	10^{63}	
decillion	10^{33}			

Metric prefixes

exa-	10^{18}
peta-	10^{15}
tera-	10^{12}
giga-	10^9
mega-	10^6
kilo-	10^3
	1
milli-	10^{-3}
micro-	10^{-6}
nano-	10^{-9}
pico-	10^{-12}
femto-	10^{-15}
atto-	10^{-18}

The exercises below refer to the chart on pages 168 and 169. Work in a group or with a partner.

1. The approximate diameter of the solar system is shown in five different ways. Below each example, the dimensions of two other objects on the chart are shown. Can you identify these objects? Use the information on pages 168 and 169 and in the tables above to help you.

Using decimal notation

Diameter of solar system:
16 000 000 000 000 m

a) 200 000 000 000 000 000 000 000 m

b) 0.0001 m

Using large number names

Diameter of solar system: 16 trillion metres

c) 8.6 quintillion metres

d) 1 quadrillionth of a metre

Using metric prefixes

Diameter of solar system: 16 terametres

e) 1.4 gigametres   **f)** 1 micrometre

Using scientific notation

Diameter of solar system: 1.6×10^{13} m

g) 1.4×10^8 m   **h)** 1.0×10^{-7} m

Using "E"

Diameter of solar system: 1.6 E13 m

i) 6.6 E20 m   **j)** 1.0 E−14 m

2. For each object you identified in exercise 1, write its approximate dimension using the other four systems.

3. Which system do you think is most useful for writing very large and very small numbers?

4. The largest number in the chart above is 10^{63}. The estimated diameter of the entire universe in metres is "only" 10^{26}. Do you think that numbers larger than 10^{26} would ever be needed? Explain your answer.

HOW MANY Ants ARE THERE?

HOW HAS SOMETHING SO SMALL AS AN ANT BECOME so astonishingly successful and important? Ants are easy to overlook. Each one stands scarcely 0.04 inch off the ground and weighs less than a millionth as much as a human being. Acting together, however, these insects are among the dominant forces of our terrestrial environment. The 8800 known species cover most of the land surfaces of the world except for the polar regions. Millions of these small animals can be found in a single acre of tropical forest. In sheer number ants far exceed all land vertebrates — that is, all Earth's mammals, birds, reptiles, and amphibians combined. The late British ecologist C. B. Williams once estimated that there are a billion billion insects alive at any given moment. If we conservatively estimate that one in 100 of them is an ant, then ants have a standing population of 10 million billion; they also have a mass over 2 billion pounds, constituting 10 percent of the entire animal biomass on dry land.

1. This passage appeared in an article in *Discover* magazine. Write each number in the passage in scientific notation.

2. The article contains an estimate of the insect population of the world.
   a) What is the human population of the world?
   b) Using your answer from part a, about how many ants are there for every human being?

3. Near the end of the excerpt there is a calculation that leads to the statement that "ants have a standing population of 10 million billion." Explain this calculation.

4. Do you think that all the figures in the article are correct? Give a reason for your answer.

5. Do you think the estimate that 1 in 100 of the world's insects is an ant is reasonable? If not, what would your estimate be? Explain your answer.

Mathematics & Science

Linking Ideas

ESTIMATING SQUARE ROOTS

Developing the Ideas

▶ ▶ *Through Discussion*

Chinese New Year's Day is celebrated on the first day of the lunar calendar. To ensure that the new year brings prosperity and good health, dances are performed for 15 days. The man in the square photographs below is taking part in a parade held in Vancouver for Chinese New Year. The banner he carries is red because this colour signifies good luck and happiness.

The photograph on the right is an enlargement of the one on the left — its area is exactly twice as large. How can you find the side length of the photograph on the right without measuring?

5 cm

5 cm

1. What is the area of the photograph on the left?

2. **a)** What is the area of the photograph on the right?
   b) Is it possible that its side length is 10 cm?

3. Without using your calculator, estimate the side length of the photograph on the right, to the nearest tenth of a centimetre.

4. Suppose two other enlargements are made of the first photograph. Their areas are 3 times as great and 4 times as great respectively. Without using your calculator, estimate the side lengths of these photographs to the nearest tenth of a centimetre.

Recall that when we square a number, we multiply it by itself:

$$7^2 = 49$$
$$(-7)^2 = 49$$

Since $7 \times 7 = 49$, we say that 7 is a square root of 49, and we write $\sqrt{49} = 7$.
Since $(-7) \times (-7) = 49$, another square root of 49 is -7.
When the radical sign, $\sqrt{}$, is used, it indicates only the positive square root.

All positive numbers have square roots. Those that have square roots which are natural numbers are called *perfect squares*. For example, 25 is a perfect square because one of its square roots is 5.

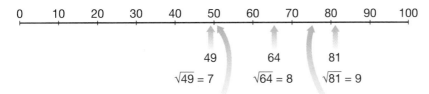

Number, n	0	1	4	9	16	25	36	49	64	81	100
Square root, $\sqrt{n}$	0	1	2	3	4	5	6	7	8	9	10

You can estimate the square roots of numbers that are not perfect squares. To estimate $\sqrt{50}$ and $\sqrt{75}$, think of the perfect squares near 50 and 75:

```
0    10   20   30   40   50   60   70   80   90   100

                        49        64        81
                    √49 = 7   √64 = 8   √81 = 9
```

50 is between 49 and 64, and is much closer to 49.
Hence, $\sqrt{50}$ is between 7 and 8, and is probably much closer to 7.
We estimate $\sqrt{50}$ to be about 7.1.

75 is between 64 and 81, and is a little closer to 81.
Hence, $\sqrt{75}$ is between 8 and 9, and is probably a little closer to 9.
We estimate $\sqrt{75}$ to be about 8.6.

BOGGLE YOUR MIND

The Hermitage art gallery in St. Petersburg, Russia has nearly 3 million works of art and historical artifacts on display. What if it takes an average of 15 s to look at each item? How many days would it take to view the entire collection?

191

Working with Mathematics

Something to talk about

1. Which of the three estimates is closest to the square root? Explain your answer.

   a) $\sqrt{13}$ 3.4   3.5   3.6

   b) $\sqrt{20}$ 4.4   4.5   4.6

   c) $\sqrt{85}$ 9.2   9.3   9.4

2. A student estimated $\sqrt{50}$ as follows:
   "Since 50 is halfway between 0 and 100, $\sqrt{50}$ should be halfway between 0 and 10. Therefore, $\sqrt{50}$ should equal 5."
   Is this reasoning correct? Explain your answer.

Work together

3. What are the square roots of each number?

   a) 36   b) 100   c) 400

   d) 1   e) $\frac{1}{4}$ f) $\frac{1}{9}$

4. Estimate each square root to one decimal place.

   a) $\sqrt{40}$ b) $\sqrt{97}$ c) $\sqrt{30}$ d) $\sqrt{65}$

5. Simplify each expression. Estimate the result where necessary.

   a) $\sqrt{64} + \sqrt{36}$ b) $\sqrt{64} + 36$

   c) $64 + \sqrt{36}$ d) $\sqrt{64} \times \sqrt{36}$

   e) $\sqrt{64 + \sqrt{36}}$ f) $\sqrt{\sqrt{64} + \sqrt{36}}$

6. a) Use a calculator to find each square root.

      i) $\sqrt{3}$ ii) $\sqrt{300}$

      iii) $\sqrt{30\ 000}$ iv) $\sqrt{3\ 000\ 000}$

      v) $\sqrt{0.03}$ vi) $\sqrt{0.0003}$

   b) Look at the results in part a. Try to explain the pattern.

On your own

7. Write the two square roots of each number.

   a) 81   b) 64   c) 900

   d) 121   e) 0.25   f) 0.01

8. Estimate each square root to one decimal place.

   a) $\sqrt{5}$ b) $\sqrt{12}$ c) $\sqrt{32}$ d) $\sqrt{69}$

9. The area of a square is given. Estimate the length of a side to the nearest millimetre.

   a) 45 cm^2 b) 54 cm^2 c) 72 cm^2 d) 86 cm^2

10. Simplify each expression. Estimate the result where necessary.

   a) $\sqrt{16 + 9}$ b) $\sqrt{16} + \sqrt{9}$

   c) $\sqrt{16 - 9}$ d) $\sqrt{16} - \sqrt{9}$

   e) $\sqrt{16} \times \sqrt{9}$ f) $\sqrt{\sqrt{16} + \sqrt{9}}$

11. Continue working on the Quest on page 162. You can use square roots in your expressions. For example, you can use $\sqrt{9} = 3$, which allows you to write 3 instead of 9.

   a) In some of the expressions you already have, replace 9 with $\sqrt{9}$. Can you get an expression for any number you still need?

   b) Try other square roots in your expressions. Can you get all the numbers from 1 to 100 now?

Extend your thinking

12. a) Use a calculator to find each square root.

      i) $\sqrt{2}$ ii) $\sqrt{20}$ iii) $\sqrt{200}$

      iv) $\sqrt{2000}$ v) $\sqrt{20\ 000}$ vi) $\sqrt{200\ 000}$

   b) Look at the results in part a. Try to explain the pattern.

COMMUNICATING

The Ideas

Look at the square roots in these exercises. Some of the square roots are less than the original numbers, while others are greater than the original numbers. How can you tell if the square root of a number is greater than or less than the number? Record your ideas in your journal, with examples.

Graphing Squares and Square Roots

Work in a group.

Group 1 Graphing Squares of Numbers

Construct a table like the one below.
Use your calculator to complete
a table of squares. Use numbers
between 0 and 2 for the numbers
in the first column.

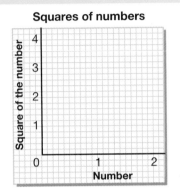

Squares of numbers

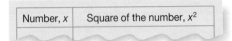

Number, x	Square of the number, x^2

Draw a grid similar to the one at the
right. Plot the data from your table.
Draw a smooth curve through the
plotted points.

Group 2 Graphing Square Roots

Construct a table like the one below.
Use your calculator to complete a
table of square roots. Use numbers
between 0 and 4 for the numbers in
the first column.

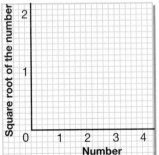

Square roots of numbers

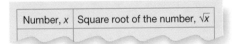

Number, x	Square root of the number, $\sqrt{x}$

Draw a grid similar to the one at the
right. Plot the data from your table.
Draw a smooth curve through the
plotted points.

All Groups

1. Compare the numbers in the two columns of your table.
   a) When are the numbers in the second column less than those in
      the first column?
   b) When are the numbers in the second column greater than those
      in the first column?
   c) How does the graph illustrate your answers to these two questions?

2. Compare your table and your graph with the table and the graph of the
   other group. What are the similarities and differences?

THE PYTHAGOREAN THEOREM

Developing the Ideas

▶ ▶ *Through an Activity*

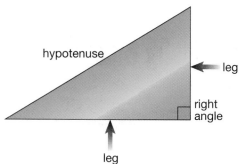

hypotenuse

leg

right angle

leg

Any triangle that has a right angle in it is called a right triangle. The side opposite the right angle is called the *hypotenuse*. The other two sides are sometimes called the *legs*.

More than 4000 years ago the Babylonians knew a special property that is satisfied by a right triangle, and no other kind of triangle. Later, Chinese and Hindu civilizations also knew this property. It was first proved by the ancient Greeks, and is named after the Greek mathematician Pythagoras. To investigate the *Pythagorean Theorem*, follow these steps.

1. Copy these squares onto 1-cm grid paper. Determine the area of each square by counting squares and part squares if necessary. Write the area on each square.

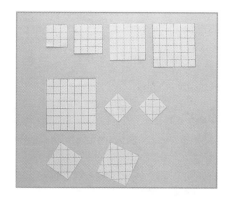

2. Cut out the squares.

3. Take three of the squares and arrange them to form a triangle, as shown at the right:

Find three squares that form a right triangle when you do this. Try to get as many different right triangles as you can. When you think you have a right triangle, how can you be certain that it is a right triangle?

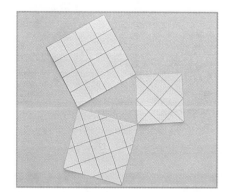

4. For each right triangle you get, record the areas of the three squares in a table.

Area of square on one leg	Area of square on the other leg	Area of square on the hypotenuse

5. In a right triangle, how does the area of the square on the hypotenuse appear to be related to the areas of the squares on the other two sides?

Save your squares for use later.

The Pythagorean Theorem

In any right triangle, the area of the square on the hypotenuse is equal to the sum of the areas of the squares on the other two sides.

For the right triangle shown,

area of square on AB	=	area of square on BC	+	area of square on AC
↓		↓		↓
c^2	=	a^2	+	b^2

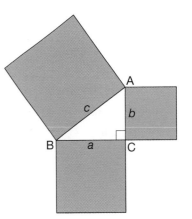

If you know the lengths of two sides of a right triangle, you can use the Pythagorean Theorem to calculate the length of the third side.

Example ....

The size of a television screen is the length of its diagonal. A television screen is 56 cm wide and 40 cm high. Calculate the length of its diagonal to the nearest centimetre.

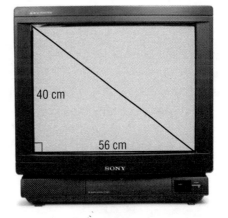

40 cm

56 cm

Solution

Let d centimetres represent the length of the diagonal. According to the Pythagorean Theorem,

$$d^2 = 56^2 + 40^2$$
$$= 3136 + 1600$$
$$= 4736$$
$$d = \sqrt{4736}$$
$$\doteq 68.8$$

The length of the diagonal is approximately 69 cm.

BOGGLE YOUR MIND

This colour enhanced micrograph shows a single human skin cell. Your body consists of about 10 000 000 000 000 cells. What if it were possible to count these cells? How many years would it take if you counted 1 cell per second?

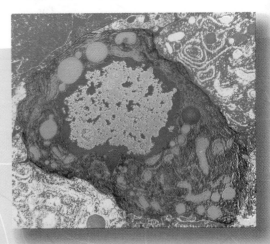

Working with Mathematics

Something to talk about

1. When you arranged three squares to form a triangle, how did you know that the triangle was a right triangle?

Work together

2. Calculate the length, to one decimal place, indicated by each letter.

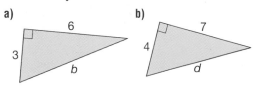

a)

b)

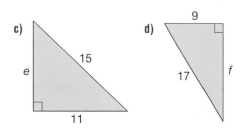

c)

d)

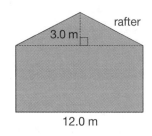

3. Calculate the length of the rafters for a building. It is 12.0 m wide and has the peak of the roof 3.0 m above the ceiling. Give the answer to the nearest centimetre.

3.0 m   rafter

12.0 m

4. A ramp is to be built from one level of one parking garage to another. Calculate the length of the ramp, to the nearest centimetre.

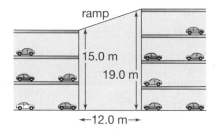

ramp

15.0 m

19.0 m

←12.0 m→

5. Get the squares you used in the activity on page 194. In this activity you should have formed four right triangles with the squares.
   a) What other kinds of triangles can you form with the squares? Are the areas of the three squares related in any way for these triangles?
   b) Which three squares form a triangle which is closest to being a right triangle, but which is still not a right triangle? Use a protractor to measure the angles of this triangle.

6. If you have access to a computer and *The Geometer's Sketchpad*® software, load the sketch entitled **Shear Pythagoras** (Macintosh version) or **shear.gsp** (Windows version), which comes with the program. Follow the instructions on the screen to see a visual demonstration of the Pythagorean Theorem. Try some of the other Pythagorean sketches which come with the program.

Pythagoras (585 B.C. – 500 B.C.)

C O M M U N I C A T I N G

The Ideas

You began this section with an activity involving squares. In your journal, describe what you did, what you discovered, and why it is important. Your description should be understandable to someone who did not do the activity, and who does not know the Pythagorean Theorem.

. . . . LENGTH OF A LINE SEGMENT

Developing the Ideas

▶▶ *Through an Activity*

1. The lines on the grid are 1 cm apart. Use the Pythagorean Theorem to calculate the lengths of the line segments AE, HF, DG, and IC to the nearest tenth of a centimetre.

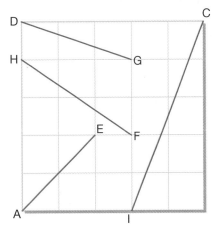

2. Plot the points A(1, 2) and B(5, 4) on graph paper. Join them to create line segment AB. Use the Pythagorean Theorem to calculate the length of AB to the nearest tenth of a unit.

▶▶ *Through a Guided Example*

If you know the lengths of two sides of a right triangle, you can use the Pythagorean Theorem to calculate the length of the third side.

Example ....

Calculate the length of the line segment joining the points P(−1, 3) and Q(4, 6). Express your answer to one decimal place.

Solution

Plot P and Q on a grid.
Draw a right triangle under the line segment.
Let h units represent the length of the hypotenuse. By counting squares, we see that the legs of this triangle have lengths 5 units and 3 units. According to the Pythagorean Theorem,

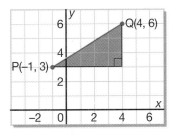

$h^2 = 5^2 + 3^2$
$\quad = 25 + 9$
$\quad = 34$
$h = \sqrt{34}$
$\quad \doteq 5.8$

The line segment is approximately 5.8 units long.

Working with Mathematics

Something to talk about

1. Can you use the Pythagorean Theorem to calculate the length of any line segment drawn on a grid?

Work together

2. Calculate the length of each line segment.

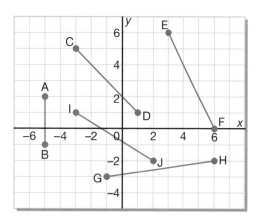

3. Plot each pair of points. Calculate the distance between them.

a) (1, 3), (5, 5) **b)** (6, 0), (8, 2)
c) (−3, 2), (1, −3) **d)** (0, 2), (1.5, 0)

4. A rectangle has vertices P(−3, −2), Q(1, 2), R(3, 0), and S(−1, −4).
   a) Draw the rectangle on graph paper. Calculate the lengths of its sides.
   b) Calculate the area of the rectangle.
   c) Calculate the lengths of the diagonals of the rectangle.

On your own

5. Calculate the length of each side of △OAB.

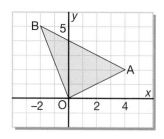

6. Plot each pair of points. Calculate the distance between them.
   a) (−4, 2), (−1, 3) **b)** (−1, −4), (2, −1)
   c) (−3, 1), (0, −1) **d)** (1, 3.5), (7, 1)

7. A triangle has vertices J(−3, 2), K(2, 3), and L(4, −1). Draw the triangle on graph paper, and calculate the lengths of its three sides.

Extend your thinking

8. Consider all the points which have integer coordinates and are 5 units from (0, 0).
   a) How many such points are there? What are their coordinates? Plot the points on graph paper.
   b) Choose four of these points to make a rectangle which has diagonals 10 units long. How many different rectangles like this can you make? To justify your answer, draw the rectangles on graph paper in a systematic way.
   c) What are the areas of these rectangles?

The Ideas

In your journal, describe how to calculate the length of a line segment if you know the coordinates of its end points. Illustrate your answer with examples. Your answer should be understandable to someone who knows the Pythagorean Theorem but has never used it to calculate the length of a line segment.

Can You Make One Large Square from Two Small Ones?

You will need a pair of scissors and two identical square pieces of paper or cardboard. Your challenge is to cut the squares into smaller pieces and arrange all the pieces to form one large square.

Understand the problem

- What are you asked to do?
- Can the pieces overlap? Do they have to overlap?

Think of a strategy

- Try cutting the squares into as few pieces as possible.
- Try cutting the squares into parts that are congruent.
- Try arranging the pieces to form a symmetrical pattern in the large square.
- If one method does not work, you will need to start again with two new squares.

Carry out the strategy

- Suppose you fold each square into two congruent parts, as shown, and then cut along the fold line. Can you arrange the four rectangles to form one large square?
- Is there another way you could fold each square into two congruent parts?
- If you then cut along the fold lines, can you form a large square using the four pieces?

Look back

- Can you find another solution to this problem?

Suppose the side length of each small square is 1 unit.
- What is the area of each small square?
- What is the area of the large square?
- How long is each side of the large square?

Communicating the Ideas

In your journal, write a description of this problem. Include diagrams to illustrate your solution.

IRRATIONAL NUMBERS

Developing the Ideas

▶ ▶ *Through Discussion*

Earlier in your study of mathematics, you encountered these
sets of numbers

Natural numbers, N 1, 2, 3, 4, 5,...	Rational numbers, Q Numbers that can be expressed in fractional form
Integers, I ... −3, −2, −1, 0, 1, 2, 3,...	Examples: $\frac{2}{3}$ $\frac{-9}{4}$ $\frac{5}{-7}$ $\frac{-1}{-2}$ 1.32 5.8 −2

1. Express each rational number in decimal form.
   Use a calculator if necessary.

   a) $\frac{3}{8}$ b) $\frac{7}{12}$ c) $\frac{-23}{16}$ d) $\frac{7}{-8}$

   e) $\frac{37}{11}$ f) $\frac{53}{99}$ g) $\frac{17}{222}$ h) $\frac{22}{7}$

Look at the results for exercise 1. The decimals in the quotients always
terminate or repeat. You can see why by looking at paper-and-pencil
division calculations such as these:

In this example, the
remainder must be
less than 8. Since
a remainder of 0
occurs, the division
terminates.

```
  0.375
8)3.000
  2 4
    60
    56
    40
    40
     0
```

We write $\frac{3}{8} = 0.375$,

which is a terminating decimal.

In this example, the
remainders must be
less than 12. Since we
get a remainder that
occurred previously,
the division repeats.

```
   0.583
12)7.000
   6 0
   1 00
     96
     40
     36
      4
```

We write $\frac{7}{12} = 0.58333333...$,

which is a repeating decimal.

One of these two cases will occur when any rational number is expressed
in decimal form. Therefore, when a rational number is expressed in
decimal form, the digits either terminate or repeat.

2. Only three of the numbers below are rational numbers.
   a) Which ones do you think they are?
   b) Why are the others not rational numbers?
      Do you think they are numbers?
      i) 1.010203040506070809010011012013001...
      ii) −238.418773
      iii) 3.14159265358979323846264338327950288419...
      iv) 88175.4754754754754754754754754754754754...
      v) 47.44444443838383838383820974449072...
      vi) −0.0792188367584920007839783978397839...

3. We use *bar notation* to indicate a repeating decimal. For example, $2.4\overline{35}$ means 2.43535353535353535353535...

a) Write a few digits of each number without using bar notation.

  i) $4.\overline{9}$ **ii)** $17.\overline{02}$ **iii)** $-8.51\overline{273}$

b) Write the two repeating decimals in exercise 2b using bar notation.

c) What are two advantages of bar notation?

If you use a calculator to calculate $\sqrt{2}$, you will obtain something like 1.414 213 562.

To check this, you can multiply 1.414 213 562 by 1.414 213 562.

But the product has more digits than most calculators can handle. Using a computer, the exact value of this product is:

1.414 213 562 × 1.414 213 562 = 1.999 999 998 944 727 844

Since the product is not exactly 2, we say that 1.414 213 562 is an *approximation* to $\sqrt{2}$. We write $\sqrt{2} \doteq 1.414\ 213\ 562$. Using a computer, we can calculate more accurate approximations to $\sqrt{2}$, such as:

$\sqrt{2} \doteq 1.414\ 213\ 562\ 373\ 095\ 048\ 801\ 688\ 724\ 209\ 698\ 078\ 569\ 671\ 875\ 376\ 94$

No matter how many digits we calculate for $\sqrt{2}$, we will never determine its exact value, and we will never find a pattern of digits that repeats.

This means that $\sqrt{2}$ cannot be expressed in fractional form $\dfrac{m}{n}$, where m and n are integers. That is, $\sqrt{2}$ is not a rational number. $\sqrt{2}$ is called an irrational number.

• • • • • • • • •

> Any number that cannot be expressed in the form $\dfrac{m}{n}$, where m and n are integers ($n \neq 0$), is an *irrational number*. In decimal form, the digits of an irrational number neither terminate nor repeat. The set of numbers is denoted $\overline{Q}$.

Examples of rational numbers	Examples of irrational numbers
Terminating decimals	Decimals that neither terminate nor repeat
−2.875 3.0	−2.718 281 828 459 045 235 36...
7.231 875 622 945 8.45×10^{-7}	1.010 010 001 000 010 000 010...
Repeating decimals	−357.575 757 575 757 877 233...
−2.333 333 333 333 333 333 33...	$\sqrt{5} \doteq 2.236\ 067\ 977\ 499\ 789\ 696\ 41$
$0.\overline{7}$	$-\sqrt{31.5} \doteq -5.612\ 486\ 080\ 160\ 912\ 078\ 38$
$3.\overline{142\ 857}$	
5.121 212 121 212 121 212 12...	
$-23.059\ 723\ 116\ \overline{894\ 5}$	

All the numbers shown above are *real numbers*. The set of real numbers consists of all the rational numbers and all the irrational numbers—that is, all numbers that can be expressed in decimal form.

Working with Mathematics

Something to talk about

1. A calculator was used to approximate $\sqrt{3}$. It displayed 1.732 050 8.
   a) Is 1.732 050 8 rational or irrational?
   b) Is $\sqrt{3}$ rational or irrational?
   c) Can a number be both rational and irrational?

2. A student wrote the formula for the circumference of a circle in the form $\pi = \frac{C}{d}$. The student claimed that this proved that π is a rational number. Do you agree with this reasoning?

3. Does each number appear to be rational or irrational? Why is the phrase "appear to be" used in this question?
   a) 1.253 253 253 253 253 253 253 253...
   b) 0.147 474 747 474 747 457 883 312...
   c) 72.041 000 000 019 875 198 751 987...
   d) −0.121 232 123 432 123 454 321 234...

On your own

4. Classify each number as natural, integer, rational, or irrational. Some of the numbers will belong to more than one set.
   a) $\frac{3}{5}$ b) $0.\overline{25}$ c) -7
   d) 23 517   e) $\sqrt{25}$ f) 2^{-1}
   g) 3×10^9 h) 2.4×10^{-6} i) $-2\frac{1}{4}$
   j) $\sqrt{7}$ k) 3.14   l) $-875.0\overline{297}$

5. Which of these numbers are irrational?
   a) $\sqrt{3}$ b) $-\sqrt{3}$ c) $6 + \sqrt{3}$
   d) $6 - \sqrt{3}$ e) $\sqrt{6+3}$ f) $\sqrt{6-3}$
   g) $\sqrt{63}$ h) $\sqrt{36}$ i) $\sqrt{6 \times 3}$

6. Only three of the numbers below are rational. Which ones are they? For each of the other numbers, explain why it is irrational.
   a) $\sqrt{9} + 7$ b) $\sqrt{9} - 7$ c) $9 + \sqrt{7}$
   d) $9 - \sqrt{7}$ e) $\sqrt{9+7}$ f) $\sqrt{9-7}$
   g) $\sqrt{9} + \sqrt{7}$ h) $\sqrt{9} - \sqrt{7}$ i) $\sqrt{9 \times 7}$

Work together

7. Give examples of two rational and two irrational numbers between the numbers in each pair.
   a) 2.47, 2.61   b) −4.825, −4.82
   c) $1.1\overline{47}$, 1.15   d) $\frac{3}{8}, \frac{4}{9}$
   e) $7.\overline{323}$, 7.323   f) $1.\overline{6}$, 1.7

8. Have you completed the Quest on page 162? If you are still missing numbers, there is another mathematical symbol you might find helpful. The product of the first n natural numbers is $1 \times 2 \times 3 \times 4 \times 5 \times ... \times n$. This product is called *factorial n* and is written $n!$. For example, 4! means $1 \times 2 \times 3 \times 4$, or 24.
   a) Calculate.   i) 2!   ii) 3!   iii) 5!   iv) 6!   v) 7!
   b) Try using the factorial sign in your expressions using the digits 1, 4, 8, and 9. For example, you can use $(4 - 1)!$, which allows you to get 6 from 4 and 1. Can you complete all the numbers from 1 to 100 now?

9. You can use envelopes to show how different sets of numbers are related. You will need five envelopes of different sizes, and 30 small pieces of cardboard or paper.

   Write each of these numbers on a small piece of cardboard.

   6,   0,   −2,   −99, $\frac{2}{3}$, 2^{10}, 3×10^6,

   2.4×10^9, $\sqrt{2}$, $\frac{12}{7}$, π, $\sqrt{900}$,   2.13,

   2^{-1},   −1, 5.8×10^{-6}, $-\sqrt{2}$,   75%,

   10^{-3},   0.762, $32.\overline{6}$, $-\frac{1}{2}$, $-17.0\overline{298}$,

   22^{22},   3 355 432,   63.172 844,

   1.212 211 222 111 222 211 111...,

   150 million,   2.5 billion,

   −17.002 900 290 029 002 900 290 029...

202 POWERS AND ROOTS

Label each of the four envelopes with one of the descriptions below. Think carefully about the size of each envelope as you label it. Place the numbers into the envelopes.

Natural numbers
N
1, 2, 3 ...

Integers
I
... –3, –2, –1, 0, 1, 2, 3, ...

Rational numbers
Q
Terminating decimals
Repeating decimals

Irrational numbers
Q̄
Decimals that neither
terminate nor repeat

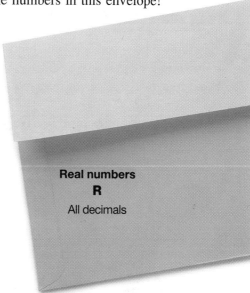

Follow this rule:

Each number must be inside every envelope containing a set of numbers to which it belongs.

For example, since –2 is an integer, –2 must be inside envelope I. Since $-2 = \frac{-2}{1}$, –2 is a rational number, and must also be inside envelope Q.

Label the fifth envelope as shown. Place all the numbers in this envelope!

Real numbers
R
All decimals

Extend your thinking

10. Is the sum of two irrational numbers always an irrational number? If your answer is no, give an example to support your answer.

11. Two students were discussing slope.

Michael: "Since slope = $\frac{\text{rise}}{\text{run}}$, the slope of a line segment is always a rational number."
Ingrid: "That's not true! I can write the coordinates of two points A and B, and the slope of the line segment AB will be irrational."
Make up an example to show that Ingrid is correct.

The Ideas

Suppose you have a number with many decimal places.
a) If you see a repeating pattern, can you be certain that the number is a rational number?
b) If you do not see a repeating pattern, can you be certain that the number is an irrational number?

Record your ideas in your journal. Include some examples to illustrate your conclusions.

Review

1. Estimate each number. Include some calculations when you need them.

   a) About how many steps do you climb up or down in a month? in a year?

   b) About how many pieces of macaroni are in a 900-g bag?

   c) About how many litres of milk have you drunk in your lifetime?

2. What does each power mean? Evaluate each power.

   a) 5^3 b) 3^5 c) 5^{-3}

   d) 3^{-5} e) $(-5)^3$ f) $(-3)^5$

   g) $(-5)^{-3}$ h) $(-3)^{-5}$ i) 3^0

3. Simplify each expression.

   a) $6^2 + 4^2$ b) $(6 + 4)^2$

   c) $2^4 + 4^3$ d) $3^2 - 2^3$

   e) $4^3 - 5^2$ f) $7^2 + 7^0$

   g) $4^{-1} - 2^{-2}$ h) $2^{-2} + 3^{-2}$

4. Which is the greater number in each pair?

   a) 8^3, 5^4 b) 8^{-3}, 5^{-4}

   c) 6^3, 4^4 d) 6^{-3}, 4^{-4}

   e) 9^2, 2^6 f) 9^{-2}, 2^{-6}

5. There is only one power of 5 between 1000 and 10 000. Which number is it?

6. Write each expression as a power.

   a) $10^4 \times 10^9$ b) $7.3^5 \times 7.3^3$

   c) $(-12)^6 \times (-12)^8$ d) $8^7 \div 8^2$

   e) $9.4^{-4} \div 9.4^{-11}$ f) $(-3)^8 \div (-3)^{-5}$

   g) $(3^2)^2$ h) $\dfrac{6.25^8}{6.25^3}$

   i) $\dfrac{8^6 \times 8^4}{8^3}$ j) $\dfrac{2^5}{2^3 \times 2^8}$

   k) $\dfrac{4^{-3} \times 4^{10}}{4^5 \times 4^{-2}}$ l) $\dfrac{(-7)^2 \times (-7)^9}{(-7)^3 \times (-7)^4}$

7. Write in scientific notation.

   a) 41 700   b) 4 170 000 000

   c) 0.000 417   d) 0.000 004 17

   e) −2 100 000   f) 0.000 003 1

   g) 97 800   h) −0.000 123 4

8. Write in scientific notation.

   a) Speed of light: 300 000 km/s

   b) Number of telephones in the world in 1989: 423 619 000

   c) Mass of Earth: 5 980 000 000 000 000 000 000 000 kg

   d) Mass of the ball in a ballpoint pen: 0.004 g

   e) Time of fastest camera exposure: 0.000 000 1 s

High speed photograph of a bursting balloon. The balloon contains some talcum powder, which holds the balloon's shape for a fraction of a second after the balloon has been destroyed.

9. In 1938, the physicist Sir Arthur Eddington estimated that the number of particles in the universe is 33×2^{259}. This number is called the cosmical number.
   a) Use your scientific calculator to express this number in scientific notation.
   b) How many digits are in this number?

10. Write the two square roots of each number.
   a) 36   b) 400   c) 441
   d) 256   e) 0.49   f) 0.01

11. Estimate each square root to one decimal place.
   a) $\sqrt{18}$ b) $\sqrt{35}$ c) $\sqrt{85}$
   d) $\sqrt{105}$ e) $\sqrt{150}$ f) $\sqrt{210}$

12. Simplify each expression. Estimate the result where necessary.
   a) $\sqrt{4} + \sqrt{81}$ b) $\sqrt{4 + 81}$
   c) $\sqrt{81} - \sqrt{4}$ d) $\sqrt{81 - 4}$
   e) $\sqrt{4} \times \sqrt{81}$ f) $\sqrt{4 \times 81}$
   g) $\sqrt{81 + \sqrt{4}}$ h) $\sqrt{\sqrt{81} - \sqrt{4}}$

13. Find the length, to one decimal place, indicated by each letter.
   a)
   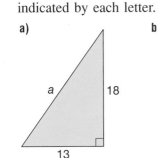
   b)
   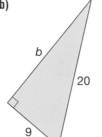
   c)
   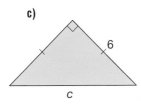
   d)
   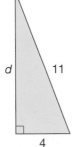

14. Can an umbrella 1.3 m long be packed flat in a box 1.1 m by 0.3 m? Give reasons for your answer.

15. Calculate the length, to one decimal place, of each line segment.
   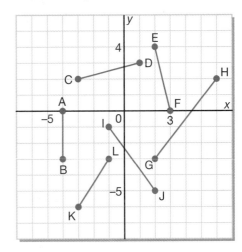

16. Plot each pair of points. Calculate the distance between them, to one decimal place.
   a) $(5,9)$, $(-2,2)$ b) $(1,-6)$, $(5,2)$
   c) $(-3,7)$, $(5,2)$ d) $(-9,-3)$, $(-3,4)$

17. Does each number appear to be rational or irrational?
   a) 2.147 474 474 474…
   b) −6.132 133 134…
   c) 72.041 296 478…
   d) 0.165 165 516 555…
   e) −2.236 067 977 749…
   f) −4.317 495

18. Classify each number as natural, integer, rational, or irrational. Some numbers will belong to more than one set.
   a) $\frac{4}{5}$ b) $0.2\overline{17}$
   c) −6   d) $\sqrt{225}$
   e) 6.121 121 12...   f) 1.8×10^{-4}
   g) 4.76×10^3 h) $\sqrt{27}$

19. Give examples of two rational numbers and two irrational numbers between the numbers in each pair.
   a) 3.65, 3.69   b) −1.476, −1.47
   c) $0.3\overline{97}$, 0.4   d) $-5.3\overline{76}$, $-5.3\overline{7}$
   e) $\frac{8}{9}$, $\frac{9}{10}$
   f) 2.236 067…, 2.236 071 23…

Designing a Scale Model of the Solar System

The Voyager 2 spacecraft was launched in 1977 on a journey of discovery that took over 10 years to complete. Its goal was to travel to the outer planets of our solar system: Jupiter, Saturn, Uranus, and Neptune. The cameras and scientific equipment it carried have provided information about these planets as well as stunning photos like those you see here.

The Apollo 11 spacecraft launched in 1969 reached the moon in only 4 days. Why did it take the Voyager so long to complete its journey?

The answer lies in the vast distances which separate the planets. The chart on pages 168 and 169 attempts to illustrate the immensity of remote astronomical objects. Another way to visualize the incredibly large is to design a scale model of the solar system.

ACTIVITY 1

Before you can begin to design your model, you will need to collect some data about the solar system.

The diameter of the sun is about 1.40×10^9 m.

DATA DISK

Do some research to find the mean diameter of each planet in our solar system and its distance from the sun, in metres. This information can be found in the *Moon and Planets* database on the student's disk. Express each measurement in scientific notation.

ACTIVITY 2

Obtain a spherical object to represent the sun. Measure and record the diameter of this object. Calculate how many times as small as the diameter of the sun is the diameter of your object. This figure establishes the scale for your model.

ACTIVITY 3

Use the scale established in Activity 2. Calculate the diameters of the objects you would need to represent the planets in your scale model. Think of as many objects as you can with these diameters. As you do this, keep in mind:

- There will probably not be objects with the exact diameters you require. Use other objects whose diameters are approximations of the diameters you require.
- If the diameters of the objects are too small, you may need a larger object to represent the sun. Conversely, if the diameters of the objects are too large, you may need a smaller object for the sun.

ACTIVITY 4

Use the scale established in Activity 2. Calculate the distances from the sun to the objects that represent the planets in your model. Try to visualize where they would be in relation to your sun.

ACTIVITY 5

After the sun, the moon is the celestial body which has the most influence on Earth. The moon has a diameter of about 3.5×10^6 m and is about 3.8×10^8 m from Earth. About how far from Earth would the moon be in your model? How does this compare with the distance from Earth to one of the planets visited by Voyager 2?

ACTIVITY 6

Research to find more information about the Voyager 2 spacecraft, its journey, and the planets it visited. Some questions you may wish to research include:

How was Voyager 2 powered and how was its flight path controlled?

What scientific equipment was on board the craft? How was the information it gathered sent to Earth?

What new information did we learn about the outer planets and their moons?

What happened to the Voyager spacecraft after it reached Neptune in 1989?

ACTIVITY 7

Construct a scale drawing showing the sun and planets as circles. You could use a Draw program that allows you to draw circles with a given radius or diameter. Since the sun is much larger than any of the planets, you might want to show only part of the sun on your drawing.

COMMUNICATING
The Ideas

Write a brief report which summarizes the results of your research and investigations. Include tables and drawings.

ALGEBRAIC OPERATIONS AND EQUATIONS

Mathematics Files

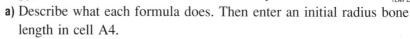

NATIONAL HOCKEY LEAGUE				
CENTRAL	**WIN**	**LOSS**	**TIE**	**POINTS**
Toronto	27	10	3	57
Dallas	24	12	4	52
St. Louis	20	18	3	43
Detroit	17	18	4	38
Chicago	16	17	6	38
Winnipeg	13	23	5	31
PACIFIC	**WIN**	**LOSS**	**TIE**	**POINTS**
Calgary	20	12	8	48
Vancouver	19	12	7	45
San Jose	17	15	7	
Edmonton				

ACTIVITY 1

Hockey Standings

1. In hockey standings, 2 points are given for a win and 1 point is given for a tie.

   a) Suppose you know the numbers of wins and ties that a hockey team had in a season. How could you determine the team's total points?

   b) Write a formula that you could use to determine a team's total points.

2. a) A team had 28 wins and 6 ties. How many points did it have?

   b) A team had 83 points. It had 37 wins. How many ties did it have?

   c) A team had 79 points. It had 11 ties. How many wins did it have?

ACTIVITY 2

Estimating Heights

Did you know that there are formulas relating the sizes of some parts of the human body? And that these formulas are the same for all people?

For example, suppose you know only the length of a person's radius bone, r centimetres. You want to estimate this person's height, h centimetres. You can substitute the value for r in the appropriate formula below. Then solve to determine her or his approximate height.

Female $h = 3.34r + 81.2$

Male $h = 3.27r + 85.9$

3. A radius bone 24.5 cm long was found. Substitute 24.5 for r in both formulas. Use your calculator to estimate the height if the person was a female and if the person was a male.

4. a) For a female, choose some values of r between 20 cm and 30 cm. Calculate the corresponding values of h. Make a table of values. Graph the height of the person against radius bone length.

   b) Repeat part a for a male.

5. Use a computer to set up a spreadsheet like the one shown below. Copy the formulas in row 5 to row 6, and beyond.

TEMPLATE DISK

   a) Describe what each formula does. Then enter an initial radius bone length in cell A4.

   b) Use the spreadsheet to check your solutions to exercise 3.

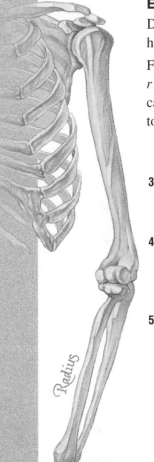

Radius

	A	B	C	D
1	Estimating heights			
2				
3	Length of radius bone	Height of female	Height of male	Difference
4		=3.34*A4+81.2	=3.27*A4+85.9	=C4-B4
5	=A4+0.5	=3.34*A5+81.2	=3.27*A5+85.9	=C5-B5

DR. SHELLEY SAUNDERS IS A PHYSICAL anthropologist at McMaster University in Hamilton, Ontario. She investigates changes in human body size and shape over time. She wondered whether there were any differences between the heights of 19th century pioneers and present-day people.

To make the comparison, she studied human remains from a pioneer graveyard. Using bone measurements and formulas like those in *Activity 2*, she found that pioneer men were roughly the same height as present-day men, but pioneer women were shorter than present-day women. Since pioneer men and women probably ate the same food, poor diet doesn't explain the women's shorter heights. Dr. Saunders is currently doing more research to try and discover a reason for this height difference.

19th century pioneer dress supplied courtesy of textile department, Royal Ontario Museum

ACTIVITY 3

Comparing the Activities

6. Compare *Activities 1* and *2*. List as many things as you can that they have in common. List as many things as you can that are different about these activities.

THE CONCEPT OF A VARIABLE

Developing the Ideas

▷ ▶ *Through Activities*

Work in a group to complete the two activities below.

ACTIVITY 1

Extending Patterns

Here is a pattern of figures made from squares.

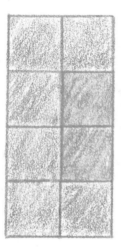  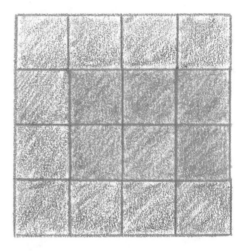

Draw two more figures in this pattern. Count the number of green squares and the number of blue squares in each figure. Record the results in a table.

Number of green squares	Number of blue squares

1. Suppose the pattern is continued.
    a) One of the figures will have 20 green squares. How many blue squares will it have?
    b) How many blue squares are there on the figure which has 100 green squares?

2. Suppose you know the number of green squares in one figure. How would you find the number of blue squares?

3. Let *s* represent the number of green squares in one figure. Write an expression for the number of blue squares. What kind of number is *s*?

4. In one figure there are 74 green squares. Use your expression to determine the number of blue squares.

5. In one figure there are 100 blue squares. Use your expression to determine the number of green squares.

6. Use your table to draw a graph. How does the graph show the way the number of blue squares is related to the number of green squares?

ACTIVITY 2

Using Measurement Formulas

A rectangular flower bed has a length of 5 m.

|←————————————— 5 m —————————————→|

7. Calculate the perimeter of the flower bed for a width of 2 m, and for a width of 3.5 m.

Width (m)	Perimeter (m)

8. Calculate the perimeters for four other widths. Record the results in a table.

9. **a)** Suppose you know the width of a flower bed with length 5 m. How would you find its perimeter?
   b) Let w metres represent the width of the flower bed. Write an expression for its perimeter.
   c) Write this expression in another way.
   d) What kind of number is w?

10. Suppose the width is 2.4 m. Use your expression to determine the perimeter.

11. Suppose the perimeter is 13 m. Use your expression to determine the width.

12. **a)** Use your table to draw a graph of perimeter against width.
    b) How could you use the graph to determine the perimeter if you know the width?
    c) How could you use it to determine the width if you know the perimeter?

13. Suppose you were to graph perimeter against length for the rectangles in this activity. What do you think the graph would look like?

In *Activity 1*, you can determine the number of blue squares by adding 4 to the number of green squares. So, if you let *s* represent the number of green squares, then $s + 4$ represents the number of blue squares.

In *Activity 2*, there are two ways to determine the perimeter:
- You can double the width and add 10. So, if you let *w* metres represent the width, then $2w + 10$ represents the perimeter.
- You can add 5 to the width and double the result. Therefore, $2(w + 5)$ represents the perimeter.

In these activities, $s + 4, 2w + 10$, and $2(w + 5)$ are called *algebraic expressions*. The parts of an expression that are added or subtracted are called *terms*. Each expression contains a letter representing a number that can vary. For this reason, these letters are called *variables*. When you use a variable, you should know the possible numbers it can represent.

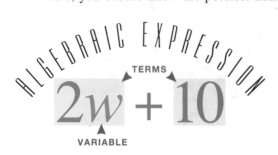

In the expression $s + 4$ in *Activity 1*, *s* must be an even number. You do not join the points on the graph because *s* cannot represent numbers between those in the table.

In the expressions $2w + 10$ and $2(w + 5)$ in *Activity 2*, *w* is a rational number. You join the points on the graph because *w* can represent numbers between those in the table. Also, *w* must be between 0 and 5.

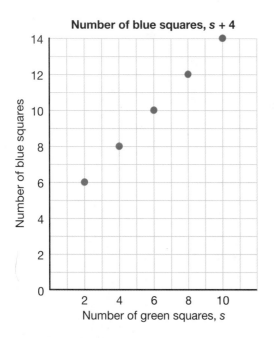

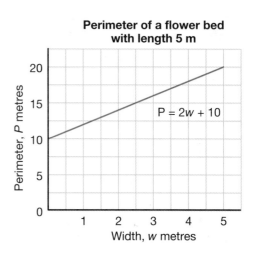

Working with Mathematics

Something to talk about

1. a) What is a variable?

b) Do you think it is correct to say that a variable is "an unknown number"? Explain.

c) Do you think you could use symbols other than letters as variables? Explain.

2. a) In the expression $s + 4$ in *Activity 1*, why must s be an even number?

b) In the expressions $2w + 10$ and $2(w + 5)$ in *Activity 2*, why must w be a rational number between 0 and 5?

3. Some common formulas are given below.

a) Identify the variables in each formula. For each variable you identify, explain what it represents, and why it is a variable.

b) Is π a variable? Explain your answer.

i)

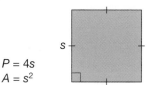

$P = 4s$
$A = s^2$

ii)

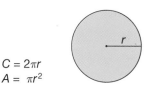

$C = 2\pi r$
$A = \pi r^2$

iii)

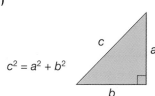

$c^2 = a^2 + b^2$

4. a) Can an expression contain more than one variable?

b) Can a variable occur more than once in an expression?

Give examples to illustrate your answers.

Work together

5. A series of cubes are grouped on a table, as shown. You can look at each group from all sides. The total number of faces that can be seen are counted. Suppose this pattern is continued.

5 faces

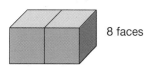

8 faces

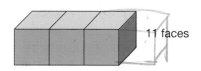

11 faces

a) In each group, check that the number of faces shown is correct.

b) Make a table showing how the number of faces that can be seen is related to the number of cubes.

c) How many faces could be seen if there are 4 cubes? 5 cubes? Include these results in your table.

d) How many faces could be seen if there are 10 cubes? 30 cubes?

e) If you know the number of cubes, how would you determine the number of faces that can be seen?

f) Let n represent the number of cubes. Write an expression for the number of faces that can be seen.

g) If there are 16 cubes, how many faces can be seen?

h) If 62 faces can be seen, how many cubes are there?

i) Use your table to draw a graph. How does the graph illustrate the way the number of faces that can be seen is related to the number of cubes?

6. A rectangular flower bed has a length of 5 m.

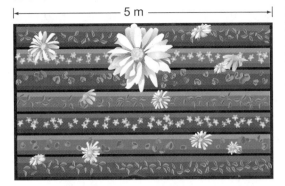

|← ———————— 5 m ———————— →|

a) Calculate the area of the flower bed if its width is 2 m and if it is 3.5 m.

b) Calculate the areas for four other widths. Record the results in a table.

c) Suppose you know the width of a flower bed with length 5 m. How would you find its area?

d) Let w metres represent the width of a flower bed. Write an expression for its area. What kind of number is w? What are the possible values of w?

e) Suppose the width is 1.2 m. Use your expression to determine the area.

f) Suppose the area is 15 m^2. Use your expression to determine the width.

g) Use your table to graph area against width.
  i) How could you use the graph to find the area if you know the width?
  ii) How could you use it to find the width if you know the area?

7. Take a calendar for any month.

august/août						
M/L	T/M	W/M	T/J	F/V	S/S	S/D
1	2	3	4	5	6	7
8	9	10	11	12	13	14
15	16	17	18	19	20	21
22	23	24	25	26	27	28
29	30	31				

a) Choose any 2 by 2 square of four dates. Write the number in the upper left corner (UL). Add the numbers in the upper right corner (UR) and the lower left corner (LL).

b) Repeat part a for other 2 by 2 squares. Repeat for 2 by 2 squares on the calendars for other months. Record the results in a table.

Number in the UL corner	Sum of the numbers in the UR and LL corners

c) Suppose you know the number in the UL corner. How would you find the sum of the numbers in the UR and LL corners?

d) Let n represent the number in the UL corner.
  i) Write an expression for the sum of the numbers in the UR and LL corners.
  ii) What are the possible values of n?

On your own

8. A pattern of squares is shown below. Each small square has sides 1 cm long.

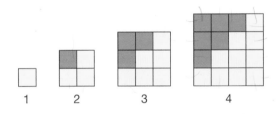

1   2   3   4

a) Determine the following information for each large square shown above. Account for any patterns you see in the results.
  i) its perimeter
  ii) the perimeter of the figure formed by the yellow squares
  iii) the perimeter of the figure formed by the red squares

b) Draw one more large square in this pattern. Repeat part a for this large square.

c) Without drawing the large squares, repeat part a for the 10th large square and the 100th large square in the pattern.

d) Suppose you know only the side length of one of the large squares. How could you use this to answer part a?

e) Let n represent the side length of one of the large squares in the pattern. Write formulas you could use to calculate the things in part a.

f) One of the large squares in the pattern has a perimeter of 60 cm. How long is the side of this square?

g) On one of the large squares, the perimeter of the figure formed by the red squares is 44 cm. How long is the side of this square?

h) Is it possible for one of the large squares to have a perimeter of 29 cm? Explain your answer.

9. In *Activity 1* on page 212, s represented the number of green squares in one diagram. Write an expression for:

a) the total number of squares in the diagram

b) the perimeter of the diagram

10. For the flower bed in *Activity 2* on page 213, decorative fencing for the flower bed sells for $1.50/m. Suppose w metres represents the width of the flower bed. Write an expression for the cost of decorative fencing to go around it.

Extend your thinking

11. Canada started using the Celsius scale for temperatures in the 1970s. Suppose a tourist from the United States wants to convert a Celsius temperature to Fahrenheit. Let C represent a temperature reading in degrees Celsius. Let F represent the equivalent reading in degrees Fahrenheit.

a) A rule of thumb for converting Celsius to Fahrenheit is "to double and add 30". Write a corresponding formula for F.

b) The exact formula for converting Celsius temperatures to Fahrenheit is $F = 1.8C + 32$. Choose some values of C. Determine how closely the rule of thumb gives the correct Fahrenheit temperatures.

12. Use a computer to set up a spreadsheet like the one below to compare the approximate and exact conversions used in exercise 11. Adjust the Celsius values by entering new numbers in cell A4. Include some negative values among those you try. When are the results of the approximate formula closest to those of the exact formula?

TEMPLATE DISK

	A	B	C	D
1	Celsius to Fahrenheit Converter			
2				
3	Celsius	Approximate	Exact	Difference
4	0	=A4*2+30	=A4*1.8+32	=C4-B4

COMMUNICATING

The Ideas

Look up the word "variable" in a dictionary. In your journal, write some examples that illustrate the use and meaning of this word in everyday speech. How does its mathematical meaning compare with these examples?

ver'ē ə bəl

What If You Saved 1¢, Then 2¢, Then 3¢, Then 4¢,...?

Suppose you save 1¢ today, 2¢ tomorrow, 3¢ the next day, 4¢ the day after that, and so on. Assume that you continue to save according to this pattern.

1. How much money would you save after 30 days? after 100 days? after one year?

2. Determine a formula you could use to calculate the amount you would have if you know the number of days that you saved.

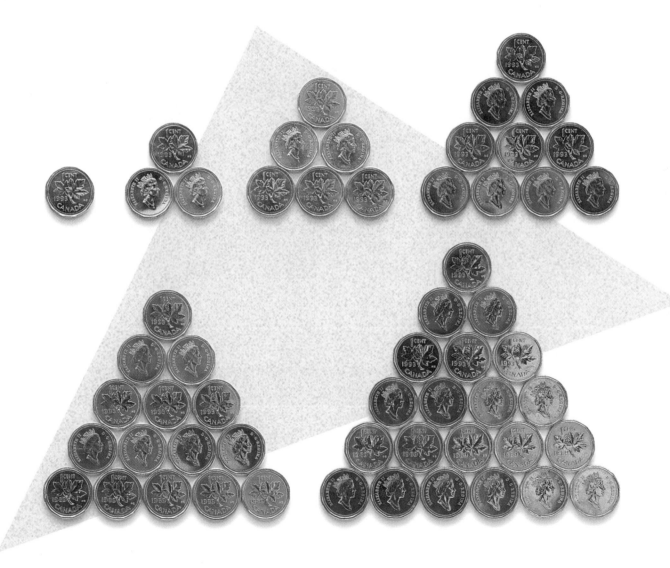

Understand the problem

- Describe the pattern.
- What are you asked to do?
- You could use cents throughout and convert to dollars at the end. How do you convert cents to dollars?

Think of a strategy

- Look at the pattern of yellow squares in the last diagram in exercise 8 on page 216. Describe a relation between the number of yellow squares in each column and the amount of money you save each day. How many days' savings are represented by these yellow squares?
- Notice how the yellow squares and the red squares fit together to form a rectangle. You might be able to answer the questions using patterns like these.

Carry out the strategy

- Using graph paper, create two identical figures like the one on the right, and cut them out. Think of each small square as representing 1¢. Each figure represents the amount you would save after 7 days.
- Fit the two figures together to form a rectangle.
- What are the dimensions of the rectangle? What is the area of the rectangle? How is the area related to the number of squares in each figure?
- Answer these questions for figures with other numbers of squares.
- What is the sum $1 + 2 + 3 + \cdots + 30$? How much would you save after 30 days?
- What is the sum $1 + 2 + 3 + \cdots + 100$? How much would you save after 100 days?
- What is the sum $1 + 2 + 3 + \cdots + 365$? How much would you save after 365 days?
- What is a formula for the sum $1 + 2 + 3 + \cdots + n$? How much would you save after n days?

Look back

- How long would it take you to save $100?
- The numbers 1, 3, 6, 10, 15, ... are called the *triangular numbers*. Why is this name appropriate? What is a formula for the nth triangular number?

Communicating the Ideas

In your journal, write a description of this problem and your solution. Illustrate with diagrams showing how the figures fit together. Explain how you can use these diagrams to answer the questions.

The Distributive Law

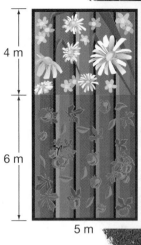

4 m

6 m

5 m

You are planting both flowers and vegetables in a rectangular garden. To buy fertilizer for the garden, you need to know its area. You can calculate the area in two ways.

Method 1

Total area = width × length

Method 2

Total area = area with flowers + area with vegetables

1. **a)** Calculate the area of the garden using both methods. Are the two results the same?
   b) Repeat part a using a rectangular garden with different measurements. Use positive rational numbers. Are the two results the same for this garden?

Since you can calculate the area of the garden above using either *Method 1* or *Method 2*, you write:

$$5(4 + 6) = 5 \times 4 + 5 \times 6$$

You get similar results with other numbers:

$$3(7 + 2) = 3 \times 7 + 3 \times 2$$
$$4.5(2.4 + 6.3) = 4.5 \times 2.4 + 4.5 \times 6.3$$

In arithmetic, you write equations such as those above. In algebra, you use variables and write only one equation $a(b + c) = ab + ac$. This equation is called the *Distributive Law* for multiplication over addition.

In question 1 above, you verified that the variables a, b, and c can be positive rational numbers. Do you think the variables could be negative?

2. Substitute some negative numbers for a, b, and c in the left side of $a(b + c) = ab + ac$. Substitute the same numbers in the right side. Do you get the same result on both sides? Repeat with other negative numbers. What kinds of numbers can a, b, and c represent in this equation?

3. There is also a Distributive Law for multiplication over subtraction. Make up some examples to illustrate this law.

> **Distributive Law**
>
> $a(b + c) = ab + ac$
> $a(b - c) = ab - ac$ $a, b,$ and c can be any real numbers

REPRESENTING VARIABLES AND EXPRESSIONS

Developing the Ideas

▶▶ *Using Manipulatives*

In the preceding section, you worked with expressions such as $s + 4$, $2w + 10$, and $2(w + 5)$. You can use algebra tiles to represent expressions like these.

This tile, called a 1-tile, represents one unit, or 1.

To represent −1, flip the tile.

This tile, called a variable-tile, represents a variable. For example, if you are using s, you can call this tile an s-tile. If you are using w, you call it a w-tile.

To represent the opposite of s, or $-s$, flip the tile.

To represent the expression $s + 4$ with algebra tiles, use one s-tile and four 1-tiles.

To represent $2w + 10$, use two w-tiles and ten 1-tiles.

To represent $2(w + 5)$, form two equal groups of tiles. Each group contains one w-tile and five 1-tiles.

In *Activity 2* on page 213, you knew that the expressions $2(w + 5)$ and $2w + 10$ are equal because they represent the perimeter of a rectangle. The algebra tiles demonstrate again that $2(w + 5) = 2w + 10$.

1. What expression does each group of algebra tiles represent?

a)

b)

2. Use algebra tiles to represent each expression.
   a) $2x + 1$ b) $3y - 5$ c) $2 - n$ d) $-4x + 3$

3. Use algebra tiles to represent each expression. Then use the tiles to write the expression without brackets.
   a) $2(x + 4)$ b) $3(2x - 1)$ c) $6(2 - a)$ d) $-2(2m - 3)$

4. In each part of exercise 3, compare the algebraic expression with the algebra-tiles expression.
   a) What patterns can you find?
   b) Without using the algebra tiles, how can you write an expression without brackets?
   c) Make up some examples to illustrate your method. Check with the algebra tiles.

▶▶ *Through Guided Examples*

Example 1 ....

   a) Use algebra tiles to represent the expression $5 - 2x$.
   b) What is the value of this expression when $x = 6$? when $x = -3$?
   c) Use algebra tiles to represent the expression $-(5 - 2x)$.

Solution

   a) Use five 1-tiles and two flipped x-tiles.

   b) Think:
   If each x-tile represents 6, each flipped x-tile represents -6. Replace each flipped x-tile with six flipped 1-tiles.

   Since a 1-tile represents $+1$ and a flipped 1-tile represents -1, a pair of opposite tiles add to 0. You can remove five 0-pairs, leaving seven flipped 1-tiles, or -7.

   In symbols, you substitute 6 for x and write:
   $$5 - 2x = 5 - 2 \times 6$$
   $$= 5 - 12$$
   $$= -7$$

   Think:
   If each x-tile represents -3, each flipped x-tile represents 3.
   Replace each flipped x-tile with three 1-tiles.
   This gives eleven 1-tiles, or 11.

   In symbols, you substitute -3 for x, and write:
   $$5 - 2x = 5 - 2(-3)$$
   $$= 5 + 6$$
   $$= 11$$

   c) Just as $-x$ represents the opposite of x, so $-(5 - 2x)$ represents the opposite of $5 - 2x$. Start with the expression in the brackets (which is the same as in part a), and flip the tiles.
   You obtain $-(5 - 2x) = -5 + 2x$, or $2x - 5$.

Example 2

Use algebra tiles to represent each expression. Use the result to write the
expression without brackets.

a) $2(3x - 4)$ **b)** $-3(p - 3)$

Solution

a) Think:

2 equal groups of tiles

Each group has three x-tiles and four flipped 1-tiles.

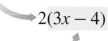

In all, there are six x-tiles and eight flipped 1-tiles.
This means that $2(3x - 4) = 6x - 8$

b) Think:

3 equal groups of tiles

$-3(p - 3)$

Each group has one p-tile and three flipped 1-tiles.   The negative sign means flip all the tiles.

There are three flipped p-tiles and nine 1-tiles.
This means that $-3(p - 3) = -3p + 9$

Instead of using algebra tiles, you can use the Distributive Law to write
expressions without brackets. This process is called *expanding*.

Example 3

Expand using the Distributive Law.

a) $6(3n + 4)$ **b)** $-3(4b - 7)$

Solution

a) $6(3n + 4) = 6 \times 3n + 6 \times 4$
$= 18n + 24$

b) $-3(4b - 7) = (-3)(4b) + (-3)(-7)$
$= -12b + 21$

Working with Mathematics

Something to talk about

1. Decide if each statement is always true, sometimes true, or never true. Explain your answers.

   a) A 1-tile is positive and a flipped 1-tile is negative.

   b) A variable-tile is positive and a flipped variable-tile is negative.

   c) x is positive and $-x$ is negative.

2. Could a variable tile have a value of 0? represent a rational number? Explain your answers.

3. How could you represent the number 0 using algebra tiles?

Work together

4. What expression does each group of algebra tiles represent?

   a)

   b)

5. Use algebra tiles to represent each expression. Determine the value of the expression when the variable represents 4 and when it represents -5.

   a) $5 + 3n$ b) $2x - 4$

   c) $-3y - 6$ d) $-4 + k$

6. Only two of the expressions below are equal. Which ones are they? Use algebra tiles to justify your answer.

   $3x + 2$ $3x - 2$ $2 + 3x$ $2 - 3x$

7. Use algebra tiles to expand each expression.

   a) $2(3 - 2x)$ b) $-(3z + 4)$

   c) $5(2 - a)$ d) $-3(-2s + 1)$

8. Expand using the Distributive Law.

   a) $3(4m + 7)$ b) $-5(x - 10)$

   c) $4(2a + b - 3)$ d) $6(x - 3y + 4z)$

On your own

9. Use algebra tiles to represent each expression. Determine the value of the expression when the variable represents 3 and when it represents -4.

   a) $-2 + 3x$ b) $4x + 3$

   c) $-5y + 2$ d) $-1 - 3h$

10. Use algebra tiles to expand each expression.

    a) $3(2a + 1)$ b) $2(3 - x)$

    c) $4(1 - 2t)$ d) $-2(4 + 3x)$

11. Expand using the Distributive Law.

    a) $6(4x + 9)$ b) $-3(5c + 3)$

    c) $11(3 - 8z)$ d) $-10(-2 + 7y)$

12. Expand using the Distributive Law.

    a) $3(x + 2y - 7)$ b) $-2(a - 5b + 2)$

    c) $-(6m - 7n)$ d) $4(9p + q - 9r)$

13. Expand each expression.

    a) $2.5(n + 2)$ b) $3.2(2 - 1.5r)$

    c) $\sqrt{2}(x - \sqrt{2})$ d) $2\pi(R - r)$

Extend your thinking

14. Do you think it is possible to illustrate expansions like those in exercise 8, parts c and d with the algebra tiles you have been using? If so, describe how you would do this. If not, describe a set of tiles for which it would be possible.

The Ideas

What do you think the word "distribute" means? Look up this word in a dictionary. Why do you think the law $a(b + c) = ab + ac$ is called the Distributive Law? Write your ideas in your journal.

Interpreting Number Properties Algebraically

Operations with numbers have certain properties.

Order Properties of Addition and Multiplication

$3 + 4 = 4 + 3 \quad 5 \times 7 = 7 \times 5$

If x and y are any two natural numbers, they can be added or multiplied in any order. You write:

$x + y = y + x \qquad xy = yx$

Grouping Properties of Addition and Multiplication

$(2 + 5) + 8 = 2 + (5 + 8) \qquad (3 \times 4) \times 5 = 3 \times (4 \times 5)$

If you add or multiply three natural numbers, it does not matter which two you add or multiply first. You write:

$(x + y) + z = x + (y + z) \qquad (xy)z = x(yz)$

Identities for Addition and Multiplication

$3 + 0 = 3$ and $0 + 3 = 3$

If you add 0 to any number, or if you add any number to 0, the number does not change.

$x + 0 = 0 + x = x$

0 is called the *identity for addition*.

$5 \times 1 = 5$ and $1 \times 5 = 5$

If you multiply any number by 1, or if you multiply 1 by any number, the number does not change.

$x \times 1 = 1 \times x = x$

1 is called the *identity for multiplication*.

Inverses for Addition and Multiplication

$4 + (-4) = 0$

If you add a number and its opposite, the sum is the identity for addition.

$x + (-x) = 0$

x and $-x$ are called *additive inverses*.

$2 \times \frac{1}{2} = 1$

If you multiply a number by its reciprocal, the product is the identity for multiplication.

$x \times \frac{1}{x} = 1 \quad (x \neq 0)$

x and $\frac{1}{x}$ are called *multiplicative inverses*.

1. Several equations above contain the letters x, y, and z. Are these letters variables in these equations? Explain your answer.

2. a) Do the integers and rational numbers satisfy the order properties? Explain.

  b) Do the integers and rational numbers satisfy the grouping properties? Explain.

3. Do you think there are properties, like those above, for subtraction and division?

COMBINING LIKE TERMS

Developing the Ideas

In arithmetic, you learned how to add, subtract, multiply, and divide numbers.

In algebra, you will learn how to add, subtract, multiply, and divide algebraic expressions.

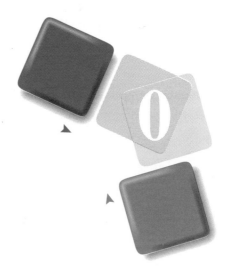

▶ ▶ *Using Manipulatives*

When you add or subtract expressions using algebra tiles, you use the Zero Principle.

The Zero Principle

You have already seen that a 1-tile and a flipped 1-tile add to 0. In fact, any two opposite tiles add to 0. This means that you can add or remove pairs of opposite tiles without changing an expression.

You see: or

You think:
The sum of each pair is 0.

You use the Zero Principle when you combine groups of tiles. For example, here are three groups of tiles, which represent $4x$, $-2x$, and 5.

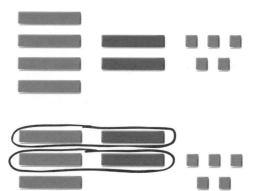

You think:
To combine them, you can use the Zero Principle to remove two pairs of opposite tiles. Then two variable tiles and five 1-tiles remain. You cannot combine the variable tiles and 1-tiles since they are not the same type.

You write: $4x - 2x + 5 = 2x + 5$

The terms $4x$ and $-2x$ are examples of *like terms*. They contain the same variable. Similarly, 7 and -3 are like terms. They contain no variables. They are called constant terms. The terms $2x$ and 5 are not like terms and cannot be combined.

You can combine like terms with algebra tiles, or by thinking about algebra tiles.

1. Use algebra tiles to combine like terms.

   a) $3x + 2x$ **b)** $4n - n - 5n$ **c)** $-4a - 2a + 3a$

2. Use algebra tiles to combine like terms.

   a) $2x + 1 + 4x + 3$ **b)** $5y - 4 - 3y + 3$ **c)** $6 - 3a - a - 1$

3. Use algebra tiles to combine like terms.

   a) $2(x - 2) + 3x + 1$ **b)** $4m - 1 - 3(m - 2)$ **c)** $3(k - 2) - (k - 3)$

▶ ▶ *Through Guided Examples*

When you use algebra tiles, the terms which are represented by the same type of tile are called like terms. The terms represented by variable tiles are all like terms. The terms represented by the 1-tiles are also like terms.

These are like terms: $2x$ $-5x$ x

These are also like terms: 4 -7

These are not like terms: $3a$ $2b$ 8

When you combine like terms you make the expression simpler than it was originally.

Example 1

Use algebra tiles to simplify the expression $4a + 3 + 2a - 4$.
What is the value of this expression when $a = 8$? when $a = -2$?

Solution

Think:

four *a*-tiles   three 1-tiles

and two *a*-tiles   and four flipped 1-tiles

$$4a + 3 + 2a - 4$$

From the tiles, $4a + 3 + 2a - 4 = 6a - 1$

When $a = 8$, the value of the expression is $6 \times 8 - 1 = 48 - 1$, or 47.

When $a = -2$, the value of the expression is $6 \times (-2) - 1 = -12 - 1$, or -13.

You could have simplified this expression without using algebra tiles.

Example 2

Simplify the expression $4a + 3 + 2a - 4$ by combining like terms.

Solution

$$4a + 3 + 2a - 4 = 4a + 2a + 3 - 4$$
$$= 6a - 1$$

Example 3

Use algebra tiles to combine like terms: $2(x + 2) - 3(2 - x)$

Solution

Think: Combine two groups   ... and flip three groups
              of these tiles ...   of these tiles.

$$2(x + 2) - 3(2 - x)$$

two x-tiles and   Flip six 1-tiles and
four 1-tiles   three flipped x-tiles

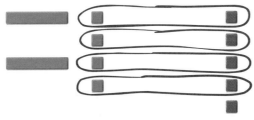

From the tiles, $2(x + 2) - 3(2 - x) = 5x - 2$

When you do not use algebra tiles, you use the distributive law.

Example 4

Simplify the expression $2(x + 2) - 3(2 - x)$.

Solution

$$2(x + 2) - 3(2 - x) = 2x + 4 - 6 + 3x$$
$$= 2x + 3x + 4 - 6$$
$$= 5x - 2$$

BOGGLE YOUR MIND

The two main cables which support the Golden Gate
Bridge in San Francisco are made of many strands of
thick steel wire – thousands more than in the cable pictured
at the right. They contain enough wire to encircle the Equator
three times. Each cable is about 4 km long. The Equator is
about 40 000 km long. How many wires are in each cable?

Working with Mathematics

Something to talk about

1. In *Example 1* on page 227, you could have found the value of the expression when $a = 8$ and when $a = -2$ without combining like terms. What advantage is there to combining like terms before substituting?

2. Which are like terms?
   - a) $5x, -2x$
   - b) $3a, 7$
   - c) $2x, -1$
   - d) $4, 8$
   - e) $2x, 3y$
   - f) $-5c, c$
   - g) $-x, 4x$
   - h) $3, 3s$
   - i) $8k, -4k, 3$

3. There are ten pairs of like terms below. Try to find all ten pairs.
   $$2x \quad -3y \quad 5x \quad -y \quad 3 \quad -x \quad 5 \quad 4x \quad -1$$

Work together

4. Combine like terms. Use algebra tiles if you like.
   - a) $2x + 4x - 3x$
   - b) $-3a + 2a - a$
   - c) $3k - 2 - k + 6$
   - d) $2(x + 2) + 3(2x - 1)$

5. Simplify each expression. Determine its value when $x = 4$ and when $x = -3$.
   - a) $4x + 2x - 2$
   - b) $5x - 6x - 2$
   - c) $2x + 3(4x - 2)$
   - d) $7(1 - x) - 3(1 - 2x)$

6. Simplify each expression.
   - a) $7a + 3a + 2b - 5b$
   - b) $-3m + 2n - 7n + 4m$
   - c) $4x - 3y - (x - y)$
   - d) $2(x - 3y + 1) - 3(x + 2y - 1)$
   $$2x - 6y + 2 - 3x + 6y + 3$$
   $$2x - 3x - 6y + 6y + 2 + 3$$
   $$-x - 12 + 5$$

COMMUNICATING

The Ideas

Your friend phones you for help in simplifying this expression:
$$3a - 2(a - 1)$$

To simulate that you are talking on the telephone, sit back-to-back with another student. Provide that student with verbal instructions for simplifying the expression.

Write another expression and reverse roles.

On your own

7. Combine like terms. Use algebra tiles if you like.
   - a) $2x + 4x - 3 + 5$
   - b) $9x - 5 + 7 - 6x$
   - c) $-x + 2 - 3x - 4$
   - d) $5a - 2(a - 4)$
   - e) $3(2 - x) - 2(3 - x)$
   - f) $2(5a - 1) - 3(2a - 2) + 4(a - 3)$

8. Simplify each expression. Determine its value when $x = 7$, $x = -5$, and $x = 0$.
   - a) $9x - 5 - 6x - 2x + 4$
   - b) $-3(x - 1) - (2x - 3)$
   - c) $8x - 2 - 6x - 6$
   - d) $2.5x - 3.2 - 1.5x$
   - e) $4.2(x - 0.5) - 2.5(x + 0.6)$

9. Simplify each expression.
   - a) $2a + 3b - c - 3a - b + 5c$
   - b) $3x - 2y + 7 - x + 6y - 7$
   - c) $m - 2n + 5m - n$
   - d) $-(a - 5) - 2(3b - 5) + 3(2c - 5)$

Extend your thinking

10. a) Do you think all expressions can be simplified? If your answer is no, give an example of an expression that cannot be simplified.
    b) Which of these expressions do you think is the simpler? Give a reason for your answer.
    $$7(x + y + z) \quad 7x + 7y + 7z$$
    c) Without using the words "simple," "simpler," or "simplest," explain what the word "simplify" means.

Number Tricks

1. Three examples are given above, each starting with a different number.
   a) Follow the steps to check the calculations.
   b) Choose another natural number and follow the same steps.
   c) Follow the steps again, using a negative integer, and then a decimal.

2. How do you know that the number at the end will always be the number you start with?

3. Change one step in the trick so that everyone will get the same number at the end, no matter what number he or she starts with.

4. Here is another number trick. Follow the steps several times, using a different number each time. Explain why the trick works.
   • Think of a number.
   • Add 2.
   • Multiply by 3.
   • Subtract the number you started with.
   • Divide by 2.
   • Subtract the number you started with.
   • What is your answer?

5. Make up your own number trick, and try it with a friend.

SOLVING EQUATIONS USING ALGEBRA TILES

Developing the Ideas

At the beginning of this chapter, you were asked this question:
A team had 79 points. It had 11 ties. How many wins did it have?
(Page 210, exercise 2c)

To answer this question you solved this equation:
$2w + 11 = 79$

You probably solved this equation by using systematic trial
or inspection.

In the next few sections you will learn an algebraic method
of solving equations like this.

CENTRAL	WIN	LOSS	TIE	POINTS
Toronto	27	10	3	57
Dallas	24	12	4	52
St. Louis	20	18	3	43
Detroit	17	18	4	38
Chicago	16	17	6	38
Winnipeg	13	23	5	31

PACIFIC	WIN	LOSS	TIE	POINTS
Calgary	20	12	8	48
Vancouver	19	12	7	45
San Jose	17	15	7	
Edmonton				

▶▶ Using Manipulatives

To solve equations using algebra tiles, you use a *work chart*.
You can make one simply by drawing a vertical line in the middle
of a piece of paper. You will use the work chart to solve an
equation such as $4x + 2 = 3x + 5$. Put algebra tiles representing
$4x + 2$ on the left side and $3x + 5$ on the right side, like this:

Think:
The expression on the left side must equal the expression on
the right side. For what value(s) of the variable is this true?

To keep both sides equal, you add the same quantity to each side
or you remove the same quantity from each side.
- Start with $4x + 2 = 3x + 5$ on your work chart.
- Remove two 1-tiles from each side. Are both sides equal?
- How many x-tiles could you remove from each side
  and keep both sides equal?
- Can you determine the value of the x-tile
  in this equation?

Recall the Zero Principle that you used to combine like tiles.
You will sometimes use this principle when you solve equations with
algebra tiles.
There are two other principles you will use.

The Opposites Principle

If two numbers are equal, you can multiply each number by -1 and
maintain equality. Similarly, when two sets of tiles are equal, you can
flip the tiles in each set and maintain equality.

The Sharing Principle

If two numbers are equal, you can divide each of them by the same
number and maintain equality. Similarly, when two sets of tiles are equal,
if you can divide both sets into the same number of groups, each of these
groups will be equal.

Use algebra tiles and a work chart to solve each equation.

1. $3x - 5 = 2x - 7$

2. $4n + 2 = 5n$

3. $3c = 6$

4. $2y = -10$

5. $-2 + 5x = 2x + 7$

6. $3t - 2 = 6 - t$

▶ ▶ *Through Guided Examples*

To solve an equation means to determine the value(s) of the variable for
which the expressions on both sides of the equals sign represent the
same number.

To solve an equation with algebra tiles, use a work chart. Do the same
thing to each side, until you have a single variable tile on one side.

Each step in a solution using algebra tiles corresponds to a step in an
algebraic solution. To solve an equation using algebra you perform the
same operation on each side until you have isolated the variable on one
side of the equation.

Gold leaf is an extremely thin sheet of gold used in ornamental
gilding. A single ounce of gold can be beaten into a sheet
measuring 25 m². Gold leaf is sold in booklets of 25 leaves, each
8.25 cm square. About how many of these booklets could be
made from a single ounce of gold?

Example 1

Solve the equation $3x - 2 = x + 4$ using algebra tiles and symbols.

Solution

Using algebra tiles	Using symbols
Step 1	**Step 1**
Start with 	Start with $$3x - 2 = x + 4$$
Step 2	**Step 2**
You want all x-tiles on one side. So, remove one x-tile from each side. 	You want all variables on one side. So, subtract x from each side. $$3x - 2 - x = x + 4 - x$$ $$2x - 2 = 4$$
Step 3	**Step 3**
You want all 1-tiles on the side opposite the x-tiles. So, add two 1-tiles to each side. This creates two pairs of 1-tiles and their opposites on the left side.  By the Zero Principle, this is the same as 	You want all constant terms on the side opposite the variable. So, add 2 to each side. $$2x - 2 + 2 = 4 + 2$$ $$2x = 6$$
Step 4	**Step 4**
You want a single x-tile on the left side. Each side can be arranged into two equal groups. By the Sharing Principle, you need use only one group from each side and still maintain equality. From the tiles, $x = 3$	Divide each side by 2. $$\frac{2x}{2} = \frac{6}{2}$$ $$x = 3$$

Example 2

Solve the equation $2 - 3c = 8$ using algebra tiles and symbols.

Solution

Using algebra tiles	Using symbols
Step 1	**Step 1**
Start with 	Start with $$2 - 3c = 8$$
Step 2	**Step 2**
Since the variable tiles are all on the left side, you want all 1-tiles on the right side. So, remove two 1-tiles from each side. 	You want all constant terms on the side opposite the variable. So, subtract 2 from each side. $$2 - 3c - 2 = 8 - 2$$ $$-3c = 6$$
Step 3	**Step 3**
You want a single c-tile on the left side. Each side can be arranged into three equal groups. By the Sharing Principle, you need use only one group from each side and still maintain equality.  By the Opposites Principle, you can flip all tiles on each side and still maintain equality. You then get a positive c-tile on the left side.  From the tiles, $c = -2$	Divide each side by -3. $$\frac{-3c}{-3} = \frac{6}{-3}$$ $$c = -2$$

Working with Mathematics

Something to talk about

1. When you finish solving an equation, there is one variable tile on one side of the equation. Does it matter if it is on the left side or on the right side? Explain.

2. There is often more than one way to solve an equation using algebra tiles. Illustrate this with an example.

3. In the last step of *Example 2*, all the tiles on each side were flipped. How could you have solved this equation differently to avoid this last step?

Work together

4. Work with a partner. You solve an equation using algebra tiles, and your partner explains the steps. Take turns using the tiles and explaining.

   a) $2x + 1 = -5$

   b) $3a = a + 10$

   c) $7x + 2 = 6x - 3$

   d) $4n + 5 = -3 + 2n$

5. Work with a partner. You solve an equation using algebra tiles, and your partner records the solution using symbols. Take turns using the tiles and recording.

   a) $4m + 1 = 9$

   b) $5a + 2 = 3a - 6$

   c) $3 - 2x = 7$

   d) $4y - 3 = 6y - 5$

On your own

6. Solve each equation using algebra tiles.

   a) $4x - 5 = 3x$

   b) $5g + 4 = 3g$

   c) $2a + 1 = -5$

   d) $2 + 3n = 4n$

   e) $3x + 1 = 2x - 4$

   f) $4t - 3 = 2t + 3$

7. Solve each equation using algebra tiles. Record the solution using symbols.

   a) $2m + 6 = m$

   b) $4x + 2 = 3x$

   c) $5 - 2x = 1$

   d) $2b - 3 = b - 5$

   e) $3y + 1 = y + 7$

   f) $4k - 2 = 3 - k$

Extend your thinking

8. When you have solved an equation, how can you check your solution? Develop a method of checking a solution using algebra tiles. Describe your method by illustrating the steps you would follow in at least two examples.

The Ideas

Your friend phones you for help in solving this equation:

$$3x + 7 = x - 5$$

To simulate that you are talking on the telephone, sit back-to-back with another student. Tell that student how to solve the equation.

Write another equation and reverse roles.

SOLVING EQUATIONS ALGEBRAICALLY

Developing the Ideas

▶ ▶ *Through Guided Examples*

When you are familiar with solving equations with algebra tiles, you should try to solve equations using symbols only. Each line in an algebraic solution corresponds to one or more steps using the tiles. You may find that it helps at first to think about the corresponding steps with the tiles.

When you have solved an equation, you can check your solution by following these steps:

- Substitute your solution for the variable in both sides of the original equation.
- Simplify both sides of the equation separately. If both sides simplify to the same number, your solution is correct.

Example 1 ....

Solve each equation algebraically. Check your solutions.   4-51

a) $3x - 17 = 28$ **b)** $4 - 5k = 8 + k$

Solution

a) $3x - 17 = 28$

Add 17 to each side.
$$3x - 17 + 17 = 28 + 17$$
$$3x = 45$$
Divide each side by 3.
$$\frac{3x}{3} = \frac{45}{3}$$
$$x = 15$$

Check: Substitute 15 for x in each side of the equation.

Left side $= 3(15) - 17$ Right side $= 28$
$$= 45 - 17$$
$$= 28$$

Since both sides are equal,
$x = 15$ is correct.

b) $4 - 5k = 8 + k$

Add $5k$ to each side.
$$4 - 5k + 5k = 8 + k + 5k$$
$$4 = 8 + 6k$$
Subtract 8 from each side.
$$4 - 8 = 8 + 6k - 8$$
$$-4 = 6k$$
Divide each side by 6.
$$\frac{-4}{6} = \frac{6k}{6}$$
$$k = -\frac{2}{3}$$

Check: Substitute $-\frac{2}{3}$ for k in each side of the equation.

Left side $= 4 - 5\left(-\frac{2}{3}\right)$ Right side $= 8 + \left(-\frac{2}{3}\right)$
$$= \frac{12}{3} + \frac{10}{3} \qquad\qquad\qquad = \frac{24}{3} - \frac{2}{3}$$
$$= \frac{22}{3} \qquad\qquad\qquad\qquad = \frac{22}{3}$$

Since both sides are equal, $k = -\frac{2}{3}$ is correct.

Example 2

The grade 9 students from Westdale High School are planning a weekend trip to Regina. The bus company will charge $1416.16 for all transportation costs, including the driver's salary and accommodations. The cost for accommodation and admission to the various attractions the students will visit will be $62.50 per student.

a) Write a formula to determine the total cost of the trip, C dollars, in terms of the number of students who go on the trip.

b) The total cost for a group of students was $3978.66. Substitute 3978.66 for C in your formula to get an equation. Solve the equation to determine how many students went.

c) Rearrange your formula so that the accounting office can figure out how many students went on the trip by looking at the total cost.

Solution

a) Choose a variable, such as n, to represent the number of students who go on the trip.
There is a fixed cost of $1416.16.
In addition, there is a cost of $62.50 for each student. This is $62.5n$ dollars for all students.
Thus, the total cost of the trip, in dollars, is
$C = 1416.16 + 62.5n$

b) $C = 1416.16 + 62.5n$
Substitute 3978.66 for C.
   $3978.66 = 1416.16 + 62.5n$
To solve for n, subtract 1416.16 from each side.
   $2562.5 = 62.5n$
Divide each side by 62.5.
      $41 = n$
Thus, 41 students went on the trip.

c) You want to rearrange the formula so you can solve for n if you are given a value for C.
First, subtract 1416.16 from each side of the formula.
$$C - 1416.16 = 1416.16 + 62.5n - 1416.16$$
$$C - 1416.16 = 62.5n$$
Divide each side by 62.5.
$$\frac{C - 1416.16}{62.5} = \frac{62.5n}{62.5}$$

The accounting office can use this formula: $n = \dfrac{C - 1416.16}{62.5}$.

Working with Mathematics

Something to talk about

1. a) Would it be possible to solve the two equations in *Example 1* using algebra tiles? Explain your answer.
   b) Would it be possible to solve the equation in *Example 2b* using algebra tiles? Explain.

Work together

2. Solve each equation. Check one another's solutions.
   a) $2x - 15 = 27$ b) $3a - 1 = 2 - a$
   c) $2 + 5y = 3y - 3$ d) $x - 2 = 7x + 2$

3. Solve, and round the answer to the nearest tenth. Compare your solutions.
   a) $1.5x - 3.2 = 4.1$
   b) $4.7 + 2.3y = 12.4$
   c) $2.6k + 7.6 = 1.2k - 8.3$
   d) $8.2 - 1.6x = 2.3x - 9.4$

4. To rent a certain model of car for one day, a car rental company charges $28.50 plus an additional charge of 15¢ for every kilometre driven. You can represent this with the formula $C = 28.50 + 0.15d$, where C is the charge, in dollars, and d is the distance driven, in kilometres.
   a) To determine the charge for driving 200 km, substitute 200 for d.
   b) Your budget allows you $75 to spend on a rental car for a day. To determine how far the car could be driven for $75, substitute 75 for C and solve the equation for d.
   c) Why do you think the rental cost depends on the distance the car is driven?

On your own

5. Solve each equation. Check your solution.
   a) $7 = 23 - 4x$ b) $3a - 10 = 10$
   c) $8 - 2z = 5 + 3z$ d) $4m + 9 = 2m$
   e) $12x + 17 = 10 - 2x$ f) $5 - 3k = -4$

6. Solve each equation. Check your solution.
   a) $5x + 4 = 40$ b) $9 - 2a = a + 5$
   c) $2 - 4x = 1 - x$ d) $3 + 7c = 2c - 3$
   e) $2 = 9a - 3$ f) $5 - 6n = 2n + 5$

7. The cost, C dollars, of producing a school yearbook is given by the formula $C = 8000 + 9n$, where n is the number of yearbooks printed.
   a) What does each term on the right side of the formula represent?
   b) The yearbook committee has a budget of $10 000. To determine the number of yearbooks that can be produced for $10 000, substitute 10 000 for C and solve the equation for n.
   c) How many yearbooks can be produced for $20 000?

8. Volcanoes and geysers provide striking evidence that the Earth's interior is very hot. The formula $T = 10d + 20$ is used to estimate the temperature, T degrees Celsius, at a depth of d kilometres.
   a) What does each term on the right side of the formula represent?
   b) To estimate the depth where the temperature is 50°C, substitute 50 for T and solve the equation for d.
   c) At what depth is the temperature 100°C?

9. The formula for the perimeter P of a rectangle with length l and width w is $P = 2l + 2w$. A rectangular field is 135 m long and requires 450 m of fencing to enclose it.

  a) To determine the width of the field, substitute 450 for P, 135 for l, and solve the equation for w.

  b) Another field is 45 m wide and requires 380 m of fencing. How long is the field?

10. Have you ever seen a flash of lightning, and then heard thunder a few seconds later? A rule of thumb which provides an estimate for the distance to a storm is to count the number of seconds between the lightning and thunderclap and divide by 3. This rule is based on the speed of sound in air being about 330 m/s, which is approximately one-third of a kilometre per second.

  a) Let d represent the distance to the storm, in kilometres, and t represent the time between the lightning and the thunder, in seconds. Express the rule of thumb as a formula.

  b) Suppose the time is 3.5 s. To estimate how far away the storm is, substitute 3.5 for t.

  c) Suppose a storm is 8 km away. Estimate the time between the lightning and the thunder.

Extend your thinking

11. Given the equation $3(x + 2) = x + 2(x + 3)$

  a) Check that $x = 5$, $x = 8$, and $x = -1$ are all solutions of this equation.

  b) Choose any other number and check that it is also a solution of the equation.

  c) Try to solve the equation algebraically. Use the result to explain why every number is a solution of this equation.

  d) Make up another equation like this one, which has infinitely many solutions.

12. Given the equation $3(x + 2) = x + 2(x + 4)$

  a) Choose any number and show that it is *not* a solution of this equation.

  b) Try to solve the equation algebraically. Use the result to explain why the equation has no solution.

  c) Make up another equation like this one, which has no solution.

COMMUNICATING

The Ideas

In your journal, describe the kinds of equations that can be solved with algebra tiles, and give some examples. Also, give some examples of the kinds of equations that would be difficult or impossible to solve with algebra tiles, and explain why.

How Do Builders Determine the Size of Steps in a Staircase?

Have you ever tripped while walking up a flight of stairs? It may not be because you're clumsy! Journey person carpenter Mickey Weinberg says that careful planning and precise measurement of the wood are extremely important when building a staircase. Rules for riser height and tread depth, such as those listed on the following page, have to be followed closely. She points out that if one riser is even slightly higher than the others, it can cause you to trip.

Find some combinations of riser heights and tread depths that satisfy these rules.

1. All risers must have the same height and all treads must have the same depth.

2. The depth of the treads must be between 250 mm and 300 mm.

3. The depth of the treads plus two times the height of the risers should be approximately 635 mm.

Understand the problem

- What is a riser? What is a tread? What do *riser height* and *tread depth* mean?
- Why should all risers have the same height and all treads have the same depth?
- Why do you think the second rule is necessary?
- How are the riser height and tread depth related?
- What are you asked to do?

Think of a strategy

- Let t millimetres represent tread depth. Let r millimetres represent riser height. Use algebra.
- Notice that t should be between 250 and 300.

Carry out the strategy

- Use one of the rules above to write an equation relating t and r.
- Substitute a reasonable value of t into the equation. Then solve to determine the corresponding value of r. Repeat for several different values of t.

Look back

- Did you use 250 and 300 for t?
- If you increase the value of t, what happens to the value of r? Explain why.
- If you know the height of the risers, how can you calculate the depth of the treads?
- In many houses the vertical height between floors is approximately 2500 mm. Choose some combinations of t and r that satisfy the rules. For each of these combinations, how many steps are in a staircase which spans 2500 mm?
- Measure some staircases in your school or in your home. Do their dimensions satisfy the above rules?

Communicating the Ideas

In your journal, write a description of this problem. Include any measurements you have made of staircases in your school or home.

Developing the Ideas

▶ ▶ *Through Discussion*

Later in this chapter you will learn how to use equations to solve problems. The equations are usually slightly more complicated than the equations you have been working with up to now. You need to simplify these equations before you solve them by performing the same operations on each side.

Group 1 Combining Like Terms

1. What do you think is the first step in solving each equation? Complete this step and continue the solution.

   a) $4x + 3x = 35$

   b) $6n - 7 - 2n = 21$

   c) $4 = 2w + 16 + w - 5$

2. Create two more equations like these and solve them.

Group 2 Using the Distributive Law

3. What do you think is the first step in solving each equation? Complete this step and continue the solution.

   a) $2(x + 3) = 14$

   b) $2(3m - 4) = 11$

   c) $9 = -3(2t - 7)$

4. Create two more equations like these and solve them.

Group 3 Solving Equations Involving Fractions

5. Solve each equation. Add terms to or subtract terms from each side until the variables are combined and the constant terms are combined, on opposite sides of the equals sign. Multiply or divide to complete the solution.

   a) $\frac{1}{4}n + \frac{1}{2} = 3$

   b) $x + \frac{3}{4} = \frac{1}{4}x + \frac{1}{2}$

   c) $\frac{2x}{3} + 1 = \frac{x}{2} + 2$

6. Solve each equation in exercise 5 again. Your first step should be to multiply every term by a common denominator. Compare the two methods of solving the equations. Which method do you think is easier?

All Groups

To the rest of the class, present the solution to one of the equations your group solved. Record the steps on the chalkboard, explaining each step as you write it.

When solving equations, simplify each side before applying the same operation to each side.

Example 1 .... *Solution* ....

Solve: $3(a - 3) + 4a + 7 = 5a - 3$

$$3(a - 3) + 4a + 7 = 5a - 3$$

Simplify the left side.

$$3a - 9 + 4a + 7 = 5a - 3$$
$$7a - 2 = 5a - 3$$

Add 2 to each side.

$$7a - 2 + 2 = 5a - 3 + 2$$
$$7a = 5a - 1$$

Subtract $5a$ from each side.

$$7a - 5a = 5a - 5a - 1$$
$$2a = -1$$

Divide each side by 2.

$$\frac{2a}{2} = \frac{-1}{2}$$
$$a = -\frac{1}{2}$$

When an equation contains fractions, multiply each side by a common denominator.

Example 2 .... *Solution* ....

Solve and check: $\frac{x}{2} + 1 = \frac{2x}{3} - 3$

$$\frac{x}{2} + 1 = \frac{2x}{3} - 3$$

Multiply each side by a common denominator, 6.

$$6\left(\frac{x}{2} + 1\right) = 6\left(\frac{2x}{3} - 3\right)$$
$$(6)\left(\frac{x}{2}\right) + (6)(1) = (6)\left(\frac{2x}{3}\right) - (6)(3)$$
$$3x + 6 = 4x - 18$$

Subtract 6 from each side.

$$3x + 6 - 6 = 4x - 18 - 6$$
$$3x = 4x - 24$$

Subtract $4x$ from each side.

$$3x - 4x = 4x - 4x - 24$$
$$-x = -24$$

Multiply each side by -1.

$$x = 24$$

Check: Substitute 24 for x in each side of the equation.

Left side $= \frac{24}{2} + 1$ Right side $= \frac{2(24)}{3} - 3$

$$= 12 + 1 \qquad\qquad = \frac{48}{3} - 3$$
$$= 13 \qquad\qquad\qquad = 16 - 3$$
$$\qquad\qquad\qquad\qquad = 13$$

Since both sides are equal, $x = 24$ is correct.

Working with Mathematics

Something to talk about

1. The solution of *Example 1* shows one way to solve $3(a - 3) + 4a + 7 = 5a - 3$. What are some other ways to solve this equation?

2. In the solution of *Example 2* both sides were multiplied by a common denominator, 6. Could other common denominators be used? Do you think this equation could be solved without starting by multiplying both sides by a common denominator?

Work together

3. Solve each equation. Check one another's solutions.
   a) $7x - 3x + 5 = 7$
   b) $6 = 4x - x + 9$
   c) $3(n + 2) = 21$
   d) $2(x + 3) = 3(5 - x)$
   e) $\frac{x}{5} - x = \frac{1}{2}$
   f) $\frac{3k}{4} - 1 = \frac{k}{3}$

4. Suppose you live in Regina, Saskatchewan and want to call a friend in Singapore. If you call between 8 a.m. and 4 p.m., the cost is $4.88 for the first three minutes and $1.22 for each additional minute. You can represent this with the formula $C = 4.88 + 1.22(n - 3)$, where C is the cost in dollars, n is the time in minutes, and n is greater than or equal to 3.
   a) To determine how long you could talk for $10, substitute 10 for C and solve the equation for n.
   b) How long could you talk for $20?
   c) If you have a graphing calculator, graph the equation $y = 4.88 + 1.22(x - 3)$. Set the range so that x is between 3 and 25 and y is between 0 and 40. Trace along the graph to check your answers to parts a and b.

On your own

5. Solve each equation. Check your solution.
   a) $4x + 6x = -20$
   b) $5c + 2c + 6 = 34$
   c) $4y - 7y = 18$
   d) $50 = 8x - x + 1$
   e) $12 = 2x - 7x - 8$
   f) $-10 = -n + 2 - 2n$
   g) $3x - 2 + x = 5 + 7x - 3$
   h) $2.5x + 1.5x = 6$
   i) $41 = 0.5a + 0.7a - 7$

6. Solve each equation.
   a) $2(x - 4) = 10$
   b) $5(x - 6) = -15$
   c) $2(4 - 3m) = 13$
   d) $-3(n + 2) = 12$
   e) $7 = -2(-3 - y)$
   f) $3(2t + 6) = 0$
   g) $2(p + 1) = 3(p - 1)$
   h) $1.6(y - 5) = 24$
   i) $6.3 = 1.8(1 - 5x)$

7. Solve each equation.
   a) $\frac{x}{2} - 1 = 4$
   b) $2 + \frac{n}{3} = 10$
   c) $\frac{x}{4} - \frac{2}{3} = 2$
   d) $\frac{a}{3} - 3 = \frac{5}{6}$
   e) $\frac{x}{3} - \frac{3x}{4} = 10$
   f) $\frac{5x}{2} - 3 = 8 + \frac{2x}{3}$

8. Solve each equation.
   a) $9x - 1 - 7x - 4 = 5x$
   b) $3(1 - 2y) + y = 2$
   c) $4 = 6 - 2(x + 1)$
   d) $-3(2 - a) - a = 1$
   e) $-2(3n - 1) + 2n = 4$
   f) $3(4x - 1) = 4 - 2(5 - 3x)$

9. Solve and round the answer to the nearest tenth.
   a) $2.5x - 4 + 1.2x = 3.5$
   b) $x + 3.2(2.5 - x) = 40$
   c) $2.3(x - 1.7) = 4.2(x + 1.3)$

10. Keyboarding speed, S, in words per minute, is calculated with the formula $S = \frac{w - 10e}{5}$, where w is the number of words input in 5 min and e is the number of errors. In keyboarding, a word is equivalent to 5 characters. So, to determine the number of words input, count the number of characters and divide by 5.

a) Marcus input 275 words in 5 min and made 8 errors. What was his keyboarding speed?

b) Sue input 1250 characters in 5 min and had a keyboarding speed of 40 words/min. How many errors did she make?

c) Dexter made 3 errors in 5 min and had a keyboarding speed of 30 words/min. How many words did he input?

Extend your thinking

11. Determine all real numbers that are solutions of each equation. Check that your solutions are correct.

a) $x^2 - 3 = 6$ **b)** $a^2 + 3 = 28$
c) $m^2 - 36 = 64$ **d)** $x^2 + 5 = 7$
e) $x^2 + 5 = 5$ **f)** $x^2 + 5 = 4$

Why do you think the word "all" is included in the above sentence? Why do you think the word "real" is included?

12. Refer to exercise 11 on page 217. Canadian weather data collected before 1970 are often expressed in degrees Fahrenheit.

a) What would be a rule of thumb for converting Fahrenheit temperatures to Celsius? Express this rule of thumb as a formula.

b) Determine an exact formula for converting Fahrenheit temperatures to Celsius.

13. Use a computer to set up a spreadsheet to compare the approximate and exact conversions in exercise 12. Enter the formulas you wrote in parts a and b in cells B4 and C4. Adjust the Fahrenheit values by entering numbers in cell A4. Include some negative values among those you try. When are the results of the approximate formula closest to those of the exact formula?

TEMPLATE DISK

	A	B	C	D
1	Fahrenheit to Celsius Converter			
2				
3	Fahrenheit	Approximate	Exact	Difference
4	0			=C4-B4

COMMUNICATING

The Ideas

You could check the solution of an equation by repeating the steps you used to solve it. Explain why you think it is better to substitute your solution into the original equation. Why should both sides be simplified separately when checking?

How Can You Design a Trundle Wheel?

A trundle wheel is a measuring tool. As you roll the wheel along the ground, an odometer displays the distance in metres that the wheel has travelled. The wheel moves forward 1 m for each complete rotation.

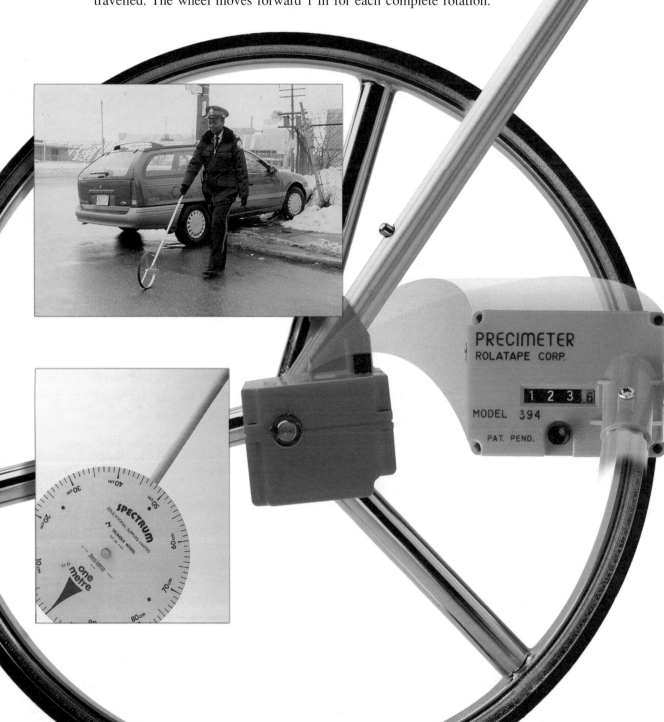

Police constable Laureen Tobias Ashbey uses a trundle wheel in her job as a traffic officer. It is one of the most useful tools she has to establish exactly what happened at the scene of an accident. Laureen takes several measurements at the scene, including the length of any skid marks on the road. Using these measurements, she can reconstruct the accident and estimate the speeds of the vehicles involved.

Suppose you are making a trundle wheel. What must the radius of the wheel be, to the nearest tenth of a centimetre?

Understand the problem

- What is a trundle wheel?
- What are you asked to find?

Think of a strategy

- How does the circumference of the wheel compare with the distance it moves in one rotation?
- How are the circumference and the radius of the wheel related?

Carry out the strategy

- Use the formula $C = \pi d$ to find the circumference of the circle, where d is the diameter. If you have a scientific calculator, use the π key; if not, use 3.1416 as an approximation for π.
- Substitute 100 for C and solve the equation for d.
- What is the diameter of the wheel? What is the radius of the wheel, to the nearest tenth of a centimetre?

Look back

- Check your solution.
- Suppose your wheel had a radius that was 0.5 cm too large. How would this affect the distances it measured?
- Suppose another trundle wheel is designed to move forward 2 m for each complete rotation. What must the radius of the wheel be?
- You could also measure distances along the ground with a tape measure. Compare these two methods. What are the advantages and disadvantages of each method?

Communicating the Ideas

In your journal, write a description of this problem and your solution. Include diagrams with your explanation.

Developing the Ideas
▶▶ Through Discussion

Juice from a vending machine costs 50¢. The vending machine contains $3.50 in dimes and quarters. There are 23 coins in all. How many dimes and how many quarters are there?

Several different ways to solve the problem are suggested below. Each group should choose a method and use it to solve the problem.

Group 1 Use systematic trial

Estimate the numbers of dimes and quarters that you think might be reasonable. What is the value of this many dimes and quarters? Compare with $3.50 and revise your estimate of the numbers of dimes and quarters. Repeat until you have a combination of 23 dimes and quarters that is worth $3.50.

Group 2 Use tables

Make two tables like these:

▶ • • • • • • • • •

NUMBER OF DIMES	VALUE OF THE DIMES ($)
0	0
1	0.10
2	0.20
3	0.30
.	.

▶ • • • • • • • • •

NUMBER OF QUARTERS	VALUE OF THE QUARTERS ($)
0	0
1	0.25
2	0.50
3	0.75
.	.

Extend your tables for several more rows.
Use your tables to help you solve the problem.

Group 3   Use an equation

Suppose you know how many dimes there are. How would you find the number of quarters? How would you find the value of the dimes? How would you find the value of the quarters?

Let x represent the number of dimes. Use your answers to these questions to write expressions in x for:

- the number of quarters
- the value of the dimes, in cents
- the value of the quarters, in cents
- the total value of the dimes and quarters, in cents

You know that the total value of the dimes and quarters is 350¢. You can write an equation in x. Solve the equation and use the result to solve the problem.

Suppose you let y represent the number of quarters. How would the equation change? Would you get the same solution if you solved the new equation? Try it.

Group 4   Reason out the solution

Suppose all 23 coins were dimes. How much money would this be?

How much more money is there? Where does this money come from?

How much more money comes from each quarter? How many quarters are there? How many dimes?

Do you think you could solve the problem in a similar way, by assuming that all 23 coins were quarters? Explain your answer.

Working with Mathematics

Something to talk about

1. What are some of the advantages and disadvantages of each method that was used to solve the problem on page 248? Which method do you prefer?

Work together

2. Solve the problem in two ways.
   1 kg of peanuts costs $4.00.
   1 kg of pecans costs $22.00.
   You want 23 kg of mixed nuts worth $236. How many kilograms of each type of nut should you use?

3. Solve the problem in two ways.
   In one week, Nigel exercised for 23 h and covered 350 km.
   In one hour, he ran 10 km.
   In one hour, he cycled 25 km.
   How much time did he spend running that week?
   How much time did he spend cycling that week?

4. Compare exercises 2 and 3 with the problem on page 248. In what ways are exercises 2 and 3 similar to this problem? In what ways are exercises 2 and 3 different from this problem?

Solve each problem in two ways.

5. A pile of nickels and dimes has a value of $4.50. There are three times as many nickels as dimes. How many nickels and how many dimes are there?

6. The mass of a can and the paint it contains is 3554 g when it is three-quarters full. When it is half full the mass of the can and the paint is 2530 g. What is the mass of the can?

7. Adrian and Jasmine live near a mountain road. There is a viewpoint on the road, higher up the mountain. The two students cycled up to the viewpoint and back. The total travelling time was 3 h. Going up to the viewpoint, they averaged 5 km/h, but returning from the viewpoint they averaged 25 km/h. How far is it to the viewpoint?

Extend your thinking

8. A piggy bank contains 69 coins which are nickels, dimes, and quarters. There are 5 more dimes than nickels, and twice as many quarters as nickels. How much money is in the piggy bank? Solve this problem in at least two ways.

The Ideas

Do you think that some methods of solving a problem are better than others? Do you think there is a "best" way to solve a problem? Be prepared to explain your answers, using a specific problem, in a class discussion.

Keeping Ships Afloat

TO KEEP A FREIGHTER BALANCED AND STABLE IN THE water, the crew must replace the mass of cargo which is offloaded at each port with sea water. This water is called ballast.

The mass of cargo offloaded is measured in kilograms. The amount of water taken on is measured in litres. How does the first mate know how many litres of water will have the same mass as the cargo that's been offloaded? The answer: use density!

Density is the mass of a unit volume of a substance. Every substance has a characteristic density at a particular temperature. A material with its molecules packed tightly together, like metal, will have a greater density than a material with more space between its molecules, like wood.

The density D of a substance is the quotient of its mass M and its volume V.
We use the formula $D = \dfrac{M}{V}$.

The mass M of a substance is the product of its density D and volume V.
We use the formula $M = DV$.

The volume V of a substance is the quotient of its mass M and its density D.
We use the formula $V = \dfrac{M}{D}$.

1. A tanker is to be loaded with 140 000 t of Kuparuk crude oil from the Alaska North Slope.

   a) The temperature in port when the oil is loaded is 21°C. At this temperature, the density of sea water is 1.030 kg/L. How much sea water must be dumped to allow for this cargo to be loaded?

   b) When the oil is offloaded at its destination, the temperature is only 15°C. At this temperature, the density of sea water is 1.025 kg/L. How much sea water must be taken on as ballast to replace the offloaded oil?

2. a) Kuparuk crude oil has a density of 0.9150 kg/L at 21°C. What is the volume of the oil loaded in exercise 1a?

   b) The density of Kuparuk crude at 15°C is only 0.8862 kg/L. What is the volume of the oil offloaded in exercise 1b?

Developing the Ideas

▶ ▶ *Through Discussion*

Problem 1

An electronics store is selling videocassette recorders for $590, with all taxes included. Customers can pay a deposit of $140 and pay the balance in 6 equal monthly payments. What will be the amount of each payment?

Problem 2

Every October, Canine Visions Canada sponsors a national Walk-a-dog-a-thon. The money raised provides blind and visually-impaired Canadians with a free 26-day dog guide handling course.

Last year, Ashok Krishnan and Lisa Crosbie took part in the walk-a-thon. Lisa twisted her ankle during the walk and had to drop out. Ashok completed the walk. Ashok walked 6 km farther than Lisa. Together they walked a total distance of 14 km. How far did Lisa walk?

Work in a group.

1. Try to solve both problems.

2. Several methods for solving problems are described on pages 248 and 249. Did your group use one of these methods?

3. Compare your group's solution to each problem with the solutions from other groups. Did every group solve the problems in the same way?

4. If you haven't done so already, try to solve *Problem 1* using an equation. Suppose you know the monthly payment. How would you calculate the total cost? What is the total cost? Let p dollars represent the monthly payment. Write an expression to represent the total cost. Since you know the total cost, write an equation. Solve the equation to obtain the answer to the problem. Check that your answer is correct.

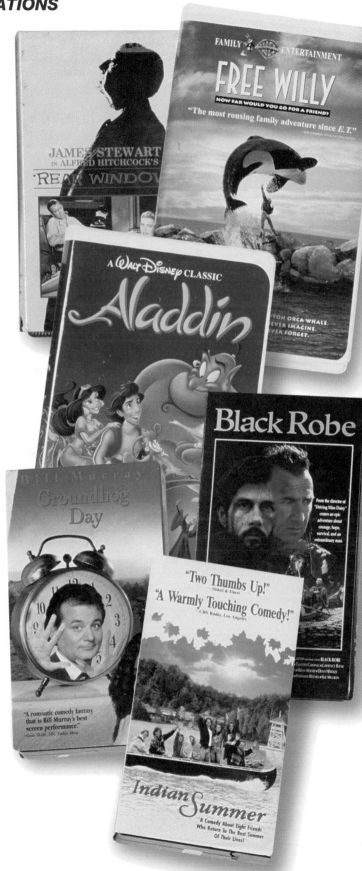

5. If you haven't done so already, try to solve *Problem 2* using an equation.

Suppose you know how far Lisa walked.

How would you determine how far Ashok walked?

What is the total distance they both walked?

Let x kilometres represent the distance Lisa walked.

Write an expression to represent the distance Ashok walked.

Since you know the total distance, write an equation.

Solve the equation to obtain the answer to the problem.

Check that your answer is correct.

▷▶ *Through Guided Examples*

You can solve a problem in many ways. One method is to use an equation. Follow these steps.

- Use a variable to represent the unknown quantity.
- Express any other unknown quantities in terms of this variable, if possible.
- Write an equation, and solve it.
- State the answer to the problem.
- Check the answer by substituting in the problem.

Example 1

An electronics store is selling videocassette recorders for $590, with all taxes included. Customers can pay a deposit of $140 and pay the balance in 6 equal monthly payments. What will be the amount of each payment?

Solution

Let p dollars represent the monthly payment. Then,

$6 \times$ amount of each payment + deposit = total cost

$$6p + 140 = 590$$
$$6p + 140 - 140 = 590 - 140 \quad \text{◀ Subtracting 140 from each side}$$
$$6p = 450$$
$$\frac{6p}{6} = \frac{450}{6} \quad \text{◀ Dividing each side by 6}$$
$$p = 75$$

Each payment will be $75.

Check: The total of the 6 monthly payments will be $6 \times \$75 = \$450$.
Since the deposit is $140, the total of all payments will be
$\$450 + \$140 = \$590$.
The solution is correct.

Example 2

Every October, Canine Visions Canada sponsors a national Walk-a-dog-a-thon. The money raised provides blind and visually-impaired Canadians with a free 26-day dog guide handling course. Last year, Ashok Krishnan and Lisa Crosbie took part in the walk-a-thon. Lisa twisted her ankle during the walk and had to drop out. Ashok completed the walk. Ashok walked 6 km farther than Lisa. Together they walked a total distance of 14 km. How far did Lisa walk?

Solution

Let x kilometres represent the distance Lisa walked.

Then, the distance Ashok walked is $(x + 6)$ kilometres.
Since the total distance they walked is 14 km,

$$x + (x + 6) = 14$$
$$2x + 6 = 14$$
$$2x + 6 - 6 = 14 - 6 \quad \text{Subtracting 6 from each side}$$
$$2x = 8$$
$$\frac{2x}{2} = \frac{8}{2} \quad \text{Dividing each side by 2}$$
$$x = 4$$

Lisa walked 4 km.

Check: Ashok walked 4 km + 6 km = 10 km.
         The total distance was 4 km + 10 km = 14 km.
         The solution is correct.

Working with Mathematics

Something to talk about

1. Suppose *Problem 2* had asked how far Ashok walked. The solution to *Example 2* provides an answer to this problem. Solve the problem by letting y kilometres represent the distance Ashok walked and using an equation. Compare your equation with the equation in *Example 2*. What are their similarities and differences?

2. **a)** What do you think is the answer to this problem? A bottle and a cork cost $1.10. The bottle costs $1 more than the cork. How much does the cork cost?

   b) Solve the problem using an equation, and by reasoning out the solution.

Work together

Solve each problem. Show all your work and check your answer.

3. Ms. Durocher bought a dining room suite. She paid $800 down and made 12 equal monthly payments. The total cost was $3800. How much was each payment?

4. Alexia sees a package deal for skis and boots costing $225. The salesperson tells Alexia that the skis cost $60 more than the boots. How much do the skis cost?

5. Barry cut a 72-cm piece of wire into two parts. One part is twice as long as the other. How long is each part?

6. Rashid has 500 cm of trim to frame a banner. If the banner is to be 22 cm wide, how long can it be?

22 cm

7. A salesperson earns $1200 per month plus 5% commission on sales. In one month, she earned $1850. Determine her monthly sales.

On your own

Solve each problem. Show all your work and check your answer.

8. Mary is three years older than Ann, and the sum of their ages is 35. How old is Ann?

9. In a class of 35 students there are 9 more boys than girls. How many girls are there?

10. Tak San earned three times as much as Paul. Together they earned a total of $68. How much did Paul earn?

11. Yvonne has equal numbers of nickels, dimes, and quarters. Their total value is $4.00. How many of each kind of coin does she have?

12. **a)** In their first season, the Toronto Blue Jays lost 53 more games than they won. They played 161 games. How many games did they win?

   b) The Toronto Blue Jays first won the World Series in 1992. That year, they won 34 more games than they lost. They played 162 regular-season games and 12 championship games. How many games did they win in 1992?

Extend your thinking

13. Joe has 500 cm of trim to frame a banner. The banner must be between 20 cm and 35 cm wide.

   a) What are the possible lengths the banner could have?

   b) If the width increases by 1 cm, what happens to the length?

   c) Draw a graph of the length of the banner against the width.

COMMUNICATING

The Ideas

Using an equation is only one method to solve a problem. What are some of the advantages and disadvantages of using an equation? Write your ideas in your journal.

Solving Problems with a Spreadsheet

A plane left Halifax, bound for Vancouver, with stops in Ottawa and Winnipeg. In Ottawa, 43 passengers left the plane and 5 others came on. In Winnipeg, half the passengers left the plane and 64 came on. There were 131 passengers on the plane when it left Winnipeg. How many were on the plane when it left Halifax?

Understand the problem

You can solve this problem by systematic trial. Suppose you estimate that 120 passengers were on the plane when it left Halifax. How many passengers were on the plane when it left Ottawa? How many were there when it left Winnipeg?

You could start with other numbers of passengers leaving Halifax and repeat the calculations until you have 131 passengers leaving Winnipeg.

You can do this more easily with a spreadsheet.

Planning the spreadsheet

TEMPLATE DISK

Use a diagram like the one below to help plan your spreadsheet. In this case, the formulas you need have been provided. What do you think each formula in cells B5 and B6 tells the computer to do?

	A	B
1	Plane Problem	
2		
3		Passengers
4	Halifax	120
5	Ottawa	=B4-43+5
6	Winnipeg	=0.5*B5+64

Using the computer

Start your spreadsheet program. Input the information from the spreadsheet shown above.

Move to cell B4 and change the number to 200. What happens to the numbers in B5 and B6? Keep changing the number in B4 until 131 appears in B6. How many passengers were on the plane when it left Halifax?

Look back

Solving a problem by systematic trial with a spreadsheet involves these steps:

Step 1 *Plan the cells you need to solve the problem.*

This is the most important step, because you are designing the spreadsheet to solve your problem. In the example, this step involves deciding that you need a cell for each number of passengers on the plane when it leaves Halifax, Ottawa and Winnipeg.

Step 2 *Enter numbers and formulas in the cells.*

To complete this step, you must know how to calculate the numbers in the cells. For example, in this problem you must know that the number in cell B5 is found by subtracting 43 from the number in B4, and then adding 5.

Step 3 *Solve the problem by changing the number in one of the cells.*

By changing the number in cell B4 you were able to solve the problem.

TEMPLATE DISK

Use a computer to solve these problems.

1. A vending machine contains $3.50 in dimes and quarters. There are 23 coins in all. How many dimes and how many quarters are there? (This is the problem on page 248.)

	A	B	C
1	Dimes and Quarters		
2			
3		Number	Value
4	Dimes		=0.1*B4
5	Quarters	=23-B4	=0.25*B5
6	Total	=B4+B5	=C4+C5

a) Explain the formulas in columns B and C.

b) Enter any natural number between 1 and 23 in cell B4.

c) By entering different numbers in cell B4, solve the problem.

Create your own spreadsheet to solve each of problems 2, 3, and 4.

2. The length of a rectangular pool is 28.5 m greater than its width. The perimeter of the pool is 143.0 m. What are the dimensions of the pool?

3. a) A salesperson earns $1400 per month plus 4% commission on sales. In one month, she earned $1825. Determine her monthly sales.

   b) How much would she have to sell to earn $2000 in a month?

4. Find four consecutive integers such that if the first is increased by 2, the second decreased by 2, the third multiplied by 2, and the fourth divided by 2, the sum of the four resulting numbers is 200.

5. Choose two problems from earlier in this chapter, and solve each problem using a spreadsheet.

Mathematics & Technology

Linking Ideas

Cheetahs can run at speeds of more than 100 km/h.

Developing the Ideas

▶ ▶ Through Discussion

Look at the pictures on this page and the next.

Let j centimetres represent Joanne's height.
You write: $j < 180$

Let v kilometres per hour represent a cheetah's fastest speed.
You write: $v > 100$

Let p represent the percent of passes a good quarterback completes.
You write: $p \geq 50$

Let r represent the percent reduction.
You write: $r \leq 70$

These statements are examples of *inequalities*.

SYMBOL	MEANING
>	"is greater than"
<	"is less than"
≥	"is greater than or equal to"
≤	"is less than or equal to"

The inequality $2x < 7x + 15$ states that two times a number is less than seven times the same number, plus 15. Inequalities like this are true for some values of the variable and false for others. To solve such an inequality, you determine the values of the variable for which it is true.

Joanne is less than 180 cm tall.

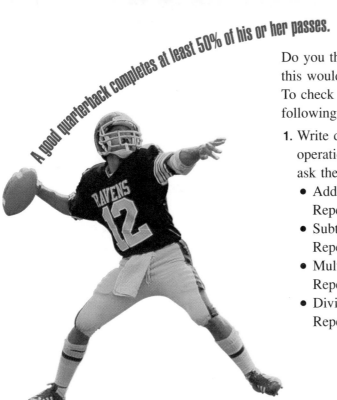

Do you think the steps for solving an inequality such as this would be the same as those for solving equations? To check your answer to this question, complete the following investigation with a partner.

1. Write down an inequality, such as $4 < 8$. Apply each operation listed below to your inequality. Each time, ask the question, "Is the inequality still true?"
   - Add the same positive number to each side. Repeat with a negative number.
   - Subtract the same positive number from each side. Repeat with a negative number.
   - Multiply each side by the same positive number. Repeat with a negative number.
   - Divide each side by the same positive number. Repeat with a negative number.

▶ ▶ *Through Guided Examples*

When you multiply or divide both sides of an inequality by the same *negative* number, the inequality is no longer true. To keep the statement true, you must reverse the inequality sign.

For example, $4 < 8$, but $-2 \times 4 > -2 \times 8$ because $-8 > -16$

To solve an inequality, you follow the same steps as for solving equations, with one exception—if you multiply or divide both sides by a *negative* number, you must reverse the inequality sign.

Example 1 ....

Solve: $2x < 7x + 15$

Solution

$$2x < 7x + 15$$
$$2x - 7x < 7x - 7x + 15 \quad \text{◀ Subtracting } 7x \text{ from each side}$$
$$-5x < 15$$
$$\frac{-5x}{-5} > \frac{15}{-5} \quad \text{◀ Dividing each side by } -5 \text{ and changing } < \text{ to } > \text{ because } -5 < 0$$
$$x > -3$$

The solution of the inequality is all real numbers greater than -3.

This is what you mean by writing $x > -3$. You can also illustrate the solution on a number line. An arrow is drawn in the direction "greater than -3." The open dot at -3 indicates that this number is not one of the solutions.

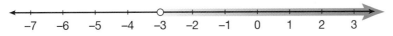

It is impossible to check all the numbers that are solutions of an inequality. To check an inequality, follow these steps:

1. Check that the number obtained is correct. Substitute it in each side of the original inequality. Each side should simplify to the same number.

2. Check the direction of the inequality sign. Choose one solution and substitute it in each side of the original inequality. The results should satisfy the original inequality.

Example 2

Solve, graph, and check: $2 + 4a \geq a - 10$

Solution

$$2 + 4a \geq a - 10$$
$$2 + 3a \geq -10 \quad \text{— Subtracting } a \text{ from each side}$$
$$3a \geq -12 \quad \text{— Subtracting 2 from each side}$$
$$a \geq -4 \quad \text{— Dividing each side by 3}$$

Graph the solution on a number line.
The solid dot at -4 indicates that this number is a solution.

Check: **1.** Substitute -4 for a in each side of the inequality.

Left side $= 2 + 4a$ Right side $= a - 10$
$= 2 + 4(-4)$ $= -4 - 10$
$= 2 - 16$ $= -14$
$= -14$

Since both sides are equal, -4 is correct.

2. Substitute any number greater than -4 in each side of the inequality.
Substitute 0 for a in $2 + 4a \geq a - 10$.

Left side $= 2 + 4a$ Right side $= a - 10$
$= 2 + 4(0)$ $= 0 - 10$
$= 2$ $= -10$

Since $2 \geq -10$, the solution is correct.

Working with Mathematics

Something to talk about

1. Compare the last steps in the solutions of *Example 1* and *Example 2*. Explain why the inequality sign was reversed in *Example 1* but not in *Example 2*.

2. State an inequality that is represented by each graph.

a)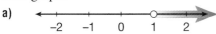

b)

c)

d)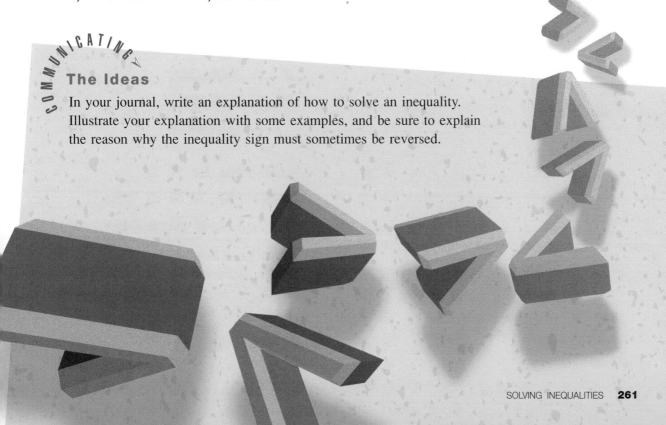

Work together

3. Solve, graph, and check each inequality.

a) $x + 3 > 2$ b) $2x + 1 \leq 7$
c) $y - 3 \geq -8$ d) $-3x + 2 > 14$
e) $4 - a < 9$ f) $4x - 7 \geq x - 1$

On your own

4. Solve and graph each inequality.

a) $x - 5 \geq -2$ b) $3x < -6$
c) $4c \leq 11$ d) $-2x > 9$
e) $5 + 3m \leq 10 + m$ f) $13.5 + 2y < 18.5$

5. Solve and check.

a) $x + 7 > 2$ b) $4x < x - 9$
c) $k + 8 \leq -7$ d) $1 - t \geq 4 + t$
e) $13 \leq 1 + \frac{3}{4}x$ f) $3.5 - 1.5a \geq 8$

Extend your thinking

6. In the second part of the check in the solution of *Example 2*, 0 was substituted for *a*. Can you always use 0 when you check the solution of an inequality? If your answer is yes, give a reason for your answer. If your answer is no, give an example of an inequality that cannot be checked by substituting 0 for the variable. Include the solution of the inequality and an explanation why you cannot use 0 to check the solution.

COMMUNICATING

The Ideas

In your journal, write an explanation of how to solve an inequality. Illustrate your explanation with some examples, and be sure to explain the reason why the inequality sign must sometimes be reversed.

Review

1. Here is a pattern made from toothpicks. Suppose the pattern is continued.

a) Count the number of squares and the number of toothpicks in each diagram. Record the results in a table.

b) How many toothpicks would you need to make 4 squares? 5 squares? 10 squares? 50 squares? 100 squares?

c) Suppose you know the number of squares in one of the diagrams. How would you find the number of toothpicks?

d) Let s represent the number of squares in one of the diagrams. Write an expression for the number of toothpicks. What kind of number is s?

e) If there are 35 squares, how many toothpicks are there?

f) If there are 100 toothpicks, how many squares are there?

g) Use your table to draw a graph. How does the graph show the number of toothpicks is related to the number of squares?

2. Take a calendar for any month. Choose any 3 by 3 square of 9 dates on the calendar.

august/août						
L/M	T/M	W/M	T/J	F/V	S/S	S/D
1	2	3	4	5	6	7
8	9	10	11	12	13	14
15	16	17	18	19	20	21
22	23	24	25	26	27	28
29	30	31				

a) Add the numbers in the four corners. How does the sum compare with the number in the middle? Repeat with other 3 by 3 squares on the same month. Repeat on calendars for other months.

b) Suppose you know the number in the middle of a 3 by 3 square on the calendar for any month. How would you find the sum of the numbers in the four corners?

c) Let n represent the number in the middle of a 3 by 3 square. Write an expression for the sum of the numbers in the four corners. What are the possible values of n?

3. A horse paddock has a width of 10 m.

a) Calculate the perimeter of the paddock if the length is 15 m and if it is 20 m.

b) Calculate the perimeter of the paddock for four other lengths. Record the results in a table.

c) Suppose you know the length of a paddock with width 10 m. How would you find its perimeter?

d) Let l represent the length of the paddock. Write an expression to represent its perimeter. What kind of a number is l? What are the possible values of l?

e) If the perimeter of the paddock is 74 m, use the expression to determine its length.

f) Use the table from part b to draw a graph of perimeter against length.

4. What expression does each group of algebra tiles represent?

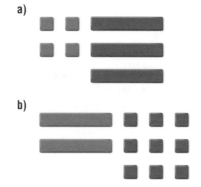

5. Use algebra tiles to represent each expression. Determine the value of the expression when the variable represents 3 and when it represents -2.

a) $4x + 3$ **b)** $3(5 - 2m)$

c) $2(6a + 1)$ **d)** $-4(2s - 5)$

6. Expand using the distributive law.
  a) $3(2x + 7)$ **b)** $-5(4 + 3n)$
  c) $12(4s - 5)$ **d)** $-2(4b - 3)$

7. Combine like terms and simplify each expression.
  a) $2x + 7 + 3x - 5$
  b) $3m - 12 - 7m + 2$
  c) $5a + 3b + 8a - 10b$
  d) $4y - 11 - 9y + 16$
  e) $6s + 5t - 2(3s + 9t)$
  f) $-2(4m - 7n) + 3(m - 13n)$

8. Simplify each expression and determine its value when $x = 4$, $x = -3$, and $x = -1$.
  a) $5x + 2x$
  b) $8x - 3 + 4x + 9$
  c) $2x - 7 - 6x + 3$
  d) $3x - 2 + 4(x - 5)$
  e) $-3(4x + 1) - (-7x - 5)$
  f) $2x + 11 - 4(3x + 7)$

9. Solve each equation using algebra tiles.
  a) $3x + 2 = 8$
  b) $2x - 3 = 1$
  c) $7 - 4x = -5$
  d) $3x + 4 = 2x - 3$
  e) $2x - 5 = 6x + 7$
  f) $3x - 1 = 5x - 9$

10. Solve each equation. Check your solution.
  a) $2x + 7 = 17$
  b) $3 - 2x = 15$
  c) $-40 = -4 + 4x$
  d) $3x - 2 = 5x + 8$
  e) $7 - 5x = 6 + x$
  f) $-11 + 6x = -6x + 13$

11. When an object falls freely from rest, its approximate speed, v metres per second after t seconds, is given by the formula $v = 9.8t$. This is because acceleration due to Earth's gravity is 9.8 m/s^2.
  a) Find its speed after each time.
    i) 2 s   **ii)** 5 s   **iii)** 8 s

  b) Find the time required for the object to reach each speed.
    i) 29.4 m/s   **ii)** 88.2 m/s   **iii)** 137.2 m/s
  c) If the object were on the moon, the formula would be $v = 1.63t$. Repeat parts a and b using this formula.
  Give the answers to one decimal place.

12. Solve each equation.
  a) $5(2x - 3) = 10$
  b) $6(-2 - x) = -5(2x + 4)$
  c) $-2(1 - x) = -3(2 - x)$
  d) $\frac{x}{6} - 5 = \frac{1}{2}x$
  e) $\frac{1}{2}x + \frac{1}{3}x = 10$
  f) $\frac{2}{3}x + 9 = \frac{3}{4}x - 6$

13. A parking meter accepts only quarters and dollars. If there are 31 coins with a value of $20.50, how many quarters and how many dollars are there?

14. For two consecutive integers, the sum of the smaller and twice the larger is 38. What are the integers?

15. A Jaguar travelled 1.2 times as fast as a Mercedes. The difference in their speeds was 24 km/h. Find the speed of each car.

16. The length of a rectangle is 5 cm longer than the width. The perimeter is 54 cm. Find the dimensions of the rectangle.

17. Solve, graph, and check each inequality.
  a) $9 > -2x$
  b) $3y + 8 < 17$
  c) $21 - 5x \geq 11$
  d) $61 \leq 13a - 4$
  e) $4.5m - 1.5 > 18$
  f) $-3x + 8 < 5 - 7x$

Investigating a Card Trick

You will need a deck of 52 playing cards. In this trick, aces count as 1, and jacks, queens, and kings count as 10. Shuffle the cards as much as you like before you start.

Step 1

Hold the pack face down and deal the top card face up on the table. Continue to deal cards face up on top of this one. To determine the number of cards to deal, subtract the value of the card on the table from 13. For example, if the first card is a queen, deal three more cards; if it is a 5, deal eight more cards. Set the pile of cards off to the side, face down.

Step 2

Repeat *Step 1*, and set the new pile off to the side, face down. Keep repeating *Step 1* until you run out of cards.

At the end you will probably not have enough cards to finish the last pile. If this happens, hold the cards that are left face down.

Step 3

Ask a friend to choose any three piles, and to turn over the top card on two of those piles. Pick up the other piles. Add the cards to those you are already holding. It does not matter if you shuffle them.

There will now be three piles on the table, with the top card turned over on two of the piles.

Step 4

Deal some cards from those you are holding. To determine how many cards to deal, add the values of the two cards you see on the table, and add 10 to the result.

Ask your friend to turn over the top card on the third pile. The value of this card should be equal to the number of cards that you have in your hand!

ACTIVITY 1

Do this trick a few times with a friend, until you are familiar with it.

ACTIVITY 2

To understand why the trick works, let a, b, and c represent the values of the top three cards on the three piles your friend chose in *Step 3*. Develop an expression for the number of cards in each of the three piles. Use these expressions to develop a formula for the number of cards you are holding just before you start dealing cards in *Step 4*.

What is the least number of piles that you can have on the table at the end of *Step 2*? What is the greatest?

ACTIVITY 3

The number 13 plays an important role in *Steps 1* and *2*. Suppose this number is replaced by 14. How can the instructions for the trick be slightly modified so that the outcome is the same? Try numbers other than 13 and 14. In each case, develop a formula for the number of cards you are holding just before you start dealing cards in *Step 4*.

In *Step 3*, ask your friend to choose four piles instead of three piles. How can the instructions for the trick be slightly modified so that the outcome is the same? Try numbers other than 3 and 4.

The Ideas

Write a brief report which summarizes the results of your investigations. Include an explanation of why the trick works, and what happens if you change the trick as suggested in *Activity 3*.

RATIO, RATE, AND SIMILARITY

WHAT'S COMING UP?

DEPARTMENTS

Linking Ideas

Mathematics File

Quests

Minds on Math

Start With What You Know

1. Canadians are realizing that smoking is a health hazard and they are giving it up.
   a) From the circle graph below, estimate the percent of Canadians in each category.

Canadian population over 15 years of age, in 1990

Former smokers

Current smokers

Never smoked

   Use the table below.
   b) What percent of females do not smoke?
   c) What percent of males do not smoke?
   d) What is the ratio of female smokers to female non-smokers?
   e) What is the ratio of male smokers to male non-smokers?

Smokers as a percent of the Canadian population over 15 years of age	
Female	Male
28%	31%

2. Monday to Friday, a 5-min phone call from Vancouver to Prince George costs $1.75 during the day.
   a) What would a 5-min call cost in the evening after 5 p.m.?
   b) What would a 5-min call cost in the early hours of the morning?

Time	Reduction
17:00 – 23:00	35% off
23:00 – 08:00	60% off

3. Here are some common sizes, in inches, for photographs and their enlargements: 3 by 5, 4 by 5, 4 by 6, 5 by 7, 8 by 10, 11 by 14, 16 by 20, and 20 by 24.
   a) Write each size as a ratio.
   b) Reduce each ratio to lowest terms.
   c) Which sizes have the same length-to-width ratios?

4. In the NHL, to determine the number of points a player has, we add the number of goals scored to the number of assists. In the 1990–91 hockey season, Wayne Gretzky had 41 goals and 122 assists.
   a) How many points did Gretzky have?
   b) What percent of his points were goals?
   c) What percent of his points were assists?
   Give the answers to the nearest whole number.

5. A boneless sirloin steak is advertised at $6.59/kg. A 0.8-kg package of centre cut sirloin sells for $5.59. Which meat has the lower unit price?

6. An electronic tuner can be used to tune a guitar. When it is tuned so that A corresponds to a frequency of 440 cycles per second, then C flat is about 264 cycles per second, and E is 330 cycles per second. Express each ratio of these frequencies in lowest terms.
   a) A to E
   b) C flat to A
   c) C flat to E
   d) A to E to C flat

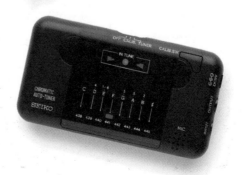

APPLICATIONS OF PERCENT

Developing the Ideas

▶ ▶ *Through Discussion*

The word "percent" comes from the Latin "per centum" meaning "out of 100." Explain the meaning of each statement.

1. The sales tax in Saskatchewan is 9%.

2. A pair of in-line skates is selling at a 40% discount.

3. A basketball player scores on 28% of her shots.

4. Canada Savings Bonds pay interest at $5\frac{1}{4}\%$ per annum.

5. A photocopy machine can enlarge an image to 142%.

Sale!

In-line Skates
40% off!

only $59.97 plus GST

regular price $99.95

▶ ▶ *Through Guided Examples*

Example 1 ....

Up to 1992, the most widely watched television program in North America was the final episode of M*A*S*H, aired on February 28, 1983. Nielsen estimates that 60.2% of the 50 150 000 households in North America that had television sets on that day watched that program. About how many households in North America watched the final episode of M*A*S*H?

Solution

The number of households watching the final episode of M*A*S*H was

$$60.2\% \text{ of } 50\ 150\ 000 = \frac{60.2}{100} \times 50\ 150\ 000$$
$$= 0.602 \times 50\ 150\ 000$$
$$= 30\ 190\ 300$$

Since the information is based on a sample, it is only an approximation. We round the number to 30 000 000. That is, about 30 000 000 households watched the final episode of M*A*S*H.

Example 2

In the 1990–91 hockey season, Wayne Gretzky was the NHL scoring leader. He scored 41 goals. This was 19.3% of all his shots on goal. How many shots on goal did Wayne Gretzky take in the 1990–91 season?

Solution

Let x denote the number of shots on goal.

19.3% of the number of shots = number of goals

We write:
$$19.3\% \times x = 41$$
$$0.193x = 41$$
$$x = \frac{41}{0.193}$$
$$\doteq 212$$

Gretzky took 212 shots in the 1990–91 season.

Example 3

A Guaranteed Investment Certificate (GIC) pays compound interest at 5.25% per annum. One $3000 certificate is bought.

a) How much interest is earned in the first year?

b) How much interest is earned in the second year?

c) What is the total value of the certificate at the end of the second year?

d) What is the total value of the certificate at the end of the third year?

Solution

a) The annual interest on $3000 is 5.25% of $3000 = 0.0525 × $3000
$$= \$157.50$$
The interest earned in the first year is $157.50.

b) At the end of the first year, the certificate is worth
$3000 + $157.50 = $3157.50
Interest is earned on this amount in the second year. That is:

5.25% of $3157.50 = 0.0525 × $3157.50
$$\doteq \$165.77$$
The interest earned in the second year is $165.77.

c) The total value of the certificate at the end of the second year is
$3157.50 + $165.77 = $3323.27

d) Interest earned in the third year is

5.25% of $3323.27 = 0.0525 × $3323.27
$$\doteq \$174.47$$
The total value of the certificate at the end of the third year is
$3323.27 + $174.47 = $3497.74

In *Example 3*, we say that the interest is *compounded*; that is, interest is earned on ever increasing amounts.

Working with Mathematics

Something to talk about

1. Explain the meaning of the statement, "A standard tip for a waiter is about 15%."

2. Find each percent. Explain how you reached your answer.

a) 75% of 1000 **b)** 80% of 10

c) 25% of 40 **d)** 60% of 3

3. Estimate the percent of each square that is shaded.

a)

b)

c)

4. A photograph is enlarged. The area of the enlargement is 50% greater than the area of the original. What is the area of the enlargement as a percent of the original area?

Work together

5. Calculate each percent.

a) 40% of 80 **b)** 60% of 5

c) 16% of 72 **d)** 0.4% of 1000

e) 125% of 150 **f)** 8% of 123 000

6. A can of tennis balls has a regular price of $5.60. It is on sale for 30% off. What is the sale price of the can of tennis balls?

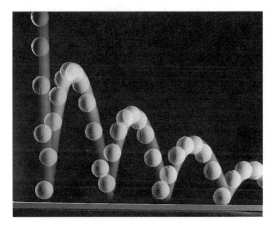

7. In all of Shakespeare's works, he used 31 534 different words. Of these, 14 356 were used only once. What percent of the words did he use only once? Give the answer to one decimal place.

8. Express each reduction as a percent of the original price. Give the answers to one decimal place where necessary.

a) A TV regularly priced at $540 is selling for $499.

b) An overcoat regularly priced at $195 is selling for $156.

On your own

9. A ten-speed bicycle regularly sells for $254.95. What will it cost during a "20% off" sale?

10. A CD sells for $18.95. What is the sales tax on it in a province with a sales tax of 8%?

11. In 1991 there were about 1 870 000 people in Canada between 15 and 19 years of age. The total population of Canada was about 27 300 000. What percent of people in Canada were between 15 and 19 years of age in that year? Give the answer to one decimal place.

12. An amount of $2000 is invested for one year at an interest rate of 6% per annum. What interest is earned after one year?

13. In 1991 there were about 4 780 000 Canadian families with children at home. This was about 65% of all Canadian families. About how many Canadian families were there in that year? Give the answer to the nearest thousand.

14. In the 1990–91 hockey season, Brett Hull scored on 22.1% of his shots on goal. He scored 86 goals that season. How many shots on goal did he take that season?

15. a) A photocopy machine will enlarge a diagram to 142% of its original length and width. A diagram measures 6.0 cm by 4.0 cm. What are the dimensions of its enlargement?
    b) What would be the dimensions of the enlargement of the enlargement?

16. On a particular day, $1 U.S. is worth $1.34 Can.
    a) What is the value of $1 U.S. as a percent of $1 Can?
    b) What is the value of $1 Can as a percent of $1 U.S.?
    Give the answers to the nearest whole number.
    c) Can we answer part b by subtracting 34¢ from $1? Explain your answer.

Extend your thinking

17. Suppose a GIC pays interest at 5.25% compounded annually. At the end of each year, the GIC is worth 105.25% of its value at the beginning of the year. Consider a GIC that was bought for $1000.
    a) Show that, at the end of 5 years, the investment has grown to $1000(1.0525)^5$.
    b) Calculate the value of the GIC after 5 years.

18. A photocopy machine enlarged a poster by 25%. The enlarged poster was too big. So the machine was used to reduce it by 25%.
    a) After the enlargement and reduction, was the poster back to its original size?
    b) If your answer to part a was no, what is the size of the final poster as a percent of its original size?

COMMUNICATING

The Ideas

In your journal, give three examples where a percent greater than 100% might be used. Explain its meaning in each case. Is it possible to have a percent which is less than 1%? If so, give an example to explain what such a percent might mean.

APPLICATIONS OF RATIO

Developing the Ideas

▶ ▶ *Through Instruction*

In most countries, approximately 105 boys are born for every 100 girls. That is, the ratio of boys to girls is 105 : 100.

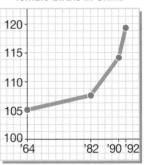

Male births for each 100 female births in China

The graph shows that in China the ratio of boys to girls born in recent years has increased dramatically. A newspaper report indicated that the ratio of boys to girls born in 1992 in China was 118 : 100. A different report indicated that in South Korea, the ratio of boys to girls was 57 : 50. In which country was the ratio of male births to female births greater?

To compare 118 : 100 with 57 : 50, both ratios should have the same second term. We can express 118 : 100 with a second term of 50. To do this, we divide each term by 2 to get 59 : 50.

In China, there are 59 boys to 50 girls. In South Korea, there are 57 boys to 50 girls. The ratio of male births to female births is greater in China.

Alternatively, we could have expressed the ratio 57 : 50 with a second term of 100. To do this, multiply each term by 2 to get 114 : 100.

Could we have said that since 118 > 57, the ratio of male births to female births was greater in China?

Example ....

In 1992 there were about 30 000 000 babies born in China.

a) Using the boys : girls ratio of 118 : 100, determine how many of each sex were born in 1992.

b) What percent of the newborns were girls?

Solution

a) The boys : girls ratio of 118 : 100 means that 118 boys are born for every 100 girls. That is, out of every 218 babies born in China, 118 are boys and 100 are girls. We can state each ratio using a fraction.
Of all babies born in China in 1992, $\frac{118}{218}$ were boys and $\frac{100}{218}$ were girls.

Therefore, the number of male babies was

$\frac{118}{218} \times 30\ 000\ 000 \doteq 16\ 238\ 532$

Expressed to the nearest million, there were about 16 million boys born.
The number of girls born was about
30 000 000 − 16 000 000 = 14 000 000

b) We convert the fraction $\frac{100}{218}$ to a percent.

The percent of newborns who were girls is $\frac{100}{218} \times 100\% \doteq 45.9\%$

There are two ways in which 2-term ratios can be used.

One way considers a whole divided into two parts. An example is the ratio of boys to girls being 118 : 100. The terms of the ratio refer to the parts of the whole.

The other way uses the terms to compare one of the parts with the whole. An example is the ratio $\frac{100}{218}$ which compares the number of girls to the number of babies.

Bombay is the financial and commercial centre of India.
It has one of the highest population densities in the world.
Some parts of the inner city have nearly 40 000 people per square kilometre.
What if the population density in your classroom were the same as in these parts of Bombay? About how many people would there be in your classroom?

Working with Mathematics

Something to talk about

1. Explain each statement.
   a) The ratio of female babies to male babies is 100 : 105.
   b) A chain saw requires gasoline and oil to be mixed in the ratio of 40 : 1.
   c) This year, domestic cars outsold foreign cars in the ratio of 7 : 4.
   d) Brass is an alloy of copper and zinc in the ratio of 3 : 2.
   e) Most television screens have a width : height ratio of 4 : 3.

2. Express each statement as a ratio.
   a) The length of a rectangle is three times its width.
   b) When a fair coin is tossed, heads should turn up 50% of the time.
   c) A map is drawn so that 1 cm on the map corresponds to an actual distance of 1 km.
   d) During the summer months of the 1993 baseball season, John Olerud's batting average was above .400.
   e) Most people spend about one-third of their lives sleeping and two-thirds awake.

3. State which is the greater ratio.
   a) $\frac{5}{10}$ or $\frac{3}{5}$ b) $\frac{6}{4}$ or $\frac{7}{8}$
   c) $\frac{6}{5}$ or $\frac{12}{11}$ d) $\frac{8}{3}$ or $\frac{13}{5}$

Work together

4. For each diagram, write the ratio of the blue area to the pink area. Write each ratio in lowest terms.

a)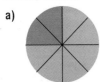

b)

c)

d)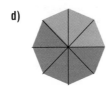

5. Write each ratio in lowest terms.
   a) 4 : 6   b) 12 : 9   c) 16 : 12
   d) 24 : 20   e) 105 : 100   f) 35 : 63

6. Sterling silver is an alloy of silver and copper in the ratio of 37 : 3.
   a) What fraction of a sterling silver spoon is silver?
   b) What percent of a sterling silver spoon is silver?
   c) A sterling silver ingot has a mass of 500 g. How much silver does it contain?

7. Doctors measure the risk of heart attacks by the ratio of total cholesterol to HDL-cholesterol in the blood. For minimum risk, this ratio should be between 3.5 : 1 and 4.5 : 1. A patient is found to have 55 mg of HDL-cholesterol in a blood sample containing 230 mg of cholesterol. Is that patient at risk of having a heart attack?

8. This photograph was taken with an electron microscope. It shows a mite, which has been magnified 180 times. Measure the length of the mite. Calculate the actual length of the mite.

On your own

9. About 37.4% of Canadians have O⁺ blood type. What is the ratio of those with O⁺ blood to those with a different blood type?

10. About 3 Canadians in 10 are nearsighted to some degree. About 6 in 10 are farsighted. How many times more likely is a Canadian to be farsighted than nearsighted?

11. In 1992, there were about 393 000 live births in Canada. The ratio of boys to girls was 21 : 20.
    a) How many girls were born?
    b) What percent of the newborns were girls? Give the answer to one decimal place.

12. Lake Superior is the largest of the Great Lakes. Lake Ontario is the smallest. Their areas are in the ratio of approximately 4 : 1. The area of Lake Ontario is about 19 500 km². What is the area of Lake Superior?

13. Scientists estimate that about one person in 9 is left-handed. The population of Canada is about 28 000 000. About how many left-handed people are there in Canada?

14. On average, a person with red hair has about 90 000 hairs on her head, a person with blond hair has about 40 000 hairs on his head, and a person with brown hair has about 100 000 hairs. Write a three-term ratio in lowest terms which compares the numbers of hairs on the heads of people with brown, red, and blond hair.

15. The average distance required to stop a car depends on its speed. The table below shows, for various speeds, the distance travelled while the driver is reacting (the *reaction time distance*), the distance travelled after the brakes were applied (the *braking distance*) and their sum, the *stopping distance*.

Speed (km/h)	Reaction time distance (m)	Braking distance (m)	Stopping distance (m)
16	3.4	2.7	6.1
32	6.7	7.0	13.7
48	10.1	13.7	23.8
64	13.4	24.7	38.1
80	16.8	40.5	57.3
96	20.1	62.8	82.9

a) Estimate the speeds at which the ratio, Braking distance : Reaction time distance, is:
   i) 1 : 1   ii) 2 : 1   iii) 3 : 1
b) Estimate the speeds at which the ratio, Stopping distance : Braking distance, is:
   i) 9 : 5   ii) 2 : 1   iii) 1.5 : 1

Extend your thinking

16. The front gear-wheels on a 10-speed bicycle have 40 and 52 teeth. The back gear-wheels have 14, 17, 20, 24, and 28 teeth.
    a) What is the largest front : back gear ratio that can be produced?
    b) How many different front : back ratios can be created from these gear-wheels?
    c) Which front and back gear-wheels must the chain connect to achieve a front : back gear ratio of 13 : 6?

COMMUNICATING The Ideas

A newspaper headline reads "Four out of every five eligible Canadians voted in the last federal election." In your journal, rewrite this headline using a ratio. Then rewrite it using a fraction and using a percent.

How Fast Can You Go?

An 18-speed mountain bike has three gears, called *pedal gears*, attached to the pedals, and six smaller gears, called *wheel gears*, attached to the back wheel. The speed of the bike is determined by the gear you are using, the size of the wheels, and your rate of pedalling.

Suppose that when the bike is in the highest gear, the chain passes around a pedal gear containing 48 teeth and a wheel gear containing 12 teeth. The diameter of the wheels is 66 cm. Suppose you can pedal at a speed of 60 turns per minute. How fast could you go on the bike?

Understand the problem

- Why does your speed depend upon the gear you use?
- Why does your speed depend upon the size of the wheel?
- What units do we use to describe the speed of the bike?

Think of a strategy

- What happens to the back wheel when the pedal gear makes one complete turn?
- How is the diameter of the wheel related to the distance the bike moves?
- How far forward does the bike move for each turn of the pedal gear?

Carry out the strategy

- When the pedal gear makes one complete turn, the chain passes over 48 teeth. How many turns does this amount of chain cause the back wheel to make?
- Use the formula $C = \pi d$ to find the circumference of the wheel. This is the distance the bike moves forward in one rotation of the wheel. How far forward does the bike move in one turn of the pedal gear?
- If you pedal at 60 turns per minute, how far does the bike move in one minute?
- How fast is this in kilometres per hour?

Look back

- Check your solution. Does the answer seem reasonable?
- Suppose the pedal gear had 36 teeth. How would this change the answer?
- Some bikes have larger wheels. How much faster would you go if the diameter of the wheels was 68.5 cm?
- Do you think you could pedal the bike any faster? How much faster? How fast would you then go on your bike?
- The speed of a bike depends upon the diameter of the wheels, the rate of pedalling, the number of teeth in the pedal gear, and the number of teeth in the wheel gear. Use these variables to write a formula to calculate speed. Set up a spreadsheet that uses these variables. Determine the speeds of the bike for different values of these variables.

Communicating the Ideas

In your journal, describe how the speed of a bike is related to the number of teeth in the gears, the size of the wheels, and the pedalling speed. Describe other factors that might affect the speed, and explain how they do.

SOME SPECIAL RATIOS

Developing the Ideas

▶ ▶ *Through Discussion*

During the third game of the 1992 World Series, Pat Borders, the catcher for the Toronto Blue Jays, made a key play. He threw out Brian Hunter, a pinch-runner for the Atlanta Braves, who was attempting to steal second base.

(second base)
S

T ◇ (third base)   (first base) ◇ F

H
(home plate)

Borders threw the ball from H to S.
Hunter ran from F to S.
How far did the ball travel?

1. What is the distance on a baseball diamond from:
   a) home plate to first base?
   b) first base to second base?

2. **a)** Which is greater: the distance HS or the distance HF + FS? Explain your answer.
   b) Estimate the distance HS on a baseball diamond.

3. For each square, measure one side and one diagonal. Calculate the quotient $\frac{\text{diagonal length}}{\text{side length}}$. Write each quotient to one decimal place.

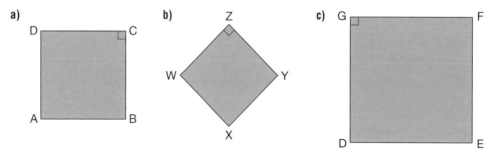

a)

D ▢ C

A ─── B

b)

Z

W ◇ Y

X

c)

G ▢ F

D ─── E

4. Use the results from exercise 3. Describe a relationship between the length of a diagonal of a square and the length of one of its sides.

5. Use this relationship and your answer to exercise 1 to calculate the distance HS from home plate to second base. How does this compare with your estimate in exercise 2b?

You should have discovered that, for any square, the length of a diagonal is approximately 1.4 times as long as the length of a side.

►► *Through Activities*

In the following activities, you will make some polygons by folding circles. You should discover some interesting ratios.

You will need 3 paper circles and a millimetre ruler.

For each polygon, begin with this first step.

Step 1

Fold the circle in half, then in quarters.

To make a square

Step 2

After the circle has been folded into quarters, open it.

Step 3

Join the points where the fold lines meet the circumference. This makes an inscribed square.

- What does *inscribed* mean?
- Is the circumference of the circle greater than or less than the perimeter of the square?

To make a hexagon

Step 2

After the circle has been folded into quarters, unfold it, then fold it again, as shown.

Step 3

Open the circle. Ignore the horizontal fold line through the centre. Join the points where the other fold lines meet the circumference. This makes an inscribed hexagon.

- Is the circumference of the circle greater than or less than the perimeter of the hexagon?

To make an octagon

Step 2	Step 3
After the circle has been folded into quarters, fold it in half again.	Open the circle. Join the points where the fold lines meet the circumference. This makes an inscribed octagon. • Is the circumference of the circle greater than or less than the perimeter of the octagon? • What is the perimeter of the octagon? • Estimate the circumference of the circle. • About how many times as great as the diameter of the circle is its circumference?

• Copy this table. Measure your figures. Complete the table.

Figure	Square	Hexagon	Octagon
Perimeter			
Diameter			

▶ ▶ *Through Instruction*

• Use the table to estimate the value of the fraction $\dfrac{\text{circumference}}{\text{diameter}}$ for a circle.
The value of this fraction has fascinated people from many civilizations for thousands of years. Mathematicians have assigned the symbol, π, (pronounced "pi") to this number. The value of π is a non-repeating decimal. π is an irrational number. Its first few billion decimal digits have been calculated, with the aid of a computer.
Expressed to 8 decimal places, the value of π is 3.141 592 65.

Alternatively, we can express this fraction as a ratio.
Circumference : diameter = π : 1
Or, circumference : diameter is simply π.
In general, when a ratio is expressed as a single number, this number is the first term, and the second term of the ratio is 1.

This relationship for circles can be expressed as a formula.

$$\frac{C}{D} = \pi$$

or $C = \pi D$

You can use this formula to calculate the circumference C of a circle when you know its diameter D, or to calculate the diameter when you know the circumference.

Working with Mathematics

Something to talk about

1. Explain the meaning of each term.
   a) polygon   **b)** perimeter of a polygon
   c) circumference   **d)** diameter of a circle

2. What is the approximate ratio of the length d of a diagonal of a square to the length l of one side? Write this relationship as a formula.

3. Explain how to use the Pythagorean Theorem to find the length of a diagonal if you know the length of a side of a square.

4. About how many times as far is it around the circumference C of a circle as it is across its diameter D? Write this relationship as a formula.

5. What is the approximate circumference of a circle with a diameter of 27 cm?

Work together

6. Earth is approximately spherical. The circumference of Earth is about 40 000 km. Calculate the approximate diameter of Earth.

7. A mountain bike wheel is 66 cm in diameter. How many rotations are made by the wheel when the bicycle travels 1 km?

On your own

8. Estimate the circumference of each circle.

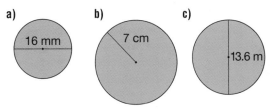

a) 16 mm   **b)** 7 cm   **c)** 13.6 m

9. Calculate the approximate length of a diagonal of a square with sides of length 21.8 cm.

Extend your thinking

10. In this diagram, all the small circles are congruent. Which of the paths from A to B described below is shortest?

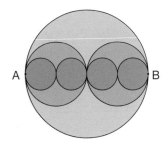

   - a path along the circumference of the large circle
   - a path along the circumferences of the two medium circles
   - a path along the circumferences of the four small circles

11. The innermost ring of Saturn is 6636 km above the surface of this planet. How much greater is the circumference of this ring than the circumference of Saturn? Give the answer to the nearest 100 km.

COMMUNICATING The Ideas

Find a mug similar to this. Estimate which is greater, the height or the circumference. Use a piece of string to check your estimate. In your journal, write about what you did, and your results.

The Search for a Fraction that Approximates π

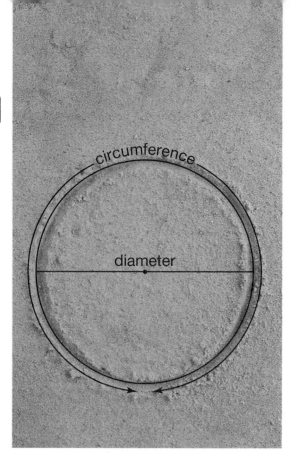

For thousands of years, people have tried to find a fraction that approximates π. From ancient times, people have known that the circumference of a circle is a little more than 3 times its diameter.

People from different civilizations have tried to find a fraction that would equal the ratio:

$$\frac{\text{circumference}}{\text{diameter}}$$

Over the years, various civilizations used these fractions as approximations for π.

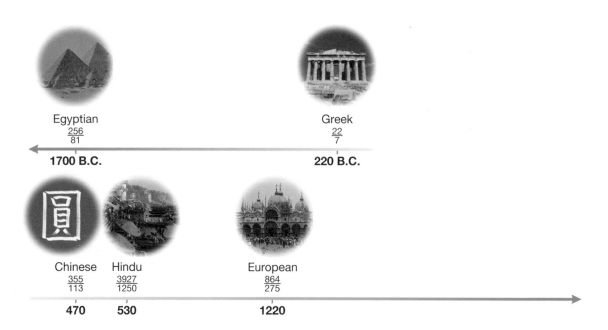

Egyptian
$\frac{256}{81}$

Greek
$\frac{22}{7}$

1700 B.C.

220 B.C.

Chinese
$\frac{355}{113}$

Hindu
$\frac{3927}{1250}$

European
$\frac{864}{275}$

470

530

1220

We know that π cannot be expressed as a rational number. In its decimal form, the value of π never repeats. We shall use a spreadsheet to find out which of the fractions mentioned above is closest to π.

Open a new spreadsheet. Enter the text and the formulas in cells D2, E2, and F2. Use the Fill Down option to copy these cells to the cells below. Make column F wide enough to display the numbers in fixed format with 12 decimal places.

TEMPLATE DISK

	A	B	C	D	E	F
1	Civilization	Numerator	Denominator	Decimal	Pi	Difference
2	Egyptian	256	81	=B2/C2	=Pi()	=D2-E2
3	Greek	22	7	=B3/C3	=Pi()	=D3-E3
4	Chinese	355	113	=B4/C4	=Pi()	=D4-E4
5	Hindu	3927	1250	=B5/C5	=Pi()	=D5-E5
6	European	864	275	=B6/C6	=Pi()	=D6-E6

1. a) Which fraction is closest to π?
   b) Which fraction is farthest from π?
   c) Which civilization used a fraction that was:
   i) larger than π?   ii) smaller than π?
   How do you know?

Perhaps you can find a fraction that is closer to π. This has not yet been done, but you may be the first to find it! Modify your spreadsheet as shown below.

TEMPLATE DISK

	A	B	C	D	E	F
1		Numerator	Denominator	Decimal	Pi	Difference
2	My try	3	1	=B2/C2	=Pi()	=D2-E2
3		=B2+1	=C2	=B3/C3	=Pi()	=D3-E3
4		=B3+1	=C3	=B4/C4	=Pi()	=D4-E4
5		=B4+1	=C4	=B5/C5	=Pi()	=D5-E5
6		=B5+1	=C5	=B6/C6	=Pi()	=D6-E6
7		=B6+1	=C6	=B7/C7	=Pi()	=D7-E7
8		=B7+1	=C7	=B8/C8	=Pi()	=D8-E8
9		=B8+1	=C8	=B9/C9	=Pi()	=D9-E9
10		=B9+1	=C9	=B10/C10	=Pi()	=D10-E10

Look at the numbers in column F. Notice where the difference changes from negative to positive. The fractions on either side of this change are closest to π.

2. a) Change the denominator in cell C2 to 7. Change the numerator in cell B2 to 21. See where the change occurs now. Notice how close $\frac{22}{7}$ is to π. Record the difference between π and $\frac{22}{7}$ as 0.001 26... .
   b) Choose any denominator and enter it in cell C2. Change the numerator in cell B2 until the negative to positive change shows in column F. For example, enter 57 in cell C2. Estimate 3 times 57 and enter that in cell B2. Does the sign change show? If all column F is negative, increase the beginning numerator. If all column F is positive, decrease the beginning numerator.
   c) How close can you get to π?

$\frac{C}{D}$ Is the Same for All Circles

This article appeared in a newspaper on Saturday, November 28, 1992. Read the article, then answer the questions.

SPECIAL TO THE STAR

Like many of us, Ann Druyan would like to know everything. The difference is that she gets paid for her efforts.

The 43-year-old writer and activist has written novels and scientific works, organized demonstrations for nuclear test bans, and selected messages to send to space aliens.

She was elected secretary of the Federation of American Scientists, a Nobel Laureate-laden group that monitors the misuse of science and high technology. Ann is a director of the Children's Health Fund, a New York City organization whose roving health-care vans for poor children have been praised and duplicated across the U.S.

She always had love, intelligence and self-confidence, but she did not have a distinguished academic career, Druyan says. She was "derailed" from her interest in science and math when a junior high school teacher ridiculed her excitement over the universality of pi, the ratio of the circumference of a circle to its diameter.

"I raised my hand and said, 'You mean this applies to every circle in the universe?' and the teacher told me not to ask stupid questions," she recalls. "And there I was having this religious experience, and she made me feel like such a fool. I was completely flummoxed from then on until after college."

1. What is pi?
2. What is meant by the "universality of pi"?
3. a) What question did Ann Druyan ask?
   b) Was this question stupid? Explain.

3.14159265358979
93238462643383
27950288419716
93993751058209
74944592307816
40628620899862
80348253421170
67982148086511
28230664709384
46095505822317
25359408128481
17450284102...
19385211055596
44622948954930
38196442881097
56659334461284
75648233786783
16527120190914
64821339360726
024914127372458700660631558817488152
92829254091715364367892590360011330
54882046652138414695194151160943305
03657595919530921861173819326117931(
85480744623799627495673518857527248?
79381830119491298336733624406566430
13949463952247371907021798609437027
92171762931767523846748184676694051
0568127145263560827785771342757789

APPLICATIONS OF RATE

Developing the Ideas

▶ ▶ *Through Discussion*

Canadian consumers are concerned about the costs of running a car.
Fuel consumption is an important factor in deciding which car to buy.

To help consumers make a decision, Transport Canada publishes an annual
report called *Fuel Consumption Guide*. For the most popular models, this
report lists the engine size, and the fuel consumption for city and for
highway driving. Fuel consumption is measured in litres per 100 km.
That is, the number of litres of fuel burned when travelling 100 km.

An excerpt from the 1994 guide is shown below.

Automobile type	Engine size (L)	Number of cylinders	Litres per 100 km (city)	Litres per 100 km (highway)
Dodge Colt 100	1.5	4	7.1	5.5
Dodge Shadow	2.2	4	9.1	6.5
Dodge Spirit	2.5	4	10.5	7.9
Eagle Vision	3.3	6	12.4	8.0
Eagle Talon TSi Turbo	2.0	4	10.9	7.5
Eagle Summit	1.5	4	7.1	5.5
Ford Crown Victoria	4.6	8	13.4	8.8
Ford Probe	2.0	4	9.2	6.5
Ford Taurus	3.0	6	11.9	7.3
Ford Tempo	2.3	4	10.0	6.5
Ford Thunderbird	3.8	6	12.5	8.5
GEO Metro	1.3	4	9.4	7.2
Honda Accord	2.2	4	9.5	6.8
Honda Civic	1.5	4	7.0	5.4
Honda Prelude	2.2	4	10.1	7.6
Hyundai Excel	1.5	4	8.3	5.9
Hyundai Scoupe	1.5	4	8.5	5.8
Lexus ES 300	3.0	6	13.1	9.0
Lincoln Continental	3.8	6	13.3	8.2
Mazda 323	1.6	4	8.5	6.3

From the table, the Ford Taurus used 11.9 L to travel 100 km in the city and 7.3 L to travel 100 km on the highway.

1. Why are the consumptions for highway and city driving listed separately?

2. Which car uses more fuel on the highway: a Ford Probe or a Honda Accord? How do you know?

3. Which car in the list has the greatest fuel consumption:

   a) on the highway?   b) in the city?

4. Which car consumes the least fuel per kilometre travelled?

5. Choose six cars with different engine sizes.

   a) Look at each car's fuel consumption on the highway. Does there appear to be a relationship between engine size and fuel consumption?

   b) Look at the number of cylinders each car has. Does there appear to be a relationship between the number of cylinders and the fuel consumption?

The fuel consumption compares two quantities: the volume of fuel in litres and the distance travelled in kilometres. Because the quantities have different units, the comparison is called a *rate*.

6. Suggest other examples of rates.

Example 1 ....

The fuel consumption of the Dodge Colt 100 is quoted as 7.1 L/100 km for city driving.

a) Find how much fuel is needed to travel 275 km in the city.

b) Find how far the car will travel in the city on 48 L of gasoline.

Solution

a) The fuel for 100 km is 7.1 L.

The fuel for 1 km would be $\frac{7.1}{100}$ L.

The fuel for 275 km would be $\frac{7.1}{100} \times 275$ L = 19.525 L.

About 20 L of fuel are needed for a trip of 275 km.

b) On 7.1 L of fuel, the car travels 100 km.

On 1 L of fuel, the car would travel $\frac{100}{7.1}$ km.

On 48 L of fuel, the car could travel $\frac{100}{7.1} \times 48$ km $\doteq$ 676.056 km.

The car travels about 676 km on 48 L of fuel.

Example 2 ....

In the 1993–94 hockey season, Kurt Muller had 18 goals in the first 12 games. Suppose he continued scoring at this rate.

a) How many goals would he have after 80 games?

b) How many games would he have to play to get 100 goals?

Solution

a) In 12 games, Muller scored 18 goals.

At this rate, in 1 game he would score $\frac{18}{12}$ goals.

In 80 games, he would score $\frac{18}{12} \times 80 = 120$ goals.

If Muller continued scoring at the same rate, he would score 120 goals in 80 games.

b) Muller scored 18 goals in 12 games.

To get 1 goal, it would take $\frac{12}{18}$ games.

To get 100 goals, it would take $\frac{12}{18} \times 100 \doteq 67$ games.

If Muller continued scoring at the same rate, he would score 100 goals in approximately 67 games.

Find out whether Muller did maintain his scoring rate for the 1993–94 season. How close are the answers for parts a and b to what actually happened?

Working with Mathematics

Something to talk about

1. Explain the difference between a ratio and a rate.

2. Give examples of familiar measurements which are expressed as rates.

3. Is a percent a ratio or a rate?

Work together

4. Use the table on page 287.
   a) About how much fuel would a Ford Probe consume on a 500-km trip which involves mainly highway driving?
   b) About how far would a Ford Probe travel on the highway on 50 L of gas?

5. Janet earned $42 for 7 h of babysitting. Her friend, Richard, earned $35 for $5\frac{1}{2}$ h of babysitting. Who earned more per hour?

6. A gold nugget with a volume of 7 cm³ has a mass of 135 g. A lead paperweight with a volume of 350 cm³ has a mass of 4 kg. Which element, gold or lead, has the greater mass per cubic centimetre? This is called density.

7. A laser printer can print 17 pages per minute. Ignore the time it takes to refill the paper tray.
   a) How many pages can the printer print in:
      i) 1 h?   ii) 1 week?
   b) Find how long it will take to print:
      i) 1000 pages   ii) 100 000 pages

8. In the first 20 games of the 1993 baseball season, Larry Walker of the Montreal Expos hit 5 home runs. If he continued at this rate, how many home runs would he hit in 160 games?

9. A 400-g box of corn flakes costs $1.89. A 525-g box of the same cereal costs $2.29.
   a) Find the unit price, in cents per 100 g, for each box of cereal.
   b) Which box is the better buy?

10. Earth orbits the sun once every 365 days (to the nearest whole number). Venus orbits the sun once every 225 days. About how many times will Venus orbit the sun in 10 Earth years?

11. Sound travels in air at approximately 335 m/s. About how long would it take for the sound of thunder to travel a distance of 5 km?

On your own

12. Adrian works in a factory making pies. He is paid $9.55 per hour for a 7.5-h shift. He is paid "time and a half" for the first 4 h of overtime in a day. Then he is paid double time for any additional hours worked that day. In one week, Adrian worked these hours.

Mon.	Tues.	Wed.	Thurs.	Fri.
15	7.5	7.5	11.5	7.5

What are Adrian's wages for this week?

13. A brand of liquid detergent is sold in 2 sizes—$1.99 for 500 mL and $2.39 for 950 mL.
   a) Find the unit price for each size of detergent. Which is the better buy?
   b) The smaller size is "on special" for one week at a price of $1.79. For this week, which is the better buy?

14. One measure that is used to compare countries of the world is population density. This measure is the average number of people per square kilometre of land. In Canada, we have a very low population density compared to Japan.

DATA DISK

Use the *Land Use* database on the student's disk. It contains information about countries of the world, including population and land area. Determine the population densities for:

a) the 5 countries which have the smallest land areas

b) the 5 countries which have the largest land areas

c) the 5 countries which have the smallest populations

d) the 5 countries which have the largest populations

15. Marilyn works in a car assembly plant. She is paid $14.50 per hour for an 8-h shift. She receives an additional 72.5¢ per hour for working the night shift. In one month, Marilyn works two 40-h weeks on the day shift and two 40-h weeks on the night shift. Find her wages for the month.

Extend your thinking

16. Milk is sold in 4 L bags, and 2 L and 1 L cartons. The milk is priced at $3.49, $2.59, and $1.49 respectively. By how much would the cost of each carton have to be reduced so that its unit price was equal to that of the 4 L bags?

17. A person is paid $8.60/h for a 40-h week and time and a half for overtime. How many hours has she worked if she earns $414.95 in one week?

COMMUNICATING
The Ideas

In your journal, explain how ratio and rate are similar and how they are different. Give 3 examples of ratios we use in everyday life. Give 3 examples of rates we use in everyday life.

BOGGLE YOUR MIND

In April 1992, it was reported in *Flight International* magazine that a McDonnell Douglas DC-9 (similar to the one shown) had completed 94 159 flights in 26 years and was still in operation. About how many flights would the plane have made each day during those 26 years?

Food for a Healthy Heart

YOU'VE PROBABLY HEARD OR READ ABOUT THE importance of reducing the amount of fat in our diets. The Heart and Stroke Foundation recommends that we eat food containing less than 30% of its total energy as fat. This helps to maintain a healthy heart and to avoid gaining weight.

Many packaged foods claim to be cholesterol free or to contain reduced amounts of fat. But it is not always clear whether the food meets the guideline of less than 30% fat energy. Here's a way you can check.

Find the nutrition information printed on a package, like this label from homogenized milk.

For each 250 mL serving	
Energy	157 Cal
	660 kJ
Protein	8.5 g
Fat	8.6 g
Carbohydrates	12.0 g

Energy is measured in calories or kilojoules.
Mass is measured in grams.
Volume or capacity is measured in millilitres.

1. a) According to the label, how much fat is there in 250 mL of homogenized milk?

   b) In 1 g of fat there are about 38 kJ. How many kilojoules are there in the fat content of 250 mL of homogenized milk?

2. a) According to the label, how many kilojoules of food energy are there in 250 mL of homogenized milk?

   b) Use your answer to exercise 1b to express the energy in the fat as a percent of the total food energy.

   c) Does homogenized milk meet the recommended guideline of the Heart and Stroke Foundation?

3. Skim milk contains 380 kJ of energy and 0.5 g of fat in every 250-mL serving. Calculate the percent of fat energy in skim milk.

Skim milk label →

NUTRITION INFORMATION NUTRITIONNELLE		
PER 250 ml SERVING (1 CUP)		
PAR PORTION DE 250 ml (1 TASSE)		
ENERGY	91 cal/380 kJ	ÉNERGIE
PROTEIN	8.8g	PROTÉINES
FAT	0.5g	MATIÈRES GRASSES
POLYUNSATURATES	0g	POLYINSATURÉES
MONOUNSATURATES	0.1g	MONOINSATURÉES
SATURATES	0.3g	SATURÉES
CHOLESTEROL	5 mg	CHOLESTÉROL
CARBOHYDRATE	13g	GLUCIDES
% RECOMMENDED DAILY INTAKE		
% DE L'APPORT QUOTIDIEN RECOMMANDÉ		
VITAMIN A	11%	VITAMINE A
VITAMIN D	44%	VITAMINE D
CALCIUM	29%	CALCIUM
PHOSPHORUS	24%	PHOSPHORE

4. a) A popular snack food contains 152 Cal, or 640 kJ of energy and 9.6 g of fat in every 28-g serving. Does it meet the recommended guideline?

   b) The ingredients are popcorn, vegetable oil, cheddar cheese, whey protein concentrate, lactose, salt, and buttermilk. What do you think the food is?

5. Examine your calculations in the above exercises. Describe a rule that you could use to tell whether packaged food meets the recommended guideline of the Heart and Stroke Foundation.

6. Record the nutrition information from three packaged foods in your home. Determine whether the foods meet the guideline for fat energy content.

7. a) Can you find any packaged foods in your home that indicate the percent of energy that is fat?

   b) Why do you think some food manufacturers do not disclose this information?

Developing the Ideas

▶ ▶ *Through Instruction*

Most television sets have a rectangular shape like this. The width-to-height ratio is 4 : 3.

The screens in many movie theatres have width-to-height ratios of 16 : 9.

The fact that these ratios are different creates a problem when a movie is shown on TV.

Suppose the movie image has the same height as the TV screen. Then part of the movie is chopped off each side.

Suppose the movie image has the same width as the TV screen. Then it will not be high enough to fill the screen.

Consider a TV screen that measures 40 cm by 30 cm. A movie with
a width-to-height ratio of 16 : 9 is to be shown on the television.

Case 1

The movie image fills the screen
vertically but its edges are cut off to
fit the screen horizontally. How much of
the movie image is cut off?

Let w represent the width of the movie
image before its edges are cut off.
The original width-to-height ratio of the
movie image is 16 : 9.
This ratio is equal to the width-to-height
ratio of the image before its edges are
cut off.
We write, $\frac{w}{30} = \frac{16}{9}$

Multiply each side by 30.
$$\frac{w}{30} \times 30 = \frac{16}{9} \times 30$$
$$w = \frac{16 \times 30}{9}$$
$$\doteq 53.33$$
The image is about 53.3 cm wide.
But the TV screen is only 40 cm wide.
The amount cut off is
53.3 cm − 40 cm = 13.3 cm
The amount cut off each side is
$\frac{13.3}{2}$ cm $\doteq$ 6.7 cm

Case 2

The movie image fills the screen
horizontally, but there are dark bands at
the top and bottom of the screen. How
much of the screen is not used?

Let h represent the height of the image.
The ratio 16 : 9 is equal to the width-to-
height ratio of the image on the screen.
That is, $\frac{40}{h} = \frac{16}{9}$
This equation is similar to the one
in *Case 1*, but the variable is in the
denominator. We'd like to solve this
equation the same way we solved the
one in *Case 1*. Since the two fractions
are equal, their reciprocals are equal. We
invert both fractions.
$$\frac{h}{40} = \frac{9}{16}$$
Multiply each side by 40.
$$\frac{h}{40} \times 40 = \frac{9}{16} \times 40$$
$$h = \frac{9 \times 40}{16}$$
$$= 22.5$$
The image is 22.5 cm high.
But the TV screen is 30 cm high.
The amount of space is
30 cm − 22.5 cm = 7.5 cm
The amount of space at the top is
$\frac{7.5}{2}$ cm, or approximately 3.8 cm.

A statement that two ratios are equal is called a *proportion*.
For example, the statement $\frac{h}{40} = \frac{9}{16}$ is a proportion.

Working with Mathematics

Something to talk about

1. A proportion can be used to compare sizes. Express each statement as a proportion.
   a) The mass of a blue whale compared to the mass of an African elephant is the same as the mass of a person compared to the mass of a chicken.
   b) The population of China compared to the population of Canada is the same as the population of Canada compared to the population of Calgary.

2. Explain why you agree or disagree with this statement: "A recipe doesn't need to list the masses of the ingredients. It need only list the proportions of the ingredients."

3. A negative from a 35-mm film has a width of 2.4 cm and a length of 3.6 cm. Prints and enlargements are available in these width-to-length ratios: $3:5$, $4:6$, $5:7$, $8:10$, $11:14$, $16:20$, and $20:24$. Which prints and enlargements can be made without omitting part of the original picture?

Work together

4. a) For *Case 1*, on page 295, write the width of the TV screen as a percent of the width of the image.
   b) For *Case 2*, on page 295, write the height of the image on the TV screen as a percent of the height of the screen.

5. Melissa is 150 cm tall. She had her photo taken beside a basketball player who is 225 cm tall. How many times as tall as Melissa will the basketball player appear to be in the photograph? Explain your answer.

6. A 5 by 7 picture is made by enlarging a negative with a length-to-width ratio of $3:2$. What percent of the picture's length was eliminated in making the enlargement?

7. a) In *Case 1*, on page 295:
      i) Calculate the area of the image that is cut off.
      ii) Express this area as a percent of the image before its edges are cut.
   b) In *Case 2*, on page 295:
      i) Calculate the area of the dark bands on the screen.
      ii) Express this area as a percent of the area of the screen.
   c) How do the percents in parts a and b compare?

8. The scale of the floor plan is $1:200$. This means that 1 mm on the plan corresponds to 200 mm, or 0.2 m in the house. Measure the plan.
   a) Calculate the dimensions, in metres, of each room.
      i) the living room
      ii) the master bedroom
      iii) the family room
   b) Does each room have the same length-to-width ratio on the plan as in the house?

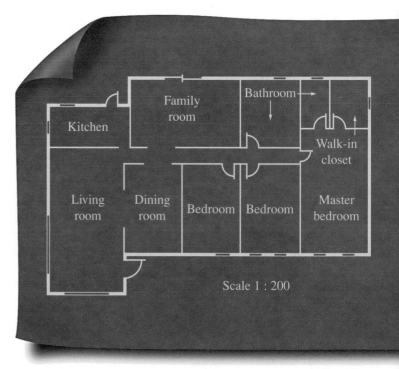

9. Solve each proportion.

a) $\dfrac{x}{3} = \dfrac{13}{15}$ b) $\dfrac{x}{9} = \dfrac{36}{27}$

c) $\dfrac{3}{x} = \dfrac{9}{48}$ d) $\dfrac{16}{24} = \dfrac{14}{x}$

On your own

10. Solve each proportion.

a) $\dfrac{3}{5} = \dfrac{x}{45}$ b) $\dfrac{1.5}{x} = \dfrac{7.2}{3}$

c) $7 : x = 16 : 9$ d) $20 : 17 = 6 : x$

11. White gold is an alloy of nickel and gold in the ratio of $3 : 8$ by mass. A white gold ring has a mass of 30.0 g. What is the mass of nickel in the ring?

12. In 1988, Canada mined 128.5 t of gold. This was 6.8% of the world's gold production. South Africa contributed 32.6% of the world's gold production. How many tonnes of gold did South Africa mine?

13. At a given time of day, the ratio of the height of a tree to the length of its shadow is the same for all trees. A tree 12 m high casts a shadow 5 m long.

a) How tall is a tree that casts a shadow 3 m long?

b) Why is the ratio of height to shadow length the same for all trees?

Extend your thinking

14. The population of China is about 1 160 000 000 and the population of Calgary is about 710 000. Use this information and the proportion in exercise 1b to calculate the population of Canada.

15. Use the information in exercise 1a. Show algebraically that the mass of a blue whale to the mass of a person is the same as the mass of an African elephant to the mass of a chicken.

16. In exercise 4, we saw that when the full height of the movie was preserved, the television screen showed only 75% of the width of the original image. When the full width was preserved, the television screen showed only 75% of the height of the original image. In both cases the percents are the same. Will the percents be equal for all other width-to-height ratios? Prove your answer algebraically.

The Ideas

Measure your TV screen at home. In your journal, explain what could happen to a movie, with a width-to-height image of $16 : 9$, if it were shown on your TV.

How Can You Estimate the Number of Fish in a Lake?

Lesley Barnes is a fisheries biologist who works for the Ontario Ministry of Natural Resources. One of her jobs is to estimate how many trout there are in Red Lake, a large lake in northwestern Ontario. She also needs to find out if trout from all parts of the lake use a spawning shoal at one end of the lake. To estimate the trout population, she used a clever idea and a proportion.

Understand the problem

- Do you think it would be possible to catch all the fish in a lake and count them?
- What are you asked to do?

Think of a strategy

This is the strategy Lesley used:
- Catch some fish and tag them. Release them into the lake.
- Wait a year and catch some fish again.
- In the second catch, count the number of tagged fish and the total number of fish.
- Let n represent the number of fish in the lake. Write an equation and solve it for n.

Carry out the strategy

- To illustrate the method, suppose Lesley obtained these results.

  Number of fish caught and tagged the first time: 38
  Number of fish caught the second time: 127
  Number of tagged fish in the second catch: 8

- You have these three numbers and a variable n to represent the number of fish in the lake. Write an equation relating these four quantities, and solve it.
- What was Lesley's estimate for the number of fish in the lake?

Look back

- What was Lesley's clever idea?
- What assumptions did Lesley make about what happened to the tagged fish after she released them into the lake?
- What assumptions did she make about the other fish in the lake?
- Do you think these assumptions are reasonable? Give reasons for your answer.
- Suppose the number of tagged fish in the second catch had been 9 instead of 8. How would this affect the result?

Communicating the Ideas

In your journal, write a description of how you could estimate the number of fish in a lake. Use some numerical examples in your explanation to help someone who reads your work to understand the method.

Remote Sensing

IN 1972, THE FIRST OF A SERIES OF SIX LANDSAT SATELLITES WAS LAUNCHED BY NASA. These satellites carry computer equipment which generates high-quality images of a country's physical geography. The process of observation from a high vantage point is known as *remote sensing*. Canada is one of the world leaders in this technology. Images produced by remote sensing can be used to determine the extent of drought or flooding, the spread of forest fires, the existence of natural resources, as well as the outline of shores, mountain ranges, bridges, dams, buildings, and other structures.

The image on the previous page shows the city of Vancouver in the centre and the Strait of Georgia to the left. The large lake in the upper right is Harrison Lake. The scale for this image is 1 : 1 250 000.

1. How long is Harrison Lake?

2. The town of Hope appears on the image near the upper right corner. It is approximately 3.0 cm from the top and 1.0 cm from the right. The Fraser River flows through Hope to the Strait of Georgia. How long is the river that flows from Harrison Lake to the Strait of Georgia?

3. What area is represented by the image on the previous page?

4. An object has to be about 30 m across before it will show up in a Landsat image.
   a) Do you think your school could be seen on a Landsat image? How can you find out?
   b) Would you be able to see a football field on such an image?

5. The Landsat satellite is about 900 km above the ground when the images are created. To get an idea how high this is, use an atlas or map to find a city in Canada or the United States that is approximately 900 km from where you live.

DATA DISK

6. Use the *Moon and Planets* database from the student's disk or an almanac to find the radius of Earth. About how far does Landsat travel in one orbit?

7. The satellite makes one complete orbit of Earth in about 100 min.
   a) How fast is Landsat travelling, in kilometres per hour?
   b) How far does it travel in one day?
   c) How many orbits would it make in:
      i) 6 h?   ii) 1 day?   iii) 1 week?   iv) 1 month?

8. A Landsat satellite circles Earth from north to south in a near-polar orbit. Estimate how long it would take to travel from the North Pole to the Canada-U.S. border.

9. Landsat makes a total of 233 different orbits before it returns to the same location. Suppose it is above your school right now.
   a) How long will it be before Landsat is above your school again?
   b) What time of day will it be then?
   c) After one complete orbit, do you think the satellite will be to the east or west of your school? Why?

10. On each orbit, the satellite scans a region on the ground that is 185 km wide.
   a) What is the smallest number of orbits that would be necessary to provide remote sensing images of all of Canada?
   b) Do you think that these images could all be taken on consecutive orbits? Why?

Developing the Ideas

▶▶*Through Discussion*

How can we tell whether two figures of different sizes have the same shape? One of these logos has a distinctly different shape from the other two. How can we determine whether the two logos that look alike actually have the same shape?

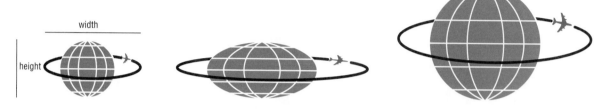

1. For each logo, measure the height and the width.
   Calculate its height-to-width ratio to one decimal place.

2. What do you discover?

Repeat these measurements with the rectangles below.

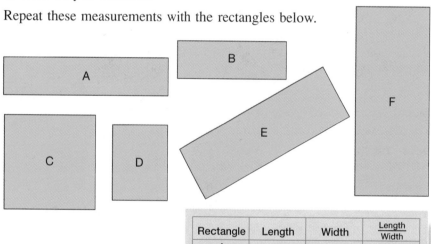

Copy and complete this table.

Rectangle	Length	Width	$\frac{Length}{Width}$
A			
B			
C			
D			
E			
F			

3. Measure and record the length and width of each rectangle.

4. Calculate and record the length : width ratio for each rectangle.
   Write the ratio as a decimal.

5. Which two rectangles have the same length : width ratio?

We say that two rectangles which have the same length : width ratio are *similar*.
Similar rectangles have the same shape but not necessarily the same size.

6. Which of the rectangles are similar?

Similar is the mathematical word meaning *same shape*. If two rectangles are similar, the ratio of the lengths of any two sides of one rectangle is equal to the ratio of the lengths of the corresponding sides of the other rectangle.

$$\frac{AB}{BC} = \frac{A'B'}{B'C'}$$

We can extend the concept of similarity to polygons.

If two polygons are similar, then the ratio of the lengths of any two sides of one polygon is equal to the ratio of the lengths of the corresponding sides of the other polygon.

The following examples show how we use this property of similar figures. We can calculate the unknown length of one side of a figure if we know the length of one of its sides and the lengths of corresponding sides of a similar figure.

Example 1............................

These two triangles are similar. Determine the length of side EF.

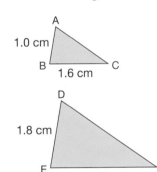

Solution ....

Since △DEF is similar to △ABC, the ratio of any two sides of △DEF is equal to the ratio of the corresponding sides of △ABC. We write a proportion.

$$\frac{EF}{DE} = \frac{BC}{AB}$$

Substitute the lengths we know.

$$\frac{EF}{1.8} = \frac{1.6}{1.0}$$

Solve the proportion.

$$EF = 1.8 \times 1.6$$
$$= 2.88$$

EF is about 2.9 cm long.

Example 2.............................

These two octagons are similar. Determine the length of diagonal B′F′.

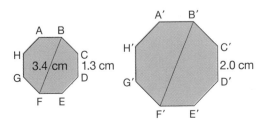

Solution ....

Since the octagons are similar, we can write a proportion relating corresponding segments.

$$\frac{B'F'}{C'D'} = \frac{BF}{CD}$$

Substitute the lengths we know.

$$\frac{B'F'}{2.0} = \frac{3.4}{1.3}$$

$$B'F' = \frac{3.4 \times 2.0}{1.3}$$

$$\doteq 5.23$$

B′F′ is approximately 5.2 cm long.

Working with Mathematics

Something to talk about

1. Explain how you can find out whether two rectangles have the same shape.

2. How can you find out whether two triangles have the same shape?

3. What does it mean when two figures are said to be *similar*?

4. Each side of the hexagon on the right is twice as long as the corresponding side of the hexagon on the left. Are the hexagons similar? Explain your answer.

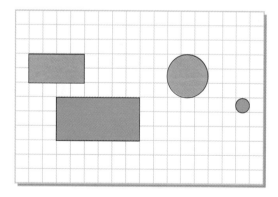

5. Recall that figures which can be made to coincide are *congruent*. Are congruent figures similar? Explain your answer.

Work together

6. **a)** Calculate the length-to-width ratio for each rectangle.

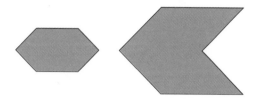

b) Are the rectangles similar?

c) How many times as great as the length of the blue rectangle is the length of the red rectangle?

d) Are the two circles similar? Explain your answer.

7. In each diagram, the triangles are similar. For each pair of triangles, write the ratio of sides which is equal to $\frac{AB}{BC}$.

a)

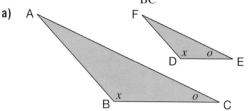

b)

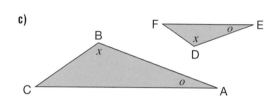

c)

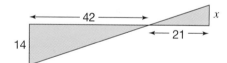

8. The two triangles in each diagram are similar. Find each length represented by x.

a)

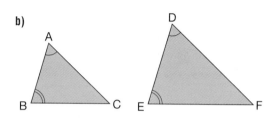

b)

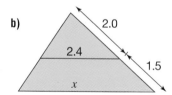

c)

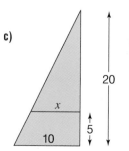

On your own

9. Which rectangle has the same shape as the yellow rectangle? Explain how you know.

10. A photocopy machine is set to reduce all dimensions to 77% of their original sizes. This picture of the Canadian flag is copied on the machine.

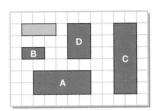

a) Measure the flag. What is its length-to-width ratio?

b) What is the length-to-width ratio of the photocopy?

c) What is the length of the flag on the photocopy?

d) What is the width of the flag on the photocopy?

e) Calculate the areas of the flag and its photocopy.

f) Write the area of the photocopy as a fraction of the area of the flag. Express this fraction as a percent, to the nearest whole number.

11. Measure AD, AB, AE, and AC. Is △ABC similar to △ADE?

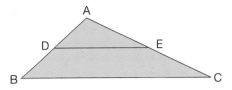

Extend your thinking

12. a) An enlargement of a triangle makes every dimension k times as large as the original, where k is greater than 1. The perimeter of the original triangle is p. What is the perimeter of the enlarged triangle?

b) The area of the original triangle is A. What is the area of the enlarged triangle?

Is a Laser Gun Better For Catching Speeders Than a Radar Gun?

A radar gun is used by a police officer to catch speeding motorists. A beam of microwave radiation is directed at an approaching car. This beam spreads out as it travels away from the gun. At a distance of 300 m from the gun, the beam has spread out approximately 32 m. The frequency of the signal, when it reflects off a car and returns to the gun, indicates the speed of the car.

Police officers in New York State have started to use laser guns to catch speeding motorists. The gun emits infrared radiation. This beam does not spread out as much as a radar beam. At a distance of 300 m from the gun, the radiation has spread out approximately 0.9 m.

A radar gun can be used at a range of 200 m. The New York State troopers claim that a laser gun is more effective for controlling speeders. Do you agree? Why?

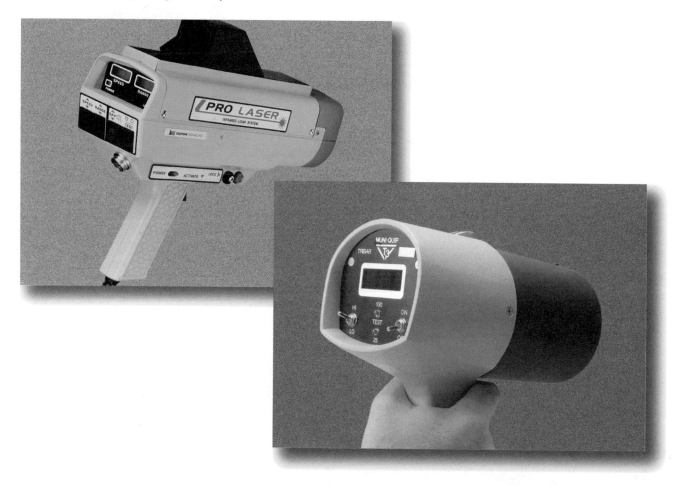

radar
gun

300 m

32 m

Diagram of radar
gun and beam

laser
gun

300 m

0.9 m

Diagram of laser
gun and beam

Understand the problem

- What are the two types of guns used by police to catch speeders?
- What is meant by one type of gun being "more effective"?
- At a range of 300 m, how many cars could be "caught" in each beam? How many cars could be "caught" in each beam at a range of 200 m?

Think of a strategy

- Use the information for the spread of each beam at 300 m. For each gun, draw a diagram to show the spread at 200 m.

Carry out the strategy

- Use similar triangles. A gun will be the vertex of an isosceles triangle. The equal sides of the triangle will be the edges of the beam.
- What is the length of the base of each triangle when its height is 200 m?

Look back

- At 200 m, how many lanes of traffic would be in the "field of vision" of a radar gun? Could a police officer determine which car was speeding if there was a car in each lane?
- When using a laser gun, would the police officer have the same difficulty? Explain your answer.
- Could the speed of a particular car at a distance of 500 m be determined using a laser gun? How could the police officer be sure that she had the right car?
- Some companies sell speed trap detectors to warn drivers they are approaching a speed trap. The companies claim that the detector usually alerts the driver that the speed trap is there, before the speed of the car is known by the police officer. This allows the driver to slow down. Why do you think it might be more difficult for a speed trap detector to warn a speeding motorist of a laser trap than a radar trap?

Communicating the Ideas

In your journal, explain why a laser gun is better for catching speeders than a radar gun is.

Constructing Similar Figures

In this activity, you will use the Draw program on a computer to create similar geometric figures.

Create a small square and two isosceles right triangles. The legs of the right triangles and the sides of the square have length 1 unit.

Use these figures (Duplicate and drag) to make the figure shown. It has a base of 4 units, and a height of 4 units. This is figure A.

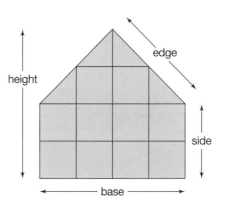

1. Make another figure that is twice as high and whose base is twice as long as figure A. Call this figure B.
   a) What is the area of figure A?
   b) What is the area of figure B?

2. Write each ratio.
   a) edge of figure B : edge of figure A
   b) side of figure B : side of figure A
   c) height of figure B : height of figure A

3. Draw figure C similar to figure A so that the ratio of the side of figure A to the side of figure C is 2 : 1. Write the ratio of the areas of these figures.

4. Create two new similar figures D and E so that the ratios of the side of E to the side of D and the edge of E to the edge of D are 5 : 3.

5. Is there a ratio that relates figure A to figure E? If so, what ratio?

6. Find a ratio that relates each figure to each other figure in the set of five figures.

7. Create two irregular figures (include some curves) which are similar. Write the ratio of their corresponding lengths. For example, these figures have corresponding lengths in the ratio 2 : 3.

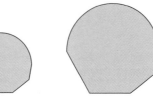

Mathematics & Technology

Linking Ideas

ENLARGEMENTS AND REDUCTIONS

Developing the Ideas

▶ ▶ *Through an Activity*

When the negative of a 35-mm film is developed, it is available as a photograph in these sizes: 3 by 4, 4 by 5, 4 by 6, 5 by 7, 8 by 12, 11 by 14, 16 by 20, 20 by 24. The negative has dimensions 2.4 cm by 3.6 cm. Which of the photographs listed above can be produced without losing any of the picture?

1. On squared paper, draw a rectangle 2.4 cm by 3.6 cm.

2. On the same piece of paper, draw each rectangle listed below, so that the rectangles have a common vertex.

3. From the common vertex, draw a diagonal of each rectangle. What do you notice?

4. Copy and complete the table.

Width (cm)	Height (cm)	Width : Height
3	4	
4	5	
4	6	
5	7	
8	12	
11	14	
16	20	
20	24	

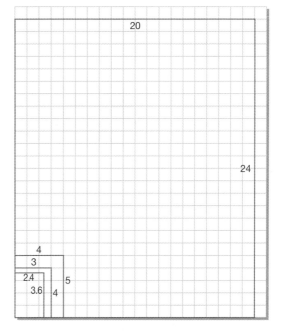

a) Which sizes of photograph have the same width : height ratio?

b) Which sizes of photograph are similar to the negative?

c) Which sizes of photograph have some of the picture missing?

Canada produces 6.5 million tonnes of toxic waste each year. How much is this for every person living in Canada? How much is this per person, per day?

Several times in this chapter we have referred to photographs and their enlargements. If the enlargement is similar to the original photograph, then they have the same length-to-width ratio.

Consider a photograph that has dimensions 4 by 5.
An enlargement of it has dimensions 8 by 10.

5

4

10

8

The width of the enlargement is 2 times the width of the original photograph. We say the *scale factor* of the enlargement is 2.

$$\text{Scale factor of the enlargement} = \frac{\text{width of enlargement}}{\text{width of original photograph}}$$

Another enlargement of the 4 by 5 photograph has dimensions 16 by 20.

The scale factor of this enlargement is $\frac{16}{4}$, or 4.

We can write the scale factor 4 as the *scale* 4 : 1.
That is, the scale of the enlargement is 4 : 1.

Suppose we have a poster with dimensions 55 cm by 85 cm.

This is reduced to 22 cm by 34 cm to fit on a sheet of paper.

The smaller poster is a reduction of the original poster. We can use scale factor to describe the reduction.

22 cm

34 cm

55 cm

85 cm

$$\text{Scale factor of the reduction} = \frac{\text{width of reduced poster}}{\text{width of original poster}}$$

For the poster, the scale factor of the reduction is $\frac{22}{55}$, or 0.4.

The scale factor of the reduction can also be calculated from a ratio of corresponding lengths; that is, $\frac{34}{85}$, or 0.4.

We can write the scale factor as the scale 0.4 : 1.
That is, the scale of the reduction is 0.4 : 1.

Example 1 ⋅⋅⋅

The Eiffel Tower was built
in Paris, France, in 1889.
It has a height of about 300 m.

Its height in this scale drawing is 4 cm.
What is the scale factor of the drawing?

4 cm

Solution

Scale factor = $\dfrac{\text{height of the Eiffel Tower in the diagram}}{\text{height of the Eiffel Tower}}$

$= \dfrac{4 \text{ cm}}{300 \text{ m}}$

$= \dfrac{4 \text{ cm}}{30\ 000 \text{ cm}}$

$\doteq 0.000\ 13$

The scale factor is approximately 0.000 13.

Example 2 ⋅⋅⋅

When it was completed in 1973, the Sears Tower in Chicago was
the world's tallest building. The scale drawing on the right has a
scale factor of 0.0005. What is the height of the Sears Tower?

Solution

We measure the height of the drawing to be 21.7 cm.
Let h centimetres represent the height of the Sears Tower.

We use scale factor = $\dfrac{\text{height of drawing}}{\text{height of building}}$ to set up a proportion.

We write the scale factor as a fraction with a denominator of 1.

$\dfrac{0.0005}{1} = \dfrac{21.7}{h}$

Invert the fractions.

$\dfrac{1}{0.0005} = \dfrac{h}{21.7}$

Multiply each side by 21.7.

$h = \dfrac{21.7}{0.0005}$

$= 43\ 400$

We convert this height in centimetres to metres.
The Sears Tower is approximately 434 m high.

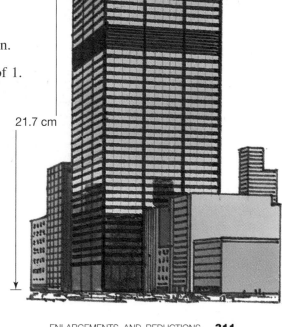

21.7 cm

Working with Mathematics

Something to talk about

1. Explain the meaning of each term.
   a) an enlargement   b) a reduction
   c) a scale factor   d) a scale drawing
   e) a scale

2. a) A scale drawing has a scale factor of 0.78. Is the drawing an enlargement or a reduction?
   b) If you know the scale factor, how can you determine whether a scale drawing is an enlargement or a reduction?

3. Write the scale factor that corresponds to each scale.
   a) 2 : 1   b) 1 : 5   c) 5 : 3
   d) 2 : 5   e) 8 : 1   f) 3 : 5

4. Write the scale that corresponds to each scale factor.
   a) 2   b) 1.5   c) 0.5
   d) 0.25   e) 2.5   f) 5

5. Is the scale factor for an enlargement defined differently from the scale factor for a reduction? Explain your answer.

Work together

6. The photograph on the right is an enlargement of the photograph on the left.

Measure the photographs.
   a) Calculate the scale factor of the enlargement to one decimal place.
   b) Calculate the length-to-width ratio of the original photo and the length-to-width ratio of its enlargement. What do you discover?

7. A passport photo is 4.5 cm long and 3.5 cm wide. It is enlarged by a scale factor of 3.
   a) How long is the enlargement?
   b) How wide is the enlargement?

8. A photocopy machine is set so that a line that is 6.0 cm long on the original becomes 8.4 cm long on the copy.
   a) Is the copy a reduction or an enlargement?
   b) What is the scale factor?
   c) Express the scale factor as a percent.

9. Suppose you want to draw one thing to scale and have it fit on this page. What might you draw for each scale?
   a) 2 : 1   b) 10 : 1
   c) 1 : 8   d) 1 cm to 1 m

On your own

10. Write the scale factor for each scale in exercise 9.

11. The Humber Estuary Bridge in the United Kingdom is the world's longest bridge. The distance between the tops of its two towers is about 1400 m. This is so long that the bridge was constructed with a slight bend so that it could follow the curvature of Earth! What is the scale factor in this drawing of the bridge, to five decimal places?

12. The tallest tree in Canada is about 73 m high. What scale factor would you use to draw a diagram in which the tree has a height of 11 cm? Give the answer to four decimal places.

13. The structures in the diagram below are drawn to the same scale.

a) Measure the height of each drawing.

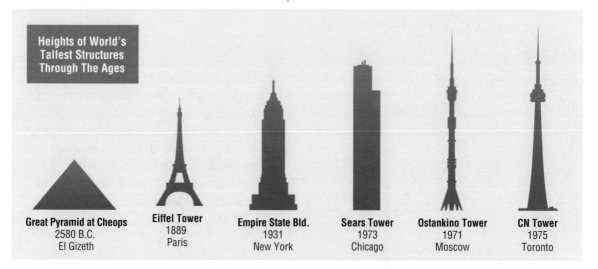

Heights of World's Tallest Structures Through The Ages

Great Pyramid at Cheops 2580 B.C. El Gizeth | **Eiffel Tower** 1889 Paris | **Empire State Bld.** 1931 New York | **Sears Tower** 1973 Chicago | **Ostankino Tower** 1971 Moscow | **CN Tower** 1975 Toronto

b) i) Use a reference book to find the height of one of the structures.

ii) What is the ratio of the height in the drawing to the height of the structure in part i? Make sure you express both heights in the same unit. This ratio is the scale for the diagram.

c) Use the scale for this diagram to find the height of the Ostankino Tower.

d) Calculate the heights of all the other structures.

e) Compare your values for the heights of the structures with those of other students.

i) How close are they?

ii) Did it make a difference which structure you used to find the scale?

Extend your thinking

14. A picture measuring 2 cm by 3 cm is enlarged to 8 cm by 12 cm.

a) What is the scale factor of the enlargement?

b) How many times as great as the original is the area of the enlargement?

c) If an enlargement has a scale factor k, what is the ratio of the area of the enlargement to the area of the original?

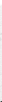
COMMUNICATING

The Ideas

Take measurements of yourself in a recent photograph. Compare these with your actual measurements to determine the scale of the photograph. What is the scale factor of your photograph? Write a report in your journal.

Fast Food, Safe Food

Jim Chan is a public heath inspector. He's one of the people who makes sure that the food we eat in restaurants is safe.

Public health inspectors inspect most restaurants every two months. Once a year they do a very detailed inspection of the preparation of food. They will also do this kind of inspection if someone complains of feeling ill after eating at a restaurant.

Some bacteria are present in almost all foods. Bacteria may even help to make the food; dairy products such as sour cream and yogurt need bacteria to give them their distinctive flavours. Most bacteria are harmless, but some will cause illness if eaten. Whether bacteria are harmless or not, there are strict standards as to how many are allowed in food.

Suppose a customer complains to the health department about feeling ill after drinking a milkshake. An inspector visits the restaurant, and takes a sample of milkshake for testing. The sample is sent to a laboratory, where a technician counts the bacteria. Because an individual bacterium is too small to see, the technician dilutes the sample and spreads it on a dish of solid bacteria food. Each bacterium will divide into two new bacteria every 20 min. Before long, there are enough bacteria to see. This group of millions of bacteria is called a colony. The technician can then count the number of colonies. Since each colony began as a single bacterium, she can determine the number of bacteria in the sample. If this number exceeds 10^5 per millilitre, the restaurant is asked to stop making milkshakes.

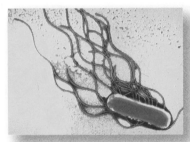

The technician mixes 10 mL of the milkshake with 990 mL of distilled water, in a flask. She spreads 0.1 mL of this mixture on a dish.

1. **a)** What is the total volume of the mixture in the flask?
   b) What is the ratio of the volume of the sample in the dish to the total volume in the flask?

2. The technician counts 147 colonies in the dish. The ratio of the number of bacteria in the dish to the number of bacteria in the flask is equal to the ratio of the volumes in exercise 1b. Set up a proportion. Solve it to determine how many bacteria were in the flask.

3. All the bacteria in the flask came from the 10-mL sample of milkshake.
   a) How many bacteria were there in 1 mL of milkshake?
   b) Does this exceed the allowable level?

Review

1. Calculate each percent.
   a) 25% of 40
   b) 6% of 150
   c) 140% of 25
   d) 0.8% of 300

2. At a school dance, there are 275 girls, 225 boys, and 15 teachers. Express each ratio in lowest terms.
   a) girls to boys
   b) teachers to girls
   c) students to teachers

3. This photograph was taken with an electron microscope. It shows two aphids on a lemon leaf, magnified 25 times. Measure the length of an aphid in the photograph. Determine its actual length in millimetres.

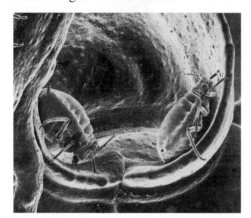

4. A *Mach number* is a ratio whose second term is 1. The Mach number of an airplane is the ratio of its speed to the speed of sound at the same altitude and temperature. Assume an airplane is at an altitude where the speed of sound is 1085 km/h.
   a) Calculate the Mach number for each speed. Give the answers to one decimal place.
      i) 3255 km/h
      ii) 1000 km/h
   b) Find the speed of the North American Aviation X-15A-2, which flies at Mach 6.72.

5. Which would drain a tank faster; one drain 4 cm in diameter or two drains each 2 cm in diameter? How many times as fast would the tank drain?

6. A car uses fuel at the rate of 7.2 L/100 km.
   a) How much fuel is needed to travel 360 km?
   b) How far will the car travel on a full tank of 85 L?

7. Solve each proportion.
   a) $\frac{11}{16} = \frac{n}{8}$
   b) $\frac{5}{8} = \frac{9}{x}$
   c) $\frac{t}{4} = \frac{5}{7}$
   d) $\frac{9}{b} = \frac{5}{6}$
   e) $5 : 13 = 10 : y$
   f) $7.2 : x = 36 : 1.5$

8. The two triangles in each diagram are similar. Find each length represented by x.

   a)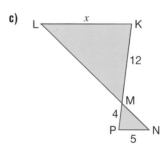

   b)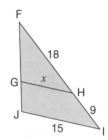

   c)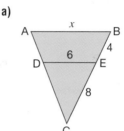

9. On grid paper, draw a rectangle that is 12 units long and 8 units wide.
   a) Draw a larger rectangle that is similar to the first rectangle.
   b) Draw a smaller rectangle that is similar to the first rectangle.
   c) How can you be sure that the rectangles you drew are similar?

10. Triangle ABC has sides AB = 5 cm, BC = 12 cm, and AC = 13 cm.
    a) Triangle ABC is enlarged by using a scale factor of 4. Find the lengths of the sides of the enlarged triangle.
    b) Triangle ABC is reduced by using a scale factor of 0.75. Find the lengths of the sides of the reduced triangle.

Bicycle Gears and Speed

How do the gears on a 12-speed bike or mountain bike work? Where is fourth gear? Are there two (or more) gears that have the same effect? Why do higher gears cause you to go faster? Is it harder to pedal in high gear? Why? How do bicycle racers use the gears? How fast can you go in high gear?

The purpose of this project is to help you understand how the gears on your bike work. You will need to look carefully at several different bikes, perform "experiments" with them, and compare the results to answer questions like those above.

ACTIVITY 1

How Many Speeds?

On a bicycle, the large gears attached to the pedals are called the *pedal gears*. The smaller gears attached to the rear wheel are the *wheel gears*. Determine the arrangement of pedal gears and wheel gears on several different bikes. How are these arrangements related to the total number of gears?

ACTIVITY 2

Gear Ratios

A *gear ratio* of a bike is the number of teeth in the pedal gear to the number of teeth in the wheel gear. Examine the pedal gears and the wheel gears on two different bikes. Determine the gear ratios for each bike. Which bike is easier to pedal? Which bike is faster?

ACTIVITY 3

Where is Fourth Gear?

Using the same two bikes, determine which pedal gear and which wheel gear are used for the lowest gear, the fourth gear, the seventh gear, and the highest gear. Are the gears arranged so that the chain engages the wheel gears in order from largest to smallest? Explain.

ACTIVITY 4

How Do The Gears Work?

As you pedal a bike, the chain moves around the pedal gear. This causes the wheel gear to turn, which then causes the back wheel to turn. Explain why it is easier to pedal the bike in low gear than it is in high gear. How do bicycle racers use this information in a race?

ACTIVITY 5

Gears and Speed

Does the gear you are using affect the speed you can achieve while riding the bike? By experimenting with several bikes, explain why you can go faster on a bike in higher gears than in lower gears.

ACTIVITY 6

Wheel Size and Speed

Does the size of the wheels on a bike affect its speed? By visiting a bicycle shop, or researching, find out what wheel sizes are available for different styles of bikes. Explain how wheel size and speed are related.

ACTIVITY 7

How Fast Can You Go?

In competitive bike racing, the rider tries to ensure that she pedals at a constant speed of 100 complete turns per minute. This is done by changing gears, when necessary, to maintain this pedalling speed. For each bike you used in this project, determine how far the rider would travel in one minute in fourth, seventh, and the highest gear. How fast would she go in each of these gears?

ACTIVITY 8

The World's Fastest Bike

A bike like the one shown below was used to set the down-hill bike speed record. It has only one pedal gear and one wheel gear. Explain why it is capable of such high speeds. Choose some pairs of values for the number of teeth in each gear. Determine how fast this bike could go for each pair of values, if the cyclist maintained a pedal speed of 100 turns per minute. How many teeth should the pedal gear and the wheel gear have to achieve a speed of more than 120 km/h? Why is this bike only good for down-hill racing?

MEASUREMENT

Mathematics File

Quests

Minds on Math

Start With What You Know

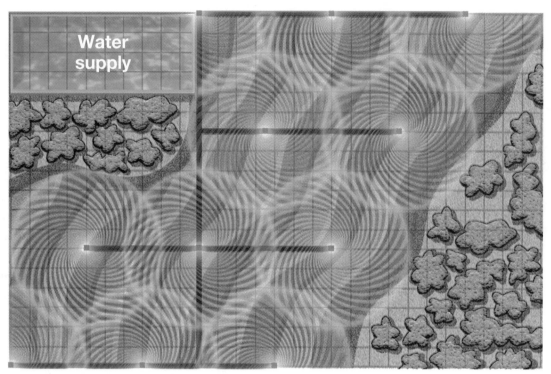

Scale: The side of 1 square = 0.25 m

The planning and use of an underground sprinkler system for a lawn involve measurement in different ways.

Four questions related to the sprinkler system are given below.
For each question:
- Discuss whether it involves length, area, or volume.
- Decide how you would answer the question.
- Answer the question.

1. How many square metres of lawn must be watered?

2. Approximately how many square metres of lawn are watered by each sprinkler?

3. Approximately how much water would be needed to cover the entire lawn with 2 cm of water?

4. Suppose you were installing this sprinkler system. How much pipe would you need to connect the sprinklers to each other and to the water supply?

5. **a)** What does *length* mean?

b) Without using any formulas, explain what *area* means.

c) Without using any formulas, explain what *volume* means.

6. In previous grades, you learned several measurement formulas.
   Some of these are listed below.

   a) Explain what each formula represents. Match each formula with one
      of the figures above.

   b) In your journal, summarize the formulas in a systematic way.
      Use diagrams to illustrate what the formulas represent.

$A = lw$ $A = s^2$ $V = lwh$ $C = 2\pi r$

$P = 2l + 2w$ $P = 4s$ $A = \pi r^2$ $V = x^3$

$C = \pi d$ $A = \frac{1}{2}bh$ $A = bh$ $P = 2(l + w)$

Designing a Lawn Sprinkler System

You are installing a sprinkler system for a lawn which is 12 m square. Each sprinkler in the system will water a circular area of the lawn. How can the sprinklers be arranged so that all parts of the lawn are covered with water? You can use the Draw program on a computer to explore various possibilities.

1. Make a grid of 12 squares by 12 squares. To do this, draw one square, Duplicate it, and drag the duplicate next to the first square. Next, Duplicate both and drag the double duplicate next to the first two squares. In this way you quickly get a row of 12 squares. Duplicate the whole row in a similar fashion to make the 12 by 12 grid. Make several copies of your grid.

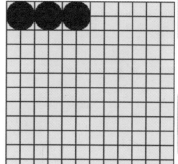

2. Use the circle/oval tool. Draw a circle to represent a sprinkler with diameter 2 m, which just fits inside 4 squares. (Note: in most Draw programs, holding the shift key down while using the circle/oval tool ensures that the object is a circle.) Place this circle in the top left 2 by 2 square. Duplicate this circle 5 times. Place the duplicates so that each covers one of the 2 by 2 squares in the top 2 rows. Duplicate to fill the grid.

3. a) What is the area of a 2 by 2 square?
   b) What is the area of a circle which just fits inside a 2 by 2 square?
   c) What area of the square is not covered by the circle? Give the answer to three decimal places.
   d) What percent of the whole grid will not be covered by this arrangement of circles? Give the answer to one decimal place.
   e) Is any part of the grid covered by more than one circle?

4. Repeat exercises 2 and 3 using larger circles on a new grid. This represents more powerful sprinklers. Is more of the lawn covered with the system of larger circles?

5. Design an arrangement of sprinklers which would cover the whole lawn. Keep the double coverage (two sprinklers covering the same part of the lawn) and the coverage outside of the lawn area to a minimum. With your design, include calculations that show it to be a good one.

6. Make some suggestions for more efficient lawn sprinkler systems. Illustrate those suggestions using the Draw program.

Developing the Ideas

▶ ▶ *Through an Activity*

You should work with a partner or in a group. You will need some tin cans with labels attached, a sharp knife, and a millimetre ruler.

Choose one of the cans. What do you think *total surface area* means? Devise a plan for calculating the total surface area of this can. Then use your plan to calculate the total surface area.

1. **a)** What did you notice about the shape of the label?
   b) How did you calculate the area of the label? What does this tell you about the area of the curved surface of the can?

2. How did you calculate the area of the bottom of the can?

3. What is the total surface area of the can?

4. Suppose a cylinder has radius r and height h. Based on what you have discovered using the can, describe how to calculate the total surface area of the cylinder.

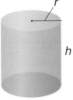

5. Write a formula for the total surface area in terms of r and h. Discuss your formula with other students.

Imagine that there is a paper label on the cylinder. When you unroll the label, it forms a rectangle with length equal to the circumference of the cylinder. The width of the rectangle is equal to the height of the cylinder. The area of the curved surface of the cylinder is equal to the area of the rectangle. The total surface area includes the two circles at the ends.

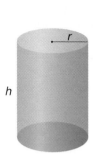

A cylinder has radius r and height h.
The area of the curved surface is:

A_{curved} = circumference × height
$= 2\pi rh$

The area of each end is:

$A_{base} = \pi r^2$

The total surface area is given by the formula:

$$A = A_{curved} + 2 \times A_{base}$$
or $\quad A = 2\pi rh + 2\pi r^2$

BOGGLE YOUR MIND

Some sources estimate that recycling one aluminum can saves the energy equivalent of 1.9 L of gasoline. What if all the students in your school recycled all the aluminum cans they use in one year? How many litres of gasoline would this represent?

Working with Mathematics

Something to talk about

1. One cylinder has a base radius of 3 cm and a height of 4 cm. Another cylinder has a base radius of 4 cm and a height of 3 cm. Do you think their total surface areas are equal? If not, which one do you think has the greater total surface area? Give a reason for your answer.

Work together

2. a) Check your answer to exercise 1 by calculating the total surface area of each cylinder.
   b) What is the ratio of the total surface areas?

3. A square piece of cardboard measuring 20 cm on a side is used to form the curved surface of a cylinder. Circles cut from another piece of cardboard are used for the top and the bottom.

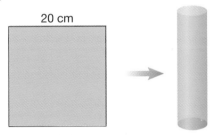
20 cm

   a) Calculate the radius of the cylinder to two decimal places.
   b) Calculate the total surface area of the cylinder.

4. A cylinder just fits inside a cubical box. Suppose the box has edges of length *x* centimetres. Find a formula for the total surface area of the cylinder.

On your own

5. A juice can has a cardboard curved surface and two metal ends.
   a) What area of cardboard is needed to make the can?
   b) What is the area of each metal end?
   c) What is the total surface area of the juice can?

|←——— 11.6 cm ———→|
6.6 cm

6. Newsprint is one of Canada's major exports. It is shipped in cylindrical rolls. The rolls shown have a diameter of 102 cm and a length of 137 cm. What is the area of the outer wrapping of the roll?

7. Calculate the total surface area of each cylinder.

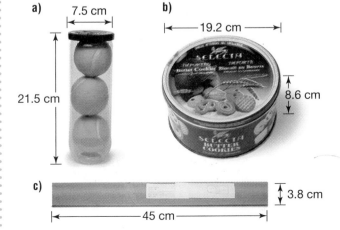

a) 7.5 cm, 21.5 cm
b) |←——— 19.2 cm ———→|, 8.6 cm
c) 45 cm, 3.8 cm

Extend your thinking

8. What happens to the total surface area of a cylinder if:

a) its radius is not changed, but its height is doubled? tripled? multiplied by n?

b) its height is not changed, but its radius is doubled? tripled? multiplied by n?

c) both the height and the radius are doubled? tripled? multiplied by n?

9. Use a computer spreadsheet program to illustrate your conclusions from exercise 8. One possible set up for the spreadsheet is shown below.

TEMPLATE DISK

a) Explain each formula in cells C4, D4, and E4.

b) Enter values for the radius and the height in cells A4 and B4. Vary one or both of these values to illustrate the effects of doubling, tripling, and multiplying by other factors, as described in exercise 8.

	A	B	C	D	E
1	Surface area of a cylinder				
2					
3	Radius	Height	Area of ends	Area of sides	Total area
4			=Pi()*A4*A4	=2*Pi()*A4*B4	=2*C4+D4

COMMUNICATING

The Ideas

In your journal, describe how you calculate the total surface area of a cylinder if you know its dimensions. Include in your account:

- a formula for the total surface area in terms of the radius r and the height h
- a formula for the total surface area in terms of the diameter d and the height h
- an explanation of why the formulas are correct

BOGGLE YOUR MIND

The amount of precipitation that falls to Earth each year is equivalent to 380 000 000 L for every Canadian. How many cubic metres of water is this? What if you were to design a container to hold this water? What dimensions would it require?

What Shapes Make Cardboard Cylinders?

Why does a frozen orange juice can have a spiral seam? Nigel Reed of Sunoco Containers Inc. says it's because it's a very efficient way of making cans out of materials other than metal. And Nigel should know: Sunoco Containers manufactures more of these cans than any other company in Canada!

A spiral can is made of 3 layers of material: an inner layer of polymer (plastic), one layer of kraft cardboard, and an outer layer of paper, on which the label is printed. Long strips of these 3 layers are wound onto a long metal rod (called a mantle) at an angle of about 40°. It's much like winding a piece of ribbon around your finger. As the layers are wound, they form a long tube. This tube is cut in 9 places to form 10 cans. An aluminum base is attached and the can is ready to be shipped to juice manufacturers. After the can is filled, the juice manufacturer puts on an aluminum lid.

1. **a)** Suppose you were to cut open a spiral can and unroll the cardboard. What shape do you think it would have?
   b) Check your prediction in part a. You will need a frozen orange juice can, a sharp knife, and a lift-type can opener. Carefully remove the bottom of the can with the can opener. Then cut the cardboard along the seam and flatten it. Was your prediction correct?
   c) Calculate the surface area of the can.

2. **a)** Construct two copies of this parallelogram, and cut them out.
   b) Tape the edges of the parallelogram in two different ways to form two cylinders, with no overlap.
   c) Calculate the base diameter and the height of each cylinder. Give the answers to the nearest millimetre. Check by measuring.

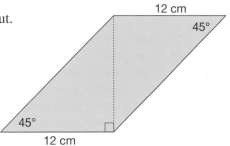

3. Every parallelogram can be used to construct two cylinders in this way. Draw an example of a parallelogram for which the two cylinders would be identical.

How Can You Fill a Can Exactly Half Full without Measuring?

You will need an empty can with no grooves in the side. A frozen juice can is ideal.

Without using a ruler or any other measuring device, and without using any other container, how can you put the right amount of water in the can so that it is exactly half full?

328

Understand the problem

- What are you asked to do?
- What are the only things you can use to solve this problem?

Think of a strategy

- You could put some water in the can and then slowly pour it out.
- As you do this, how do you think the space occupied by the water will compare with the empty space in the can above the water?
- How should these compare when the can is exactly half full?

Carry out the strategy

- Fill the can with water and then slowly pour it out.
- As you do this, look at the empty space and the space occupied by the water.
- Stop pouring when the space occupied by the water is the same as the empty space above the water.

Look back

- Can you think of any other way to solve this problem?
- Suppose you were allowed to use a ruler and other measuring devices, or containers. How many different ways can you half fill the can with water?
- Partly fill a can with water and hold it vertically above a sink or overflow container. The surface of the water has a circular shape. If you tilt the can, what other shapes can you obtain for the surface of the water? Draw diagrams of the different shapes you discover.

Communicating the Ideas

In your journal, write a description of this problem and your solution. Include diagrams to illustrate your solution.

VOLUMES OF A CYLINDER AND A CONE

Developing the Ideas
▶ ▶ *Through Activities*

Work in a group.

ACTIVITY 1

Working with a Cylinder

You will need an empty tin can, some centimetre cubes, and a millimetre ruler.

1. How many centimetre cubes will fit in one layer on the base of the can?

2. **a)** Describe a way you could use the centimetre cubes to determine the volume of the can.
   b) Estimate the number of centimetre cubes you would need.

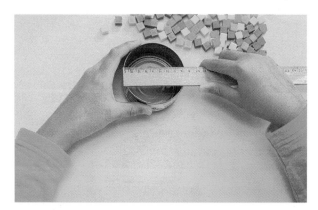

3. Measure the height and the diameter of the can.
   a) How could you use your measurements to calculate the volume of the can?
   b) Calculate the volume in cubic centimetres.
   c) Compare your result with your previous estimate. If they are different, explain why.

4. Suppose a cylinder has radius r and height h.

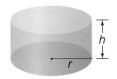

    a) Use your previous ideas to write a formula for the volume of the cylinder in terms of r and h.

    b) Compare your formula with those of other groups.

ACTIVITY 2

Working with a Cone

You will need an empty tin can, scissors, paper, tape, some clean sand or water, and an overflow container.

1. Use scissors, paper, and tape to make a paper cone that just fits inside the can.

2. a) Suppose you fill the cone with water or sand, and then empty it into the can. How many times do you think you could do this until the can is full?

    b) Check using water or sand.

3. Suppose you have a cone that just fits inside a cylinder.

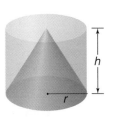

    a) Based on your observations, if you know the volume of the cylinder, how could you determine the volume of the cone?

    b) A cylinder and a cone have base radius r and height h. Write formulas for their volumes.

    c) Compare your formulas with those of other groups.

Imagine that a cylinder is filled
with layers of centimetre cubes. The
number of cubes, including part cubes,
needed to cover the base is equal to
the area of the base. If you multiply
this by the number of layers, the result
is the total number of cubes that fill
the can. This is the volume of the can.

The volume of a cylinder with radius r
and height h is given by the formula:

V = base area × height

or $V = \pi r^2 h$

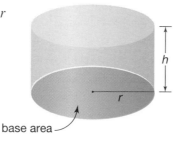

base area

Example 1

Depending what a building is used for, it must have
a regulation number of air changes per hour. To
plan a building's ventilation system to meet these
regulations, a mechanical engineer needs to know the
volume of space each floor of the building encloses.

The Peachtree Westin Plaza in Atlanta features a
cylindrical hotel. The hotel has a base diameter of
60 m. Each floor of the hotel has an interior height
of 3.5 m. Calculate the volume of space occupied by
each floor of the hotel.

Solution

The base radius is 30 m. Substitute 30 for r and 3.5
for h in the formula for the volume of a cylinder.
Use the π key on your scientific calculator. If you
have a 4-function calculator, substitute 3.14 for π.

$V = \pi r^2 h$

$= \pi \times 30^2 \times 3.5$

$\doteq 9896$

The volume of space enclosed by each floor of the
hotel is about 9900 m^3.

If a cone just fits inside a cylindrical can, you can fill the cone three times and pour its contents into the can. Then the can will be full.

These three volumes
taken together ...

... are equal
to this volume.

This is because the volume of a cylinder is exactly three times the volume of a cone with the same height and the same base radius. That is, the volume of the cone is one-third the volume of the cylinder.

The volume of a cone with radius r and height h is given by the formula:

$$V = \frac{1}{3} \times \text{base area} \times \text{height}$$

or $\quad V = \frac{1}{3}\pi r^2 h$

base area

Example 2 ....

Coke is one by-product of Suncor's crude oil plant in Fort McMurray, Alberta. This fuel is used to produce electricity and steam for other parts of Suncor's operations. Because such vast quantities of coke are produced, it is stored in large, conical piles. As Patti Lewis explains, when Suncor's engineers have to assess how much coke is in a pile, they survey it to measure the height and the diameter of the base. They input this information in a computer which then calculates the volume of the pile. Suppose a coke pile has a base diameter of 20 m and a height of 8 m. Calculate the volume of coke in the pile.

Solution

The base radius is 10 m. Substitute 10 for r and 8 for h in the formula for the volume of a cone. Use the π key on your scientific calculator. If you have a 4-function calculator, substitute 3.14 for π.

$V = \frac{1}{3}\pi r^2 h$

$\quad = \frac{1}{3} \times \pi \times 10^2 \times 8$

$\quad \doteq 838$

The volume of the pile is about 840 m³. Allowing for air spaces, the volume of coke in the pile is less than this. We cannot be certain, but the volume of coke is probably between 600 m³ and 800 m³.

Working with Mathematics

Something to talk about

1. One litre is often represented by a cube measuring 10 cm along each edge.
   a) Calculate the volumes of a cylinder and a cone which fit inside the cube.
   b) What percent of the space in the cube is occupied by the cylinder? by the cone? Give the answers to one decimal place.

Work together

2. Calculate the volume of the cylinder formed if rectangle ABCD is rotated about:
   a) side AB   b) side BC

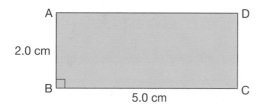

3. A can of paint is marked 978 mL. It has a base diameter of 10.4 cm and a height of 12.5 cm. Calculate the volume of the can, in cubic centimetres. Does the result confirm that the can's capacity is 978 mL?

4. a) What happens to the volume of a cylinder if its radius is not changed, but its height is doubled? tripled?
   b) What happens to the volume of a cylinder if its height is not changed, but its radius is doubled? tripled?
   c) What happens if both the height and the radius are doubled? tripled?

5. A circular log has a mass of 100 kg.
   a) A second log cut from the same tree has the same radius as this one but is half as long. What is the mass of the second log?
   b) A third log cut from the same tree has the same length as the first log but is one and a half times as thick as this one. What is the mass of the third log?
   c) A fourth log cut from the same tree is half as long and one and a half times as thick as this one. What is the mass of the fourth log?

6. a) Calculate the volume of the roll of newsprint described in exercise 6 on page 325.
   b) Measure a newspaper. Estimate how many newspapers like the one you measured could be printed from one roll of newsprint.

7. A roll of tape has an outside diameter of 58 mm and an inside diameter of 32 mm. The tape is 19 mm wide and 10 m long.
   a) Calculate the volume of tape in the roll, in cubic millimetres.
   b) Calculate the thickness of the tape.

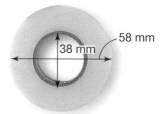

8. Construct the three figures shown. Make a cone from each figure by joining the straight edges and securing them with tape.

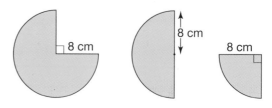

Without measuring, determine the base radius, the height, and the volume of each cone to the nearest tenth of a unit. Save your cones for use later (page 351).

9. Find the volume of each cylinder with the given dimensions. Give each answer to the nearest cubic centimetre.
   a) radius 5.00 cm; height 3.18 cm
   b) radius 7.50 cm, height 1.42 cm
   c) radius 3.99 cm; height 5.00 cm
   d) radius 3.26 cm; height 7.50 cm
   What do you notice about the volumes?

On your own

10. A machine bales hay in rolls 1.8 m in diameter and 1.2 m long.
    a) What is the radius of each roll?
    b) What volume of hay is in each roll?

11. Sand is discharged from a conveyor and forms a conical heap with a diameter of 5.4 m and a height of 2.7 m. What is the volume of the sand in the heap?

12. A cylindrical hot-water tank has a diameter of 56 cm and a height of 132 cm.
    a) Calculate the volume of the tank to the nearest cubic centimetre. What is the capacity of the tank in litres?
    b) Calculate the surface area of the tank to the nearest square centimetre.

13. Calculate the volume of the cone formed if right △ABC is rotated about:
    a) side AB   b) side BC

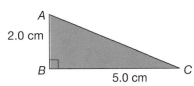

14. A refinery has five cylindrical storage tanks each measuring 12.2 m in diameter and 24.4 m high. The tanks are full.
    a) What is the total storage capacity of the refinery?
    b) Tanker trucks have cylindrical tanks 11 m long and 1.8 m in diameter. How many truck loads would be needed to empty all the tanks of the refinery?

Extend your thinking

15. Get two tin cans with different sizes. Measure the cans. Suppose you were to fill the smaller can with water and then pour the water into the larger can.
    a) Calculate how deep the water would be in the larger can.
    b) Try the activity and measure the depth of the water. How does it compare with your calculations?

16. Two identical jars contain equal quantities of water and milk. Suppose a cup of milk were removed and mixed with the water. Then a cup of the mixture were removed and mixed with the milk. Would there be more milk in the water or more water in the milk? Explain your answer.

COMMUNICATING

The Ideas

In your journal, describe how you calculate the volumes of a cylinder and a cone if you know their dimensions. Include in your account:
- an explanation of how the volume of a cone is related to the volume of a cylinder with the same base radius and the same height
- formulas for the volumes in terms of the radius r and the height h
- formulas for the volumes in terms of the diameter d and the height h

Which Cylinder Has the Greater Volume?

You can roll a rectangular piece of paper into a cylinder in two different ways. If there is no overlap, do the cylinders have the same volume? If not, then which has the greater volume—the one with the long side of the rectangle as its height or the one with the short side of the rectangle as its height?

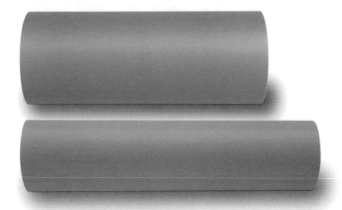

Understand the problem

- Do the two cylinders have the same height? Do they have the same radius?
- What are you asked to do?

Think of a strategy

- You could take two sheets of paper and make the two cylinders.
- What information would you need to calculate the volumes of the cylinders?

Carry out the strategy

- Before making the cylinders, measure the length and the width of the paper.
- When you roll the paper to form a cylinder, how does the circumference and the height of the cylinder compare with the dimensions of the paper?
- Determine the height and the base radius for each cylinder.
- Calculate the volumes of the cylinders.
- Are the volumes the same? If not, which cylinder has the greater volume?

Look back

- What shape would the paper have to be for the volumes to be equal?
- Suppose another piece of paper had the same width, but was twice as long. How would the volumes of the two cylinders compare?
- Suppose another piece of paper had the same length, but was half as wide. How would the volumes of the two cylinders compare?
- Determine the dimensions of a sheet of paper for which the volume of one cylinder is two times the volume of the other cylinder.

Communicating the Ideas

In your journal, write a description of this problem and your solution. Include drawings of the cylinders.

Designing Package Sizes

Suppose you are asked to design a cylindrical can to have a specific volume. As you discovered in exercise 9 on page 335, you could try many different combinations of height and base diameter for your can and still have the same volume. How can you decide which dimensions to use? Which dimensions would require the least amount of material?

You can answer this question using a spreadsheet. You will need a can which has the capacity in millilitres marked on the label. You will use the spreadsheet to determine the dimensions of a can which has the same capacity as yours, and which can be made from the least amount of material.

Start your spreadsheet program and enter the information shown below. You can use the numbers shown in cells C3 and C4 (which represent a pasta sauce can), or you can use the volume and diameter of your own can.

TEMPLATE DISK

1. Look at the formulas in cells C6 to C10. What does each formula tell the computer to do?

	A	B	C
1	Minimizing the surface area of a can		
2			
3	Enter :	Volume	725
4		Base diameter	8.2
5			
6	Calculate :	Radius	=C4/2
7		Height	=C3/(Pi()*C6*C6)
8		Area of base	=Pi()*C6*C6
9		Area of label	=2*Pi()*C6*C7
10		Total area	=2*C8+C9

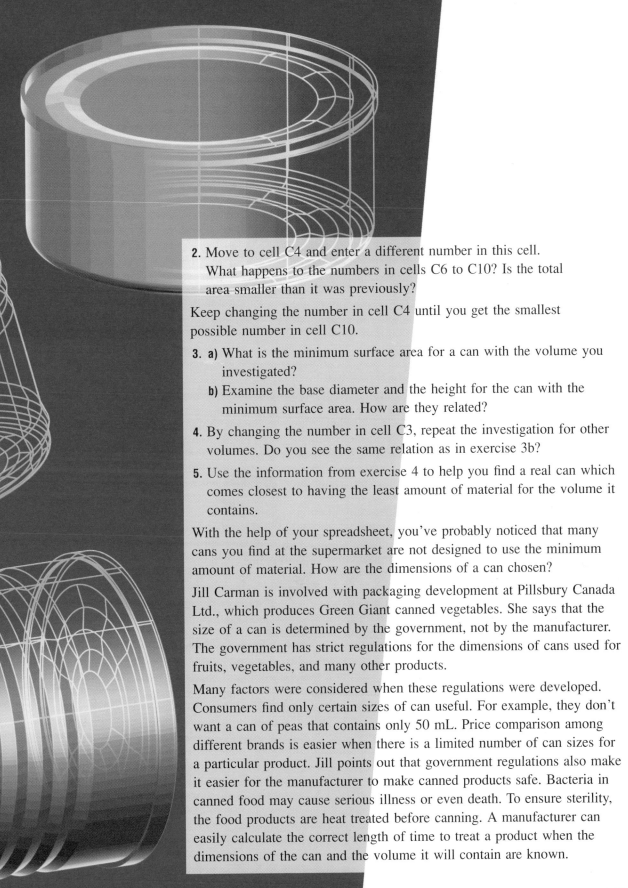

2. Move to cell C4 and enter a different number in this cell. What happens to the numbers in cells C6 to C10? Is the total area smaller than it was previously?

Keep changing the number in cell C4 until you get the smallest possible number in cell C10.

3. a) What is the minimum surface area for a can with the volume you investigated?
   b) Examine the base diameter and the height for the can with the minimum surface area. How are they related?

4. By changing the number in cell C3, repeat the investigation for other volumes. Do you see the same relation as in exercise 3b?

5. Use the information from exercise 4 to help you find a real can which comes closest to having the least amount of material for the volume it contains.

With the help of your spreadsheet, you've probably noticed that many cans you find at the supermarket are not designed to use the minimum amount of material. How are the dimensions of a can chosen?

Jill Carman is involved with packaging development at Pillsbury Canada Ltd., which produces Green Giant canned vegetables. She says that the size of a can is determined by the government, not by the manufacturer. The government has strict regulations for the dimensions of cans used for fruits, vegetables, and many other products.

Many factors were considered when these regulations were developed. Consumers find only certain sizes of can useful. For example, they don't want a can of peas that contains only 50 mL. Price comparison among different brands is easier when there is a limited number of can sizes for a particular product. Jill points out that government regulations also make it easier for the manufacturer to make canned products safe. Bacteria in canned food may cause serious illness or even death. To ensure sterility, the food products are heat treated before canning. A manufacturer can easily calculate the correct length of time to treat a product when the dimensions of the can and the volume it will contain are known.

SURFACE AREA AND VOLUME OF A SPHERE

This photograph of Mars is composed of about 100 images taken in 1980 by the Viking Orbiter. It clearly shows not only that Mars is round, but that it appears to be a sphere.

A sphere is like a ball. The points on the sphere are all the same distance from the *centre*. A line segment joining the centre to any point on the sphere is called its *radius r*. The *diameter d* of a sphere is twice as long as its radius.

Developing the Ideas

▶▶ ▶ *Through Activities*

Work in a group.

ACTIVITY 1

Surface Area of a Sphere

You will need an orange which is nearly spherical, a millimetre ruler, and some 1-cm graph paper.

Step 1

Measure the diameter of the orange as accurately as you can.

Step 2

Peel the orange and arrange the pieces on the graph paper. Press them down to make them as flat as possible, and trace around them.

Step 3

By counting full squares and part squares, estimate the area of the orange peel in square centimetres.

Step 4

Divide the area by the square of the diameter of the orange. Record the result.

1. Repeat *Steps 1* to *4* with a different orange. Find the mean of the results in *Step 4*.

2. How does the area of the peel in *Step 3* compare with the surface area of the orange?

3. What probable conclusion can you make about the ratio of the surface area of a sphere to the square of its diameter?

4. Suppose a sphere has diameter d. Write a formula for its surface area.

ACTIVITY 2

Volume of a Sphere

You will need an empty 355-mL frozen orange juice can, a millimetre ruler, an old tennis ball, a sharp knife, masking tape, some water, and an overflow container.

Step 1

Measure the diameter of the tennis ball. Carefully cut the can so that its inside height is equal to the diameter of the ball.

Step 2

Place the can in the overflow container. Fill the can to the top with water, but do not allow it to overflow. Make sure there is no water in the overflow container.

Step 3

Soak the ball with water. Then slowly place it in the can, allowing the water to overflow into the container. Push the ball right down to the bottom of the can.

Step 4

Take the can out of the overflow container, remove the ball, and empty the can. Then pour the water from the overflow container into the can. Measure the depth of the water.

1. How do you think the volume of the water in the can at the end of *Step 4* compares with the volume of the ball? Discuss your answer with other students.

2. At the end of *Step 4*, what fraction of the can is filled with water?

3. In this activity, the diameter of the cylinder is equal to its height. The sphere has the same diameter as the cylinder. What probable conclusion can you make about the volume of the sphere compared with the volume of the cylinder?

4. Suppose the cylinder and the sphere both have radius r. Write formulas for the volumes of the cylinder and the sphere.

▶▶ *Through Instruction*

In *Activity 1*, you probably discovered that the surface area of a sphere is approximately 3 times the square of its diameter. Using more advanced mathematics, it can be shown that the surface area A of a sphere with diameter d is exactly πd^2.

Since $d = 2r$,

we write: $A = \pi(2r)^2$
$= 4\pi r^2$

The surface area of a sphere with radius r is $A = 4\pi r^2$.

In *Activity 2*, you probably discovered that the volume of a sphere is approximately $\frac{2}{3}$ the volume of the cylinder into which it just fits.

Using more advanced mathematics, it can be shown that the volume of the sphere is exactly $\frac{2}{3}$ the volume of the cylinder.

If the sphere has radius r, then the cylinder has base radius r and height $2r$. Hence, the volume of the sphere is:

$V = \frac{2}{3} \times$ volume of cylinder

$= \frac{2}{3} \times \pi r^2 h$

$= \frac{2}{3} \times \pi r^2 \times 2r$

$= \frac{4}{3}\pi r^3$

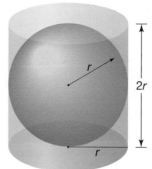

The volume of a sphere with radius r is $V = \frac{4}{3}\pi r^3$.

Working with Mathematics

Something to talk about

1. The Dutch artist, M.C. Escher, produced many striking prints and drawings. In this self-portrait he is shown holding a reflecting sphere. Estimate the actual diameter of the sphere. Then use your estimate to calculate the surface area and the volume of the sphere.

2. Which has the greater volume, a sphere with radius r or a cube with edges of length r?

Work together

3. The mean radius of the moon is approximately 1740 km. Determine the surface area and the volume of the moon.

4. A spherical balloon is blown up from a diameter of 20 cm to one of 60 cm. By how many times has its:
   a) surface area increased?
   b) volume increased?

5. What happens to the surface area and the volume of a sphere if its radius is doubled? tripled?

6. If we did not know that the moon is spherical, we might think that it was a circle. How does the surface area of the part of the moon we see when the moon is full compare with the area of the circle that it appears to be?

On your own

7. Determine the surface area and the volume of each ball listed.

	Sport	Diameter of Ball (cm)
a)	Baseball	7.4
b)	Golf	4.3
c)	Table tennis	3.7
d)	Volleyball	20.9

8. A sphere just fits inside a cube with edges of length 10.0 cm. Calculate the surface area and the volume of the sphere.

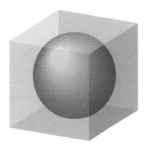

9. Repeat exercise 8 for a cube with edges of length x centimetres.

10. A basketball has a circumference of 75 cm. Determine:
   a) its radius
   b) its surface area
   c) its volume

11. Use an astronomy book or the *Moon and Planets* database from the student's disk to determine the mean radius of each planet in our solar system. Use this information to calculate the surface area and volume of each planet.

DATA DISK

12. Determine formulas for the surface area and the volume of a sphere with:
   a) diameter d **b)** circumference C

TEMPLATE DISK

13. It's been said that packing a ball in a box into which it just fits leaves about half the space in the box empty. Does this seem reasonable? To test this theory, set up the following spreadsheet on the computer.

	A	B	C	D	E
1	Volumes of a ball and a box				
2					
3	Radius	Side length of box	Volume of box	Volume of ball	Empty space
4		=2*A4	=(2*A4)^3	=4/3*PI()*A4^3	

a) Explain each formula in cells B4, C4, and D4.

b) Enter a formula in cell E4 to calculate the amount of empty space in the box.

c) Enter several different values for the radius in cell A4. Is the statement about half the space in the box reasonable? Does the length of the radius affect your answer?

COMMUNICATING

The Ideas

In this chapter, formulas were given for the surface areas and the volumes of several objects.

a) In your journal, summarize the formulas in a systematic way. (You will be adding another formula to your summary later in this chapter.)

b) How can you tell, just by looking at one of the formulas, whether it is a formula for surface area or a formula for volume?

Extend your thinking

14. A spherical soap bubble with radius 2.0 cm lands on a flat surface. Its shape changes to that of a hemisphere.

a) Assuming that none of the air inside the bubble escapes, determine the radius of the hemisphere.

b) Repeat part a for a soap bubble with a radius of r centimetres.

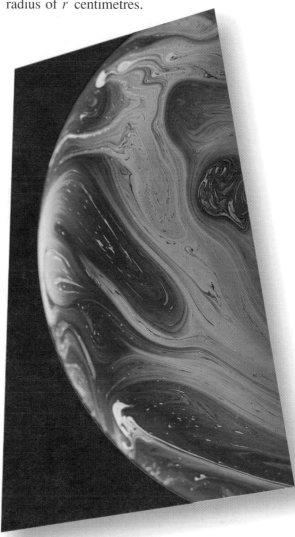

Raindrops rarely exceed 6 mm in diameter. Find out as much as you can about the number of raindrops it would take to fill a pop can.

Total Surface Areas and Volumes of Cylinders with the Same Radius

Some cylinders have the same radius but different heights. How might their total surface areas be related? How might their volumes be related?

To answer these questions you will need as many different cans as you can find which have the same radius and different heights.

Work in a group.

1. Why do you think manufacturers would make cans with the same radius but different heights?

2. Without measuring, how can you be certain that all the cans have the same radius?

3. Measure the diameter and the height of each can. Then calculate its radius and total surface area. Record the height and the total surface area of each can in a table.

Height (cm)	Surface area (cm²)

4. a) Graph the data on a grid like this. Draw a straight line or smooth curve through the plotted points.

   b) Use your graph. Estimate the total surface areas of cans with the same radius as the others and with heights of 1 cm, 2 cm, 3 cm, and 10 cm.

   c) Discuss your results with other groups. Did everyone get similar results?

5. a) All the cans have the same radius r. Substitute your value of r into the formula $A = 2\pi rh + 2\pi r^2$. You obtain an equation expressing the total surface area of a can in terms of its height h.

   b) Use your equation to verify your estimates from exercise 4b.

Surface area of cans with the same radius

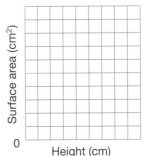

6. Conduct a similar investigation to determine how the volumes of the cans are related. Follow the same steps: create a table; graph your results; from your graph, estimate volumes of cans with different heights; and obtain an equation expressing the volume of a can in terms of its height h.

7. Conduct similar investigations using cylinders which have the same height, but different radii. How are their total surface areas and their radii related? How are their volumes and their radii related?

How Do Sled Dogs Keep Warm?

In still air, a thin layer of warm air surrounds the skin and helps maintain body heat, even at low temperatures. But body temperature drops rapidly in wind. The records of Sir Douglas Mawson's Antarctic expedition show that the mean wind speed at the base hut for the month of May 1912 was 98 km/h. In the cold, windy Antarctic conditions, shelter was essential to human survival. Yet the sled dogs used by the explorers slept outside, curled up, and covered by drifting snow.

Scientists know that a mammal produces heat in proportion to its body size and loses heat in proportion to its surface area. How do sled dogs maintain their body heat in extremely cold and windy conditions?

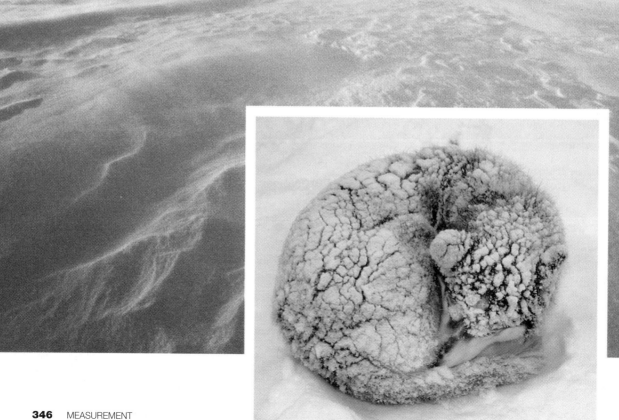

Understand the problem

- What does "produce heat in proportion to its body size" mean?
- What does "lose heat in proportion to its surface area" mean?
- Which animals do you think would be better adapted to cold climates — those with small values of the ratio $\frac{\text{surface area}}{\text{volume}}$ or those with large values of this ratio?
- What could an animal do to change the ratio of its exposed surface area to its volume?

Think of a strategy

- Consider the dog lying stretched out as a cylinder.
- Consider the dog lying curled up as a sphere.
- You could determine the ratio $\frac{\text{surface area}}{\text{volume}}$ for both sleeping positions.

Carry out the strategy

- Choose reasonable estimates for the radius and the length of the cylinder representing the dog.
- Choose a reasonable estimate for the radius of the sphere representing the dog.
- Use your estimates to calculate the ratio $\frac{\text{surface area}}{\text{volume}}$ for each sleeping position.

Look back

- How do the results explain why sled dogs curl up to sleep?
- Sled dogs allow a layer of snow to cover them as they sleep. What effect do you think this has on the dog's temperature?
- What attributes do sled dogs have that would help them to keep warm?
- Animals living in the cold regions of the world have smaller appendages (limbs, ears, and tails) than animals in tropical areas. This principle is called *Allen's rule*. How can Allen's rule be explained mathematically?

Communicating the Ideas

In your journal, write a description of this problem and your solution.

SURFACE AREA OF A CONE

Developing the Ideas

▶ ▶ *Through an Activity*

Work with a partner. You will need paper, a millimetre ruler, a protractor, a pair of compasses, scissors, and some tape.

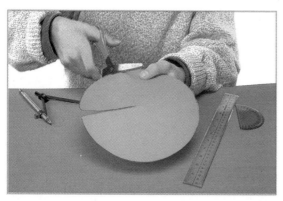

Step 1

Construct a circle with any convenient radius. Draw a radius, and draw another radius perpendicular to it. Cut out the larger part of the circle. What fraction of the circle is this part?

Step 2

Tape your part circle to form a cone. Measure the height h of the cone. What shape is the base of the cone? What is the radius r of the base? Record your values of h and r. Use these values to do the calculations in *Steps 3* and *4*.

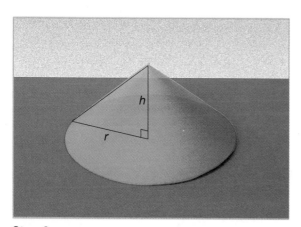

Step 3

h and r are the measures of two sides of a right triangle. Use the Pythagorean Theorem to calculate the length of the third side. How is the length of this side related to the part circle you cut out in *Step 1*?

Step 4

Calculate the circumference of the base of the cone. How does this compare with the circumference of the circle in *Step 1*?

1. How does the surface area of the cone compare with the area of the circle in *Step 1*?

2. Calculate the area of the curved surface of the cone.

▶ ▶ *Through a Guided Example*

Suppose a cone has base radius *r* and height *h*. There is a formula for the area of the curved surface, but it is not as simple as the other formulas in this chapter. Instead of using a formula, it is better to calculate the area as follows.

The area of the curved surface is equal to the area of part of a circle. Calculate the radius of the part circle using the Pythagorean Theorem.

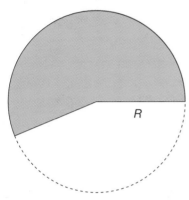

Then calculate the area of the curved surface of the cone using this proportion:

$$\frac{\text{Area of cone}}{\text{Area of circle}} = \frac{\text{Circumference of cone}}{\text{Circumference of circle}}$$

The total surface area of a cone is the sum of the area of the curved surface and the area of the base.

BOGGLE YOUR MIND

The Banff Springs Hotel in Banff, Alberta uses about 87 000 rolls of toilet paper every year. What is the volume of toilet paper used at the hotel in one year? About how far would the paper reach if it were unrolled and put in a line?

Example ....

Hands Fireworks manufactures 6 different conical fireworks. One of these, the Volcano, has a base radius of 3.3 cm and a height of 18 cm. What area of paper is needed to cover the curved surface of this firework?

Solution

Visualize cutting the curved surface and flattening it. The paper will form part of a circle. The area of the curved surface of the cone is equal to the area of the part of the circle.

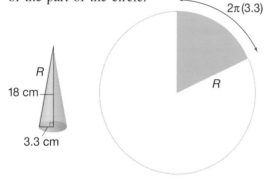

We calculate the radius R of the part circle using the Pythagorean Theorem:

$$R^2 = 3.3^2 + 18^2$$
$$= 334.89$$
$$R = \sqrt{334.89}$$

We calculate the area of the curved surface of the cone using this proportion:

$$\frac{\text{Area of cone}}{\text{Area of circle}} = \frac{\text{Circumference of cone}}{\text{Circumference of circle}}$$

$$\frac{\text{Area of cone}}{\pi \times (\sqrt{334.89})^2} = \frac{2\pi \times 3.3}{2\pi \times \sqrt{334.89}}$$

$$\frac{\text{Area of cone}}{334.89\,\pi} = \frac{3.3}{\sqrt{334.89}}$$

$$\text{Area of cone} = \sqrt{334.89}\,\pi \times 3.3$$
$$\doteq 189.72$$

The area of paper needed to cover the curved surface of the firework is approximately 190 cm^2.

Working with Mathematics

Something to talk about

1. The method used in this section only applies to a *right circular cone*. Examine the diagram on page 349. What information on the diagram suggests why the cone is called a right circular cone?

2. One cone has a base radius of 4 cm and a height of 3 cm. Another cone has a base radius of 3 cm and a height of 4 cm. Do you think their total surface areas are the same? If not, which one do you think has the greater total surface area? Give a reason for your answer.

Work together

3. **a)** Check your answer to exercise 2 by calculating the total surface area of each cone.
   b) What is the ratio of the total surface areas?

4. Get the cones you constructed in exercise 8 on page 334. Determine the area of the curved surface of each cone to the nearest tenth of a square centimetre.

5. For Halloween, a clown's hat is made by stapling together the straight edges of a quarter of a circle with radius 30 cm.
   a) What is the radius of the base of the hat?
   b) How high is the hat?
   c) What is the area of the material used to make the hat?

On your own

6. Determine the area of the curved surface of each cone.

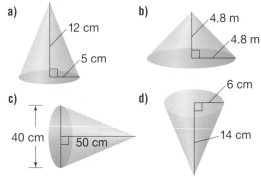

a) 12 cm, 5 cm
b) 4.8 m, 4.8 m
c) 40 cm, 50 cm
d) 6 cm, 14 cm

7. Determine the total surface area of each cone.

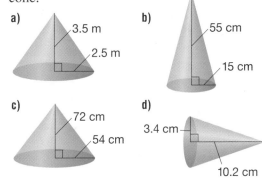

a) 3.5 m, 2.5 m
b) 55 cm, 15 cm
c) 72 cm, 54 cm
d) 3.4 cm, 10.2 cm

Extend your thinking

8. A cone has base radius r and height h. Find a formula in terms of r and h for:
   a) the area of the curved surface
   b) the total surface area

9. A cone just fits inside a cubical box. The box has edges of length x centimetres. Find a formula for the total surface area of the cone.

The Ideas

In your journal, describe how you can calculate the surface area of a cone. Include an explanation of why it is not as simple to write a formula for the total surface area of a cone as it is for a cylinder.

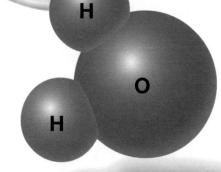

Measuring a Molecule

When you look at a drop of water, do you ever wonder what it's made of? Water, like almost every substance in the universe is made up of billions of tiny particles called molecules. A molecule is the smallest part of a substance which has all the properties of that substance. Each molecule of a substance is identical. It is also different from a molecule of any other substance.

You can estimate the size of a detergent molecule using a few household items.

You will need:

water
pepper
dish detergent
a large tray 30 cm to 40 cm wide
    and long and 1 cm to 2 cm deep
a toothpick
a ruler or measuring tape
    marked in millimetres

Step 1

Fill the tray with water. Cover the surface of the water with a light sprinkling of pepper.

Step 2

Pick up a drop of detergent using the narrow end of the toothpick. Measure its diameter. Do this a few times. Record your best estimate of the diameter, in millimetres.

Step 3

Let one drop of detergent fall onto the surface of the water in the tray. Measure the diameter of the circle that forms. Record your measurement, in millimetres.

1. Empty the tray. Repeat *Steps 1* to *3* two more times. Calculate the average radius of the drop and the resulting circle.

2. Assume the drop of detergent is a sphere. Write an expression for the volume of detergent in the drop.

3. When the drop of detergent hits the water, it spreads out on the surface of the water in a layer one molecule thick. You can think of this layer as a very flat cylinder. Write an expression for the volume of the detergent when it has spread out. Let the height of the cylinder be h.

4. Since the volume of the detergent does not change when its shape changes, the expressions in exercises 2 and 3 are equal. Equate your expressions and solve to determine the height h of the cylinder.

Every detergent molecule is charged at one end. Because of this, each molecule aligns with its charged end in the water and the other end in the air. So, the height of the cylinder is the approximate length of a detergent molecule.

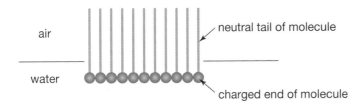

VOLUME OF A RECTANGULAR PYRAMID

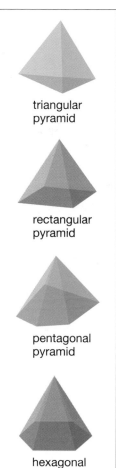

triangular
pyramid

rectangular
pyramid

pentagonal
pyramid

hexagonal
pyramid

In ancient times people built large pyramids as burial chambers for their leaders. Pyramids have also been built in modern times to serve as art galleries and conservatories.

A *pyramid* is a solid with a base that is a polygon. The other faces are triangles with a common vertex.

Developing the Ideas

▶ ▶ *Through an Activity*

In this activity, you will calculate the volume of a pyramid with a rectangular base. You will need an open rectangular box, some pieces of cardboard, scissors, a millimetre ruler, some popcorn or clean sand, and tape. Work with a partner to make a pyramid with its height equal to the height of the box.

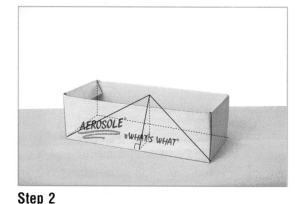

Step 1

Measure the length, width, and height of the box. Recall that this is a rectangular prism. Record the results.

Step 2

Imagine one face of the pyramid. One edge of this face coincides with the length of the prism. The other two edges meet at the vertex at the centre of the top of the prism. Use the Pythagorean Theorem to find the height of the triangle. This is the slant height of the face.

Step 3

Construct two cardboard isosceles triangles with this height, and with bases equal to the length of the prism.

Step 4

Repeat *Steps* 2 and *3* for two faces whose bases are the width of the prism. Then tape the four triangles together to form a rectangular pyramid. Use tape on both the inside and the outside, to make it as rigid as possible.

Step 5

Suppose the pyramid were filled with popcorn or sand, and then emptied into the prism. Estimate how many times you could do this until the prism is full. Check your estimate.

1. What probable conclusion can you make about the volume of the pyramid compared with the volume of the prism?

BOGGLE YOUR MIND

A 30 g drink box holds the same amount of beverage as a 400 g glass bottle. What if drink boxes replaced all glass containers? Do you think this would be a good idea? Why?

When a rectangular pyramid just fits inside a rectangular prism, you can fill the pyramid three times and pour its contents into the prism. Then the prism will be full.

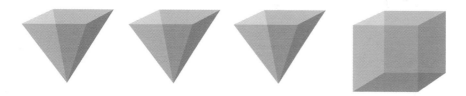

This is because the volume of a prism is exactly three times the volume of a rectangular pyramid with the same base and the same height. That is, the volume of the pyramid is one-third the volume of the prism.

The volume of a rectangular pyramid with base dimensions l and w, and height h is given by the formula:

$$V = \frac{1}{3} \times \text{base area} \times \text{height}$$

or $\quad V = \frac{1}{3}lwh$

Working with Mathematics

Something to talk about

1. How does the formula for the volume of a rectangular pyramid compare with the formula for the volume of a cone?

2. The diagrams show three views of the same rectangular prism. How do the volumes of the three pyramids compare? Explain your answer.

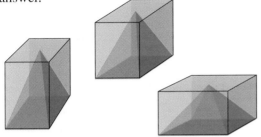

3. **a)** Suppose the base of a pyramid has 3 sides. How many faces, vertices, and edges does the pyramid have?
   b) Repeat part a for a pyramid whose base has 4 sides.
   c) Repeat part a for a pyramid whose base has 5 sides.
   d) Repeat part a for a pyramid whose base has 6 sides.

4. Suppose you know the number of sides in the base of a pyramid. How could you determine the numbers of its faces, edges, and vertices?

Work together

5. A cube is divided into six congruent pyramids. The base of each pyramid is a face of the cube. The edges of the cube are 30 cm long. What is the volume of each pyramid?

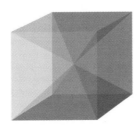

6. What happens to the volume of a rectangular pyramid if:
   a) its base is not changed, but its height is doubled? tripled?
   b) its height and base width are not changed, but its base length is doubled? tripled?
   c) its height is not changed, but both its base length and width are doubled? tripled?
   d) all three of its dimensions are doubled? tripled?

On your own

7. The Louvre is a famous art gallery in Paris, France. It is housed in a historic palace and was opened in 1793. In 1989 there was widespread controversy over its expansion. One of the additions is a large glass pyramid which covers the main entrance to the museum. This square-based pyramid is about 35.4 m wide and 21.6 m high.

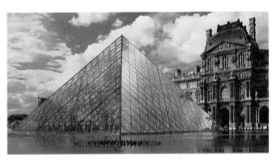

   a) Calculate the volume of the pyramid.
   b) Why do you think there was a controversy about the expansion of the Louvre?

8. The Great Pyramid in Egypt has a square base of 230 m. Its original height was 147 m.
   a) Calculate the volume of stone that was used to build the pyramid.
   b) About 2.3×10^6 blocks of stone were used to build the pyramid. Calculate the average volume of one block.
   c) The average mass of one block is about 2760 kg. Calculate the total mass of stone in the pyramid.
   d) Why do we use the word "original" in the second sentence?

9. The Muttart Conservatory in Edmonton consists of two large and two small pyramids. Each small pyramid has a square base of side length 21.0 m and a height of 13.7 m. The dimensions of each large pyramid are about 1.3 times as great as these.

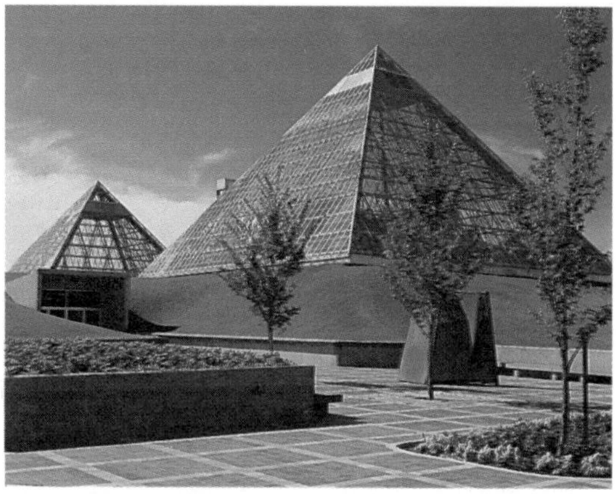

a) How many times as great as the volume of a small pyramid is the volume of a large pyramid?

b) Compare the method you used to solve part a with the method used by other students. Did everyone use the same method to solve this problem?

Extend your thinking

10. Suppose you were to trace this net, cut it out, and fold it to form a rectangular pyramid. By taking measurements from this diagram, determine the volume of the pyramid.

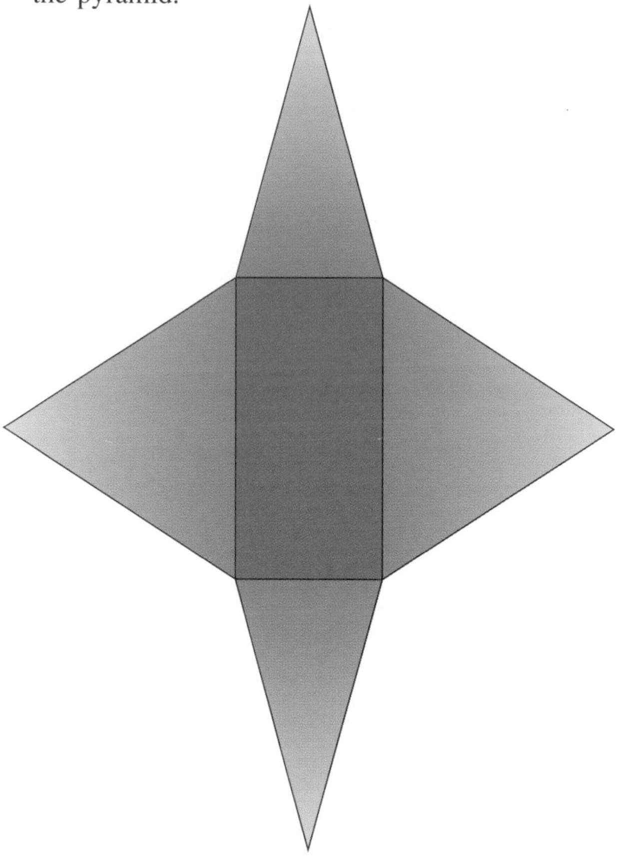

COMMUNICATING The Ideas

In your journal, describe how you calculate the volume of a rectangular pyramid if you know its dimensions. Include in your account:

- an explanation of how the volume of a rectangular pyramid is related to the volume of a rectangular prism with the same base and the same height
- formulas for the volumes in terms of l, w, and h

Include the formula for the volume of a pyramid in your formula summary referred to on page 344.

Review

1. Calculate the volume and the total surface area of each solid to the nearest unit.

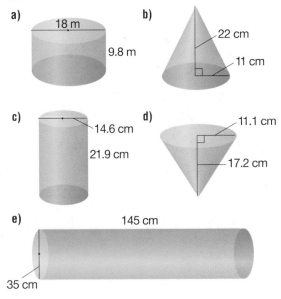

a)

18 m
9.8 m

b)

22 cm
11 cm

c)

14.6 cm
21.9 cm

d)

11.1 cm
17.2 cm

e)

145 cm
35 cm

2. Two rectangular pieces of cardboard each measuring 30 cm by 50 cm are used to form the curved surfaces of two different cylinders. Circles cut from another piece of cardboard are used for the tops and the bottoms.

   a) Calculate the radius of each cylinder to two decimal places.

   b) Calculate the total surface area of each cylinder.

   c) Calculate the volume of each cylinder.

3. What is the volume of sawdust in a conical pile that is 3.2 m in diameter and 2.8 m in height?

4. Determine the surface area and the volume of each ball listed below.

	Sport	Diameter of ball
a)	Basketball	24 cm
b)	Table tennis	4.0 cm
c)	Tennis	6.5 cm

5. The mean radius of the sun is approximately 694 000 km. Determine the surface area and the volume of the sun.

6. A sphere just fits inside a cylinder with base radius 12 cm and height 24 cm. Calculate the surface area and volume of the cylinder and of the sphere to two decimal places.

12 cm
24 cm

7. A cylindrical silo has a height of 12.5 m and a base diameter of 6.4 m. Its top is half a sphere with the same diameter. Calculate the total volume of the silo to the nearest cubic metre.

8. Tennis balls are packed in cans 8.4 cm in diameter and 25.5 cm high. Three dozen of these cans are packed in a box 51 cm by 51 cm by 26 cm. What is the total volume of wasted space?

9. Calculate the volume of each pyramid to the nearest unit.

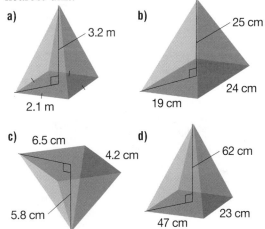

a)

3.2 m
2.1 m

b)

25 cm
24 cm
19 cm

c)

6.5 cm
4.2 cm
5.8 cm

d)

62 cm
23 cm
47 cm

10. A square-based pyramid is 24 cm wide and 52 cm high. It is cut, as shown, to create a pyramid 39 cm high with base 18 cm square. The other piece is discarded. What is the volume of the discarded portion, to the nearest unit?

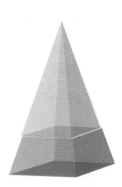

How Many Stars Can You See?

Work with a partner.

An astronomy column in a newspaper gave instructions for estimating the number of stars you can see on a clear, dark night. You will need a piece of cardboard, a sharp knife, a millimetre ruler, and a tape measure.

ACTIVITY 1

Step 1

Cut a 5-cm square hole in a piece of cardboard. What is the area of the hole? This hole is your window.

Step 2

On a clear, dark night, hold the cardboard at arm's length and count the number of stars you can see through the window. Record the result. Repeat this procedure several times, facing different directions. Calculate the mean number of stars.

Step 3

When you hold the cardboard at arm's length, the window represents about $\frac{1}{800}$ of the sky. Multiply the mean number of stars by 800. The answer is your estimate of the number of stars you can see.

ACTIVITY 2

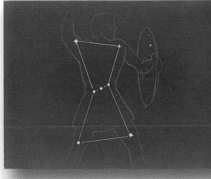

ORION

Step 1

Hold the cardboard at arm's length. Move your arm in all possible directions as you turn and look at different parts of the sky. Ask your partner to watch the cardboard as you do this, and to describe a three-dimensional object that is traced out by the cardboard.

Step 2

Ask your partner to use the tape measure to measure the radius of this object as accurately as she can. Then calculate its surface area.

Step 3

How many times as great as the area of the window is the surface area of the object? What fraction of the sky is sampled through the window each time you count the stars in *Activity 1*? Use your answer to refine your estimate in *Step 3* of *Activity 1*. How many stars can you see?

BIG DIPPER AND LITTLE DIPPER

ACTIVITY 3

Why do you multiply the mean number of stars by 800? Do you think your arm is longer or shorter than the arm of a person who should use the number 800?

If you used a 6-cm square hole, would you multiply by a number larger or smaller than 800?

Another newspaper article stated that about 3000 stars are visible to the naked eye. If this is true, then approximately how many stars could be seen through the window?

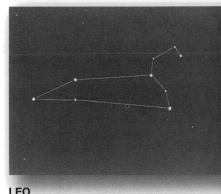

LEO

COMMUNICATING

The Ideas

Write a brief report which summarizes the results of your investigation. Include an explanation of the method you used.

POLYNOMIALS

WHAT'S COMING UP?

DEPARTMENTS

Linking Ideas

Quests

Minds on Math

Start With What You Know

Packaging is important in the food industry. If the surface area of a can of food can be reduced, without changing its volume, the packaging is cheaper and costs are reduced.

Recall that the formula $A = 2\pi rh + 2\pi r^2$ expresses the total surface area A of a cylinder in terms of its radius r and height h.

The volume V of the cylinder is given by $V = \pi r^2 h$.

All the cans in the photograph have radii 4.1 cm, but different heights. Substitute $r = 4.1$ and $\pi = 3.14$ in each formula.

$$A \doteq 2(3.14)(4.1)h + 2(3.14)(4.1)^2$$

That is, $A \doteq 25.8h + 105.6$

$$V \doteq (3.14)(4.1)^2 h$$

That is, $V \doteq 52.8h$

h is in centimetres, A is in square centimetres, and V is in cubic centimetres.

We now have the formulas in terms of h only.

Use these formulas to complete these exercises.

1. a) Calculate the surface areas and volumes of cans with radii 4.1 cm and heights of 7.6 cm, 9.0 cm, and 14.9 cm.
   b) Calculate the height of a can with radius 4.1 cm and surface area 363.6 cm². What is the volume of this can?
   c) Suppose a manufacturer doubles the height of a can. Would the surface area double? Would the volume double? Explain how you know.

The cans in these photographs have heights of 12.0 cm but different radii.

Substitute $h = 12.0$ and $\pi = 3.14$ into the formulas for A and V.

$$A \doteq 2(3.14)(12.0)r + 2(3.14)r^2$$

That is, $A \doteq 75.4r + 6.28r^2$

$$V \doteq 3.14(12.0)r^2$$

That is, $V \doteq 37.7r^2$

r is in centimetres, A is in square centimetres, and V is in cubic centimetres.

We now have the formulas in terms of r only.

Use these formulas to complete these exercises.

2. a) Calculate the surface area and the volume of each can shown.
   b) Suppose a manufacturer doubled the radius of a can. Would the surface area double? Would the volume double? Explain how you know.

All the cans on a supermarket shelf arrived at the store in cartons. Cans of Cloverleaf tuna are sometimes packaged in cartons of 24. The cans are arranged in 2 layers. Each layer is 4 cans long and 3 cans wide.

Recall that 2, 3, and 4 are factors of 24 and $2 \times 3 \times 4 = 24$.

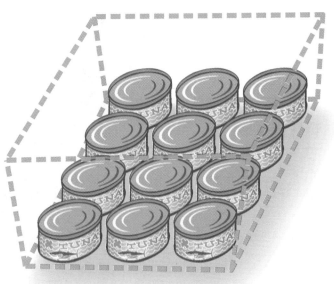

3. a) Suppose the carton containing the tuna had different dimensions.
   i) How many different ways could the tuna be arranged in the carton?
   ii) Use the answer to part i to list as many sets of three factors of 24 as you can.
   b) Other cans of Cloverleaf tuna are packaged in cartons of 48. Repeat part a for this carton.

THE CONCEPT OF A POLYNOMIAL

Developing the Ideas

▶ ▶ ▶ *Through Instruction*

Jennifer brought some money home from her vacation in the United States. She had some Canadian and some U.S. bills.

To calculate the amount of money she has, Jennifer adds the U.S. money: $20 + $10 + $10 + $5 + $1 = $46 U.S. and the Canadian money: $10 + $5 + $5 = $20 Can

The terms which represent Canadian money are *like* terms. They can be combined into a single value. Similarly, the terms which represent U.S. money are like terms. However, a term that represents Canadian money and a term that represents U.S. money are unlike terms. They cannot be combined into a single value.

We can say only that Jennifer has $46 U.S. and $20 Can.

In an earlier chapter, you worked with like and unlike terms in the form of algebra tiles.

Recall:
This tile is called a 1-tile.

It measures 1 unit on each side.
It has an area of 1 square unit.

This tile is called a variable-tile.
We call it an x-tile.

It measures 1 unit by x units.
It has an area of x square units.

We now add a new algebra tile:

This tile is a square measuring x units on each side.
It has an area of $x \times x$ or x^2 square units.

Since x is a variable, we cannot combine the areas of a 1-tile, an x-tile, and an x^2-tile to form a single term. That is, these tiles represent unlike terms.

How would we represent the tiles shown below?

We think: 3 x^2-tiles + 2 x-tiles + 5 1-tiles
We write: $3x^2 + 2x + 5$

▶ ▶ *Through Discussion*

There are special names for terms and combinations of terms.
Look at the table below. Answer each question in the last column.

All of these are monomials.	None of these is a monomial.	Which of these is a monomial?
$3x^2$ $4x$ $-6m^3$ $7x^2y$ $-\frac{1}{2}bc$	$3x + 4$ $4y^2 - y$ $\frac{-2}{z}$	$3x + 2$ $\frac{-5y^2}{x}$ $-6xy$

All of these are binomials.	None of these is a binomial.	Which of these is a binomial?
$3x + 7$ $2y^2 - y$ $4 - x^4$ $\frac{1}{2}z^3 - 4zy$	$3x^5$ $x^2 - 5x + 7$ $+1$ $\frac{1}{a} + \frac{1}{b}$	$\frac{1}{2}x^2 - 4xy$ $-2x^2y^3$ $3a^2 - 2a + 4$ $\frac{1}{a} - 5$

All of these are trinomials.	None of these is a trinomial.	Which of these is a trinomial?
$3x^4 + 7x - 6$ $4ab - 2bc + c^3$ $1 - 4x - 3y^2$	$5x^4 - 2xy$ $3a + 7$ $6x^3 - \frac{2}{y^2} + 2z$	$1 - 2x^5 + \frac{1}{x}$ -4 $x^2 - 3a^2 + 4$ $x^2 + \frac{1}{y^2} - x$

All of these are polynomials.	None of these is a polynomial.	Which of these is a polynomial?
$-3xy$ $3a^3 - 5z^2 - 14$ $11 - d^2$ $3x^3 - 5x + y - 7$	$4a^2 - \frac{2}{b} + 1$ $-\frac{2}{z}$ $\frac{1}{x}$	$2x^2 + \frac{3y}{x} - 4y^3$ $3x + 2$ $\frac{-5y^2}{-x}$

A *polynomial* is one term or the sum of two or more terms.
A *monomial* is a polynomial with one term.
A *binomial* is a polynomial with two terms.
A *trinomial* is a polynomial with three terms.

Expressions such as $3x^2 + 2y + 5$, $7x^2 - 4$, and $-x$ are polynomials.
In a polynomial, the exponents that occur with variables are whole numbers.
The coefficients are real numbers. Since $\frac{1}{x} = x^{-1}$, $\frac{1}{x}$ is not a polynomial.
Similarly, $-\frac{3}{y^2}$ is not a polynomial.

We represented the polynomial $3x^2 + 2x + 5$ using algebra tiles. This polynomial has terms that have positive coefficients. We can also represent a polynomial such as $3x^2 - 2x + 5$, which has a term with a negative coefficient. We flip the two x-tiles.

We see: $3x^2 - 2x + 5$
We think: 3 x^2-tiles, 2 flipped x-tiles, and 5 1-tiles
We display:

1. Represent each polynomial using algebra tiles.

   a) $-3x^2 + 1$ **b)** $6 - x$ **c)** $3x^2 - x - 4$ **d)** 5   **e)** $4x$

▶ ▶ **Through a Guided Example**

We can combine algebra tiles to form a rectangle.
We can write the area and the perimeter of the rectangle as a polynomial.

Example ....

Write polynomials that represent the perimeter and area of each rectangle.

a)

b)

Solution

a) The rectangle comprises 5 x-tiles.
Its length is 5.
Its width is x.
The perimeter is $x + 5 + x + 5 = 2x + 10$
The area is $5 \times x = 5x$

b) The rectangle comprises 3 x^2-tiles.
Its length is $3x$.
Its width is x.
The perimeter is $x + 3x + x + 3x = 8x$
The area is $3x \times x = 3x^2$

Working with Mathematics

Something to talk about

1. How much money is represented?

2. Explain how adding money in the same currency is similar to adding like terms.

3. Which of these expressions are polynomials? Give reasons.

a) $5x - 3$ **b)** $6x + 7x^2 - 1$

c) $2x + 3y - x^2$ **d)** $2 + \dfrac{1}{x}$

e) 3 **f)** $-\dfrac{4}{y^2}$

4. State whether each expression is a monomial, a binomial, or a trinomial. Give reasons.

a) $3x + 4$ **b)** $-x^2$

c) $-2 - y^2$ **d)** 10

e) $5 - 2x + 3y$ **f)** $4x$

g) $5x^2 + 4y^2 + x$ **h)** $-3 - y$

5. For each display of tiles, state a polynomial that represents the total area.

a)

b)

c)

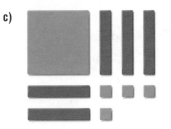

6. Refer to *Start With What You Know* on page 364. What sort of polynomial is the expression on the right side of the formula for:

a) the surface area of a cylinder?

b) the volume of a cylinder?

Work together

7. Use algebra tiles to represent each polynomial. Take turns to explain how you did it.

a) $x^2 + 3x + 2$ **b)** $2x^2 + x + 7$

c) $-2x^2 - 3$ **d)** $2x^2 - 5x - 4$

e) $-x^2 - 3x + 2$ **f)** $x^2 - 4x$

8. Some of these polynomials cannot be represented with algebra tiles. Identify them.

a) $4 - x^2$ **b)** $xy + x^2 - 3$

c) $y^3 - x^2 + 4$ **d)** $-7x$

e) x^4 **f)** $xy - yz - 4$

9. Write a polynomial that represents the perimeter of each rectangle.

a)

b)

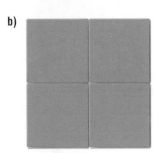

c)

10. Write a polynomial that represents the area of each rectangle in exercise 9.

11. Represent each rectangle using algebra tiles.

a)
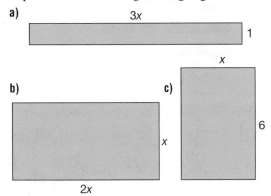
3x
1

b)
2x
x

c)
x
6

12. For each rectangle in exercise 11, write a polynomial that represents its perimeter and a polynomial that represents its area.

On your own

13. **a)** Write an example of an algebraic expression which is *not* a polynomial.
    b) Write an example of a polynomial which does not use the variable x.
    c) Write an example of a polynomial that cannot be represented with algebra tiles.

14. Write a polynomial that represents the perimeter of each rectangle.

a)
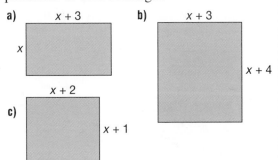
x + 3
x

b)
x + 3
x + 4

c)
x + 2
x + 1

15. **a)** Write a polynomial that represents the area of a square of side length $2s$.
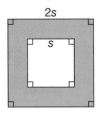
2s
s

b) Write a polynomial that represents the area of:
   i) the large square
   ii) the small square
   iii) the shaded region

Extend your thinking

16. **a)** Write a polynomial that represents the circumference of a circle with diameter $2x$ (below left).
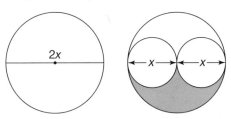
2x
x   x

b) Write a polynomial that represents the perimeter of the shaded region (above right).

c) Write a polynomial that represents the area of each small circle, and a polynomial that represents the area of the large circle (above right).

d) Write a polynomial that represents the area of the shaded region.

POLY

The Search for a Polynomial to Generate Prime Numbers

A prime number is any whole number, greater than 1, that is divisible by only itself and 1. Since the discovery of prime numbers, mathematicians have attempted to find a polynomial for generating them.

In 1772, the great Swiss mathematician, Leonhard Euler, devised the polynomial $n^2 - n + 41$ for the generation of primes.

We will use a spreadsheet to check that this polynomial does generate primes.

TEMPLATE DISK

1. Set up the spreadsheet as shown.
   Enter different numbers, up to 10, in cell A2.
   Are all the numbers generated in cell B2 primes?

	A	B
1	N	Euler's polynomial
2		=A2*A2-A2+41

2. Enter several other numbers, up to 40, in cell A2. Use your calculator to check that each number in cell B2 is prime.

3. a) Enter 41 in cell A2.
   b) What is 41^2?
   c) Does Euler's polynomial generate a prime number when $n = 41$?

In 1879, E.B. Escott devised the polynomial $n^2 - 79n + 1601$. We'll insert this polynomial on the spreadsheet beside Euler's polynomial.

	A	B	C
1	N	Euler's polynomial	Escott's polynomial
2		=A2*A2-A2+41	=A2*A2-79*A2+1601

4. Test Escott's polynomial for several values of N. Use your calculator to check if each number in cell C2 is prime.

5. Compare the numbers in column C with those in column B.
   a) Do you notice any similarities?
   b) What patterns can you find in the numbers in column C?

6. a) Enter 80 in cell A2. Show that the number in cell C2 is *not* prime.
   b) Find another value of N for which the number in cell C2 is not prime.

7. Adapt the spreadsheet to find a value of n for which each of the following polynomials does *not* produce a prime number.
   a) $n^2 + n - 1$ b) $n^2 - n + 17$ c) $n^2 - n + 41, n \neq 41$

Currently, there is no known polynomial that produces *only* prime numbers. There is also no known polynomial that will produce all the prime numbers.

Mathematics & Technology

Linking Ideas

ADDING AND SUBTRACTING POLYNOMIALS

Developing the Ideas

Polynomials, like numbers, can be added and subtracted. To add two polynomials, we combine like terms. Recall how you combined like terms in Chapter 5. The only difference now is that we include x^2-tiles.

▶ ▶ *Using Manipulatives*

We can use algebra tiles to add polynomials.
Suppose we add $2x^2 + 3x + 1$ and $-x^2 + 2x - 4$.

We write: We display:

$(2x^2 + 3x + 1) + (-x^2 + 2x - 4)$

We think:
Combine like terms. Use the Zero Principle. Each pair of opposite tiles forms a 0-pair. 1 x^2-tile, 5 x-tiles, and 3 flipped 1-tiles remain.
From the tiles, $(2x^2 + 3x + 1) + (-x^2 + 2x - 4) = x^2 + 5x - 3$

1. Use algebra tiles to add each pair of polynomials.
- **a)** $(x^2 + 2x - 1) + (2x^2 + 3x + 3)$
- **b)** $(3x^2 - x + 5) + (x^2 - 2x - 4)$
- **c)** $(-2x^2 - 3x - 4) + (-2x^2 - 5x - 1)$
- **d)** $(x^2 - 2x - 4) + (-x^2 + 2x + 4)$

2. a) How are the polynomials in exercise 1d alike?
- **b)** How are the polynomials different?

You should have discovered that $x^2 - 2x - 4$ and $-x^2 + 2x + 4$ have a sum of 0. Polynomials that have a sum of 0 are called *opposites*.
Recall that flipping the tiles representing $x^2 - 2x - 4$ gives its opposite, $-x^2 + 2x + 4$. We can use this to subtract one polynomial from another.

Suppose we subtract $-2x^2 + x - 9$ from $3x^2 + 5x - 6$.
We write: $(3x^2 + 5x - 6) - (-2x^2 + x - 9)$
We think: We display:
Flip the tiles representing $(-2x^2 + x - 9)$.

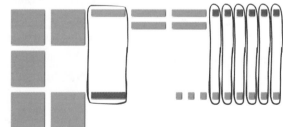

Combine like terms. Use the Zero Principle.
5 x^2-tiles, 4 x-tiles, and 3 1-tiles remain.
From the tiles,
$(3x^2 + 5x - 6) - (-2x^2 + x - 9) = 5x^2 + 4x + 3$

3. Use algebra tiles to perform each subtraction.
- **a)** $(-x^2 + 5x + 4) - (2x^2 + 3x + 3)$
- **b)** $(3x^2 + 4) - (x^2 + 2)$

To add polynomials, we group like terms and simplify.

Example 1 ⋅⋅

Simplify. $(-2x^2 + 6x - 7) + (3x^2 - x - 2)$

Solution

$$(-2x^2 + 6x - 7) + (3x^2 - x - 2) = -2x^2 + 6x - 7 + 3x^2 - x - 2$$

$$= -2x^2 + 3x^2 + 6x - x - 7 - 2 \quad \text{◄ Grouping like terms}$$
$$= x^2 + 5x - 9$$

When we subtract a polynomial from itself, we get zero.
For example, $(x^2 - 2x - 4) - (x^2 - 2x - 4) = 0$

We get the same result if we add the polynomial and its opposite.
For example, $(x^2 - 2x - 4) + (-x^2 + 2x + 4) = 0$

So, to subtract a polynomial, we add its opposite.

Example 2 ⋅⋅⋅

a) Simplify. $(3x^2 + 5x - 6) - (-2x^2 + x - 9)$

b) Find the value of the polynomial when:

  i) $x = 2$ **ii)** $x = -1$

Solution

a) $(3x^2 + 5x - 6) - (-2x^2 + x - 9)$
$$= (3x^2 + 5x - 6) + (2x^2 - x + 9) \quad \text{◄ The opposite of } -2x^2 + x - 9$$
$$= 5x^2 + 4x + 3$$

b) i) When $x = 2$, the value of the polynomial is:
$$5(2)^2 + 4(2) + 3 = 5(4) + 8 + 3$$
$$= 20 + 11$$
$$= 31$$

ii) When $x = -1$, the value of the polynomial is:
$$5(-1)^2 + 4(-1) + 3 = 5(1) - 4 + 3$$
$$= 5 - 1$$
$$= 4$$

Recall that some polynomials cannot be represented with algebra tiles.
We use the above principles to combine these polynomials.

Example 3 ⋅⋅

Simplify. $(3x^4 - 2x^2 + 3x - 9) - (x^2 - 4x + 2)$

Solution

$$(3x^4 - 2x^2 + 3x - 9) - (x^2 - 4x + 2) = (3x^4 - 2x^2 + 3x - 9) + (-x^2 + 4x - 2)$$
$$= 3x^4 - 3x^2 + 7x - 11$$

Working with Mathematics

Something to talk about

1. Show each polynomial using algebra tiles. Then flip the tiles and state its opposite.
   - a) $3x^2 + 7$
   - b) $2x^2 - 5x + 3$
   - c) $-4n^2 + 3n - 5$

2. What is the sum of a polynomial and its opposite?

3. Is there a polynomial which is equal to its opposite? Explain.

4. a) State the opposite of the polynomial $3x^2 - 2x - 1$.
   - b) Then state the opposite of your answer.
   - c) What do you discover?
   - d) Do you think this is true for all polynomials? Explain.

5. a) Suppose you have a display of algebra tiles representing a polynomial. How do you obtain the tile display for the opposite polynomial?
   - b) How do you determine the opposite of a polynomial without using algebra tiles?

6. State each subtraction as an addition.
   - a) $(3x^2 + 5) - (2x^2 + 1)$
   - b) $(x^2 + 2x) - (-x - 1)$
   - c) $(x^2 + 3x - 2) - (-x^2 - x + 1)$

7. Explain how 0-pairs are used with algebra tiles to simplify two polynomials.

Work together

8. Take turns to explain why the two polynomials are not opposites.
   - a) $5x^2 - 3x - 2$
        $5x^2 + 3x + 2$
   - b) $x^2 + 7x - 9$
        $-x^3 - 7x + 9$
   - c) $-4y + y^2 + 11$
        $4y - y^2 + 11$
   - d) $x^3 - 4x^2 + 9$
        $-x^3 + 4x^2 - x$

9. Simplify. Use algebra tiles if you wish.
   - a) $(3x^2 - 2x + 4) + (x^2 + 3)$
   - b) $(3x^2 - 2x + 4) - (x^2 + 3)$
   - c) $(5m - 2m^2) + (m^2 - 6)$
   - d) $(5m - 2m^2) - (m^2 - 6)$

10. Simplify. Find the value of the polynomial when: **i)** $x = 1$ **ii)** $x = -2$
    - a) $(1 - 2x^2 - x) + (2x - 3x^2 - 7)$
    - b) $(3 - 2x^2 - x) - (2x - 3x^2 - 7)$

11. Each rectangle is divided into squares and rectangles. Write one polynomial for the area of each piece and one polynomial for the area of the entire rectangle.

    a)

    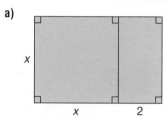

    b)

    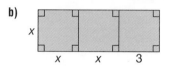

    c)

    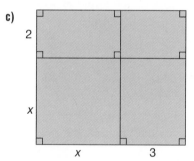

On your own

12. Simplify.
    - a) $(3x^2 - 7x + 4) + (5x - 7x^2 + 6)$
    - b) $(6 - 3x + x^2) + (9 - x)$
    - c) $(1 - 7x^2 + 2x) + (x^3 - 3x^2 + 7)$
    - d) $(5x - x^2) + (3x + x^2 - 7)$

13. Simplify.
    - a) $(5x^2 + 7x + 9) - (3x^2 + 4x + 2)$
    - b) $(11m^2 - 5m + 8) - (7m^2 + m - 3)$
    - c) $(4a^2 - 3a^3 - 7) - (a^2 - 2a^3 - 13)$
    - d) $(-6x^2 + 17x - 4) - (3x^2 + 12x + 8)$

14. Simplify. Find the value of the polynomial when: **i)** $x = -2$ **ii)** $x = 3$
    - a) $(3x^2 - 8x + 6) - (-2x^2 + 7x + 3)$
    - b) $(x^2 - 4x + x^3) - (3x + 5 - x^3)$

15. Choose any month on a calendar. Then choose a 3 by 3 square of 9 dates. Let x represent the date at the centre of the square.

a) Write a polynomial for:
  i) the date one week before x
  ii) the date one week after x
  iii) the sum of the dates in each column
  iv) the sum of all 9 dates
b) If you knew the sum of all 9 dates, how could you determine the value of x?

Extend your thinking

16. When the terms of a polynomial in x are arranged from the lowest to the highest powers of x, the polynomial is in *ascending* powers of x.
  a) Simplify. Write the polynomial in ascending powers of x.
$$7 - (3x^2 + 2x) - (5x + x^2 - 6) - (3x + 3x^2 - 12)$$
  b) Find the value of the polynomial when $x = -0.5$.

C O M M U N I C A T I N G

The Ideas

Look through this text. In your journal, record three formulas or expressions which cannot be represented with algebra tiles. Explain why they cannot be represented this way.

BOGGLE YOUR MIND

According to the *Guinness Book of Records*, Mrs. Shakuntala Devi is the fastest calculating prodigy in the world. In 1980, in a supervised test at the Computer Department of Imperial College, in London, England, she correctly multiplied 7 686 369 774 870 by 2 465 099 745 779 in 28 seconds without mechanical aid. How many digits are there in the product?

A Magic Birthday Card

Do you recognize the birthday card shown below?

It was a big seller in North America. People who were given the card were probably amused and mystified by the "magic" trick which appeared inside.

Using your birthday and the year of your birth, follow the procedure one step at a time. Why does it work?

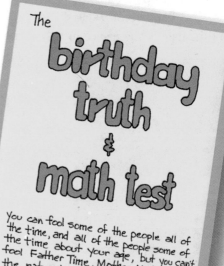

The birthday truth & math test

You can fool some of the people all of the time, and all of the people some of the time about your age, but you can't fool Father Time, Mother Nature, or the natural laws of mathematics.

Follow the steps inside and the secret of your Birthday will be magically revealed.

Tools: use a calculator, or scratch paper and pencil. Toes and fingers are permitted.

1. Write the number of the month you were born here. → ☐
2. Multiply that by four. ___ × 4
3. Now add unlucky "13" (that's both hands and 3 toes) ___ + 13
4. Multiply this (number) by twenty five and write the answer here → ☐ ___ × 25
5. Subtract two hundred ___ − 200
6. Add your birthdate (day of the month) ___ + ___
7. Double that and write the answer in this box → ☐ ___ × 2
8. Now transfer this number to 9

9. Subtract 40 from the number transferred from 8. ___ − 40
10. Multiply by 50 and write the answer on the line right here → ___ × 50 ___
11. Now (whew!), add the last 2 digits of your birth**year** (the **truth**!) → ___ + ___
12. Think of a number between 10,499 and 10,501 and **subtract** it from #11 and write the answer in this box → ☐ * mo/day/year ___ − 10,500

Gottacha! Have a Happy Birthday!

Love Shelly

*(If the answer is wrong, two possibilities exist: ① You Lied ② You got thru school by cheating in math. Try it again.)

Understand the problem

- How many digits appear in the final answer in Step 12?
- What digits in this number tell you the year of your birth?
- What digits in this number tell you the month of your birth and the day?

Think of a strategy

- How many pieces of data are needed to specify your birth date?
- What variables might you use to specify an arbitrary birth date?

Carry out the strategy

- The first step in the procedure requires that you multiply the month of your birth by 4.
  Use the variable you chose to represent the number of the month.
  Write an expression for 4 times the number of the month.
- Add 13 to the expression you have written.
- Multiply this expression by 25 and expand.
- Then subtract 200.
- Add the variable that represents the day of your birthday.
- Multiply the expression you have by 2 and then subtract 40.
  Simplify your answer by collecting like terms.
- Multiply your answer by 50.
- Then add the variable representing the birth year and subtract 10 500.

Look back

- Look at your expression. Substitute a few different birth dates into your expression to see if it yields the appropriate numbers. Choose dates for which either or both the month and the day are single and double-digit numbers.
- Does the expression show the year of birth as the last two digits?
- When does it show the day of birth as:
  a) the third and fourth digits?
  b) the second and third digits?
- When does it show the month of birth as:
  a) the first digit?
  b) the first two digits?
- Explain why the trick works for everyone's birthday.

Communicating the Ideas

In your journal, write a description of this problem and your solution.

MULTIPLYING AND DIVIDING MONOMIALS

Developing the Ideas

▷ ▶ *Through Instruction*

In the previous section, we added and subtracted polynomials.

We will begin the multiplication of polynomials by investigating products of polynomials with one term. Recall that a polynomial with only one term is called a monomial.

How would we simplify the product $(3x^2)(5x^3)$?

We recall the meaning of the exponents.

$$
\begin{aligned}
(3x^2)(5x^3) &= (3 \cdot x \cdot x)(5 \cdot x \cdot x \cdot x) \quad \text{◄ Writing each term as a product of factors} \\
&= (3)(5)(x \cdot x \cdot x \cdot x \cdot x) \quad \text{◄ Rearranging the factors} \\
&= 15x^5 \quad \text{◄ Writing } x \cdot x \cdot x \cdot x \cdot x \text{ as } x^5
\end{aligned}
$$

This example and others like it illustrate the following rule for multiplying monomials.

> To multiply two monomials, we multiply their coefficients and multiply their variables.

If the variables are the same, we add their exponents.
For example, to multiply $3x^2$ by $5x^3$:

Multiply the coefficients: $3 \times 5 = 15$

$$(3x^2)(5x^3) = 15x^5$$

Add the exponents: $2 + 3 = 5$

Similarly, to simplify the quotient, $\dfrac{7x^6}{3x^2}$, we recall the meaning of the exponents.

$$
\begin{aligned}
\frac{7x^6}{3x^2} &= \frac{7 \cdot x \cdot x \cdot x \cdot x \cdot x \cdot x}{3 \cdot x \cdot x} \quad \text{◄ Writing each term as a product of factors} \\
&= \frac{7}{3} \times \frac{x \cdot x \cdot x \cdot x \cdot {}^1\!\!\!\!x \cdot {}^1\!\!\!\!x}{{}^1\!\!\!\!x \cdot {}^1\!\!\!\!x_1} \quad \text{◄ Dividing common factors} \\
&= \frac{7}{3}x^4 \quad \text{◄ Writing } x \cdot x \cdot x \cdot x \text{ as } x^4
\end{aligned}
$$

This example and others like it illustrate the following rule for dividing monomials.

> To divide two monomials, we divide their coefficients and divide their variables.

If the variables are the same, we subtract their exponents.

For example, to divide $7x^6$ by $3x^2$:

Subtract the exponents: $6 - 2 = 4$

$$\frac{7x^6}{3x^2} = \frac{7}{3}x^4$$

Divide the coefficients: $7 \div 3 = \frac{7}{3}$

Sometimes we multiply monomials which are powers.

For example, to simplify $(3x^2)^2(2x^3)^3$, we think of its meaning:

$(3x^2)(3x^2)(2x^3)(2x^3)(2x^3)$

This expression is the product of five monomials. To determine the product, we multiply the coefficients and multiply the variables.

The product of the coefficients is $(3)(3)(2)(2)(2) = 72$

The product of the variables is $(x^2)(x^2)(x^3)(x^3)(x^3) = x^{13}$

$(3x^2)^2(2x^3)^3 = 72x^{13}$

▶▶ *Through Guided Examples*

Example 1..

Simplify.

a) $(3x^2)(-2x^3)$

b) $(8x^4y) \div (6x^2y)$

Solution

a) $(3x^2)(-2x^3) = (3)(-2)(x^2)(x^3)$

$= -6x^{2+3}$

$= -6x^5$

b) $(8x^4y) \div (6x^2y) = \dfrac{8x^4y}{6x^2y}$

$= \dfrac{8}{6} \cdot \dfrac{x^4}{x^2} \cdot \dfrac{y}{y}$

$= \dfrac{4}{3}x^{4-2}$

$= \dfrac{4}{3}x^2$

Example 2............................. *Solution* ....

Simplify. $(2a^2)^4(-5a^3)$

$(2a^2)^4(-5a^3) = (2a^2)(2a^2)(2a^2)(2a^2)(-5a^3)$

$= -80a^{11}$

Example 3............................. *Solution* ....

Simplify. $\dfrac{(2b^2)^4}{(-b)^2}$

$\dfrac{(2b^2)^4}{(-b)^2} = \dfrac{(2)^4(b^2)^4}{(-b)(-b)}$

$= \dfrac{16b^8}{b^2}$

$= 16b^{8-2}$

$= 16b^6$

Working with Mathematics

Something to talk about

1. List the factors of each monomial.

a) $3x^2$ **b)** $4x^3$

c) $-x^2$ **d)** $2x^6$

e) $-\frac{1}{2}a^4$ **f)** $9x^2y$

g) $-6a^2b^2$ **h)** $5m^2n^3$

2. State each product.

a) $(3x^2)(4x^3)$ **b)** $(-x^2)(2x^6)$

c) $\left(-\frac{1}{2}a^2\right)\left(-\frac{1}{2}a^4\right)$ **d)** $(-5a)(6a^2)$

3. State each quotient.

a) $\dfrac{5m^5}{2m^3}$ **b)** $\dfrac{-25x^5}{10x^2}$ **c)** $\dfrac{30x^6}{-6x^2}$

4. Name a pair of monomials that will satisfy each equation. Is there only one possible answer for each equation?

a) $\boxed{} \times \boxed{} = 3x^6$ **b)** $\boxed{} \times \boxed{} = -5b^3$

c) $\boxed{} \times \boxed{} = -6x$ **d)** $\boxed{} \div \boxed{} = 2x^2$

e) $\boxed{} \div \boxed{} = \frac{3}{2}x^3$ **f)** $\boxed{} \div \boxed{} = \frac{1}{4}$

Work together

5. Find each product.

a) $(x^3)(-x^2)$ **b)** $(2p^2)(3p^3)$

c) $(6y^3)(-2y)$ **d)** $(3a^2b)(2ab^2)$

e) $(3x^2)^2(2y)^2$ **f)** $(-2x)^2(-y^2)^3$

6. The base area and height of each solid are given. State the volume of each solid.

a)   **b)**

7. Find each quotient.

a) $15x^3 \div 3x$ **b)** $-6y^2 \div 2y$

c) $20a^3 \div (-4a^2)$ **d)** $\dfrac{6b^3n^2}{2b^2n}$

e) $\dfrac{15m^5a^3}{3m^2a}$ **f)** $\dfrac{21y^6x^2}{7y^3x^2}$

8. The volume and base area of each solid are given. State the height of each solid.

a)   **b)**

On your own

9. Find each product.

a) $(3m^4)(7m^5)$ **b)** $(2x^2)(4x^3)$

c) $(8a^3)(7a^{11})$ **d)** $(-5b^3)(2b^4)$

e) $(6x^5)(-3x^3)$ **f)** $(-8p^4)(-6p^2)$

g) $\left(\frac{2}{3}y^4\right)\left(\frac{3}{5}y^7\right)$ **h)** $\left(-\frac{5}{8}s^5\right)\left(-\frac{3}{10}s^3\right)$

10. Find each quotient.

a) $\dfrac{-28a^7}{4a^2}$ **b)** $\dfrac{20s^3}{-5s}$

c) $\dfrac{-32c^8}{-8c^2}$ **d)** $45x^9 \div 9x^3$

e) $18y^4 \div 3y^2$ **f)** $42m^{12} \div 6m^4$

Extend your thinking

11. a) Write the volume of the cube as a product of monomials.

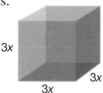

b) Write the volume of the cube as a monomial.

c) Simplify. $(2x^2)(3x^3)(7x^4)$

The Ideas

In your journal, write a brief answer to each question. Provide examples to support your answers.

a) When is the sum or difference of two monomials a monomial?

b) When is the product of two monomials a monomial?

c) When is the quotient of two monomials a monomial?

Developing the Ideas

▶ ▶ *Using Manipulatives*

In Chapter 5, you expanded a product such as $3(x + 4)$ using the Distributive Law. You represented this product using algebra tiles by combining 3 sets of tiles like this.

We can represent a product such as 3×5:

with a rectangle and...   with algebra tiles arranged in a rectangle

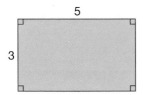

In each case, the area is $3 \times 5 = 15$

In a similar way, we can represent the product $2(x + 4)$ with algebra tiles to form a rectangle.

The area is $2(x + 4) = 2x + 8$

Instead of writing the length and width as algebraic terms, we use algebra tiles.

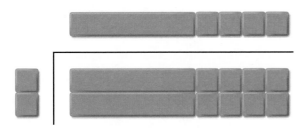

To represent the product $2x(x + 4)$ with algebra tiles, we make a rectangle that is $2x$ units wide and $(x + 4)$ units long. We place tiles to represent the length and the width.

We now fill in the rectangle with tiles. We need 2 x^2-tiles and 8 x-tiles. The area of the rectangle is $2x^2 + 8x$. We write: $2x(x + 4) = 2x^2 + 8x$

1. Illustrate each product with algebra tiles.

a) $3(x + 2)$ **b)** $3x(x + 1)$ **c)** $4(2x + 3)$ **d)** $3x(2x + 1)$

This table compares the Distributive Law in arithmetic and in algebra.

• • • • • • • • • •

To multiply in arithmetic, we use the Distributive Law.	To multiply in algebra, we use the Distributive Law.
$3 \times 27 = 3(20 + 7)$ $ = 3(20) + 3(7)$ $ = 60 + 21$ $ = 81$	$2x(x + 4) = 2x(x) + 2x(4)$ $ = 2x^2 + 8x$

▷ ▶ *Through Guided Examples*

When we multiply a polynomial by a monomial using the Distributive Law, we say we are *expanding* the product. The following examples show how we expand the product of a monomial and a polynomial.

Example 1 ··

Expand. $8x(x - 3)$

Solution

$8x(x - 3) = 8x(x) + 8x(-3)$ ◁ Applying the Distributive Law
$ = 8x^2 - 24x$

We apply the same method when the polynomial has more than two terms. Since some polynomials cannot be represented with algebra tiles, sometimes we have to use the Distributive Law.

Example 2 ··

Expand. $(-5a)(a^2 - 4a - 7)$

Solution

$(-5a)(a^2 - 4a - 7) = (-5a)(a^2) + (-5a)(-4a) + (-5a)(-7)$ ◁ Applying the Distributive Law
$ = -5a^3 + 20a^2 + 35a$

Working with Mathematics

Something to talk about

1. State the product that each diagram represents.

a)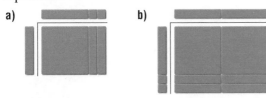

b)

c)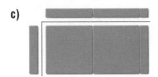

2. a) Explain the advantages of expanding by using algebra tiles.
   b) Explain the advantages of expanding by using the Distributive Law.
   c) Which method do you prefer? Why?

Work together

3. Use algebra tiles to expand each expression. Take turns explaining what you are doing.
   a) $x(x + 1)$
   b) $x(3x + 2)$
   c) $2(x^2 + x + 3)$
   d) $2x(x + 2)$

4. Expand. Before you begin, decide for which expressions you can use algebra tiles.
   a) $x(5x^2 - 6)$
   b) $2(x + 3x^2)$
   c) $(-3b)(b^3 - b^2)$
   d) $2a(3a + 1)$
   e) $(-4m)(m^2 - m)$
   f) $x^2(1 - x^3)$

5. a) Use the Distributive Law to multiply 7×236.
   b) Use the Distributive Law to expand $7(2x^2 + 3x + 6)$. Evaluate this polynomial for $x = 10$.
   c) Compare your answers in parts a and b. Explain any relationship you discover.

On your own

6. Expand.
   a) $5x(2x + 3)$
   b) $3c(5 - 2c)$
   c) $(-4n)(2n - 1)$
   d) $(-7y)(2y^2 - 5y)$
   e) $4a(3a^2 - 2a)$
   f) $(-2x)(-3x - 5x^3)$
   g) $5s(3s^2 - 2s - 7)$
   h) $3p(2 - 3p - p^2)$
   i) $(-7a)(3a^2 - 2a - 4)$

7. Expand each expression.
   a) $3x(2x - 1)$
   b) $(-3x)(-2x - 1)$
   c) $2x(-3x - 4)$
   d) $4x^2(3x + 2)$

Extend your thinking

8. The height of any television screen is about $\frac{3}{4}$ of its width.
   a) Write an expression for the height of a television screen that is x units wide.
   b) Write an expression for the height of a television screen that is 4 units wider than the screen in part a.
   c) Write a polynomial for the area of the television screen in part b.
   d) Write an expression for the difference in the areas of the screens in parts a and b.
   e) Suppose the difference in areas of the screens in part a and part b is 120 square units. What is the area of each screen?

COMMUNICATING

The Ideas

In your journal, draw a rectangle with a length of $2x$ units and a width of $(x + 3)$ units. Write the area as a product. Use the Distributive Law to write the area as a sum of the areas of two smaller rectangles. Divide the large rectangle into two smaller rectangles and show their lengths and widths.

Recursive Processes and Growth of Populations

Biologists, ecologists, and mathematicians study the way populations grow. Predicting population size is important when an organism causes disease or is a pest like the gypsy moth caterpillar.

The gypsy moth lives during the summer and dies in the cold weather after laying its eggs. The growth of its population follows a recursive process.

Before we learn about the recursive process that describes the population of the gypsy moth, we will investigate recursive processes in general.

Use your calculator. Enter any large positive number, such as 1000, and press the $\sqrt{\ }$ key many times. What happens to the display? Try this with other positive numbers, either larger or smaller than 1000. Try it with very small positive numbers, such as 0.000 001. Do you always get the same result?

Pressing the $\sqrt{\ }$ key repeatedly is an example of a *recursive process*. In a recursive process, the same operation is repeated many times. Any recursive process requires a starting number, called a *seed*. We can represent the above recursive process by a flowchart.

According to the flowchart, the process never stops. However, in practice, we usually stop when we see a pattern, or when we suspect that no pattern is likely to develop.

1. Investigate each recursive process. Use several different seeds for each process. Does the result depend on the seed?

a)

b)

c)

2. a) In the flowchart below, there is the expression $\frac{x}{2} + 1$. The variable x is used to represent the number at each stage of the recursive process. For this expression, you divide each number by 2 and then add 1.

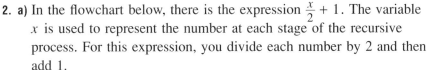

Investigate this recursive process using several different seeds. Does the result appear to be related to the expression in the flowchart?

b) Based on your result from part a, make a prediction about what will happen with the recursive process defined by this flowchart.

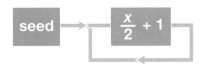

Check your prediction. Is the result what you expected? Does the result appear to be related to the expression in the flowchart?

3. The recursive processes in exercise 2 are similar. They can be represented by a single flowchart, where k is a constant:

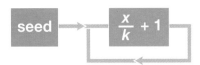

You can use a spreadsheet to investigate these recursive processes for different values of k. Set up your spreadsheet as shown below. The numbers in row 3 are the whole numbers from 2 to 7. The numbers in row 5 can be any numbers you wish, and you will be changing them. Some typical numbers are shown here.

TEMPLATE DISK

	A	B	C	D	E	F	G
1	Investigating a Recursive Process						
2							
3	Value of k	2	3	4	5	6	7
4							
5	Seed	5	8	-12	2.76	0.5	-0.22

a) In cell B6, enter the formula **=B5/2+1**. Copy this formula down column B for at least 15 more rows. What happens to the numbers in column B? Try different seeds in cell B5. How do the numbers in column B change as you change the number in cell B5?

b) In cell C6, enter the formula **=C5/3+1**. Copy this formula down column C for several rows. What happens to the numbers in column C? Try different seeds in cell C5. How do the numbers in column C change as you change the number in cell C5?

c) Repeat for the other columns. Use the formulas below in the cells in row 6. The number after the division slash in each formula is the number in the corresponding cell in row 3.

cell D6: **=D5/4+1**   cell E6: **=E5/5+1**

cell F6: **=F5/6+1**   cell G6: **=G5/7+1**

Try several different seeds, including numbers such as 999 999, −999 999, and numbers very close to 0. For some of these, you may have to copy the formulas farther down the spreadsheet.

d) What happens to the numbers in each column? How are the numbers in the columns related to the value of k in row 3?

As mentioned earlier, the growth of the population of the gypsy moth follows a recursive process. Here is the flowchart.

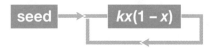

The seed is the initial population. The values of x also represent populations. The value of k has a dramatic effect on the population, as you will discover in exercise 4. But the values of x are not actual counts of the caterpillars. They are numbers between 0 and 1, which represent a fraction of the maximum possible population. For example, a value of 0.5 represents 50% of the maximum possible population. Biologists do not need to know whether the population is in the hundreds or thousands. They are more interested in comparing one year's population with the preceding year's, or with the next year's predicted population.

4. The value of k has a dramatic effect on the population, as you will discover. Set up a spreadsheet as follows:

	A	B	C
1	Growth of Gypsy Moth Caterpillar		
2			
3	Value of k		0.8
4	Initial population		0.5
5			
6		Generation	Population
7		0	=C4
8			
9			
10			

a) In cell B8, enter the formula **=B7+1**. Copy this formula down at least 15 more rows.

b) In cell C8, enter the formula **=C$3*C7*(1−C7)**. Copy this formula down at least 15 more rows. The dollar sign between the C and the 3 is used to prevent this cell from changing as you copy the formula down the column.

c) Format column C to show numbers rounded to two decimal places.

d) What do the numbers in column C tell you about the population? Change the initial populations in cell C4 to other numbers between 0 and 1. Does this affect the result?

e) Draw a graph showing how the population changes for the 15 generations. Use the graphing features of your spreadsheet program, if possible.

5. a) The value of k in cell C3 is less than 1. Change this number to other numbers less than 1. Does this affect your previous results?

b) Investigate what happens for values of k as outlined below. Try different values of the initial population for each value of k you use. Does the result depend on the initial population?

  i) values of k between 0 and 1

  ii) values of k between 1 and 3

  iii) values of k greater than 3

c) Draw graphs showing some of the different situations that can occur. What does each kind of graph tell you about the population?

In your journal, write a report of your findings.
Include tables and graphs in your report.

FACTORING POLYNOMIALS

Developing the Ideas

▷ ▶ *Using Manipulatives*

In the preceding section, we knew the length and width of a rectangle, and we had to decide which tiles completed the rectangle.

In this section, we'll reverse the procedure.

We'll begin with a set of tiles which we arrange as a rectangle, and then determine its length and width.

- Use 3 x-tiles and 6 1-tiles. What polynomial do they represent?
- Arrange these tiles to form a rectangle.
- Write the length of the rectangle as a polynomial.
- Write the width of the rectangle as a polynomial.
- Write the area of the rectangle as a product of the length and width.
- Check the rectangles of other students. Did you all arrange your tiles the same way?

Let's consider another example.

Suppose you have the tiles representing $4x + 8$.

They can be arranged in a rectangle in three ways.

The length is $4x + 8$. The width is 1. The area is $1(4x + 8)$.

The length is $2x + 4$. The width is 2. The area is $2(2x + 4)$.

The length is $x + 2$. The width is 4. The area is $4(x + 2)$.

We say that 1 and $4x + 8$ are *factors* of $4x + 8$.
Similarly, 2 and $2x + 4$ are factors of $4x + 8$,
and 4 and $x + 2$ are factors of $4x + 8$.

There are three ways to factor $4x + 8$, shown above.
The first two ways: 1, $4x + 8$ and 2, $2x + 4$ are incomplete because the
second factor in each case: $4x + 8$ and $2x + 4$, can be factored again.
The third way is complete. We say that $4x + 8$ is factored *fully* when we
write $4x + 8 = 4(x + 2)$.

The following chart compares factoring and expanding in arithmetic and
algebra.

In Arithmetic	In Algebra
We *multiply* factors to form a product.	We *expand* an expression to form a product.
$(3)(5) = 15 \leftarrow$ product factors	$4(x + 2) = 4x + 8 \leftarrow$ product factors
We *factor* a number by expressing it as a product of factors.	We *factor* a polynomial by expressing it as a product of factors.
factors number $\rightarrow 15 = (3)(5)$	factors polynomial $\rightarrow 4x + 8 = 4(x + 2)$

The operations of expanding and factoring are inverses;
that is, each operation reverses the other.

BOGGLE YOUR MIND

According to the *Guinness Book of Records*,
the greatest distance a single car has been
driven is 2 180 279 km, by a Volkswagen
"Beetle." Ask a friend or relative the average
distance he or she drives in a week. How many
weeks would it take that person to drive as far
as the Beetle? How many years is this?

Example 1 ....

Factor fully. $2x^2 + 6x$

Solution

Use 2 x^2-tiles and 6 x-tiles to represent $2x^2 + 6x$.
Arrange the tiles to form a rectangle.

The width and length of this rectangle are x and $2x + 6$.
But $2x + 6$ can be factored again.

So we arrange the tiles in a different rectangle.

The length and width are $2x$ and $x + 3$.
From the diagram, $2x^2 + 6x = 2x(x + 3)$

As before, some polynomials cannot be represented with algebra tiles.
They have to be factored algebraically.

Example 2 ....

Factor fully. $2x^3 + 4x^2$

Solution ....

Factor each term of the polynomial.
$2x^3 = 2 \cdot x \cdot x \cdot x$
$4x^2 = 2 \cdot 2 \cdot x \cdot x$

We identify the factors that are common to each term.
Each term has the factors 2 and x and x in common.
We say that $2x^2$ is the *greatest common factor*.

We write each term as a product of the greatest common factor and another monomial.
$2x^3 + 4x^2 = 2x^2(x) + 2x^2(2)$
We use the Distributive Law to write the sum as a product.
$2x^3 + 4x^2 = 2x^2(x + 2)$

We use the same method to factor a polynomial with more than two terms.

Example 3 ....

Factor fully. $-6y + 3y^2 - 3y^3$

Solution ....

$6y = 2 \cdot 3 \cdot y$
$3y^2 = 3 \cdot y \cdot y$
$3y^3 = 3 \cdot y \cdot y \cdot y$

Each term has the factors 3 and y in common.
$3y$ is the greatest common factor.
$$-6y + 3y^2 - 3y^3 = 3y(-2) + 3y(y) + 3y(-y^2)$$
$$= 3y(-2 + y - y^2)$$

Working with Mathematics

Something to talk about

1. Factor each set of monomials. State the greatest common factor.

   a) $3x$, x^2 b) $3b^3$, $3b$

   c) $-5y$, $25y^2$ d) $-3x$, $6x^3$, $9x^2$

   e) $2x^2$, $6x^3$, $-8x$ f) $2y^2$, $4xy$, $-8y^3$

Work together

2. Use algebra tiles to factor each polynomial.

   a) $2x + 2$ b) $3x + 9$

   c) $4x + 10$ d) $3x + 15$

3. Use algebra tiles to factor each polynomial. Sketch the tiles.

   a) $x^2 + 2x$ b) $2x^2 + 4x$

   c) $3x + 9$ d) $4x^2 + 8x$

On your own

4. Factor each polynomial.

   a) $16x + 40$ b) $15n - 24$

   c) $-2a^2 - 6a$ d) $18n^2 - 12n$

   e) $a^3 + 9a^2 + 3a$ f) $3x^2 + 9x$

5. Factor each polynomial.

   a) $10x + 15$ b) $6x - 9$

   c) $15x + 25$ d) $2x^2 - 4x$

   e) $4x^2 - 16x$ f) $3y^3 + 9y^2$

   g) $2x^2 + 4x + 8$ h) $12x^3 - 9x^2 + 6x$

6. Factor.

   a) $a^3 - 9a^2 + 3a$ b) $-27x^2 - 9x + 3$

   c) $5x^3 + 3x^2 - x$ d) $9a^3 + 7a^2 + 18a$

   e) $-8d - 24d^2 - 8d^3$ f) $17k - 85k^2 - 51k^3$

7. Refer to *Start With What You Know* on page 364. The total surface area A of a cylinder of radius r and height h is given by this formula. $A = 2\pi rh + 2\pi r^2$ Factor this formula.

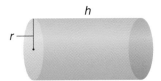

Extend your thinking

8. Using algebra tiles, attempt to factor each polynomial. Interpret those that do factor in terms of area.

   a) $2x - 6$ b) $2x^2 - 6x + 4$

   c) $2x^2 + 6$ d) $2x^2 - 6$

9. Write the formula, for the total surface area in exercise 7, in terms of the circumference C and height h, instead of r and h.

The Ideas

In your journal, explain how factoring and multiplying are related. Use examples to illustrate your explanation.

According to the *Guinness Book of Records*, the most popular surname in China is Zhang. It is estimated that between 10% and 12% of the approximately 1 160 000 000 people living in China have this surname. How many people is this? How does this number compare with the population of your province or territory?

Developing the Ideas

▷▶ *Through Guided Examples*

To divide a polynomial by a monomial, we divide each term of the polynomial by the monomial. In this way, we *simplify* the expression.

Example 1 ....

Simplify. $\dfrac{5x^2 - 10x}{5}$

Solution

$$\frac{5x^2 - 10x}{5} = \frac{5x^2}{5} - \frac{10x}{5}$$
$$= x^2 - 2x$$

Example 2 ....

Simplify. $\dfrac{3b^3 - 6b^2 + 9b}{6b}$

Solution

$$\frac{3b^3 - 6b^2 + 9b}{6b} = \frac{3b^3}{6b} - \frac{6b^2}{6b} + \frac{9b}{6b}$$
$$= \frac{1}{2}b^2 - b + \frac{3}{2}$$

There is another way to divide a polynomial by a monomial.

We factor the polynomial, and then divide the monomial into the common factor. If necessary, we factor the monomial before dividing.

For *Example 1*:

$$\frac{5x^2 - 10x}{5} = \frac{5(x^2 - 2x)}{5}$$
$$= \frac{1\cancel{5}(x^2 - 2x)}{\cancel{5}_1}$$
$$= x^2 - 2x$$

For *Example 2*:

$$\frac{3b^3 - 6b^2 + 9b}{6b} = \frac{3b(b^2 - 2b + 3)}{6b}$$
$$= \frac{3b(b^2 - 2b + 3)}{(3b)(2)} \quad \text{◄ Factoring the monomial}$$
$$= \frac{b^2 - 2b + 3}{2}$$
$$= \frac{1}{2}b^2 - b + \frac{3}{2}$$

Working with Mathematics

Something to talk about

1. Simplify.

a) $\dfrac{5x^2}{2x^2}$ **b)** $\dfrac{3m^2n}{2m}$ **c)** $\dfrac{4y^3}{-2y}$

2. Simplify.

a) $\dfrac{3m^3 - 2m}{m}$ **b)** $\dfrac{5x^2 - 10}{2}$

c) $\dfrac{21y - 7y^3}{7y}$ **d)** $\dfrac{6a^2 - 2a}{-2a}$

3. a) Factor. $3x^2 - 12x + 6$

b) Simplify. $\dfrac{3x^2 - 12x + 6}{-3}$

4. a) Describe two different ways to simplify $\dfrac{3x^2 - 12x + 6}{-3}$.

b) Which is easier for you? Explain.

Work together

5. Simplify.

a) $\dfrac{8a + 4}{4}$ **b)** $\dfrac{12y - 3}{3}$

c) $\dfrac{18x^2 - 6}{6}$ **d)** $\dfrac{6a + 15}{3}$

e) $\dfrac{24x - 4}{4}$ **f)** $\dfrac{-10 + 4m}{-2}$

g) $\dfrac{15 - 5n}{-5}$ **h)** $\dfrac{18x^2 - 6x + 30}{6}$

On your own

6. Simplify.

a) $\dfrac{3x^2 - 6x}{3x}$ **b)** $\dfrac{5x^2 - 10x}{5x}$

c) $\dfrac{18a - 21a^2}{3a}$ **d)** $\dfrac{-28n^2 - 7n}{7n}$

e) $\dfrac{36y^3 - 9y^2}{-9y}$ **f)** $\dfrac{32b^4 + 8b^3}{-4b^2}$

7. Simplify.

a) $\dfrac{-21 + 7x}{-7}$ **b)** $\dfrac{-5 - 15c + 10c^2}{-5}$

c) $\dfrac{4x^3 - 12x^2 + 8x}{4x}$ **d)** $\dfrac{8a + 2a^2 - 2a^3}{2a}$

e) $\dfrac{15x^4 - 30x^3 + 5x^2}{5x^2}$ **f)** $\dfrac{18a^4 + 6a^3 - 12a^2}{-6a^2}$

Extend your thinking

8. A closed rectangular box has length l. Its depth and width are both x units. Write a polynomial for the surface area A of the box. Write A as a product of two factors.

The Ideas

In your journal, explain how dividing a polynomial by a monomial is related to factoring. Illustrate with examples.

BOGGLEYOUR**MIND**

D.W. Friesen, one of Canada's largest printing companies, is located in Altona, Manitoba. Their largest order was to print 530 000 copies of one book. It took more than 4 months to print these books. The presses ran 18 h a day, 6 days a week. What if there had been a power failure and the presses stopped for 3 h? How many books would not be printed during this time?

Developing the Ideas

▷▶ *Using Manipulatives*

Recall that a binomial is a polynomial with two terms.
We can multiply two binomials by using algebra tiles. We follow the
same procedure we used to multiply a polynomial by a monomial.

To expand $(x + 2)(x + 4)$

- We make a rectangle that is $(x + 4)$ units long and $(x + 2)$ units wide.
  We place tiles to represent the length and the width. We then fill in the
  rectangle with tiles.

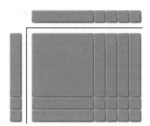

- We used 1 x^2-tile, 6 x-tiles, and 8 1-tiles.
  The area of the rectangle is $x^2 + 6x + 8$.
  We write: $(x + 2)(x + 4) = x^2 + 6x + 8$

1. Use algebra tiles to expand each product.

    a) $(x + 1)(x + 2)$ **b)** $(2x + 1)(x + 3)$

▷▶ *Through Instruction*

We can illustrate the product of two binomials with a diagram.

	x	7
x	x^2	$7x$
2	$2x$	14

The length of the large rectangle is $(x + 7)$ units and its width
is $(x + 2)$ units.

The area of the rectangle is
$(x + 7)(x + 2)$.

The area is also the sum of the areas of the
four small rectangles, $x^2 + 7x + 2x + 14$.

Therefore, $(x + 7)(x + 2) = x^2 + 7x + 2x + 14$
$$= x^2 + 9x + 14$$

This method shows that there are four terms in the product.

Example 1...

Expand. $(3x + 2)(x + 4)$

Solution

With algebra tiles, make a rectangle that is $(3x + 2)$ units long and $(x + 4)$ units wide. Fill in the rectangle with tiles.

From the diagram, $(3x + 2)(x + 4) = 3x^2 + 14x + 8$

We can multiply two binomials without using algebra tiles.

Example 2...

Expand. $(3x + 2)(x + 4)$

Solution

$(3x + 2)(x + 4)$
Multiply each term of one binomial by each term of the other binomial. We draw lines to show which terms are multiplied.

$$(3x + 2)(x + 4) = 3x(x) + 3x(4) + 2(x) + 2(4)$$
$$= 3x^2 + 12x + 2x + 8$$
$$= 3x^2 + 14x + 8$$

The lines form a pattern. We can use this pattern to check that we have all the terms.

Example 3...

Expand. $(2x + 1)(7x - 3)$

Solution

$$(2x + 1)(7x - 3) = 14x^2 - 6x + 7x - 3$$
$$= 14x^2 + x - 3$$

Working with Mathematics

Something to talk about

1.

a) State the area of the tiles as the product of the length and width of the rectangle.

b) State the area as the sum of the areas of the tiles.

2.

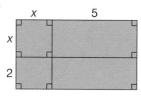

a) State the area of the rectangle as the product of its length and width.

b) State the area of the rectangle as the sum of the smaller areas.

3. State the number that belongs in each square.

a) $(x + 3)(x - 2) = x^2 + \boxed{}x - 6$

b) $(a + 5)(a + 7) = a^2 + \boxed{}a + 35$

c) $(n - 4)(n - 6) = n^2 + \boxed{}n + 24$

d) $(x - 7)(x + 1) = x^2 + \boxed{}x - 7$

Work together

4. For each diagram of algebra tiles:

  i) Write the product of its length and width.

  ii) Write the area as a sum of the areas of the tiles.

a)

b)

c)

d)

5. For each rectangle:

  i) Write the area as the product of its length and width.

  ii) Write the area as the sum of the smaller areas.

a)

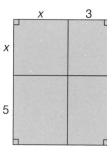

b)

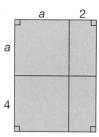

c)

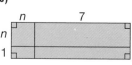

6. Expand. Use algebra tiles. Check your answers with your partner.

a) $(x + 3)(x + 4)$ **b)** $(n + 2)(n + 6)$

c) $(a + 5)(a + 3)$ **d)** $(n + 1)(n + 9)$

7. Expand.

a) $(t - 1)(t - 4)$ **b)** $(x - 2)(x + 5)$

c) $(n + 3)(n - 4)$ **d)** $(a + 6)(a - 8)$

e) $(x + 9)(x - 7)$ **f)** $(x + 12)(x - 5)$

8. Choose any month on a calendar. Then choose a 3 by 3 square of 9 dates. Let x represent the date at the centre of the square.

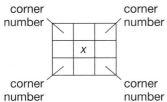

December

Sun	Mon	Tue	Wed	Thur	Fri	Sat
			1	2	3	4	5
6	7	8	9	10	11	12
13	14	15	16	17	18	19
20	21	22	23	24	25	26
27	28	29	30	31		

corner number   corner number

x

corner number   corner number

a) Write a polynomial for:
  i) each corner number
  ii) the square of each corner number
  iii) the sum of the squares of the corner numbers
b) If you knew the sum of the squares of the corner numbers, how could you determine the value of x?

9. Expand.
  a) $(2a + 1)(2a + 1)$ **b)** $(3n + 1)(3n + 1)$
  c) $(x - 6)(x - 6)$ **d)** $(a - 3)(a - 3)$
  e) $(2y - 5)(2y - 5)$ **f)** $(3b + 5)(3b + 5)$

10. What pattern do you see in the products in exercise 9?

11. Expand.
  a) $(x - 3)(x + 3)$ **b)** $(2a + 1)(2a - 1)$
  c) $(8n - 3)(8n + 3)$ **d)** $(4a + 3)(4a - 3)$
  e) $(3x - 2)(3x + 2)$ **f)** $(5x + 1)(5x - 1)$

12. What pattern do you see in the products in exercise 11?

On your own

13. Expand.
  a) $(6x - 3)(2x - 5)$ **b)** $(3b + 2)(3b - 2)$
  c) $(5a + 1)(4a - 7)$ **d)** $(a + 8)(8a + 1)$
  e) $(2a - 3)(2a - 3)$ **f)** $(3a + 4)(2a - 3)$

14. Expand.
  a) $(3x + 2)(x - 1)$ **b)** $(2a - 5)(a - 3)$
  c) $(4n - 7)(n + 5)$ **d)** $(x + 3)(6x - 5)$
  e) $(12x + 1)(3x - 1)$ **f)** $(5n - 1)(2n - 2)$

15. Expand.
  a) $(7c - 5)(2c + 1)$ **b)** $(6x - 2)(3x + 1)$
  c) $(3x - 1)(x + 2)$ **d)** $(3a + 1)(2a - 5)$
  e) $(8y - 3)(5y - 1)$ **f)** $(2x - 3)(4x + 7)$

Extend your thinking

16. Use algebra tiles to expand.
  a) $(x - 2)(x + 1)$ **b)** $(2x + 1)(x - 3)$
  c) $(2x - 3)(2x - 4)$ **d)** $(x + 3)(-2x - 1)$
  e) $(-3x + 1)(-3x - 1)$ **f)** $(-x - 4)(-x - 4)$

COMMUNICATING

The Ideas

Suppose you are talking with your friend about your homework. How would you explain, over the telephone, how to multiply two binomials? Write your answer in your journal.

A Student's Letter

This letter was received from a student, Amy Carter, who discovered an unusual way to add certain numbers. Explain why her method always works.

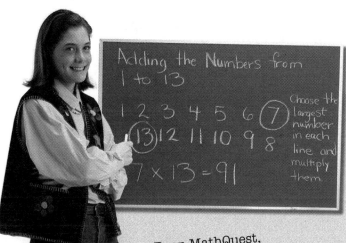

Adding the Numbers from 1 to 13

1 2 3 4 5 6 ⑦   Choose the largest number in each line and multiply them.

⑬ 12 11 10 9 8

7 × 13 = 91

Dear MathQuest,

My name is Amy Carter. I am working in your Grade 6 textbook. Today in class on pages 94 and 95 we were trying to figure out the sum of all the numbers from 1 to 100. When we had it figured out, we tried to find out what the sum of all the numbers from 1 to 13 was.

Our teacher rounded 13 to 14 and wrote:

$$
\begin{array}{cccccccc}
 & 1 & 2 & 3 & 4 & 5 & 6 & 7 \\
+ & 14 & 13 & 12 & 11 & 10 & 9 & 8 \\
\hline
 & 15 & 15 & 15 & 15 & 15 & 15 & 15
\end{array}
$$

We then multiplied:

$$
\begin{array}{r}
15 \\
\times 7 \\
\hline
105
\end{array}
$$

Since we added the extra 14, we took 14 from 105 and ended up with a sum of 91. I then looked more closely at the question and thought of a faster way to do it. Although my idea only works with odd numbers, I wrote:

$$
\begin{array}{cccccccc}
1 & 2 & 3 & 4 & 5 & 6 & 7 \\
 & 13 & 12 & 11 & 10 & 9 & 8
\end{array}
$$

You then find the greatest number in each line. In this case they are 7 and 13. If you multiply 7 times 13 you come up with 91. You automatically have the sum.

Please write to me with any comments.

Sincerely

Amy Carter

Understand the problem

- Read Amy's letter. What was her method?
- Try the teacher's method. How do you know how many numbers to write in the first line?
- Try Amy's method.
- What are you asked to do?

Think of a strategy

- Let $2n - 1$ represent an odd number, and try the two methods again.

Carry out the strategy

In the teacher's method:

- Write an expression for the first number in the second line.
- Above this expression, write the first number in the first line.
- How is the last number in the first line related to the first number in the second line?
- Write an expression for the last number in the first line.
- Below this expression, write an expression for the last number in the second line.
- Write an expression for the next to last number in the first line.
- Below this expression, write an expression for the next to last number in the second line.
- What is the sum of each pair of expressions?
- How many of these sums are there?
- Multiply this number by the sum of one pair of expressions.
- Subtract the extra number that was added at the beginning.
- What is the sum of the natural numbers from 1 to $2n - 1$?

In Amy's method:

- Write an expression for the greatest number in each line.
- What is the product of these expressions?
- Is this the same as the answer in the teacher's method?

Look back

- Why doesn't Amy's method work for even numbers?
- Try to modify her method so that it does work for even numbers. If you can do this, explain why your method works.

Communicating the Ideas

In your journal, write a letter to Amy Carter with your comments.

SPECIAL PRODUCTS OF BINOMIALS

Developing the Ideas

Square of a Binomial

When we multiply a binomial by itself, we *square* the binomial.
Consider the product $(x + 3)^2$. We call this a *binomial square*.
It means $(x + 3)(x + 3)$.

▷ ▶ *Using Manipulatives*

1. **a)** Copy and complete this diagram.
   b) Use algebra tiles to show the product $(x + 3)^2$.
   c) What shape is formed by the tiles in the product?
   d) Is there a pattern in the product that makes the x-tiles
   easy to count?
   e) What is the area of the tiles in the product $(x + 3)^2$?

2. Use tiles to expand the binomial square $(x + 4)^2$.

▷ ▶ *Through an Activity*

1. Copy and expand each binomial square.
   a) $(x + 1)^2$
   b) $(x + 2)^2$
   c) $(x + 3)^2$
   d) $(x + 4)^2$

2. Describe the patterns you see.

▷ ▶ *Through Instruction*

We can also square a binomial algebraically.

$(x + 3)^2 = (x + 3)(x + 3)$

$$= x^2 + 3x + 3x + 9$$
$$= x^2 + 6x + 9$$

The diagram shows how the square
of the binomial is represented.

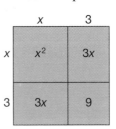

▷ ▶ *Through Guided Examples*

When a product involves two equal binomials, there is a
pattern in the terms.

$(x + 3)^2 = x^2 + 6x + 9$ the squares of the first and last terms

twice the product of the terms

This pattern can be used to square a binomial directly.

Example 1 .... *Solution* ....

Expand. $(x - 4)^2$

$$(x - 4)^2 = (x)^2 + 2(x)(-4) + (-4)^2$$
$$= x^2 - 8x + 16$$

Example 2 .... *Solution* ....

Expand. $(3x - 2)^2$

$$(3x - 2)^2 = (3x)^2 + 2(3x)(-2) + (-2)^2$$
$$= 9x^2 - 12x + 4$$

When you are familiar with the pattern, you may not need to write each step.
You can write the product directly, as in the following example.

Example 3 .... *Solution* ....

Expand. $(5 + 6n)^2$

$$(5 + 6n)^2 = 25 + 60n + 36n^2$$

Product of a Sum and a Difference

Consider the product $(x + 3)(x - 3)$.
The first binomial contains a + sign. It is the sum of two terms.
The second binomial contains a − sign. It is the difference of two terms.
We say that the product of these binomials is the *product of a sum and a difference*.

▶ ▶ *Through an Activity*

1. Copy and expand each expression.
   a) $(x + 1)(x - 1)$
   b) $(x - 2)(x + 2)$
   c) $(x + 3)(x - 3)$
   d) $(x - 4)(x + 4)$

2. Describe the patterns you see.

▶ ▶ *Through Guided Examples*

For each product above, you should have noticed that the middle
terms are opposites. They add to zero. This is illustrated further in the
following examples.

Example 4 .... *Solution* ....

Expand. $(x + 3)(x - 3)$

$$(x + 3)(x - 3) = x^2 - 3x + 3x - 9$$
$$= x^2 - 9$$

Example 5 .... *Solution* ....

Expand. $(3 - 2y)(3 + 2y)$

$$(3 - 2y)(3 + 2y) = 9 + 6y - 6y - 4y^2$$
$$= 9 - 4y^2$$

Working with Mathematics

Something to talk about

1. Give an example of a product which is:
   a) a binomial square
   b) a product of a sum and a difference

2. Use the diagram at the bottom of page 400. Explain why $6x$ is twice the product of the terms of the binomial.

Work together

3. Expand. Take turns to explain how you got your answer.
   a) $(x + 4)^2$
   b) $(x - 3)^2$
   c) $(2y + 6)^2$
   d) $(7 - 3x)^2$

4. Expand. Take turns to explain how you got your answer.
   a) $(x - 5)(x + 5)$
   b) $(4 - y)(4 + y)$
   c) $(1 + 2m)(1 - 2m)$
   d) $(2x - 3)(2x + 3)$

On your own

5. Expand.
   a) $(x + 1)^2$
   b) $(x - 2)^2$
   c) $(x - 5)^2$
   d) $(x + 5)^2$
   e) $(2x + 1)^2$
   f) $(2x - 1)^2$
   g) $(1 - 2x)^2$
   h) $(3x + 2)^2$

6. Expand.
   a) $(x - 1)^2$
   b) $(2b + 1)^2$
   c) $(3p + 2)^2$
   d) $(4m - 3n)^2$

7. a) Calculate 41^2 by expanding $(40 + 1)^2$.
   b) Calculate 68^2 by expanding $(70 - 2)^2$.
   c) Calculate 99^2 in a similar way.

8. Calculate each product by expressing it as a product of a sum and a difference.
   a) 21×19
   b) 32×28
   c) 45×55

Extend your thinking

9. a) Pick any two numbers. Calculate the square of the sum of the two numbers and the square of the difference of the two numbers.
   b) Add the two results in part a. How is the answer related to the two numbers you started with?
   c) Subtract the two results in part a. How is the answer related to the two numbers you started with?
   d) Repeat parts a to c, using other numbers. Are your conclusions in parts b and c the same as before?
   e) Prove your conclusions algebraically by using x and y to represent the numbers you picked in part a.

COMMUNICATING The Ideas

In your journal, write in words a rule for squaring a binomial. Explain how your rule can be used to perform these computations mentally.
   a) 15^2
   b) 21^2
   c) 19^2
   d) 99^2

A Shortcut for Squaring Numbers Ending in 5

Here is an example of the square of a two-digit number ending in 5: $65^2 = 4225$

Problem 1	**Problem 2**
Determine a shortcut for squaring any two-digit number ending in 5.	Use algebra to explain why this shortcut works.

Understand Problem 1
- What kinds of numbers can be squared using the shortcut?
- What are you asked to do?

Understand Problem 2
- What are you asked to do?

Think of a strategy
- Use your calculator to determine each product:
  15^2 25^2 35^2 45^2 55^2
  65^2 75^2 85^2 95^2
- Look for a pattern.

- Use a variable to represent the first digit of a 2-digit number.

Carry out the strategy
- What are the last two digits of each product?
- Examine the first number in each of the products 15^2 and 25^2, and the 2-digit number formed by the first two digits of each remaining product. How is this number related to the first digit of the number that was squared?
- What is the shortcut for squaring any two-digit number ending in 5?

- Let x represent the first digit of a 2-digit number.
- Write an expression for the 2-digit number which has x as its first digit and 5 as its second digit.
- Write an expression for the square of the 2-digit number.
- Expand the expression.
- Use factoring to write the expression in a form that explains why the shortcut works.

Look back
- Is there a shortcut for squaring other two-digit numbers?

- Does the shortcut work for squaring three-digit numbers ending in 5?

Communicating the Ideas

In your journal, write a description of what you discovered, and why it works. Your explanations should be understandable to someone who has never seen this shortcut for squaring two-digit numbers ending in 5.

FACTORING TRINOMIALS

Developing the Ideas

Recall that a polynomial with three terms is a trinomial.

As we learned in the previous section, the product of two binomials is often a trinomial.

For example, $(x + 3)(x + 4) = x^2 + 7x + 12$

Factoring is the reverse process.

To factor a trinomial, such as $x^2 + 7x + 12$, is to write it as the product $(x + 3)(x + 4)$.

▶▶ *Using Manipulatives*

We'll begin with a set of tiles which we will try to arrange as a rectangle. Then we'll determine its length and width.

1. Use 1 x^2-tile, 7 x-tiles, and 10 1-tiles.
What polynomial do they represent?

2. a) Arrange these tiles to form a rectangle.
   b) Write the length of the rectangle as a binomial.
   c) Write the width of the rectangle as a binomial.
   d) Write the area of the rectangle as a product of the length and the width.

3. Check the rectangles of other students.
Did you all arrange your tiles the same way?

4. What are the factors of the polynomial?

Let's consider another example.
Suppose you have the tiles representing $x^2 + 5x + 6$.

They can be arranged like this.

The length is $x + 3$.
The width is $x + 2$.
The area is $x^2 + 5x + 6$.
We write: $x^2 + 5x + 6 = (x + 2)(x + 3)$
We say: The factors of $x^2 + 5x + 6$ are $x + 2$ and $x + 3$.

5. Use algebra tiles to factor each trinomial.
   a) $x^2 + 5x + 4$ **b)** $x^2 + 6x + 8$ **c)** $x^2 + 4x + 4$

404   POLYNOMIALS

Consider this expansion.

$$x^2 + 7x + 12 = (x + 3)(x + 4)$$

7 is the sum of 3 and 4

12 is the product of 3 and 4

We use these relationships to factor a trinomial.

Example 1 ·

Factor. $x^2 + 7x + 6$

Solution

$x^2 + 7x + 6$

We want to find two numbers whose sum is 7 and whose product is 6.
We list pairs of factors of 6. We add each pair of factors.
We look for the factors that have a sum of 7. They are 1 and 6.
We write these numbers as the second terms in the binomials.

$x^2 + 7x + 6 = (x + 1)(x + 6)$

Factors of 6	Sum
1, 6	$1 + 6 = 7$
–1, –6	$-1 - 6 = -7$
2, 3	$2 + 3 = 5$
–2, –3	$-2 - 3 = -5$

Example 2 ·

Factor. $a^2 - 8a + 12$

Solution

$a^2 - 8a + 12$

We want two numbers whose sum is -8 and whose product is 12.
The factors that have a sum of -8 are -2 and -6.

$a^2 - 8a + 12 = (a - 6)(a - 2)$

Factors of 12	Sum
1, 12	$1 + 12 = 13$
–1, –12	$-1 - 12 = -13$
2, 6	$2 + 6 = 8$
–2, –6	$-2 - 6 = -8$
3, 4	$3 + 4 = 7$
–3, –4	$-3 - 4 = -7$

When you factor, you can check your work by expanding.

Example 3 ·

Factor $m^2 - 5m - 14$, then check.

Solution

$m^2 - 5m - 14$

We want two numbers whose sum is -5 and whose product is -14.
The factors that have a sum of -5 are 2 and -7.

$m^2 - 5m - 14 = (m + 2)(m - 7)$

Check: Expand $(m + 2)(m - 7)$.

Factors of –14	Sum
–1, 14	$-1 + 14 = 13$
1, –14	$1 - 14 = -13$
–2, 7	$-2 + 7 = 5$
2, –7	$2 - 7 = -5$

$$(m + 2)(m - 7) = m^2 - 7m + 2m - 14$$
$$= m^2 - 5m - 14$$

Since this is the trinomial we started with, the factors are correct.

Working with Mathematics

Something to talk about

1. a) Name the pairs of numbers you would test to factor $x^2 - 9x + 14$.
   b) Which pair has a sum of -9 and a product of 14?
   c) What are the factors of $x^2 - 9x + 14$?

2. Is the product of two binomials always a trinomial? Explain.

Work together

3. For each diagram:
   i) Write the trinomial represented by the algebra tiles.
   ii) Rearrange the tiles into a rectangle.
   iii) Use the result to factor the trinomial.

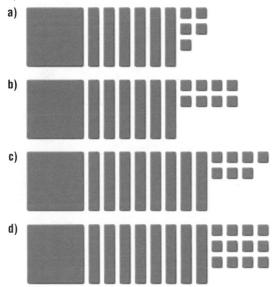

a)

b)

c)

d)

4. Use algebra tiles to factor each trinomial.
   a) $x^2 + 2x + 1$ b) $x^2 + 3x + 2$
   c) $x^2 + 4x + 3$ d) $x^2 + 5x + 4$

5. a) Describe a pattern in the terms of the trinomials in exercise 4.
   b) Describe a pattern in the algebra-tile rectangles for the trinomials.
   c) Extend the pattern by writing three more trinomials.

6. Factor. Take turns with your partner to check each other's answers.
   a) $x^2 + 6x + 5$ b) $a^2 + 8a + 12$
   c) $m^2 + 6m + 9$ d) $x^2 - x - 2$
   e) $x^2 - 5x + 6$ f) $p^2 + 2p - 8$

7. Factor. Check your partner's answers.
   a) $x^2 - 6x + 8$ b) $x^2 + 9x + 18$
   c) $a^2 - 11a + 18$ d) $m^2 + 11m + 28$
   e) $n^2 - 10n + 25$ f) $n^2 - 13n + 30$
   g) $p^2 + 16p + 64$ h) $y^2 - 13y + 42$
   i) $x^2 + 15x + 56$ j) $x^2 - 10x - 56$

On your own

8. Use algebra tiles to factor each trinomial.
   a) $x^2 + 5x + 6$ b) $a^2 + 7a + 12$
   c) $x^2 + 8x + 15$ d) $n^2 + 9n + 14$

9. Factor.
   a) $r^2 - 9r + 14$ b) $a^2 - 8a - 20$
   c) $n^2 - 8n + 16$ d) $m^2 - 9m + 20$
   e) $k^2 - 8k + 15$ f) $x^2 + 10x + 24$
   g) $a^2 - 2a - 15$ h) $m^2 + 9m + 20$
   i) $n^2 - 5n - 14$ j) $a^2 + 13a - 14$

Extend your thinking

10. Use algebra tiles to factor each trinomial.
    a) $x^2 - 2x + 1$ b) $x^2 - 3x - 4$
    c) $x^2 + x - 6$ d) $x^2 - 6x + 9$
    e) $x^2 - 6x - 7$ f) $x^2 - 10x + 16$

COMMUNICATING The Ideas

In your journal, explain how you would factor a trinomial as a product of two binomials. Give an example of a trinomial that cannot be factored in this way. By looking at a trinomial, how can you tell whether or not it can be factored as a product of two binomials?

. . . FACTORING A DIFFERENCE OF SQUARES

Developing the Ideas

▶▶ *Through Discussion*

In our expansions of products of binomials, we discovered that the
product of a sum and a difference produces a binomial.

For example, $(x + 3)(x - 3) = x^2 - 9$

Each term of the binomial is a perfect square.

That is, $x^2 = x \times x$ and $9 = 3 \times 3$

For this reason, we say that $x^2 - 9$ is a *difference of squares*.

We can think of $x^2 - 9$ geometrically as the difference between the areas
of a square of side x units and a square of side 3 units. That is, $x^2 - 9$ is
the area remaining when a 3 by 3 square is cut from an x by x square.

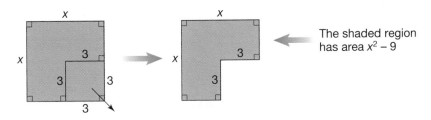

The shaded region
has area $x^2 - 9$

We can cut and paste the shaded region to form a rectangle.

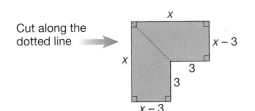

Cut along the
dotted line

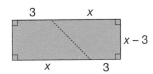

Flip one piece and paste
along the dotted line

The rectangle has length $x + 3$ and width $x - 3$.
Its area is $(x + 3)(x - 3)$.

That is, $x^2 - 9 = (x + 3)(x - 3)$
We can use this pattern to factor a difference of squares directly.

▶▶ *Through Guided Examples*

Example 1 .... *Solution* ....

Factor. $x^2 - 16$

$x^2 - 16 = x^2 - 4^2$ ◀ Writing each term as a square
$\qquad\quad = (x - 4)(x + 4)$

Example 2 .... *Solution* ....

Factor. $36x^2 - y^2$

$36x^2 - y^2 = (6x)^2 - y^2$
$\qquad\qquad = (6x - y)(6x + y)$

Working with Mathematics

Something to talk about

1. State the factors of each binomial.

a) $x^2 - 4$ b) $x^2 - 25$

c) $a^2 - 16$ d) $x^2 - 1$

e) $a^2 - 100$ f) $b^2 - 64$

2. Calculate mentally.

a) $20^2 - 19^2$ b) $80^2 - 79^2$

c) $91^2 - 89^2$ d) $201^2 - 199^2$

Work together

3. Draw a diagram to illustrate the factoring of each difference of squares. In each case, did you and your partner draw similar diagrams?

a) $x^2 - 1$ b) $x^2 - 16$

c) $x^2 - 36$ d) $x^2 - 4$

4. Factor. Compare your answers with those of your partner.

a) $25 - x^2$ b) $9 - x^2$

c) $81 - x^2$ d) $49 - x^2$

5. Choose any month on a calendar. Then choose a 3 by 3 square of 9 dates. Let x represent the date at the centre of the square.

May						
Sun	Mon	Tue	Wed	Thur	Fri	Sat
1	2	3	4	5	6	7
8	9	10	11	12	13	14
15	16	17	18	19	20	21
22	23	24	25	26	27	28
29	30	31				

a) Write a polynomial for:

  i) each corner number

  ii) the square of each corner number

  iii) the difference between the squares of numbers in diagonally opposite corners

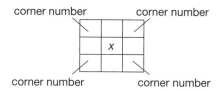

b) If you knew the difference between the squares in diagonally opposite corners, how could you determine the value of x?

On your own

6. Factor.

a) $4a^2 - 4$ b) $36 - n^2$

c) $y^2 - 49$ d) $9a^2 - 4$

e) $25x^2 - 9$ f) $16s^2 - 1$

7. Factor.

a) $36 - 100n^2$ b) $100x^2 - 121$

c) $144p^2 - 49$ d) $49a^2 - 1$

e) $4 - 36x^2$ f) $9 - 64m^2$

Extend your thinking

8. Factor completely.

a) $2x^2 - 18$ b) $3n^2 + 30$ c) $a^3 - 49a$

9. a) In the diagram, R is the radius of the larger circle and r is the radius of the smaller circle. Write a formula for the area of the shaded region.

b) Express your formula as a product.

10. Use algebra tiles to factor each difference of squares.

a) $x^2 - 1$ b) $4x^2 - 9$ c) $9x^2 - 4$

Review

1. Use algebra tiles to represent each polynomial.

a) $2x^2 + 5x + 3$ **b)** $x^2 - 3x + 2$

c) $4x^2 - 2x - 3$ **d)** $-3x^2 - 4x$

2. Write a polynomial that represents the perimeter and a polynomial that represents the area of each rectangle.

a)

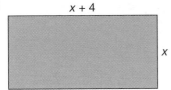

$x + 4$

x

b)

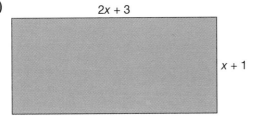

$2x + 3$

$x + 1$

c)

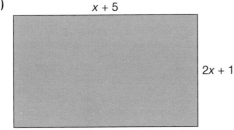

$x + 5$

$2x + 1$

3. Simplify.

a) $(5x^2 - 3y^2) + (x^2 + 4y^2)$

b) $(-2x - 7) - (-14x - 6)$

c) $(8a^2 + 2a - 3) - (-6a^2 + 4a + 7)$

d) $(3x - 2) - (x - 1) + (4x - 3)$

e) $(4x^2 - 3x) - (x^2 + 2x) + (3x^2 - x)$

f) $(3x^2 + 5x + 7) - (2x^2 - 4x + 9)$

4. Simplify. Find the value of the polynomial when: **i)** $x = 2$ **ii)** $x = -3$

a) $(5 - 2x) - (3 - x) + (7x - 2)$

b) $(5x^2 - 5x + 7) - (2x^2 - 3x - 5)$

5. Simplify.

a) $(-25n^2)(8n^2)$ **b)** $(-35c^3)(-4c^2)$

c) $(17x^2)(5x^3)$ **d)** $(-28n)(5n^3)$

6. Simplify.

a) $\dfrac{-45y^6}{-5y^4}$ **b)** $\dfrac{3n^6}{5n^4}$

c) $\dfrac{25x^4}{-5x^4}$ **d)** $\dfrac{36c^5}{24c^2}$

e) $18x^4 \div 3x$ **f)** $(-52y^6) \div 13y^5$

7. Expand.

a) $3c(5 - 2c)$ **b)** $(-4n)(2n - 1)$

c) $(-7y)(2y^2 - 5)$ **d)** $6k(3 - k + k^2)$

e) $5s(3s^2 - 2s - 7)$ **f)** $3p^2(2 - 3p - p^2)$

8. Factor each polynomial.

a) $5y - 10$ **b)** $12a + 18$

c) $-3x^2 + 6x - 12$ **d)** $2a^2 - 10a + 2$

e) $4w + 3w^2 - 7w^3$ **f)** $8y^3 - 4y^2 + 2y$

9. Simplify.

a) $\dfrac{3x^2 - 6x}{3x}$ **b)** $\dfrac{5x^2 - 10x}{5x}$

c) $\dfrac{18a - 21a^2}{3a}$ **d)** $\dfrac{-28n^2 - 7n}{7n}$

e) $\dfrac{36y - 9y^2}{-9y}$ **f)** $\dfrac{32b^4 + 8b^3}{-4b^2}$

10. Expand.

a) $(x - 3)(5x + 2)$ **b)** $(2a + 1)(2a + 3)$

c) $(8n - 3)(2n - 1)$ **d)** $(4a + 3)(4a + 3)$

e) $(3x - 2)(4x - 3)$ **f)** $(5x + 1)(6x - 4)$

11. Expand.

a) $(n - 7)^2$ **b)** $(c + 4)^2$

c) $(x - 1)^2$ **d)** $(3x + 2)(3x - 2)$

e) $(4x - 3)(4x + 3)$ **f)** $(3 - 5x)(3 + 5x)$

12. Factor.

a) $x^2 + 10x + 16$ **b)** $a^2 + 4a - 12$

c) $x^2 - 10x + 25$ **d)** $c^2 - 2c - 35$

e) $x^2 - x - 12$ **f)** $a^2 + a - 30$

13. Factor.

a) $a^2 - 49$ **b)** $m^2 - 64$

c) $h^2 - 144$ **d)** $81y^2 - 49$

e) $16a^2 - 81$ **f)** $64x^2 - 121$

The SET Game

Have you ever played the game SET? It can be played alone or with two or more people. This game was invented by Marsha J. Falco, a mathematician and computer programmer.

Marsha Falco didn't start out to make a popular game of logic. In 1974, she was working as an applied mathematician at the University of Cambridge in England. She was trying to determine whether epilepsy in German Shepherd dogs was inherited. While compiling her research, she wrote information about each dog on file cards. Because blocks of information were the same on each file card, rather than writing the data, she drew a symbol to represent a piece of data. If the information was slightly different, she would make the symbol a different colour. The veterinarians she was working with would look over her shoulder at the cards spread out on the table. They tried to find patterns in the shapes and colours of the symbols on the different cards. This gave her the idea for the game SET. She invented the game for her co-workers. Her daughter and son enjoyed SET so much that they urged Marsha to sell the game. Since 1991, SET has been a popular game enjoyed by young and old all over North America.

The game has 81 cards. Each card has 4 attributes.
- Number — each card has one, two, or three symbols
- Shape — each symbol is an oval, a squiggle, or a diamond
- Colour — each symbol is red, green, or purple
- Shading — each symbol is solid, striped, or unshaded

The purpose of the game is to find a set of three cards. In a set, each of the 4 attributes must be the *same* on every card or *different* on each card.

The three cards above right form a set.

Each card has a *different* number of symbols.
The symbols are the *same*.
The colours are the *same*.
The shadings are *different*.

Do the three cards on the right form a set? Why or why not?

The game is played by laying down 12 cards in a rectangle. The first person to see a set calls out "Set!". This person shows the set to the other players. If it is agreed that the cards form a set, this person is given 1 point. The three cards are removed and replaced by three cards from the deck. The game is over when all the cards have been used or no set can be made.

In this project, you will produce your own SET game, using mathematical expressions.

Each card should have a mathematical expression of the form $a \times b^c + d$. The four attributes are the values of a, b, c, and d. In the original game, each attribute has three possibilities. Let's use three different numbers for each of a, b, c, and d. It really does not matter which three numbers, so let's use 2, 3, and 5. There will be 81 cards altogether. Three examples are shown on the right. Do the three cards form a set?

Let's check. The values of a (2,2,2) are all the *same*, the values of b (3,5,2) are all *different*, the values of c (5,5,5) are all the *same*, and the values of d (5,3,2) are all *different*. These three cards *do* form a set.

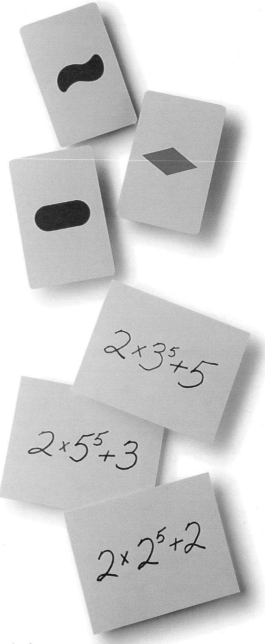

ACTIVITY 1

Make a complete set of these cards. Play the game on your own or with some friends.

ACTIVITY 2

How many cards would be in the set if each attribute had 4 different values? In such a version, would sets occur more often?

ACTIVITY 3

Design your own version of SET with or without mathematical expressions. You might try to use more than three attributes per card. Investigate whether this makes the game too complicated to play. Or you could use less than three attributes and see if this makes the game so simple that it loses its appeal.

WHAT'S COMING UP?

DEPARTMENTS

Mathematics Files

Quests

Minds on Math

Start With What You Know

Fazlur Khan

John Hancock Center

The innovative, 100-storey John Hancock Center opened in Chicago in 1970. Its exterior diagonal braces provide support and stability. Each diagonal beam spans 18 storeys. Engineer Fazlur Kahn played a vital role in the building's design.

1. Describe each of these items in your own words. Then find an example of each item in the photographs on these pages. If you have questions about any of these items, check the glossary at the end of this book.
   a) parallel lines
   b) perpendicular lines
   c) an equilateral triangle
   d) an isosceles triangle
   e) a right triangle
   f) an acute triangle
   g) an obtuse angle
   h) congruent triangles
   i) similar triangles
   j) a rectangle
   k) a square
   l) a parallelogram
   m) a rhombus

2. Find the side length of the square with each area.
   a) 16 m^2 b) 6.25 cm^2
   c) 10^4 m^2 d) 4900 m^2

3. A guy wire is attached 50 m up a tower and 12 m from its base. Calculate the length of the guy wire to the nearest tenth of a metre.

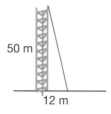

50 m

12 m

4. A ladder, 8.2 m long, is placed on horizontal ground with its foot 1.8 m from a vertical wall. How high up the wall will the ladder reach?

Bank of China

I.M. Pei

The Bank of China in Hong Kong is a dramatic structure which rises over 350 m. Architect I.M. Pei and engineer Leslie Robertson used a triangular glass and metal grid instead of a traditional interior steel frame. The bank required 40% less steel than most buildings of this height.

National Gallery of Canada

Moshe Safdie

The National Gallery of Canada, in Ottawa, was completed in 1988. This striking building contains great works of art from around the world. It was designed by architect Moshe Safdie. From the Great Hall, visitors can look out to the city of Ottawa or enter the galleries.

Angles and Intersecting Lines

Work with a partner to explore some properties of intersecting lines.
You'll need a piece of waxed paper and a protractor.

Step 1
Fold the paper along a slanted line. Unfold it
to show a crease.

Step 2
Fold the paper along a line that intersects the
first one. Unfold the paper to show two creases.

1. Four angles are formed by the creases.
   a) Which of these angles are equal?
   b) Check your answers by measuring with a protractor or folding the
   paper. Then use your paper model to explain why the angles are
   equal. These pairs of equal angles are called *opposite angles*.

An *angle bisector* is a line which divides an angle into two equal angles.
You can use your paper model to explore angle bisectors.

Step 3
Fold the paper so that one arm of one angle lies on top of the other arm.
Make a crease and unfold the paper. This crease is the angle bisector.

Repeat with one of the other angles.

2. What do you notice about the bisectors? Why do you think this
   happened? Compare your result with other students. Did everyone get
   the same result?

3. In your classroom, find an example of intersecting lines. To your
   partner, describe the angles that are formed.

Developing the Ideas

▶ ▶ *Through an Activity*

Work in a group. You'll need paper, a ruler, and scissors.

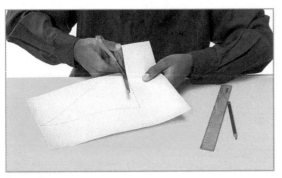

Step 1

Use a ruler to draw a large, acute scalene triangle. Be sure all the sides have different lengths. Cut out the triangle.

Step 2

Find the midpoint of one side of the triangle. To do this, fold the side in half and make a small crease at the edge of the paper. The crease marks the midpoint.

Step 3

Repeat the previous step to find the midpoint of another side of the triangle. Join the two midpoints with a ruler.

Step 4

Fold the paper along the line segment you drew. Where does the vertex at the top of the triangle end up?

Step 5

Carefully fold the triangle so that one of the other vertices ends up at the same point as the first vertex. Repeat with the third vertex.

1. Discuss your observations with your group. These questions should help you.

   a) What happened to the three vertices of the triangle?

   b) What does this tell you about the sum of the angles in the triangle? Compare your result with other groups. Did everyone get the same result?

2. Repeat your exploration using a right triangle, an isosceles triangle, or an equilateral triangle. What do you discover about the sum of its angles?

3. What else can you demonstrate about the angles in your triangle by paper folding?

Choose someone in the group to report your findings to the class when all the groups have finished their investigations.

▷▶ *Through a Guided Example*

In any triangle, the sum of the angle measures is 180°.

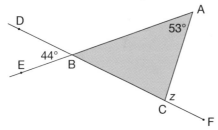

$\angle A + \angle B + \angle C = 180°$

Example ....

Determine the angle measure indicated by z.

Solution

Since $\angle ABC$ and $\angle DBE$ are opposite angles,

$\angle ABC = \angle DBE$

$\qquad = 44°$

Since the sum of the angle measures in $\triangle ABC$ is 180°,

$44° + \angle BCA + 53° = 180°$

$\qquad \angle BCA + 97° = 180°$

$\qquad\qquad \angle BCA = 83°$

Since $\angle BCF$ is a straight angle,

$\angle BCA + \angle ACF = 180°$

$\qquad 83° + z = 180°$

$\qquad\qquad z = 97°$

Working with Mathematics

Something to talk about

1. Take turns explaining how to find the angle measure indicated by each letter in the diagrams below. You may make sketches or rough calculations if you wish.

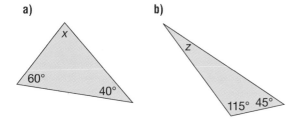

a) **b)**

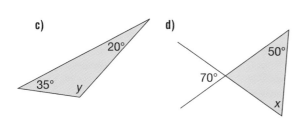

c) **d)**

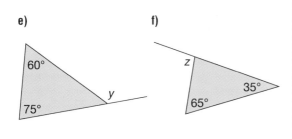

e) **f)**

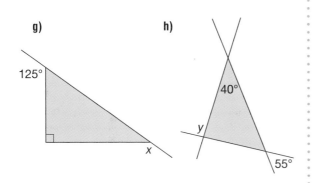

g) **h)**

On your own

2. Each pair of angles represents the measures of two angles in a triangle. Determine the measure of the third angle. Then classify each triangle by angle and by side.
- **a)** $32°, 67°$
- **b)** $70°, 75°$
- **c)** $40°, 26°$
- **d)** $60°, 30°$

3. Determine the angle measure indicated by each letter.

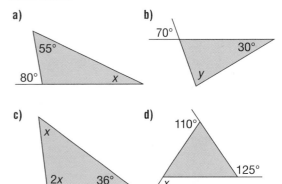

a) **b)**

c) **d)**

4. Make up a question involving the sum of the angles in a triangle. Exchange your question with someone in your class. Solve the question you are given. Explain your reasoning to the person who made up the question.

Work together

5. A triangle on graph paper can be described by the coordinates of its vertices. Draw the triangle formed by each set of points. Then classify each triangle by angle and by side.
- **a)** A(4, 4), B(7, 0), C(−1, −1)
- **b)** D(5, 0), E(−4, 6), F(−3, 1)
- **c)** G(−1, 6), H(7, 4), I(2, 1)

6. a) How many triangles are there in the diagram below?
- **b)** How many of these triangles are right? obtuse? acute? isosceles? equilateral? scalene?

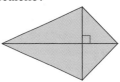

7. How many line segments are there in the diagram in exercise 6? Draw a figure, using the least number of line segments, that has at least one triangle of all 6 types.

8. Do you think that it is possible for a triangle to have these angles? Give reasons for your answers.
   a) 2 acute angles
   b) 3 acute angles
   c) 2 right angles
   d) 2 obtuse angles
   e) a straight angle
   f) 1 right angle, 1 obtuse angle

9. a) If you know the measure of one of the acute angles in a right triangle, how can you determine the measure of the other acute angle? List some possible values in a table. Then use the data to draw a graph on a grid like the one shown below.

One acute angle	The other acute angle

Angles in a right triangle

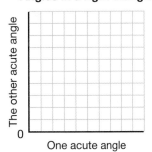

One acute angle

b) Describe the pattern formed by the plotted points. Try to explain why this pattern occurs.

Extend your thinking

10. In mathematics, we often look for ways to extend our results to other situations. For example, since we know that the sum of the angle measures in a triangle is 180°, we might try to extend this property to polygons with more than 3 sides.
    a) Sketch a quadrilateral. Divide it into 2 triangles by drawing a diagonal. What does your sketch tell you about the sum of the angle measures in a quadrilateral?
    b) Sketch a pentagon. Use the idea from part a to find the sum of its angles. Then repeat for a hexagon.
    c) If you know the number of sides a polygon has, how can you find the sum of its angles?
    d) What is a formula for the sum of the angles in a polygon with n sides?

COMMUNICATING

The Ideas

How can you find the measure of an angle in a triangle if you know the measures of the other two angles? Describe a step-by-step procedure in your journal.

BOGGLE YOUR **MIND**

The total floor space of all of the office space in the Bank of China building, shown on page 415, is 132 895 m². A typical 1-storey, 3-bedroom bungalow has a floor space of about 140 m². How many times as great as the floor space of one of these houses is the floor space of the Bank of China building?

A Property of a Right Triangle

Here's a neat fact about right triangles that you can discover by paper folding. You'll need paper, a ruler, scissors, a protractor, and a pair of compasses, cardboard, and glue.

Step 1

Draw a large right triangle on a sheet of paper. Cut out the triangle.

Step 2

Fold the triangle so that one of the vertices lies on the vertex at the right angle. Do the same with the other vertex.

Step 3

Unfold the triangle. It should look something like the one above.

1. What do you notice about the creases in your triangle?

2. **a)** What do you notice about the distances from the three vertices to the point where the creases meet?
   b) Compare your results with other students.

3. In a right triangle, the side opposite the right angle is called the *hypotenuse*. In your journal, describe a property of the midpoint of the hypotenuse that the paper folding has demonstrated.

4. Glue your triangle to a piece of paper or cardboard. Draw a circle which passes through the three vertices of your triangle.
   a) How are the triangle and the circle related? Explain why this happens.
   b) In your journal, describe the property of the midpoint of the hypotenuse that you have demonstrated.

Investigating Properties of Angles in Triangles

The Geometer's Sketchpad enables you to investigate geometric relationships in a way that is impossible without a computer. You can construct a diagram on the screen. You can then change your diagram by simply dragging with the mouse or by creating an animation.

In this investigation you will use *The Geometer's Sketchpad* to explore the following problem.

△ABC is any triangle. BD and CD are the bisectors of ∠ABC and ∠ACB respectively. How are ∠A and ∠D related? That is, if ∠A changes by a certain number of degrees, by how many degrees does ∠D change? If you know the measure of ∠A, how can you determine the measure of ∠D?

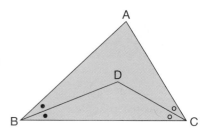

Step 1 Constructing the triangle

Start the program.

Choose the Point tool and use it to create three points which will be the vertices of your triangle. Label each point with the Text tool. You may need to change the labels so they are the same as those shown here. To change a label, double click on the label with the Text tool still in effect. Enter the label you wish to use for that point in the dialog box which appears. Shift-click the three points to select them. To shift-click, use the Selection tool, and, holding the shift key, click each point. From the **Construct** menu, choose **Segment**. The computer will draw the triangle. Click any blank area of the screen to deselect the triangle.

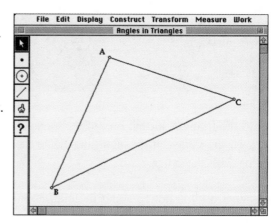

Step 2 Constructing the angle bisectors and point D

Shift-click the three vertices in the order A, B, C.
From the **Construct** menu, choose **Angle Bisector**.
Click any blank area of the screen to deselect the bisector.
Shift-click the three vertices in the order A, C, B.
From the **Construct** menu, choose **Angle Bisector**.
Choose the Point tool. Click the point where the bisectors intersect.

With the Text tool, label this point D.
Click any blank area of the screen to deselect the point.

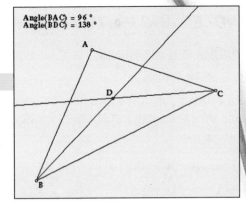

Step 3 Measuring angles A and D

Shift-click the vertices B, A, C in this order.
From the **Measure** menu, choose **Angle**.
Click any blank area of the screen to deselect the vertices.
Shift-click the vertices B, D, C in this order.
From the **Measure** menu, choose **Angle**.

Step 4 Collecting the data and graphing the results

Copy this table.

∠BAC	∠BDC
20°	
40°	
60°	
80°	
100°	
120°	
140°	
160°	

Using the Selection tool, drag point A to different positions.
Observe how the two angle measurements change. Try to
get the measures shown for ∠BAC in the table. Record the
measure of ∠BDC for each of these. You may need to drag
points B or C to get some of the results you need.

Draw a graph of the measures of ∠D against the measures
of ∠A.

Step 5 Analysing the results

1. Describe the change in the measure of ∠D when the
   measure of ∠A:

   a) increases by 20°   **b)** increases by 10°   **c)** decreases by 10°

2. How are these changes shown in the table and on the graph?

3. Why do you think the changes in ∠D are related to the
   changes in ∠A?

4. Write an equation that you could use to determine the
   measure of ∠D if you know the measure of ∠A.

In your journal, describe the problem you investigated
and the properties you discovered. Illustrate your report
with diagrams.

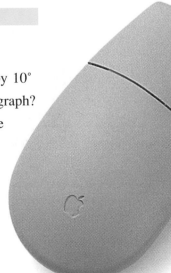

Developing the Ideas

▶ ▶ *Through an Activity*

You can use paper triangles like the ones you made earlier to investigate some properties of parallel lines. You'll need paper, scissors, a ruler, and a protractor.

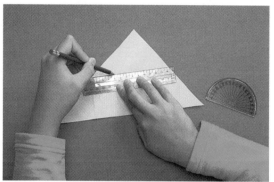

Step 1

Get the triangle you used on page 417 or follow the steps on that page to make another triangle.

Step 2

Look at the angles shown above. How do you think their measures compare? Check your prediction. Mark the angles on your triangle to show what you have discovered.

1. The base of the triangle and the line joining the midpoints are *parallel lines*. The side of the triangle is a *transversal*. The marked angles are called *corresponding angles*.

   a) When a transversal intersects two parallel lines, what do you think is true about the corresponding angles?

   b) Find another pair of corresponding angles. Mark these angles.

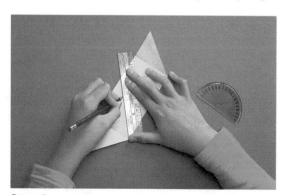

Step 3

Fold the triangle along the line joining the midpoints, so that the top vertex lies on the base. Draw a line along each edge of this folded portion.

Step 4

Look at the angles shown above. How do you think their measures compare? Check your prediction. Mark the angles on your triangle to show what you have discovered.

2. The marked angles are called *alternate angles*.

    a) When a transversal intersects two parallel lines, what do you think is true about the alternate angles?

    b) Find another pair of alternate angles. Mark these angles.

3. Repeat your exploration using a right triangle, an isosceles triangle, or an equilateral triangle. Did you get the same results? Describe any differences or special cases that you see. Share your discoveries when all the groups have finished their investigations.

▶ ▶ *Through a Guided Example*

The diagrams show related angles. The lines do not have to be parallel.

- Angles forming a Z-pattern are called *alternate angles*.

- Angles forming an F-pattern are called *corresponding angles*.

When a transversal intersects two *parallel* lines:
- the alternate angles are equal
- the corresponding angles are equal

Example

Determine the angle measure indicated by x.

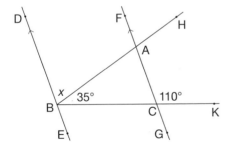

Solution

Since ∠BCK is a straight angle,

∠BCA + 110° = 180°

       ∠BCA = 70°

Since FG ∥ DE and ∠EBC and ∠BCA are alternate angles,

∠EBC = ∠BCA

      = 70°

Since ∠DBE is a straight angle,

x + 35° + 70° = 180°

         x = 75°

Working with Mathematics

Something to talk about

1. In this figure:
   a) name two pairs of alternate angles
   b) name four pairs of corresponding angles

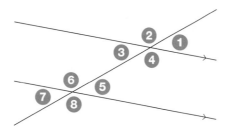

2. Find at least two sets of parallel lines and transversals in each photograph on pages 414 and 415. In each example, point out which lines are parallel, which line is the transversal, one pair of corresponding angles, and one pair of alternate angles.

3. In the *Example*, the angle measure indicated by *x* can be determined in many different ways. Find as many of these ways as you can.

4. Take turns explaining how to find the angle measures indicated by *x*, *y*, and *z*. You may make sketches or rough calculations if you wish.

a)

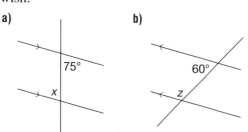

b)

c)

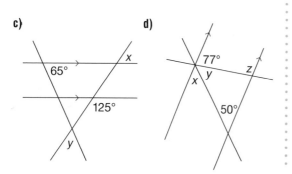

d)

On your own

5. Determine the measures of the three angles in △ABC.

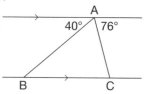

6. Determine the angle measure indicated by each letter.

a)

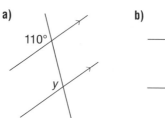

b)

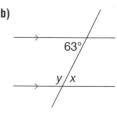

c)

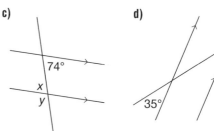

d)

e)

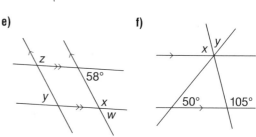

f)

7. Make up a question involving angles and parallel lines like those in exercises 4 to 6. Exchange questions with a classmate. Answer the question you receive. Explain your reasoning to the person who wrote the question.

Work together

8. Do you think that two intersecting lines can both be parallel to a third line? Draw a diagram to support your answer.

9. Do you think that two intersecting lines can both be perpendicular to a third line? Draw a diagram to support your answer.

Extend your thinking

10. Two lines can intersect in 0 points or 1 point, as shown below.

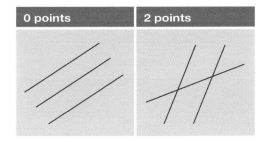

Two possibilities for three lines are also shown.

a) What other possibilities are there for three lines? Draw diagrams to support your answer.

b) What is the greatest number of points in which four lines can intersect? What is the least number? Try to find examples of four lines intersecting in all the possible numbers of points from the least to the greatest.

c) What is the greatest number of points in which five lines can intersect? six lines can intersect?

d) If you know the number of lines, how can you find the greatest number of points in which they can intersect?

COMMUNICATING

The Ideas
A transversal intersects two lines that are not parallel. Do you think any of the pairs of angles formed are equal? Record your ideas in your journal.

BOGGLE YOUR MIND

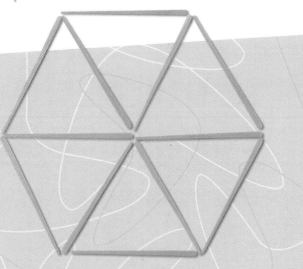

Arrange 12 toothpicks as shown. Then try to complete each of these challenges.

1. Create 4 identical diamonds by moving 4 toothpicks.
2. Create 3 equilateral triangles by moving 4 toothpicks.

Extending the Pythagorean Theorem

In Chapter 4, you reviewed the Pythagorean Theorem which relates the areas of squares on the sides of a right triangle.

Pythagorean Theorem

In a right triangle, the area of the square on the hypotenuse is equal to the sum of the areas of the squares on the other two sides.

$$b^2 = a^2 + c^2$$

Do you think that this property of a right triangle might be true for figures other than squares? Work in a group to investigate this question. You will need geometrical instruments.

- Construct the diagram shown below for your group. In each case, AB has measure 3 cm, BC has measure 4 cm, and AC has measure 5 cm.
- Make the measurements indicated. Then calculate the areas of the three figures in colour.
- Compare the sum of the areas of the two smaller figures with the area of the larger figure. What do you notice?

Group 1 Isosceles right triangles

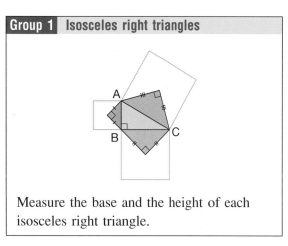

Measure the base and the height of each isosceles right triangle.

Group 2 30°–60°–90° triangles

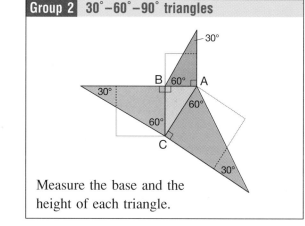

Measure the base and the height of each triangle.

Group 3 Circles

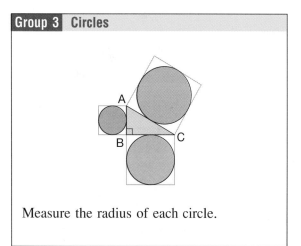

Measure the radius of each circle.

Group 4 Equilateral triangles

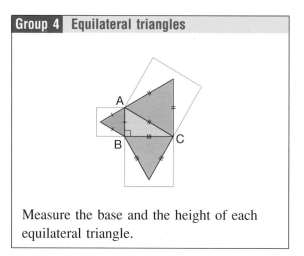

Measure the base and the height of each equilateral triangle.

1. Each group constructed similar figures on the sides of a right triangle. Compare the results of your investigations.

   a) What did you discover about the areas of these figures?

   b) What do you think is meant by the Extended Pythagorean Theorem?

2. Do you think the Extended Pythagorean Theorem would apply to these figures? Explain your answers.

   a) Rectangles with length twice the width

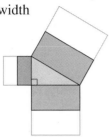

   b) Triangles with height half the base

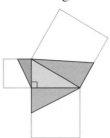

   c) Semicircles

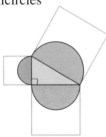

   d) Quarter circles

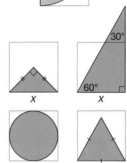

3. The Pythagorean Theorem relates the areas of squares on the sides of a right triangle. When you draw other figures on the sides of a right triangle, their areas are related to the areas of the squares. For example, the figures used by Groups 1 to 4 are shown. Each figure is drawn in a square with side length x and area x^2.

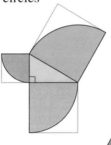

   The figures cover different amounts of the squares. For example, the area of the isosceles right triangle is one-quarter, or 25%, of the area of the square. So, the area of the isosceles right triangle is $0.25x^2$.

   a) Determine an expression in x for the area of each of the other figures.

   b) Determine an expression in x for the area of each figure in exercise 2.

   c) What do you observe about the expressions for the areas of all the figures? Explain how this proves the Extended Pythagorean Theorem for these figures.

Prepare a display or presentation of the results of your investigations.

The Triangle in Engineering and Architecture

This building is called a geodesic dome. The larger a geodesic dome is, the stronger it is. This contrasts with other buildings, whose structures would not be strong enough to support their weights if they exceeded certain dimensions.

Look closely at the dome. You should see that its framework is constructed in triangular sections. Triangles are also part of many simpler structures, such as metal bridges or scaffolding. What characteristics do triangles have that make them such an important part of a structural framework? You can investigate this question by making models. You'll need 32 toothpicks and a glue gun.

Step 1

Build two identical cubes using glue and toothpicks.

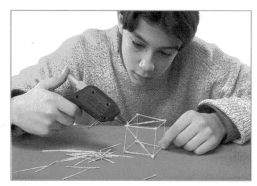

Step 2

Add a diagonal crossbeam to each side of one cube. You will need two toothpicks to make each diagonal beam.

Step 3

When the glue has dried, lay a flat palm on each cube and push gently back and forth.

1. Record your observations from *Step 3* in your notebook. Compare how the two cubes reacted to the pressure of your palm.

2. Design and carry out a simple test to compare how much weight the two cubes can support. Record your results in your note book.
   a) Describe the test.
   b) How did you keep your comparison fair?
   c) What did you discover when you attempted your test?

3. Look around your neighbourhood. Describe any buildings or other structures that use triangles in their designs.

Developing the Ideas

▶ ▶ *Through an Activity*

You can use paper triangles like the ones you made earlier to investigate some properties of isosceles and equilateral triangles. You'll need paper, scissors, a ruler and a protractor.

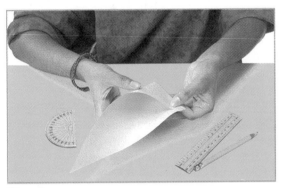

Step 1
Follow *Step 1* on page 417 to make a triangle. Mark the midpoints of two sides.

Step 2
Draw a perpendicular line from the third side of the triangle to one of the midpoints.

Step 3
Fold along the line you have drawn. Draw a line along the edge of the folded piece.

Step 4
Unfold the paper. The line you have drawn forms a triangle with two sides of the large triangle.

1. **a)** What kind of triangle have you drawn?
   b) What special properties does it have? How does your triangle illustrate those properties?

2. Fold and draw another triangle of the same kind on your paper triangle. Does it have the same properties?

3. Repeat the investigation using a right triangle, an isosceles triangle, or an equilateral triangle. Did you get the same results? Describe any differences or special cases that you see. Share your discoveries when all the groups have finished their investigations.

In an isosceles triangle, the angles opposite the equal sides are equal.

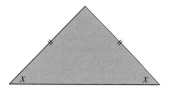

In an equilateral triangle, all three angles are equal. Since the sum of the angle measures is 180°, each angle measures 60°.

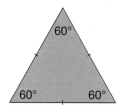

Example ·······································

Determine the angle measure indicated by y.

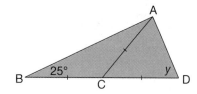

Solution

Since $\triangle ABC$ is isosceles, $\angle BAC = 25°$

Since the sum of the angle measures in $\triangle ABC$ is 180°,

$25° + 25° + \angle BCA = 180°$
$\qquad\qquad \angle BCA = 130°$

Since $\angle BCD$ is a straight angle,

$130° + \angle ACD = 180°$
$\qquad\quad \angle ACD = 50°$

Since the sum of the angle measures in $\triangle ACD$ is 180°,

$50° + \angle CAD + \angle CDA = 180°$
$\qquad\quad \angle CAD + \angle CDA = 130°$

Since $\triangle ACD$ is isosceles, $\angle CAD = \angle CDA$, so $\angle CAD + \angle CDA = 2y$.

$2y = 130°$
$\ y = 65°$

Working with Mathematics

Something to talk about

1. Take turns explaining how to find the angle measure indicated by each letter. You may make sketches or rough calculations if you wish.

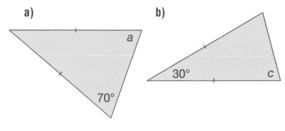

a)

b)

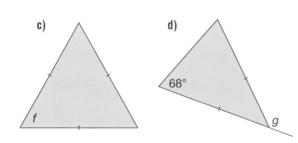

c)

d)

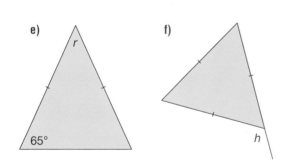

e)

f)

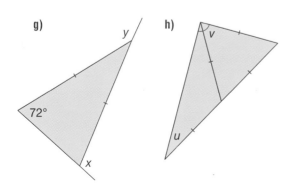

g)

h)

On your own

2. Determine the angle measure indicated by each letter.

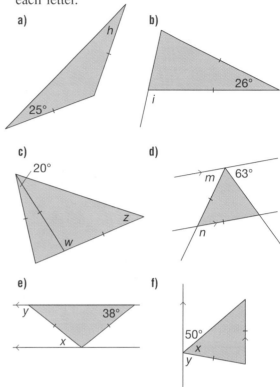

a)

b)

c)

d)

e)

f)

Work together

3. In a certain isosceles triangle, one angle is double another angle. What are the measures of the angles in this triangle?

4. There are two different isosceles triangles, each of which has a 30° angle. What are the measures of the other two angles in each triangle?

5. There are two different isosceles triangles, each of which has one angle that is 30° greater than another angle. What are the measures of all the angles in these triangles?

6. Do you think that it is possible to have each kind of triangle? Give reasons for your answers.

   a) an isosceles right triangle

   b) an isosceles obtuse triangle

   c) an isosceles acute triangle

   d) a scalene isosceles triangle

Extend your thinking

7. You'll need a straw, a length of string, cardboard, a protractor, and some tape.

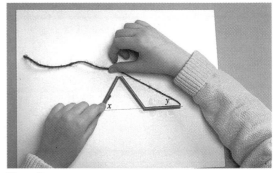

Step 1

Cut the straw into three equal lengths. Thread the string through the straws. Tape the string at one end and pull the extra string to the other end. This hinges the straw pieces.

Step 2

Draw a baseline on a piece of cardboard. Tape the straw with the extra string to the baseline. Arrange the straws so that the free end is also on the baseline. Pull the string to meet the top vertex, as shown.

Look at the angles marked x and y in *Step 2*. Move the free end of the straw along the baseline and observe how the angles change. You will need to adjust the string each time so it meets the vertex.

a) Determine the value of y for each value of x: 70°, 65°, 40°, 30°, 15°.

b) If you know a value of x, how can you find the corresponding value of y?

c) Determine an equation relating x and y.

d) Use your model to show the largest possible value of x. What is the corresponding value of y?

e) Use your model to show the smallest possible value of x. What is the corresponding value of y?

f) Draw a graph showing how the value of y depends on the value of x.

COMMUNICATING
The Ideas

Suppose you know the measure of one angle in an isosceles triangle. In your journal, describe how to calculate the measures of the other two angles.

Calculating Angles in House Construction

Dormer

Fascia

A dormer is a small structure that projects from a sloping roof and has a window set into its outer wall.

The dormer roof of this cottage is inclined at an angle of 64°, as shown. To construct the fascia boards around the dormer, the builder needs to know the measures of the two angles indicated. You can use your knowledge of isosceles triangles to calculate these angles.

64°

Understand the problem

- What kind of triangle is formed by the dormer roof and the baseline? How do you know this?
- How are the angles to be cut related to the angles in the triangle?

Think of a strategy

- Without measuring, can you find a way to calculate the measures of the other angles in the triangle?
- How are the angles in the triangle related to the angles the builder needs to know to make the fascia boards?

Carry out the strategy

- What are the measures of the angles the builder requires?

Look back

- Compare this problem with exercise 1b on page 433. In both cases, the measure of one angle of an isosceles triangle is given. Explain the differences in the ways that you determined the other two angles.
- In this problem, you determined the measures of some angles without measuring them. Why do you think a person would need to do this when the angles could be measured with a protractor?

Communicating the Ideas

In your journal, write a description of this problem and your solution. Someone reading your solution should be able to use your ideas to solve similar problems with different angles for the dormer roofs.

Patterns in the Angles in Isosceles Triangles

Work in a group to complete this activity. All groups will be investigating the relationships among angles in isosceles triangles.

Group 1

Copy this table. For each isosceles triangle on pages 432 and 433, record the measures of its angles in the table. Then use the data to draw a graph on a grid like the one shown on the right.

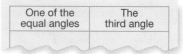

One of the equal angles	The third angle

1. Describe the pattern formed by the plotted points. Try to explain why this pattern occurs.

2. Let x represent the measures of the angles in the first column of your table. Let y represent the measures of the angles in the second column.
   a) Determine an equation relating x and y.
   b) What are the possible values of x and y in your equation?

3. Compare your graph and your equation with those of Group 2.

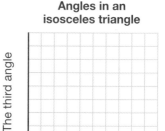

Angles in an isosceles triangle

The third angle / One of the equal angles

Group 2

Copy this table. For each isosceles triangle on pages 432 and 433, record the measures of its angles in the table. Then use the data to draw a graph on a grid like the one shown on the right.

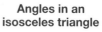

The smallest angle	The largest angle

1. Describe the patterns formed by the plotted points. Try to explain why these patterns occur.

2. Let x represent the measures of the angles in the first column of your table. Let y represent the measures of the angles in the second column.
   a) Determine an equation relating x and y for each part of your graph.
   b) What are the possible values of x and y in each equation?

3. Compare your graph and your equations with those of Group 1.

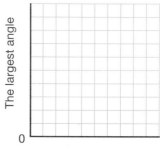

Angles in an isosceles triangle

The largest angle / The smallest angle

GEOMETRY & ALGEBRA

Linking Ideas

PROPERTIES OF CHORDS IN CIRCLES

Developing the Ideas

▶▶ *Through Activities*

Work in a group. You will need paper, a ruler, a protractor, and a pair of compasses.

A line segment joining any two points on a circle is called a *chord*.

ACTIVITY 1

1. Construct a circle. Draw any chord AB. Construct the perpendicular bisector of the chord. Through what point does the perpendicular bisector appear to pass?

2. Repeat exercise 1 for other chords and other circles. Did you always get the same result?

ACTIVITY 2

1. Construct a circle. Draw any chord CD. Locate the midpoint M of the chord. Join it to the centre O of the circle. Measure ∠OMC and ∠OMD. What do you notice?

2. Repeat exercise 1 for other chords and other circles. Did you always get the same result?

ACTIVITY 3

1. Construct a circle. Draw any chord EF. Construct a line through the centre O of the circle, that is perpendicular to EF. Let N be the point where the perpendicular meets EF. Measure NE and NF. What do you notice?

2. Repeat exercise 1 for other chords and other circles. Did you always get the same result?

In *Activities 1* to *3*, you should have observed the following properties of chords:

Property 1

The perpendicular bisector of any chord passes through the centre of the circle.

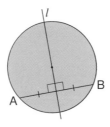

l passes through the centre.

Property 2

The line segment joining the midpoint of a chord to the centre of the circle is perpendicular to the chord.

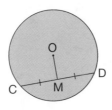

The angles at M are right anges.

Property 3

The line which is perpendicular to a chord, and passes through the centre of the circle, passes through the midpoint of the chord.

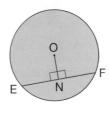

N is the midpoint of the chord.

Example ....

A circle with centre O has radius 6.0 cm. A chord AB is 8.4 cm long. Calculate how far the chord is from the centre of the circle.

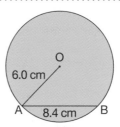

Solution

Construct the perpendicular from O to the chord, meeting the chord at C. According to Property 3, C is the midpoint of AB.
So, AC = 4.2 cm

Use the Pythagorean Theorem in right $\triangle$OAC.

$$OA^2 = AC^2 + OC^2$$
$$6.0^2 = 4.2^2 + OC^2$$
$$OC^2 = 36.00 - 17.64$$
$$= 18.36$$
$$OC = \sqrt{18.36}$$
$$\doteq 4.3$$

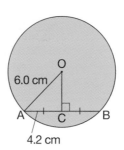

The chord is approximately 4.3 cm from the centre of the circle.

Working with Mathematics

Something to talk about

1. A diameter is a special chord. Do you think that the three properties of chords apply to chords that are diameters? Explain your answers.

2. Determine the length indicated by each letter. Give the answers to one decimal place where necessary. Which chord properties did you use?

a)

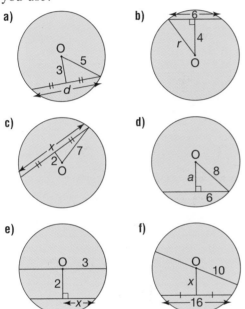

b)

c)

d)

e)

f)

On your own

3. Calculate the length indicated by each letter. Give the answers to one decimal place where necessary. Which chord properties did you use?

a)

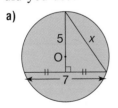

b)

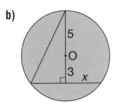

c)

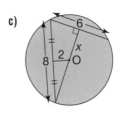

d)

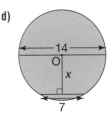

4. △PQR is inscribed in a circle with centre O, such that QR = 8.0 cm and PO extended is perpendicular to QR at M. The radius of the circle is 5.0 cm. Calculate:
   a) the distance from O to QR
   b) the length of PM
   c) the length of PQ
   d) the distance from O to PQ

Work together

5. A circle has radius 5.0 cm. A chord in the circle is x centimetres from the centre.
   a) Find an expression in terms of x for the length y of the chord.
   b) What are the smallest and largest possible values of x? What are the corresponding values of y?
   c) Draw a graph showing how the value of y depends on the value of x.

Extend your thinking

6. An equilateral triangle is inscribed in a circle with radius 6.0 cm.
   a) Calculate the lengths of the sides of the triangle.
   b) Calculate the area of the triangle.
   c) What percent of the circle is covered by the triangle?

COMMUNICATING The Ideas

In your journal, explain what a chord is. Then describe three different properties of chords. Illustrate each property with a diagram.

Locating the Centre
of a Circle

A meteor is a mass of stone or metal that enters Earth's atmosphere from space. If a meteor passes through Earth's atmosphere and strikes the planet's surface, it is called a meteorite. Large meteorites create craters at the point where they collide with Earth. Many of the world's largest meteorite craters have been found in Canada.

Some people believe that the circular outline of part of the eastern shore of Hudson Bay was created when a meteorite struck Earth millions of years ago. If these people are correct, how far from the shoreline did the meteorite hit?

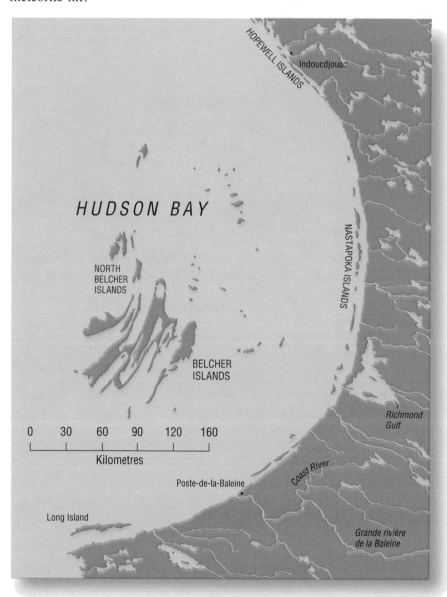

The Manicouagen Reservoir, in Quebec, is one of Canada's largest meteorite crators. As seen in this satellite image, the force of the impact created a raised circular mound surrounded by a ring of water.

Understand the problem

- What are you asked to do?
- Is it reasonable to assume that the meteorite would have hit Earth at the centre of the circle formed by the shoreline?

Think of a strategy

- You could trace the map.
- You could use geometrical instruments to locate the centre of the circle.
- The centre of a circle lies on a diameter. How many diameters would you need to construct to locate the centre?
- How could you construct the diameter of a circle, when only part of the circle is given?

Carry out the strategy

- Make a tracing of the circular arc formed by the eastern shore of Hudson Bay.
- Mark any two points on this arc and join them to form a chord. Use one of the chord properties to construct a diameter. Construct another diameter in the same way.
- Measure the distance from the centre to the shoreline on your tracing.
- Use the scale to determine how far from the shoreline the meteor hit Earth.

Look back

- Check your construction with a pair of compasses.
- Approximately what percent of the entire circle is formed by the shoreline? If the shoreline formed a smaller part of the circle, could you still use your method to locate the centre?

Communicating the Ideas

In your journal, describe a step-by-step procedure someone could follow to locate the centre of a circle. Include diagrams when you feel they would help the reader to understand your instructions.

PROPERTIES OF ANGLES IN CIRCLES

Developing the Ideas

▶▶ *Through Activities*

Work in a group. You will need several sheets of paper, some light
cardboard, a piece of corrugated cardboard, some tacks, scissors, a ruler,
a protractor, and a pair of compasses.

ACTIVITY 1

1. Construct a circle. Draw any diameter AB.

2. Mark a point C on the circle. Join AC and BC.

3. Measure ∠C.

4. Repeat exercises 2 and 3 for other positions of C on the circle.
What do you notice?

5. Repeat exercises 1 to 4 for other circles. Are the results the same?

ACTIVITY 2

1. Place a sheet of paper on the corrugated cardboard, and insert two tacks.
Cut a piece of cardboard to form a right angle. Position the corner of
the cardboard against the tacks. Move the cardboard, keeping it against
the tacks. Observe how the position of the corner of the cardboard
changes. Use a pencil to mark some of these positions. What figure do
you think is formed by the corner of the cardboard?

2. How is this related to your observations in *Activity 1*?

ACTIVITY 3

1. Construct a circle. Draw any chord DE (not a diameter).

2. Mark a point F on the circle. Join DF and EF.

3. Measure ∠F.

4. Repeat exercises 2 and 3 for other positions of F on the circle.
What do you notice?

5. Repeat exercises 1 to 4 for other circles. Are the results the same?

ACTIVITY 4

1. Place a sheet of paper on the corrugated cardboard, and insert two tacks. Cut a piece of cardboard to form an acute angle. Position the corner of the cardboard against the tacks. Move the cardboard, keeping it against the tacks. Observe how the position of the corner of the cardboard changes. Use a pencil to mark some of these positions. What figure do you think is formed by the corner of the cardboard?

2. How is this related to your observations in *Activity 3*?

ACTIVITY 5

1. Construct a circle. Mark the centre O.

2. Draw any chord GH. Join GO and HO.

3. Mark a point J on the circle. Join GJ and HJ.

4. Measure ∠O and ∠J. What do you notice?

5. Repeat exercises 3 and 4 for other positions of J on the circle.

6. Repeat exercises 2 to 5 for other chords, including the diameter. Did you always get the same result?

ACTIVITY 6

1. Construct a circle.

2. Mark any four points A, B, C, and D on the circle. Join the points to form a quadrilateral.

3. Measure ∠A and ∠C. Measure ∠B and ∠D. What do you notice?

4. Repeat exercises 2 and 3 for other positions of the points on the circle. Did you always get the same result?

▶▶ *Through Guided Examples*

An angle with its vertex on the circumference of a circle and having chords for arms is called an *inscribed angle*. In the diagram, ∠C and ∠D are two of the inscribed angles.

To describe how these angles are related to the chord AB, we say that ∠C and ∠D are *subtended* by the chord AB.

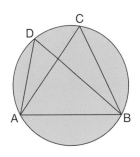

In *Activities 1* to *5*, you should have observed the following properties of inscribed angles:

Property 1

The angle inscribed in a semicircle is a right angle.

$\angle C = 90°$

Property 2

Inscribed angles subtended by the same chord, and on the same side of the chord, are equal.

$\angle F = \angle G$

Property 3

The measures of two inscribed angles subtended by the same chord, and on opposite sides of the chord, add to 180°.

$\angle F + \angle G = 180°$

Property 4

The measure of the angle at the centre of a circle is double the measure of an inscribed angle subtended by the same arc.

$\angle O = 2 \angle J$

A quadrilateral with its vertices on a circle is called a *cyclic quadrilateral*. Figure ABCD is a cyclic quadrilateral.

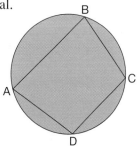

In *Activity 6*, you should have observed the following property of a cyclic quadrilateral.

Property 5

In a cyclic quadrilateral, the measures of the opposite angles add to 180°.

$\angle A + \angle C = 180°$
$\angle B + \angle D = 180°$

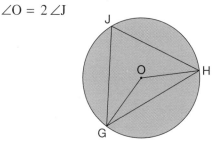

Example 1

BC is a diameter of a circle, centre O.
A is any point on the circumference.
Find the measure of ∠C.

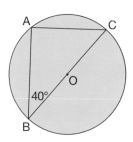

Solution

Since ∠A is an angle in a semicircle, ∠A = 90°
Since the sum of the angle measures in a triangle is 180°,

$$∠C = 180° − 90° − 40°$$
$$= 50°$$

Example 2

O is the centre of a circle.
A, B, C, D, and E are points on the
circumference.
Find the measure of each angle.

a) ∠E

b) ∠O

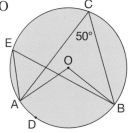

Solution

a) Since ∠E and ∠C are subtended by arc AB,

$$∠E = ∠C$$
$$= 50°$$

b) Since ∠O is the angle at the centre subtended by
arc AB,

$$∠O = 2∠C$$
$$= 2(50°)$$
$$= 100°$$

BOGGLE YOUR MIND

You're probably familiar with the classical
tangram set. It consists of 7 pieces that fit
together to form a square. These pieces
can be arranged to form outlines of animals,
people, and geometric figures. But did you
know that a tangram set doesn't have to be
square? You can make or buy a set that
forms a circle, an oval, or even a heart!

Trace the 2 circles on the right. Cut out your
tracings along the white lines. Use all 7
pieces to form each of the figures shown.

Working with Mathematics

Something to talk about

1. Find the angle measure indicated by each letter. O is the centre of the circle.

a)

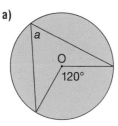

b)

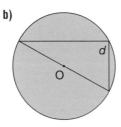

c)

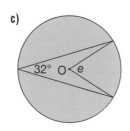

d)

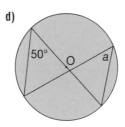

e)

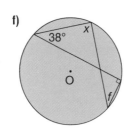

f)

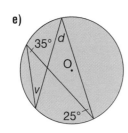

2. Find the value of x in two different ways.

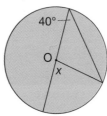

On your own

3. Find the angle measure indicated by each letter. O is the centre of the circle.

a)

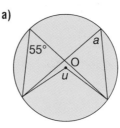

b)

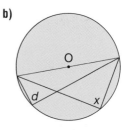

c)

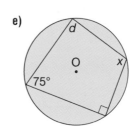

d)

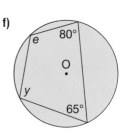

e)

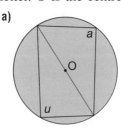

f)

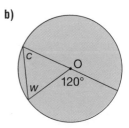

4. Find the angle measure indicated by each letter. O is the centre of the circle.

a)

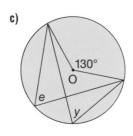

b)

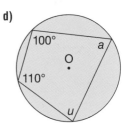

c)

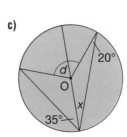

d)

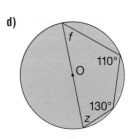

Work together

5. Answer these questions for each diagram below. O is the centre of the circle.
   a) If you know the value of x, how can you determine the value of y?
   b) Write an equation relating x and y.
   c) What are the smallest and largest possible values of x? What are the corresponding values of y?
   d) Draw a graph showing how the value of y depends on the value of x.

   i)
   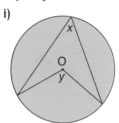

   ii)
   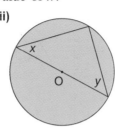

   iii)
   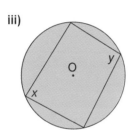

6. In the Quest on page 440, you investigated how to locate the centre of a circle. Use a circular object to draw a circle. Use one of the properties of inscribed angles in a circle to construct diameters to locate the centre of your circle.

Extend your thinking

7. Use this diagram and some geometrical properties you learned earlier to explain why the angle inscribed in a semicircle is a right angle.

   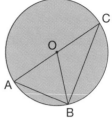

8. This question refers to the five properties on page 444.
   a) If Property 4 is true, explain why Properties 1, 2, and 3 must be true.
   b) If Property 3 is true, explain why Property 5 must be true.

COMMUNICATING

The Ideas

Suppose point P moves around a circle. A and B are any two fixed points on the circle. In your journal, describe what happens to the measure of $\angle APB$ as P moves around the circle.

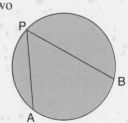

The surface area of all the windows at the National Gallery of Canada, shown on page 415, is 28 680 m². It is estimated that a 10 m² window can be cleaned in 2 min. At this rate, how many hours would it take to clean all the windows in the gallery?

Investigating Properties of Angles in a Circle

In this investigation you will use *The Geometer's Sketchpad* to explore some properties of angles in a circle by drawing a triangle inscribed in a circle.

Step 1 Constructing a triangle inscribed in a circle

Start the program.

Use the Circle tool to construct a large circle.

Use the Point tool to mark three points on the circle.

Label the points with the Text tool.

Using the Selection tool, shift-click the three points to select them.

From the **Construct** menu, choose **Polygon Interior**. This draws a triangle with vertices at the three points you selected.

Click on any blank area of the screen to deselect the polygon.

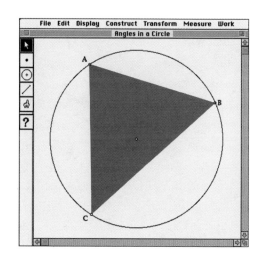

Step 2 Measuring the angles of the triangle

Shift-click the three vertices to select them again.

From the **Measure** menu, choose **Angle**.

How is the angle the computer measured related to the order in which you clicked the vertices?

Click any blank area of the screen to deselect the vertices. Measure the other two angles in a similar way.

Step 3 Adding the angle measures

Click on any blank area of the screen to deselect the vertices.

Shift-click the three measurements to select them.

From the **Measure** menu, choose **Calculate...** .

Choose one of the measurements in the **Value** pop-up menu, then click +.

Choose another measurement, and click +.

Choose the third measurement. Then click **OK**.

Click any blank area of the screen to deselect the angle measurements.

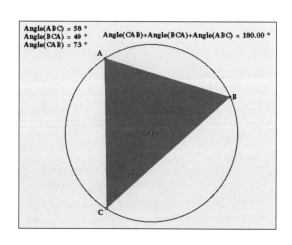

Step 4 Changing the positions of the vertices on the circle

Select one vertex. Drag it back and forth along the circle.
What happens to the three angle measurements as you drag the
vertex? What happens to their sum? What happens if you drag the
vertex all around the circle?
Repeat, using the other two vertices.
What can you conclude about how the measures of the angles
change as you drag one of the vertices around the circle?

Step 5 Animating the motion

Shift-click one of the points and the circle. From the **Display** menu,
choose **Animate…** . In the dialog box that appears, click **Animate**.
What happens to the angle measurements as the vertex moves around
the circle? What happens as it moves past one of the other vertices?
To stop the animation, press and hold the mouse button. Animate the
other vertices in a similar way.

Step 6 Comparing the angles with the angle at the centre

Label the centre with the Text tool. Using the Selection tool, shift-
click the centre and one of the vertices of the triangle to select them.
From the **Construct** menu, choose **Segment**.
Click any blank area of the screen to deselect the segment.
Join the other two vertices to the centre in the same way.
Measure the three angles at the centre. What is the sum of these
three angles? Drag one vertex along the circle, or set up an
animation to do this automatically.
As one of the vertices moves around the circle, what relationships
do you see among the angles at the centre and the angles in the
triangle?

Step 7 Investigating a special case

What happens if one of the angles in the triangle is a right angle?

Step 8 Looking back

How do the results of this investigation illustrate the properties of
angles in a circle you studied in this chapter?
Compare the triangle in *Step 6* with the triangle in the investigation
on page 422. Try to arrange the vertices of the triangle such that
the angle at the centre and the angle on the circle satisfy the same
relationship that $\angle D$ and $\angle A$ satisfied in the earlier investigation.
Does this mean that the radii bisect the other two angles of the triangle?

Mathematics & Technology

Linking Ideas

Saving Wood by Growing Square Trees

WHEN ROBERT FALLS BEHOLDS A FOREST, HE sees something very like a vicious circle. The shape that nature gave trees disturbs Falls. For he, a resource management scientist, is only too aware of how much man will waste in reshaping round logs into square timbers. To be precise, only 60% of a round log can be cut into straight-edged lumber. The rest is whittled away at such an alarming rate that it produces what Falls calls "a moonscape" of harvested timberlands.

But as a scientist, Falls has become one of Canada's most unusual angle players. In fact, he believes he may have the waste problem squared away. His solution? Square trees. "I figured we had to get more efficient about making wood," says Falls.

From *Globe & Mail Report on Business*

Carry out calculations to verify the statement that only "60% of a round log can be cut into straight-edged lumber."

Understand the problem

- What are you asked to calculate?

Think of a strategy

- Sketch a cross-section of a circular log, showing how it could be cut into one square piece of lumber.
- Let the radius of the circle be r. Calculate the areas of the square and the circle.

Carry out the strategy

- Mark the position of the centre of the circle and draw some radii.
- What is the area of the circle? What is the area of the square?
- What is the ratio of the area of the square to the area of the circle?

Look back

- Does your result agree with the 60% figure mentioned above?
- Give a reason why the percent of a round log that can be cut into straight-edged lumber might be somewhat greater than 60%. Give another reason why it might be less than 60%.
- Suppose the radius of the log is r. What are the dimensions of the largest square piece of lumber that can be cut from it?
- Suppose a square piece of lumber is cut into a round pole. What percent is wasted?
- Explain which circle properties are involved in this problem.

Communicating the Ideas

In your journal, write a description of this problem and your solution.

Review

1. Determine the angle measure indicated by each letter.

a)
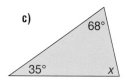

b)
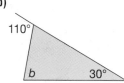

c)
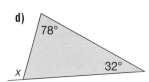

d)
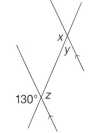

e)
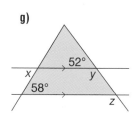

f)
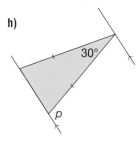

g)
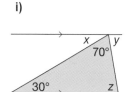

h)
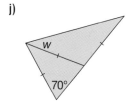

i)
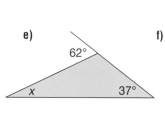

j)
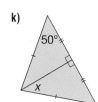

k)
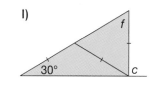

l)

2. Calculate the length indicated by each letter to one decimal place. O is the centre of the circle.

a)
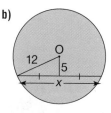

b)
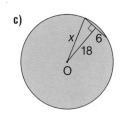

c)
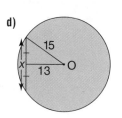

d)

3. What is the length of a chord of a circle with diameter 10 cm when the distance of the chord from the centre is:

a) 1 cm?   **b)** 2 cm?

c) 3 cm?   **d)** 4 cm?

Give the answers to one decimal place.

4. Determine the angle measure indicated by each letter. O is the centre of the circle.

a)
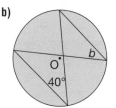

b)

c)
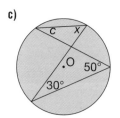

d)

e)
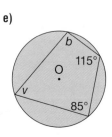

f)
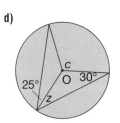

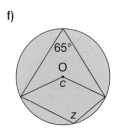

Geometry on Earth's Surface

The geometry in this chapter is called *plane geometry* because the figures are all drawn on a plane. Geometry on the surface of Earth is called *spherical geometry* because the figures are drawn or visualized on a sphere. In this project you will investigate some of the differences between spherical geometry and plane geometry. You will need a globe, tape, thread, a ruler, and a protractor.

ACTIVITY 1

Investigating the distance between two points

The distance between two points can be represented by joining them with a thread. On a plane, this is a straight line.

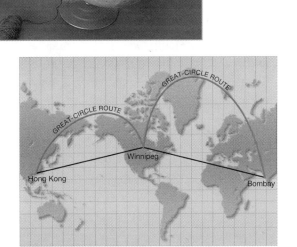

On a globe, the distance between two points is an arc of a *great circle* — the circle formed when a plane passes through the two points and Earth's centre.

The shortest distance between two cities is an arc of a great circle, but it does not look that way on most maps. On this map the straight line joining Winnipeg and Bombay crosses the Atlantic Provinces and North Africa. This route, however, is actually much longer than the great-circle route which passes near the North Pole. Similarly, the shortest route from Winnipeg to Hong Kong is the great-circle route along the north coast of Alaska.

1. On a globe, using tape and thread, show the great-circle routes from Winnipeg to Hong Kong and Bombay. Compare your routes with those shown on the map. Then measure the lengths of the threads in centimetres.

DATA DISK

2. Establish a scale for your globe by measuring its diameter as accurately as you can. Then, from a reference book or the *Moon and Planets* database on the student's disk, determine the diameter of Earth. How many kilometres on Earth is represented by 1 cm on the globe?

3. Combine the results of exercises 1 and 2 to calculate the great-circle distances from Winnipeg to Hong Kong and Bombay.

4. Describe how this information about great-circle routes would help you if you were planning flight paths for an international airline.

Investigating the sum of the angle measures in a triangle

When you draw a triangle on a plane, you know that its three sides are line segments. However, when you draw a triangle on a sphere, its three sides are arcs of great circles. The triangle is called a *spherical triangle*.

1. On a globe, with tape and thread, show the spherical triangles with vertices at the following cities. Measure their angles with a protractor. What is the sum of the angle measures in each spherical triangle? Do you notice anything unusual about the results?

a) St. John's, Vancouver, Miami

b) Winnipeg, Cairo, Rio de Janeiro

c) Honolulu, Caracas, Nairobi

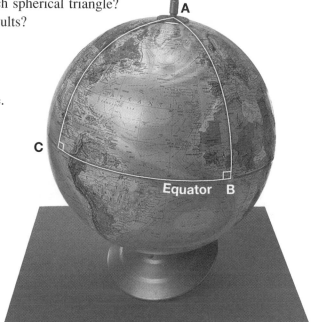

2. Let A represent the North Pole on your globe. Locate the 0° longitude line, which passes near London, England. Follow this line to where it meets the Equator, just south of Ghana in Africa. Let B represent this point. Locate the 90°W longitude line. Follow it to point C on the Equator, near the Galapagos Islands in the Pacific Ocean. Examine spherical △ABC on your globe carefully. What are the measures of its three angles? What is the sum of the measures of these angles? What kind of triangle is spherical △ABC?

3. a) In exercise 2, suppose A and B are fixed and C moves along the Equator. What happens to the sum of the angle measures in spherical △ABC? What is the minimum sum of the angle measures in this triangle? What is the maximum sum of the angle measures in this triangle?

b) Suppose B is fixed and C moves along the Equator to the 180°W longitude line. Suppose also that A moves along the 90°E longitude line through Russia towards the Equator. What happens to the sum of the angle measures in spherical △ABC? What is the maximum sum of the angle measures in this triangle?

c) State a conclusion about the minimum and maximum sums of the angle measures in a spherical triangle.

ACTIVITY 3

Investigating the angle measures in an equilateral triangle

1. Naila, Kadir, and Janice use some elastic rope to form an equilateral triangle. Without letting go of the rope, they start walking away from the centre of the triangle at the same rate. Suppose that the elastic rope can stretch forever without breaking. Also suppose that Earth is perfectly smooth, and that Naila, Kadir, and Janice can walk as long as it takes for them to meet again. Visualize what happens to the triangle formed by the elastic rope.

   a) Is the triangle always an equilateral triangle?

   b) Is there any change in the measures of the angles of this triangle as Naila, Kadir, and Janice travel around Earth in this way? Describe the change.

   c) What measures are possible for the angles in a spherical equilateral triangle?

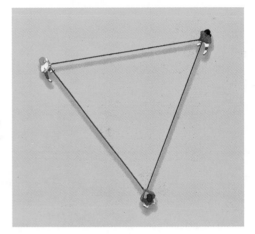

2. How far apart will Naila, Kadir, and Janice be when the spherical triangle formed by the elastic rope contains three right angles?

ACTIVITY 4

Investigating an old riddle

"A naturalist photographs a bear. Then she travels 1 km south, 1 km east, and 1 km north. After doing this, she has returned to the place where she photographed the bear. What colour is the bear?"

1. a) The customary solution to this riddle states that there is only one point on Earth's surface where the naturalist could have travelled 1 km south, 1 km east, 1 km north and ended up where she started. What point do you think this is?

   b) There are actually infinitely many points on Earth's surface where this could be done. Where do you think all these other points are? Explain your answer using a globe.

ACTIVITY 5

Investigating intersecting and parallel lines

1. Determine whether each statement is true or false for spherical geometry.

   a) When two lines intersect, the opposite angles are equal.

   b) Parallel lines never meet.

The Ideas

Prepare a report or a display to illustrate the results of your investigations. Include a comparison of geometric properties on a plane and on Earth's surface.

FUNCTIONS

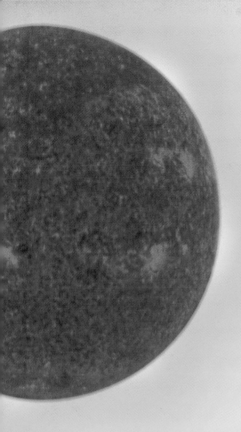

0000

STOP

PLAY

0251

Start With What You Know

This graph shows how the postal rates for first-class letters within Canada have changed since 1900.

1. **a)** In what year did the postal rate increase the most?
   b) What was the percent increase in postal rate that year?

2. **a)** In which years did the postal rate increase by 1¢?
   b) What was the percent increase in each of those years?

3. **a)** In what year did the postal rate decrease?
   b) What was the percent decrease that year?

4. **a)** Why is the graph a series of horizontal segments?
   b) Why are there gaps at the ends of the segments?

5. Could you use the graph to determine the postal rate for any year since 1900? Explain your answer.

6. **a)** What does it cost to send a first-class letter within Canada today?
   b) Copy and complete the table of values showing the postage cost for up to 10 letters.
   c) Draw a graph showing how the postage cost depends on the number of letters.

Number of letters, n	Postage cost, C dollars

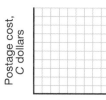

Postage cost, C dollars

Number of letters, n

7. **a)** What does the word "rate" mean?
   b) Why do you think postal rates are called rates?

8. Determine the slope of each line segment.

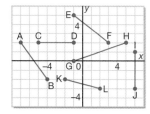

9. Determine the slope of the line segment joining each pair of points.
   a) A(−4, 1), B(3, 5) **b)** C(−3, 2), D(5, 1)
   c) E(2, 3), F(−3, 3) **d)** G(7, 3), H(7, 1)

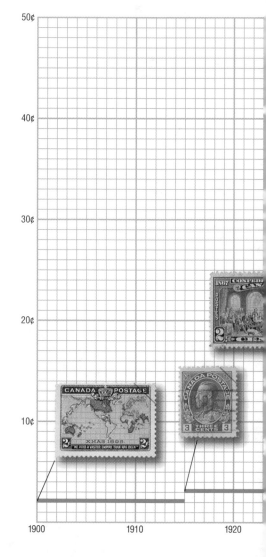

50¢

40¢

30¢

20¢

10¢

1930   1940   1950   1960   1970   1980   1990   1995

WHAT IS A FUNCTION?

Developing the Ideas

▶ ▶ *Through Instruction*

Many calculators have an x^2 key.

You input a number, press x^2, and you get a number out.

Input		Output
5 →	Press x^2 →	25

The number you put in is called the *input number*.
The number you get out is called the *output number*.

The x^2 key illustrates the idea of a function.

> A *function* is a rule that gives a single output number for every valid input number.

The rule defining a function can be expressed in different ways. For the above function we can express the rule as follows.

- In words:

    Multiply the number by itself.

- As an equation:

    $y = x^2$

In this equation, we use x for the input numbers and y for the output numbers.

We can make a table of values and draw a graph of the function defined by $y = x^2$.

Input number x	Output number $y = x^2$
−4	16
−3	9
−2	4
−1	1
0	0
1	1
2	4
3	9
4	16

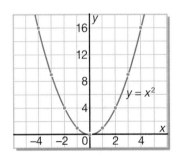

The plotted points appear to lie on a curve. Through the plotted points, we draw a smooth curve, and imagine that it is extended. To help draw a better curve, we could include more points corresponding to input numbers such as −4.5, −3.5, ... , 2.5, 3.5.

▶▶ Through an Activity

The rules defining several functions are given below. For each function:

a) Make a table of values.

b) Draw a graph of the function.

c) Decide if there are any input numbers that cannot be used.

d) Write an equation for the function.

> *Rule 1*: Add 3 to the number.
> *Rule 2*: Multiply the number by 3.
> *Rule 3*: Double the number and add 3.
> *Rule 4*: Subtract the number from 10.
> *Rule 5*: Determine the positive square root of the number.

▶▶ Through Guided Examples

We can describe a function in various ways. Some simple functions can be described easily using a rule expressed in words. We can also use a table of values, an equation, or a graph to describe a function.

Example 1

Monique has a part-time job at a garden centre. She is paid at the rate of $5.50 per hour. Employees are expected to work for whole numbers of hours only; they are not paid for parts of hours worked. Let h hours represent the time she works in a week. Let p dollars represent her pay.

a) Make a table of values. Draw a graph of p against h.

b) Write an equation for the function.

c) Suppose Monique gets a raise to $6.00 per hour.
   How would the graph and the equation change?

Solution

a)

Hours worked, h	Pay, p dollars
0	0
1	5.5
2	11
3	16.5
4	22
5	27.5

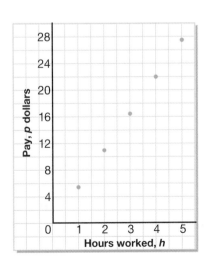

b) Each value of h was multiplied by 5.5 to get the corresponding value of p.
   An equation for the function is $p = 5.5h$.

c) The points on the graph lie along a straight line. We do not join the points because employees work for whole numbers of hours only. If Monique gets a raise to $6.00 per hour, she would still get $0 for 0 h, but would get $30 for 5 h. The points would lie along a slightly steeper line. The equation would be $p = 6h$.

Example 2

These days, it's more important than ever to wear sunscreen. According to Dr. Daniel Sauder, professor and chief of dermatology at Sunnybrook Health Science Centre, for each 1% decrease in the ozone layer, there is a 4 to 6% increase in skin cancer rates.

There are two ways to prevent ultraviolet rays reaching your skin. A sunblock forms a physical barrier through which the rays cannot pass. A sunscreen forms a chemical barrier. For the chemical compounds in sunscreen to absorb the ultraviolet rays, they must first react with proteins in your skin. So it's important to put on sunscreen at least 15 minutes *before* you go out in the sun.

The effectiveness of a sunscreen is indicated by a number called the *sunscreen protection factor*. When you know the protection factor s of a sunscreen, you can determine the percent p of the sun's ultraviolet rays that pass through it by using this formula: $p = \dfrac{100}{s}$

a) Some typical sunscreens have protection factors of 2, 8, 15, 25, and 45. Determine the percent of the sun's ultraviolet rays that pass through each of these sunscreens.

b) Draw a graph showing how the percent of the sun's ultraviolet rays that pass through a sunscreen depends on the protection factor.

Solution

a) Substitute 2, 8, 15, 25, and 45 for s in the formula $p = \dfrac{100}{s}$ to obtain the following table of values.

Sunscreen protection factor, s	Percent of ultraviolet rays passing through, p
2	50.0
8	12.5
15	6.7
25	4.0
45	2.2

b)

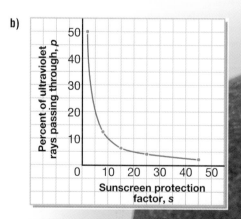

Working with Mathematics

Something to talk about

1. Look at the graph on page 459 showing how postal rates have changed since 1900. Does it illustrate a function? Explain your answer.

2. Two statements about functions are given below. Decide if each statement is true or false. Explain your answers.
   a) A table of values always shows all possible input numbers.
   b) When you graph a function you always join the plotted points.

3. a) Your calculator may have the keys √x and 1/x . Does each of these keys illustrate the concept of a function?
   b) Are there any values of x which cannot be used as input numbers for the functions defined by $y = \sqrt{x}$ and $y = \frac{1}{x}$? Explain your answer.

4. Three functions are graphed below.
   a) Describe how the graphs are similar.
   b) Account for the differences in the graphs.

   i)

   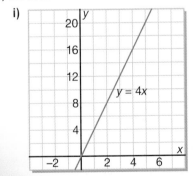

   ii)

   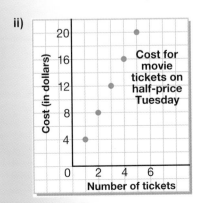

   iii)

   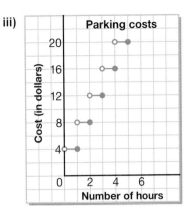

Work together

5. The rules defining three functions are given below. For each function:
   a) Make a table of values.
   b) Draw a graph of the function.
   c) Decide if there are any input numbers that cannot be used.
      i) *Rule 1*: Add 2.5 to the number.
      ii) *Rule 2*: Multiply the number by 0.5.
      iii) *Rule 3*: $y = \sqrt{x} + 2$

6. Graph each function on a separate grid.
   a) *Rule 1*: The output number is the same as the input number.
   b) *Rule 2*: The output number is always 3.
   c) *Rule 3*: $y = (x + 1)(x - 1)$

7. a) Graph these functions on the same grid.
      Rule 1: Double the number and add 3 to the result.
      Rule 2: Add 3 to the number and double the result.
      Rule 3: $y = 2x - 3$
      Rule 4: $y = 2(x - 3)$
   b) Account for the similarities and the differences in the graphs.

8. You will need a thermometer, a clock or watch with a second hand, an electric kettle, a mug, water, and some hot chocolate powder.

　a) Make a mug of hot chocolate. Measure and record its temperature every minute for 15 min. Record your results in a table.

　b) Draw a graph showing the temperature of the hot chocolate as a function of time.

　c) Did the temperature of the hot chocolate change as much during the tenth minute as it did during the first minute?

　d) Do you think you would get different results if you repeated the experiment with plain hot water? Explain your thinking.

On your own

9. Graph each function on a separate grid.

　a) *Rule 1*: The output number is the opposite of the input number.

　b) *Rule 2*: $y = -1$

　c) *Rule 3*: $y = \dfrac{x(x-1)}{2}$

10. a) Graph these functions on the same grid.

　　Rule 1: Square the number and subtract 2 from the result.

　　Rule 2: Subtract 2 from the number and square the result.

　　Rule 3: $y = x^2 + 2$

　　Rule 4: $y = (x + 2)^2$

　b) Account for the similarities and the differences in the graphs.

11. The graphs below were produced by a graphing calculator. The equations of the functions are also shown below. Identify the equation which corresponds to each graph.

i)

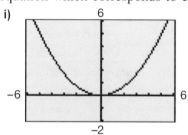

ii)

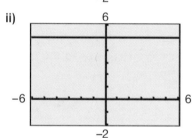

iii)

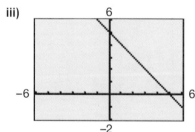

iv)

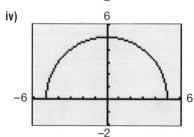

a) $y = 5 - x$　　　　**b)** $y = \dfrac{x^2}{5}$

c) $y = 5$　　　　　　**d)** $y = \sqrt{25 - x^2}$

12. Psychologists have experimented to measure how much a person remembers of material that was learned. The results of one experiment are shown in the table. p represents the percent of the material remembered after t days.

Time in days, t	1	5	15	30	60
Percent remembered, p	84%	71%	61%	56%	54%

a) Draw a graph of p against t.

b) Suppose q represents the percent forgotten instead of the percent remembered. How would the graph of q against t differ from the graph you drew in part a?

13. You will need a thermometer, a watch or clock, and a glass of cold water.

a) Record the temperature of the cold water.

b) Record the temperature of the water at various times during the next half hour.

c) Draw a graph showing the temperature of the water as a function of time.

d) Compare this graph with the graph in exercise 8.
   i) In what ways are these graphs similar?
   ii) In what ways are they different?

Extend your thinking

14. In *Example 1*, suppose the garden centre changes its policy for paying employees who work parts of hours.

a) How would the graph change if employees are paid for:
   i) half-hour time periods worked?
   ii) quarter-hour time periods worked?

b) Would it ever be possible for the graph to be drawn as a straight line? Explain your answer.

COMMUNICATING The Ideas

In your journal, give a few examples of functions in everyday life. Explain why they are functions. Try to be original.

BOGGLE YOUR MIND

Some species of bamboo, one of the fastest growing plants in the world, can grow 91 cm in a single day. What if a bamboo plant could grow at this rate indefinitely? How long would it take for the plant to grow as high as the CN Tower? Why do you think bamboo plants do not reach such heights?

Is the Fuel Gauge in a Car Accurate?

Every time Chandra buys gas she resets the trip odometer to 000.
The photographs below show the odometer readings and the fuel gauge at
different times since the last fill up. Is the fuel gauge giving accurate readings?

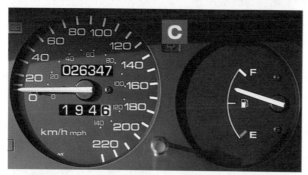

Understand the problem

- What is an odometer?
- What is a trip odometer?

Think of a strategy

- You could draw a graph showing how the amount of fuel indicated by the gauge is related to the distance travelled.

Carry out the strategy

- Use the information above to complete a table of values.
- Draw a graph.

Distance travelled (km)	Fuel gauge reading

Look back

- Give some possible reasons why the graph is not a straight line.
- Do you think the fuel gauge in Chandra's car is accurate?
- Suppose the gas tank is full and Chandra does not stop for gas. About how far will her car have travelled when the gauge reads empty?
- Ask someone who drives a car to record the odometer reading when the fuel tank is full, and later when the fuel gauge registers $\frac{3}{4}$, $\frac{1}{2}$, and $\frac{1}{4}$. Use the results to repeat the above investigation.

Communicating the Ideas

In your journal, write a description of this problem and your solution. Include drawings to illustrate your solution.

Does 64 = 65?

Of course, you know that 64 does not equal 65, but consider the following diagrams.

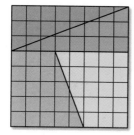
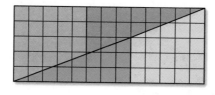

- How many unit squares are there in the large square on the left?
- How many unit squares are there in the rectangle on the right?

The square and the rectangle are each divided into four parts. Check that the parts with the same colour are congruent.

If $64 \neq 65$, then something must be wrong with one or both diagrams. To discover what is wrong, complete the following exercises.

1. Calculate the slopes of these line segments on each graph: AB, BC, AD, BD.

2. On graph paper, draw two graphs similar to those on the right. One graph should be a straight line and the other should not be a straight line. Mark points A, B, C, and D on both graphs. Calculate the slopes of these line segments on each graph: AB, BC, AD, BD.

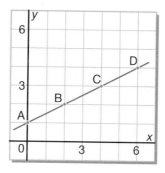
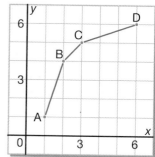

3. Compare your results in exercise 2 with those of other students. Did everyone get similar results?

4. What conclusion can you make about the slopes of line segments along a straight line?

5. Use your conclusion in exercise 4 to help you explain what might be wrong with the second diagram above. What could you do to be sure that this is what is wrong with the diagram?

6. Another way to discover the flaw in the diagrams is to use a Draw program on a computer. Start a new file. Create a grid of 8 by 8 squares. Use the Polygon tool to draw the four figures in the first diagram above, using the grid as a guide. Drag the four figures to a new location and try to assemble them as shown in the second diagram. You will have to rotate the two trapezoids 90°. Use the Enlarge feature to look at how the figures match. Describe the flaw.

LINEAR FUNCTIONS

Developing the Ideas

▷ ▶ *Through Discussion*

A clothing store gives a 25% discount coupon to some of its most valued customers. This means the customer will pay 75% of the retail price.

Suppose that you find some items that you wish to purchase. Let p dollars represent the retail price of these items. Let a dollars represent the amount (before tax) that you pay for them.

If you have the coupon, then $a = 0.75p$

We can make a table of values and draw a graph of a against p.

Retail price, p dollars	Amount you pay, a dollars
0	0
10	7.50
20	15.00
30	22.50
40	30.00

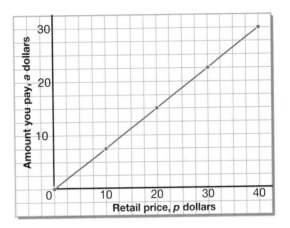

This function is an example of a linear function.

Why do you think this is a good name for this type of function?

To determine the slope of the line, choose any two points on it, such as O(0, 0) and B(40, 30).

$$\text{Slope of OB} = \frac{\text{rise}}{\text{run}}$$
$$= \frac{30 - 0}{40 - 0}$$
$$= \frac{3}{4}, \text{ or } 0.75$$

The slope of the line represents the amount you pay for every dollar of the retail price. That is, you pay at the rate of 75¢ per dollar.

1. Suppose you forgot your coupon.
   a) How would the equation change?
   b) How would the graph change?
   c) What would the slope of the line be?

2. Suppose you had a 50% discount coupon.
   a) How would the equation change?
   b) How would the graph change?
   c) What would the slope of the line be?

The slope of a line is equal to the slope of any segment along the line. To determine the slope of the line, choose any two points A and B on the line and determine the slope of the line segment joining them. A linear function is one whose graph is a straight line. The slope of the line is the change in the output number when the input number increases by 1.

Example

When you exercise, it is recommended that you do not allow your pulse rate to exceed a given maximum. This maximum pulse rate (m beats per minute) is related to your age (a years) by this formula: $m = 220 - a$

a) Make a table of values for this equation, for people between the ages of 18 and 50.

b) Draw a graph of m against a.

c) Determine the slope of the line. What does the slope represent?

Solution

a) Choose some values of a. Substitute them into the formula $m = 220 - a$. Determine the corresponding values of m.

Age, a years	Maximum pulse rate, m
18	202
25	195
40	180
50	170

b)

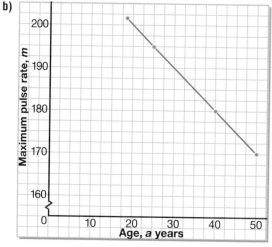

The jagged line at the base of the vertical axis indicates that part of the axis is not shown.

c) The graph in part b is a straight line. Choose any two points on the line, such as A(40, 180) and B(50, 170).

$$\text{Slope of AB} = \frac{\text{rise}}{\text{run}}$$
$$= \frac{170 - 180}{50 - 40}$$
$$= -1$$

The slope of the line is -1.

This represents the rate of change of the maximum pulse rate with age. That is, for each year a person's age increases, the maximum pulse rate decreases by 1.

Working with Mathematics

Something to talk about

1. Which of these graphs represent linear functions?

a)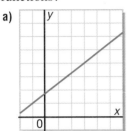

b)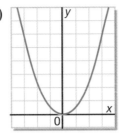

c)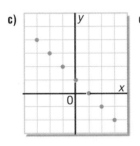

d)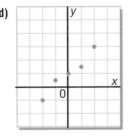

2. On pages 460 to 464, find some examples of linear functions. On these pages, are any of the functions *not* linear?

Work together

3. Suppose a parent decides that her children should receive a weekly allowance from age 6 to 16. The amount is 75¢ the first year and increases by 75¢ each year.
   a) Let *a* dollars represent the allowance of a child whose age is *n* years. Make a table of values and draw a graph of *a* against *n*.
   b) Determine a formula expressing *a* in terms of *n*.

4. After finishing a roll of film, you take it for processing.

NUMBER OF EXPOSURES	COST
12	$9.18
24	$13.38
36	$17.58

a) Let *n* represent the number of exposures. Let *C* dollars represent the processing cost. Draw a graph of *C* against *n*.

b) Sometimes, it is possible to take an extra picture at the end of a roll of film. Use your graph to estimate the cost for: 13 exposures; 25 exposures; 37 exposures.

c) Sometimes, a few pictures on a roll may not turn out. The customer is not usually charged for such photographs. Make a table that sales staff in the store could use showing the costs for other numbers of exposures.

d) The points on your graph should lie on a straight line. Determine the slope of the line. What does this represent?

On your own

5. Turkeys should be cooked at an oven temperature of 165°C. The cooking time depends on the turkey's mass. For turkeys between 3 kg and 8 kg, the recommended cooking time is 30 min per kilogram.
   a) Let *m* kilograms represent the mass of a turkey. Let *t* hours represent the time to cook it. Draw a graph of *t* against *m* for reasonable values of *m*.
   b) What does the slope of the graph represent?
   c) Larger turkeys require slightly less cooking time per kilogram. How would the graph change if you made this adjustment?
   d) Turkeys which contain stuffing require an extra 10 min per kilogram. How would the graph change if the turkey were stuffed?
   e) Many American cookbooks use pounds instead of kilograms. One pound is slightly less than half a kilogram. How would the graph change if *m* were measured in pounds instead of in kilograms?

6. Transport Canada still uses feet as the units to describe the position of an aircraft. After take-off, a Beechcraft 19-passenger aircraft climbs 40 ft vertically for every 250 ft travelled horizontally until it reaches its cruising altitude. The coordinates of the aircraft after 1 s are shown in the graph.

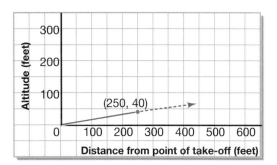

a) Copy the graph. Show the coordinates of the aircraft after 2 s, 3 s, 4 s, and 5 s.
b) What is the slope of the path of the aircraft?
c) How high is the aircraft when it has travelled a horizontal distance of 60 000 ft?
d) How long does it take to reach a cruising altitude of 20 000 ft?
e) Write an equation relating the height h feet of the aircraft to the horizontal distance d feet from the point of take-off.

7. On its approach to landing, a Beechcraft 19-passenger aircraft descends 32 ft vertically for every 500 ft of horizontal movement.
a) Draw a graph showing the aircraft's position for horizontal distances of up to 10 000 ft from the runway.

b) What is the slope of the path of the aircraft?
c) How high is the aircraft when its horizontal distance is 7500 ft from the runway?
d) Compare the slope of the graph in this exercise with the slope of the graph in exercise 6. Why do you think these slopes are so different?

Extend your thinking

TEMPLATE DISK

8. Refer to exercise 4. You can use a spreadsheet to determine the mean cost per exposure for different numbers of exposures.
a) Set up a spreadsheet as shown below. Copy the formulas in row 3 down to row 39.

	A	B	C
1	Number of exposures	Cost	Mean cost per exposure
2	0	$4.98	
3	=A2+1	=B2+0.35	=B3/A3

b) Explain the formula in each cell.
   i) A3   ii) B3   iii) C3
c) What happens to the mean cost per exposure as the number of exposures increases? Explain your answer.
d) Use the spreadsheet to draw a graph showing the mean cost per exposure as a function of the number of exposures.
e) Explain why the function is not a linear function.

COMMUNICATING

The Ideas

In your journal, explain the meaning of slope and how it is related to linear functions.

THE EQUATION OF A LINE

Developing the Ideas

▶ ▶ *Through an Activity*

Up to now, the rules defining functions have all stated what to do to an input number to produce the output number. Sometimes the rule defining a function can be expressed in a different way. For example, we can define a function by this rule:

- In words:
    The sum of the input number and the output number is 4.
- As an equation:
    $x + y = 4$

1. Make a table of values for $x + y = 4$. Graph the function.

2. **a)** When $x = 0$, what is the value of y? This number is called the *y-intercept* of the graph. Why do you think this name is appropriate?

   b) When $y = 0$, what is the value of x? This number is called the *x-intercept* of the graph. Why do you think this name is appropriate?

3. **a)** When the input number increases by 1, how does the output number change?

   b) How is this change shown in the table and on the graph?

▶ ▶ *Through Guided Examples*

Any equation of the form $Ax + By = C$ has a graph which is a straight line.

The x-intercept is the x-coordinate of the point where the line crosses the x-axis. To determine the x-intercept, substitute 0 for y and solve for x. The y-intercept is the y-coordinate of the point where the line crosses the y-axis. To determine the y-intercept, substitute 0 for x and solve for y.

Example 1 ....

A function is defined by this rule:
When you double the input number and then add the output number, the result is 4.

a) Write an equation for the function.

b) When the input number is 0, what is the output number?
When the output number is 0, what is the input number?
Determine two other pairs of input and output numbers for this function.

c) Make a table of values and graph the function.

d) When the input number increases by 1, how does the output number change? How is this change shown on the graph?

Solution

a) An equation for the function is $2x + y = 4$.

b) Think: Double 0 and add a number to get 4.
The output number must be 4.
That is, when $x = 0$, $y = 4$
Think: Double a number and add 0 to get 4.
The input number must be 2.
That is, when $y = 0$, $x = 2$
Think: Double a number and add another number to get 4.
Some other possibilities are: $x = 1$, $y = 2$ and $x = -3$, $y = 10$.

c) Write the results of part b in a table.
Use the table to graph the function.

Input x	Output y
-3	10
0	4
1	2
2	0

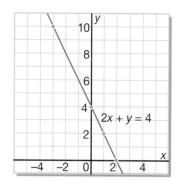

d) When the input number increases by 1 the output number decreases by 2. The slope of the line on the graph is -2.

Since an equation of the form $Ax + By = C$ has a graph which is a straight line, you only need to plot two points to draw the graph. However, it is advisable to plot a third point as a check.

Example 2

A line is defined by the equation $2x - 5y = 10$.

a) Graph the line.

b) What is the slope of the line?

Solution

a) Two of the easiest points to find are those where the line intersects the axes. To find the y-intercept, substitute $x = 0$ in the equation $2x - 5y = 10$.

$$2(0) - 5y = 10$$
$$-5y = 10$$
$$y = -2$$

One point on the graph is $(0, -2)$.

To find the x-intercept, substitute $y = 0$ in the equation $2x - 5y = 10$.

$$2x - 5(0) = 10$$
$$2x = 10$$
$$x = 5$$

Another point on the graph is $(5, 0)$.

To determine a third point, choose any value of x, for example, $x = 10$. Substitute $x = 10$ in the equation $2x - 5y = 10$.

$$2(10) - 5y = 10$$
$$20 - 5y = 10$$
$$-5y = -10$$
$$y = 2$$

A third point on the graph is $(10, 2)$.

Plot these points on a grid, and draw a straight line through them.

Input x	Output y
0	−2
5	0
10	2

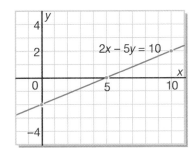

b) To determine the slope of the line, choose any two points on the line, such as A(0, −2) and B(5, 0).

$$\text{Slope of AB} = \frac{\text{rise}}{\text{run}}$$
$$= \frac{0 - (-2)}{5 - 0}$$
$$= \frac{2}{5}$$

The slope of the segment AB is $\frac{2}{5}$.
Since the slopes of all segments along a line are equal, the slope of the line is $\frac{2}{5}$.

BOGGLE YOUR MIND

The train route from Myrdal to Flåm in Norway is an engineering marvel. The 50-minute trip takes you through a narrow mountain valley to a fjord 865 m below. The track is so steep that the train is equipped with 5 different braking systems, each of which is capable of stopping the train. In one section, the track descends from 669 m to 556 m in 1.94 km. What is the slope of this section of track?

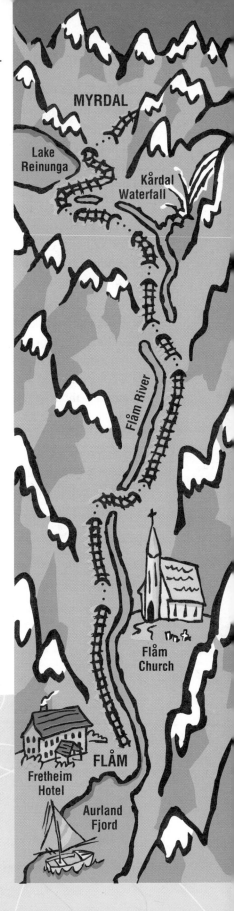

Working with Mathematics

Something to talk about

1. Suppose the graph of a function is a straight line. What is the minimum number of points you need to graph the line? Why might it be a good idea to plot more points when you graph a line?

2. a) When you want to find the x-intercept, why do you substitute 0 for y and not for x?

  b) When you want to find the y-intercept, why do you substitute 0 for x and not for y?

3. a) What can you say about the intercepts and the slope of a line that is parallel to the x-axis? to the y-axis?

  b) Does every line have both an x-intercept and a y-intercept?

  c) What would be an equation for a line that is parallel to the x-axis and has a y-intercept of 3?

  d) What would be an equation for a line that is parallel to the y-axis and has an x-intercept of 3?

Work together

4. Determine the intercepts and the slope of each line.

a)
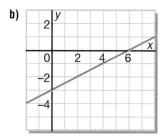

b)
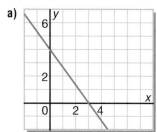

c)
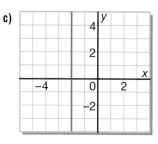

d)
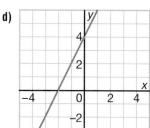

e)
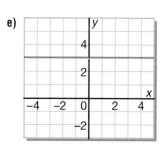

f)
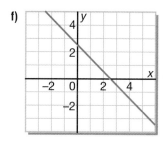

5. Make a table of values for each function. Graph these functions on the same grid. Account for the similarities and differences in the graphs.
   Rule 1: Double the input number plus the output number equals 12.
   Rule 2: The input number plus double the output number equals 12.

6. Make a table of values for each equation. Graph these equations on the same grid. Account for the similarities and differences in the graphs.
   Rule 1: $3x + 2y = 6$
   Rule 2: $3x - 2y = 6$

7. These two patterns were produced on a graphing calculator. The equation of one of the lines in one of the patterns is $x + y = 4$.
   a) i) Which pattern contains a line with this equation?
      ii) What are the equations of the other lines in this pattern?

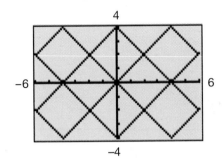

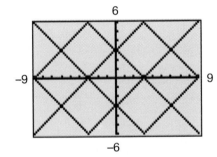

   b) What are the equations of the lines in the other pattern?

On your own

8. Determine the intercepts of the line defined by each equation.
   a) $x + 5y = 10$
   b) $4x - 3y = 12$
   c) $3x + 6y = -4$
   d) $3x + 4y = 18$
   e) $7x - 4y = -28$
   f) $y = 2x - 6$

9. Make a table of values for each equation. Graph these equations on the same grid. Account for the similarities and differences in the graphs.
   Rule 1: $2x + 3y = 6$
   Rule 2: $-2x + 3y = 6$

10. Graph the line defined by each equation. Determine the slope of each line.
    a) $x - 3y = 9$
    b) $3x - y = 9$
    c) $-2x + 3y = -12$
    d) $4x + 5y = 10$
    e) $2x + 3y = 0$
    f) $2x - 4y = 1$

11. An equation relating Celsius and Fahrenheit temperatures is given on page 217.
    a) Determine the F- and C-intercepts of the line defined by this equation.
    b) Explain what these intercepts represent.

Extend your thinking

12. The equations of the lines containing three sides of a square are $x + y = 4$, $x + y = 8$, and $x - y = 2$. What do you think the equation of the line containing the fourth side is? Explain your answer.

13. a) Make a table of values and draw the graph corresponding to this rule: The input and output numbers have a difference of 4.
    b) Does this rule define a function? Explain your answer.

COMMUNICATING The Ideas

Suppose you know the equation of a line. In your journal, write a description of how you could determine the x-intercept, the y-intercept, and the slope of the line. Illustrate your explanation with an example.

Intersecting Lines

The Nguyen family live in Vancouver. The Berg family live in Kamloops. At 12 noon the Nguyens leave by car on a trip to Kamloops. They drive at an average speed of 50 km/h. At the same time, the Bergs leave by car on a trip to Vancouver. They drive at an average speed of 60 km/h. It is approximately 360 km from Kamloops to Vancouver.

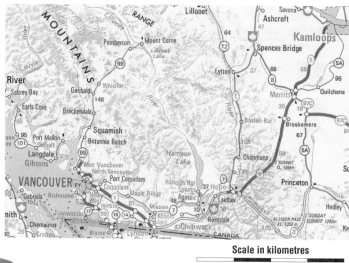

Scale in kilometres

| 0 | 40 | 80 | 120 | 160 |

1. **a)** Copy and complete the table of values showing how far the Nguyen family are from Vancouver after each hour of their trip.

Time (h)	0	1	2	3	4	5	6	7	8
Distance from Vancouver (km)	0								

b) Draw a graph of distance from Vancouver against time for the Nguyen family.

2. **a)** Copy and complete the table of values showing how far the Berg family are from Vancouver after each hour of their trip.

Time (h)	0	1	2	3	4	5	6	7	8
Distance from Vancouver (km)	360								

b) Using the same grid as in exercise 1b, draw a graph of distance from Vancouver against time for the Berg family.

3. The two lines you drew in exercises 1 and 2 should intersect. What are the coordinates of the point where the lines intersect? What do these coordinates tell you about the locations of the two cars?

4. Use the map to determine the approximate location of the two cars when they meet.

Use your graph to answer exercises 5 and 6.

5. Suppose the Berg family leave Kamloops at 1 p.m. instead of 12 noon. About how far would they be from Vancouver when their car meets the Nguyens' car?

6. Suppose the Nguyen family average only 45 km/h. About how far would they be from Vancouver when their car meets the Bergs' car?

The point where two lines meet is called their *point of intersection*. You can determine the coordinates of the point of intersection of two lines from their graphs, and occasionally from their tables of values.

7. Six pairs of lines are defined by the tables of values below.

a) For two of these pairs, you can determine the coordinates of the points of intersection from the tables. Which pairs are these? What are the coordinates of the points of intersection?

b) Graph the other pairs of lines. Determine the coordinates of the points of intersection as accurately as you can from the graphs.

i)

x	y
0	2
1	3
2	4
3	5

x	y
0	5
1	3
2	1
3	-1

ii)

x	y
0	5
1	3
2	1
3	-1

x	y
0	0
1	1
2	2
3	3

iii)

x	y
-2	3
0	-1
2	-5
3	-7

x	y
-1	-5
1	-3
2	-2
5	1

iv)

x	y
-5	6
-3	3
-1	0
1	-3

x	y
-5	0
1	3
3	4
5	5

v)

x	y
-4	3
0	1
2	0
6	-2

x	y
-1	-6
2	0
3	2
5	6

vi)

x	y
-4	1
-1	2
5	4
8	5

x	y
1	-4
2	-1
4	5
5	8

8. Graph each pair of lines. Determine the coordinates of the point of intersection as accurately as you can from the graph.

a) $2x + y = 7$
$x - y = 5$

b) $3x + y = 6$
$x + y = 4$

c) $2x - y = 5$
$x = 3$

d) $4x + 3y = 12$
$y = -2$

e) $x + 5y = 10$
$x + y = 4$

f) $2x - 3y = -6$
$x + y = 6$

9. Examine your results in parts a and b of exercise 8. Compare them with the given equations.

a) Find a way to solve these equations algebraically.

b) Find ways to solve the other equations in exercise 8 algebraically.

FINDING RELATIONSHIPS IN DATA

Developing the Ideas

▶ ▶ *Through an Activity*

Graphing calculators and some scientific calculators are programmable. You can program calculators like these to calculate output numbers for a function defined by an equation. When you enter an input number and press a certain key, the calculator uses your equation to calculate the corresponding output number. For example, this result was obtained with a programmable calculator:

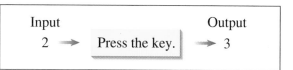

Input			Output
2	→	Press the key.	→ 3

1. Determine three different rules which give an output number 3 when the input number is 2.

2. Is a single pair of input and output numbers sufficient to determine the rule?

3. The table on the right shows several results that were obtained using the same rule. Now can you tell what the rule is?

Input	Output
2	3
5	9
−1	−3
0	−1
−7	−15

▶ ▶ *Through a Guided Example*

Example ....

For each table of values, determine a rule which expresses y as a function of x.

a)

x	y
1	4
−2	−8
6	24
0	0
−5	−20
3	12

b)

x	y
0	1
1	2
2	5
3	10
4	17
5	26

c)

x	y
2	−1
5	2
−3	−6
7	4
0	−3
−4	−7

Solution

a) Each y-value is 4 times the corresponding x-value.
   A rule is $y = 4x$.

b) Each y-value is 1 more than the square of the corresponding x-value.
   A rule is $y = x^2 + 1$.

c) Each y-value is 3 less than the corresponding x-value.
   A rule is $y = x - 3$.

Working with Mathematics

Something to talk about

1. Determine three different rules which give an output number 4 when the input number is 2.

2. Determine a rule for each table of values.

a)
x	y
1	2
2	4
3	6
4	8
5	10

b)
x	y
1	11
2	21
3	31
4	41
5	51

Work together

3. Determine a rule for each table of values.

a)
x	y
2	6
7	21
-1	-3
0	0
-3	-9

b)
x	y
6	-3
-4	2
0	0
8	-4
3	-1.5

4. On each graph below, four points are labelled.

i)
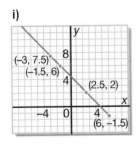

ii)
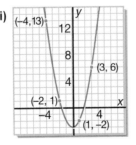

a) Make a table of values for each graph.
b) Determine a rule for each table of values.

c) Use the rule to obtain three other entries in each table. Do the points corresponding to these entries lie on the graph?

On your own

5. Write a rule for each table of values.

a)
x	y
0	2
1	3
2	4
3	5
4	6

b)
x	y
3	7
-2	-3
7	15
-5	-9
0	1

c)
x	y
0	-3
2	-5
-4	1
8	-11
-1	-2

d)
x	y
0	0
1	2
2	6
3	12
4	20

e)
x	y
3	27
-2	-8
0	0
1	1
5	125

f)
x	y
2	6
-4	-3
-1	-12
3	4
24	0.5

Extend your thinking

6. A function is defined by this equation:
$$y = 2x + 0.1(x-1)(x-2)(x-3)(x-4)(x-5)$$

a) Use the equation to determine the values of y for $x = 1, 2, 3, 4, 5,$ and 6. Show the results in a table.
b) How does your table compare with the table in exercise 2a?
c) Are the rules for the two tables the same?

COMMUNICATING

The Ideas

Make up a rule of your own and use it to generate a table of values. Give your table to a friend. Challenge your friend to write a rule for the table and explain how he or she found the rule. If you have access to a programmable calculator, you could program your rule into the calculator. Challenge a friend to discover the rule by inputting numbers and looking for patterns in the corresponding output numbers.

Predicting Long Jump Records

The world record for the women's long jump has increased steadily for many years. If it continues to increase at the same rate, when might the record be 7.75 m?

Selected Women's Long Jump World Records, 1964–1988		
Name	Year	Distance (m)
Mary Rand (Great Britain)	1964	6.76
Viorica Viscopoleanu (Romania)	1968	6.82
Heidemarie Rosendahl (West Germany)	1970	6.84
Siegrun Siegl (East Germany)	1976	6.99
Vilma Bardauskiene (Soviet Union)	1978	7.09
Valeria Ionescu (Romania)	1982	7.20
Aniscara Stanoiu-Cusmir (Romania)	1983	7.43
Heike Drechsler (East Germany)	1985	7.44
Heike Drechsler (East Germany)	1986	7.45
Galina Chistyakova (Soviet Union)	1988	7.52

Understand the problem

- What does "increased steadily for many years" mean?

Think of a strategy

- You could try graphing the data.
- If the data appear to lie on a straight line, you could use the line to estimate when the world record might be 7.75 m.

Carry out the strategy

- Graph the data.
- Use a ruler to draw a straight line which passes through or as close as possible to the plotted points.
- Extend the line until it passes the point where the length is 7.75 m.
- Approximately what year corresponds to this point?

Look back

- The line you drew is called the *line of best fit*. Why do you think this name is appropriate?
- What major assumption are you making when you solve this problem by extending the line of best fit? Do you think this assumption is justified?
- If you have a graphing calculator, or a calculator with statistical functions, you may be able to use it to determine the equation of the line of best fit. Use the equation to estimate the year when the world record might be 7.75 m. Does this agree with the result you obtained using the graph?

DATA DISK

- Use the *Olympic Summer Games* database from the student's disk. Choose a track-and-field event. Investigate how the winning distances or times have changed over time. Do the data you chose appear to lie along a straight line? Could you use the data to predict winning distances or times for future Olympic games?

Communicating the Ideas

In your journal, write a description of this problem and your solution. Include diagrams to illustrate your solution.

Finding a Rule

Look at the numbers in the table. Each number in column B was calculated using the number in the same row of column A. For example, in row 1, the number 10 was calculated by applying some rule to the number 4. This same rule was used to calculate each number in column B.

What was the rule?

A	B
4	10
3	7
−5	−17
1	1
−3	−11

TEMPLATE DISK

1. You can use a spreadsheet to help determine the rule. Follow these steps.
   a) Start a new spreadsheet document. Enter the numbers in the first column in cells A1 to A5.
   b) Now enter a formula in cell B1. The formula should use the value in cell A1 to get a 10 to appear in cell B1. Copy this formula down to cell B5.
   c) Do the numbers which appear in column B match those in the original table? If so, you have found the rule. If not, change the formula in cell B1 and repeat part b. Keep repeating this procedure until you have found the rule. What is the rule?

2. Make up a rule of your own. Use the spreadsheet to create a table of x- and y-values for your rule. Print the resulting table. Give it to a classmate and challenge her or him to determine the rule you used to create the table.

3. Think about the strategies you used to solve this problem. In your journal, describe these strategies. If you think of any additional steps you could take that would simplify the problem, include these in your description.

Review

1. The rules defining three functions are given below. For each function:
   a) Make a table of values.
   b) Draw a graph of the function.
   c) Decide if there are any input numbers that cannot be used.
   d) Write an equation to define the function.
      i) *Rule 1*: Double the number and subtract 1.
      ii) *Rule 2*: Square the number, then subtract the answer from 8.
      iii) *Rule 3*: Add 3 to the square root of the number.

2. Graph these functions on the same grid. Describe each function in words.
   a) $y = x^2 - 3$
   b) $y = (x - 3)^2$
   c) $y = x^2 + 3$
   d) $y = (x + 3)^2$

3. In a bike-a-thon to raise money for cancer research, Silvia has pledges totalling $5.00 per kilometre. Each participant is asked to round the distance he or she rides to the nearest kilometre.
   a) How much money would Silvia raise by riding 12 km? 20 km? 36 km?
   b) How far did she ride if she raised $95.00? $125.00? $215.00?
   c) Draw a graph of money raised against distance biked.

4. Determine the slope and the intercepts of each line on the graph.

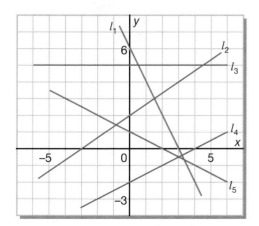

5. Determine the intercepts of the line defined by each equation. Graph the lines on the same grid. Determine the slope of each line.
   a) $3x - 4y = 12$
   b) $5x - 2y = 10$
   c) $-x + 2y = 4$
   d) $2x - y = -4$

6. Make a table of values for each equation. Graph these equations on the same grid. Account for any similarities or differences in the graphs.
   a) $3x + 2y = 12$
   b) $3x - 2y = 12$

7. Determine a rule for each table of values.

a)

x	y
1	-2
2	-4
3	-6
4	-8
5	-10

b)

x	y
2	5
3	8
4	11
5	14
6	17

8. Here is a number triangle.

   a) Assume that the pattern continues. Determine the sum of the numbers in each of the first ten rows of the triangle. Write the results in a table of values.

Row	Sum of the numbers
1	
2	
3	

   b) Use the patterns in your table to determine the sum of the numbers in the 100th row and the 101st row.
   c) Determine a formula for the sum of the numbers in the *n*th row when:
      i) *n* is even
      ii) *n* is odd
   Explain why each formula is correct.

Investigating Tape Counters

Why do you think video cassette recorders have tape counters? In this project you will investigate how the number on the counter is related to the playing time. You will need a video cassette recorder (VCR), or an audio tape recorder that has a counter, and a watch or clock.

ACTIVITY 1

Insert a tape into your VCR. Set the counter to 0000. Start playing the tape, and note the counter numbers after different times. Be sure to do this for the entire playing time of the tape. Record the results in a table. Draw a graph to show how the counter number depends on the playing time. Don't forget to rewind the tape when you have finished.

Playing time (minutes)	Counter number

Is the graph a straight line? If not, can you think of a reason why the graph is not a straight line?

Do you think the counter numbers for recording would be the same as for playing? How could you find out?

ACTIVITY 2

Your VCR may have a tape speed selector which you can use to play tapes at different speeds. Repeat *Activity 1* for each of the other speeds. For slow speeds it will take several hours for the tape to run its course. You will need to plan when to do this activity and how you will remember to check the tape.

How do the graphs compare with your graph in *Activity 1*?

The manual for your VCR may have a table showing the counter numbers for different playing times. How do your results compare with the numbers in the manual?

ACTIVITY 3

Insert a tape into your VCR and set the counter to 0000. Press the fast forward button. Note the time it takes for the counter to reach certain numbers. Do this for the entire length of the tape. Record the results in a table and a graph.

Rewind the tape. Note the time it takes the counter to reach the same numbers you used previously. Record the results in a table and a graph.

How do the graphs compare with your graph in *Activity 1*?

ACTIVITY 4

If possible, carry out *Activities 1* to *3* using a different VCR. Are the results the same?

COMMUNICATING

The Ideas

Write a report that summarizes the results of your investigations. Include tables and graphs.

Number of hours of television watched each week

Teens	**Males**	**Females**
17 h 01 min	23 h 37 min	26 h 25 min
	Children	**All people over**
	(ages 2 to 11)	**the age of 2**
	18 h 42 min	23 h 24 min

BOGGLE YOUR MIND

The art above shows some statistics about the number of hours of television watched by Canadians every week. Over the next few weeks, keep track of your television viewing times. Ask your family or a few friends to do the same. Calculate the mean number of hours of television viewed for each person and for the group. How do the numbers compare with the statistics given here?

Answers

CHAPTER 1 CHANGE

Start With What You Know, page 22

Answers may vary.

Numeracy

Developing the Ideas, page 24

1. a) It increases by 3 to 18.
   b) It would have increased by 6 to 21.
   c) The sum decreases by 3 to 12.

2. a) 3
   b) Answers may vary. Subtract 5 from every number and have integers in the square.
   c) Answers may vary. Add $\frac{1}{3}$ to each number.

3. a) It increases by a factor of 3 to 45.
   b) The sum becomes 1.

4. Yes, because what happened in exercise 3a will occur.

5. 10   6. Answers may vary.

16	2	3	13
5	11	10	8
9	7	6	12
4	14	15	1

Working with Mathematics, page 25

1. a) 50 000, 100 000, 1 000 000
   b) i) Each CD in a set is counted separately.
      ii) To bring Canada in line with the U.S.
   c) i) 10   ii) 5000, 10 000, 100 000
   d) 4   e) Answers may vary.

2. a) $24.50, $27.35   b) $2.85

3. a) Answers may vary. With the exception of $10 bills, the number of bills of each denomination increased.
   b) $20
   c) $10 821 million; $24 000 million; increased by $13 179 million

4. a) It adds the numbers in cells A4, B3, and C2. It adds the numbers in cells A2, B3, and C4.
   b)

7	2	9
8	6	4
3	10	5

   c) Answers may vary.

5. The numbers are listed in this order: $2, $5, $10, $20, $50.
   1, 0, 1, 0, 1; 1, 0, 0, 3, 0; 1, 0, 2, 2, 0; 1, 0, 4, 1, 0; 1, 2, 0, 0, 1; 1, 2, 1, 2, 0; 1, 2, 3, 1, 0; 1, 4, 0, 2, 0; 1, 4, 2, 1, 0; 1, 6, 1, 1, 0; 1, 8, 0, 1, 0; 1, 0, 6, 0, 0; 1, 2, 5, 0, 0; 1, 4, 4, 0, 0; 1, 6, 3, 0, 0; 1, 8, 2, 0, 0; 1, 10, 1, 0, 0; 1, 12, 0, 0, 0; 6, 0, 0, 0, 1; 6, 0, 1, 2, 0; 6, 0, 3, 1, 0; 6, 2, 0, 2, 0; 6, 2, 2, 1, 0; 6, 4, 1, 1, 0; 6, 6, 0, 1, 0; 6, 0, 5, 0, 0; 6, 2, 4, 0, 0; 6, 4, 3, 0, 0; 6, 6, 2, 0, 0; 6, 8, 1, 0, 0; 6, 10, 0, 0, 0; 11, 4, 0, 1, 0; 11, 2, 1, 1, 0; 11, 0, 2, 1, 0; 11, 0, 0, 2, 0; 11, 0, 4, 0, 0; 11, 2, 3, 0, 0; 11,
   4, 2, 0, 0; 11, 6, 1, 0, 0; 11, 8, 0, 0, 0; 16, 2, 0, 1, 0; 16, 0, 1, 1, 0; 16, 0, 3, 0, 0; 16, 2, 2, 0, 0; 16, 4, 1, 0, 0; 16, 6, 0, 0, 0; 21, 0, 0, 1, 0; 21, 0, 2, 0, 0; 21, 2, 1, 0, 0; 21, 4, 0, 0, 0; 26, 0, 1, 0, 0; 26, 2, 0, 0, 0; 31, 0, 0, 0, 0
   a) 53   b) $2   c) $50   d) No change

Fractions

Working with Mathematics, page 28

1. a) , b) Answers may vary. It is possible but unlikely.

2. The average number of boxes is the number in the set multiplied by the sum of all the fractions with a numerator of 1, and a denominator from 1 to the number in the set.

3. 1; $2 \times (1 + \frac{1}{2})$; $5 \times (1 + \frac{1}{2} + \frac{1}{3} + \frac{1}{4} + \frac{1}{5})$;
   $6 \times (1 + \frac{1}{2} + \frac{1}{3} + \frac{1}{4} + \frac{1}{5} + \frac{1}{6})$;
   $8 \times (1 + \frac{1}{2} + \frac{1}{3} + \frac{1}{4} + \frac{1}{5} + \frac{1}{6} + \frac{1}{7} + \frac{1}{8})$;
   $9 \times (1 + \frac{1}{2} + \frac{1}{3} + \frac{1}{4} + \frac{1}{5} + \frac{1}{6} + \frac{1}{7} + \frac{1}{8} + \frac{1}{9})$;
   $10 \times (1 + \frac{1}{2} + \frac{1}{3} + \frac{1}{4} + \frac{1}{5} + \frac{1}{6} + \frac{1}{7} + \frac{1}{8} + \frac{1}{9} + \frac{1}{10})$
   a)

Number of items in the set	Average number of boxes needed
1	1
2	3
3	6
4	8
5	11
6	15
7	18
8	22
9	25
10	29

   c) The average number of boxes needed increases as the number in the set increases. Up to 5 items, the average number of boxes is approximately double the number of items. But for 10 items, the average number of boxes is approximately 3 times the number of items.

4. a) The fraction increases.   b) The fraction decreases.
   c) The fraction increases.

5. a) The fraction increases.   b) The fraction decreases.
   c) The fraction decreases.

6. It appears that when the numerator is larger than the denominator, and each is increased by 1, the fraction decreases. When the numerator is smaller than the denominator, and each is increased by 1, the fraction increases.

7. a) To get each denominator, add the numerator and denominator of the preceding fraction. To get each numerator, add the denominator to the preceding denominator.
   b) Answers may vary.
   c) Answers may vary. The values appear to approach 1.414 214…

8. a) To get each denominator, add the numerator and denominator of the preceding fraction. To get each numerator, add the denominator to twice the preceding denominator.
   b) Answers may vary.
   c) Answers may vary. The values appear to approach 1.732 051…

Linking Ideas: Mathematics and Technology
How Many Cereal Boxes?, page 29

Answers may vary.

Quest: A Ring Around Earth, page 30

For a circle, the distance is always 2π m, or approximately 6.3 m.

Ratios
Developing the Ideas, page 32

$10:5$; $2:1$; $3:2$

Working with Mathematics, page 33

1. a) $1:1000$ **b)** 980 **c)** 125 000, 98 000

2. a)

Distance to Portage la Prairie (km)	Distance to Winnipeg (km)	Distance to Portage la Prairie : distance to Winnipeg
75	150	$1:2$
70	145	$1:2.07$
65	140	$1:2.15$
60	135	$1:2.25$
55	130	$1:2.36$
50	125	$1:2.5$
45	120	$1:2.67$
40	115	$1:2.88$
35	110	$1:3.14$
30	105	$1:3.5$
25	100	$1:4$
20	95	$1:4.75$
15	90	$1:6$
10	85	$1:8.5$
5	80	$1:16$
1	76	$1:76$

b)

Distance to Portage la Prairie (km)	Distance to Winnipeg (km)	Distance to Portage la Prairie : distance to Winnipeg
75	150	$1:2$
80	155	$1:1.94$
85	160	$1:1.88$
90	165	$1:1.83$
95	170	$1:1.79$
100	175	$1:1.75$
105	180	$1:1.71$
110	185	$1:1.68$
115	190	$1:1.65$
120	195	$1:1.625$

c) The distance to Portage la Prairie is 150 km and the distance to Winnipeg is 225 km.

3. a) As we get older, the ratio decreases.
b) The increasing ages are similar to the increasing distances. In both cases, the ratios decrease.

4. a) 0.70 **b)** $87.52 more

Linking Ideas: Mathematics and Design
The Fibonacci Sequence, page 35

1. a) Add first two terms.
b) Add second and third terms.
c) Add the two preceding terms.

2. 34, 55, 89, 144, 233, 377, 610

3. a) $1.625:1$

b)

Width (cm)	Length (cm)	Length : width
3	5	$1.666\ 666\ 667:1$
5	8	$1.6:1$
8	13	$1.625:1$
13	21	$1.615\ 384\ 615:1$
21	34	$1.619\ 047\ 619:1$
34	55	$1.617\ 647\ 059:1$
55	89	$1.618\ 181\ 818:1$
89	144	$1.617\ 977\ 528:1$
144	233	$1.618\ 055\ 556:1$
233	377	$1.618\ 025\ 751:1$

c) Each pair of width and length is adjacent terms.
d) Successive values decrease and increase, but approach 1.618.

4. 9.0 cm, 5.6 cm, $1:6.07$ **5.** Answers may vary.

6. To three decimal places, the last 5 rectangles are golden.

Rates
Developing the Ideas, page 36

1. a) Canada receives more from Greece.
b) 18 000 kg **c)** $72 000

2.

Year	Canada to Greece		Greece to Canada	
	Mass (kg)	Money (× $1000)	Mass (kg)	Money (× $1000)
1	30 000		48 000	72
2	34 000		49 000	60
3	38 000		50 000	48
4	42 000		51 000	36
5	46 000		52 000	24
6	50 000		53 000	12
7	54 000		54 000	0
8	58 000	12	55 000	
9	62 000	24	56 000	
10	66 000	36	57 000	

Working with Mathematics, page 37

1. The distance increases by 20 km each hour.

2. a) About 500 **b)** About 15 000 **c)** About 5.5 years

3. Answers may vary.

4. a) 5.477 billion
b) The population, in billions, each year will be: 5.663, 5.756, 5.849, 5.942, 6.035
c) Answers may vary.

5. a) i) 56 per year **ii)** 80 per year
b) 2800 people per year
c) 370 units per year; approximately 31 units per month
d) February, 1996

Percents
Developing the Ideas, page 39

1. a) Increase **b)** 17 425 **c)** $\frac{17\ 425}{20\ 830}$ **d)** About 84%

2. a) Increase **b)** 108 960 **c)** $\frac{108\ 960}{1\ 043\ 015}$ **d)** About 10%

3. English **4.** Punjabi

Working with Mathematics, page 40

1. Student: +$1000; +83%
   Other person: +$1000; +0.22%

2. a) i) Compact disk/digital tape equipment
      ii) Compact disk/digital tape equipment
   b) i) Colour televisions   ii) Colour televisions
   c), d) Answers may vary.

3. a) For each 10% decrease in exam mark, the final mark decreases by 2%.

Term mark	Examination mark	Final mark
84%	100%	87%
84%	90%	85%
84%	80%	83%
84%	70%	81%
84%	60%	79%
84%	50%	77%
84%	40%	75%
84%	30%	73%
84%	20%	71%
84%	10%	69%
84%	0%	67%

c) For each 10% decrease in exam mark, the final mark decreases by 4%.

Term mark	Examination mark	Final mark
84%	100%	90%
84%	90%	86%
84%	80%	82%
84%	70%	78%
84%	60%	74%
84%	50%	70%
84%	40%	66%
84%	30%	62%
84%	20%	58%
84%	10%	54%
84%	0%	50%

d) 100%, 90%, 80%, 70%, 60%, 50%, 40%, 30%, 20%, 10%, 0%
e) 105%   f) Answers may vary.

4. Answers may vary.

5. a) Answers may vary.   b) Answers may vary.
   c) We need to know the total number of players in 1991–92. There are now more teams so the total number of Canadians may be greater but their percent may be less.

Linking Ideas: Mathematics and the Consumer
The Cost of Natural Gas, page 43

1. a) $181.02   b) $176.46   c) Zone 1, zone 11
2. a) $201.34   b) $17 673.45

Integers
Developing the Ideas, page 44

1. a) Wind-chill equivalent temperature every hour: 4°C, −2°C, −7°C, −12°C, −18°C, −23°C, −28°C, −33°C, −39°C, −44°C
   b) It did drop about 5°C every hour; but some hours it dropped 6°C.

Working with Mathematics, page 45

1. a) −4; the product of a positive number and a negative number is a negative number.
   b) −3, −2, −1, 0, 1
   c) The product of two negative numbers is a positive number.

2. a)

Temperature (°C)	Temperature (°F)
30	86
25	77
20	68
15	59
10	50
5	41
0	32
−5	23
−10	14
−15	5
−20	−4
−25	−13
−30	−22

b) As the temperature in degrees Celsius decreases by 5°, the temperature in degrees Fahrenheit decreases by 9°.
c) −35°, −31°; −40°, −40°; −45°, −49°; −50°, −58°; −55°, −67°
d) Answers may vary.

3. a) The wind-chill equivalent temperature changed by −8°C or −7°C per hour.
   b) After the first hour, the wind-chill equivalent temperature changed by −18°C every 2 h.

4. Answers may vary.

5. a) Answers may vary. For example:

Wind speed (km/h)	50	27	18	12	8
Temperature (°C)	−10	−15	−20	−25	−30

Measurement
Developing the Ideas, page 47

1. Each dimension of the Post decreased by 50%, one-half. For the Star, its width decreased by 2 cm and its length decreased by 3 cm.

2. The Post decreased by 75%. The Star decreased by approximately 11%.

3. 963 000 m^2 4. Answers may vary.

Page 48

1. The length and width have each been reduced by 50%.
2. The area has been reduced by 75%.
3. The mass has been reduced by 75%.

Working with Mathematics, page 49

1. a) Answers may vary.   b) Answers may vary.

2. a) 2

b) Surface area would quadruple and the volume would increase by a factor of 8.

c) Answers may vary.

3. a) The volume increases to a maximum when the length of the cut-out square is 4 cm, and then decreases.

Length of the cut-out square (cm)	Length of the box (cm)	Width of the box (cm)	Height of the box (cm)	Volume of the box (cm³)
1	24	18	1	432
2	22	16	2	704
3	20	14	3	840
4	18	12	4	864
5	16	10	5	800
6	14	8	6	672
7	12	6	7	504
8	10	4	8	320
9	8	2	9	144

b) i) Yes   **ii)** Yes

ii) Answers may vary. For a length of 0.5 cm for the cut-out square, the volume is 237.5 cm³. For a length of 9.5 cm for the cut-out square, the volume is 66.5 cm³.

c) ii) Answers may vary. Using the minimum amount of packaging for maximum volume of a product packed in a box

4. Answers may vary.

Review, page 51

1. Each result is 32 768. Each number in the square in the picture is the power to which 2 is raised to get the corresponding number in this square.

2. a) 1758   **b)** 2061 or 2062

3. a) 95   **b)** 1 min 19 s

4. a) $486.11   **b)** $437.50   **c)** $421.69   **d)** $469.80

5. Sarah : Evan

a) 2 : 1, 3 : 2, 4 : 3, 5 : 4, 6 : 5, 7 : 6

b) i) 11 : 10   **ii)** 21 : 20   **iii)** 31 : 30

6. a) $700   **b)** $707.25   **c)** $879.75   **d)** About 29%

7. a) $7649.15   **b)** $8796.52

8. Answers may vary.

a) $(-6) + (-5)$ **b)** $(+5) + (+6) + (+7)$

c) $(-5) + (-4) + (-3) + (-2)$ **d)** $(-9) + (-8)$

e) $(+6) + (+7) + (+8)$

f) $(+2) + (+3) + (+4) + (+5) + (+6)$

CHAPTER 2 STATISTICS AND PROBABILITY

Start With What You Know, page 56

1. 43%   **2.** 486   **3.** By using a bar graph

4. 17%   **5.** 70–79   **6.** 14%

7. 2   **8.** April to October   **9.** March

10. Answers may vary.

a) In a pictograph, a symbol represents a certain number of items. In a bar graph, the length of a bar is proportional to the number of items in a set of data.

b) In a broken-line graph, straight-line segments join adjacent points. In a continuous-line graph, the points are joined by one straight line or a smooth curve.

c) In a bar graph, each bar represents a category of data, and there is a space between adjacent bars. In a histogram, the data are continuous and there is no space between the bars.

11. Your friend is more likely to pay for the movie.

12. Bag A   **13.** $\frac{2}{5}$ **14.** $\frac{1}{3}$

Collecting Data

Working with Mathematics, page 60

1. Answers may vary.

2. Answers may vary. Who constitutes a family? Parents and children? Grandparents? Aunts, uncles, cousins, and so on?

3. , 4. Answers may vary.

5. a) i   **b)** ii   **c)** i   **d)** i or ii   **e)** ii

    f) ii   **g)** i   **h)** ii   **i)** i

6. , 7. , 8. Answers may vary.

Presenting Data

Developing the Ideas, page 63

1. 58%   **2.** 49%

3. Non disabled men, aged 35–54

4. Disabled women, aged 55–64

5. a) The percent decreases.

b) Answers may vary. The people may become more debilitated and be unable to work.

Working with Mathematics, page 64

1. a) i) The tens place of marks: 3, 4, 5, 6, 7, 8, 9

    ii) The units place of marks: 0, 1, 2, 3, 4, 5, 6, 7, 8, 9

b) 0 to 9

2. 107, 109, 112, 112, 113, 114, 115, 117, 117, 118, 119, 120, 121, 123, 124

3. Answers may vary.

a) Bar graph or circle graph   **b)** Bar graph

c) Broken-line graph or continuous-line graph

d) Bar graph   **e)** Continuous-line graph

f) Bar graph or pictograph

4. a) 5%   **b)** Approximately 7 min

5. a) Swimming   **b)** 930 kJ   **c)** 27.5 min

6. c) Answers may vary. The circle graph is more useful. We cannot complete the histogram because we do not know the age of the oldest person.

d) 14 840 000   **e)** 22 120 000

7. a)

42.	1233334
42.	5555556666777778899
42.	0111

b) 20%   **d)** There are more undersized balls.

8. Answers may vary.

9. b) The statement appears to be true, especially for the disabled population.

c) Answers may vary.

10. a) The distance travelled before the driver starts using the brakes

b) The distance travelled by the vehicle from the start of using the brakes till it comes to a stop

d) Answers may vary. From the graph:

  i) 35 m   **ii)** 72 m

  e) A wet road is slippery and the stopping distances increase.

11. Answers may vary.

  c) Because the data are continuous and a bar graph suggests discrete data

12. a) Answers may vary.

Stem-and-leaf diagram:

```
2 | 34
3 | 28
4 | 1446
5 | 11235566679
6 | 011122333334555566666677888899999
7 | 1123334556678899
8 | 0244689
9 | 028
```

Frequency table:

Interval	Number of students	Frequency
20 - 29	II	2
30 - 39	II	2
40 - 49	IIII	4
50 - 59	₩ ₩ I	11
60 - 69	₩ ₩ ₩ ₩ ₩ ₩ III	33
70 - 79	₩ ₩ ₩ I	16
80 - 89	₩ II	7
90 - 99	III	3

The data can be displayed in a bar graph.

b) , c) Answers may vary.

Linking Ideas: Mathematics and Science
Electricity Use, page 67

Answers may vary.

Measures of Central Tendency
Working with Mathematics, page 71

1. Answers may vary.

  a) Mean   **b)** Median **c)** Mean   **d)** Mean   **e)** Mean   **f)** Mode

2. 40.1, 40.5, there are four modes: 23, 32, 41, 54

3. a) 16, 16   **b)** 3.4, 4   **c)** 10.3, 10

4. $15.88, $14.99   **5.** 18   **6.** Answers may vary.

7. a) The mean and median both increase by 5.

  b) The mean and median both double.

  c) The mean and median do not change.

8. a) The mean is $50 571.43. The median is $55 000. The modes are $55 000 and $33 000.

  b) Answers may vary. The median and mean most fairly represent the pay structure. There are 8 out of 14 people who earn at least these amounts.

9. Answers may vary.

  a) 6, 8, 10, 13, 14, 15, 18   **b)** 41, 63, 64, 65, 66, 67, 68

  c) 0, 5, 5, 10, 11, 12, 13   **d)** 7, 8, 9, 12, 15, 15, 39

Box-and-Whisker Plots
Working with Mathematics, page 74

1. For exercise 2: the quartiles are 30.5 and 50, the range is 36.
For exercise 3a: the quartiles are 14 and 18, the range is 10.

For exercise 3b: the quartiles are 2.5 and 4, the range is 4.
For exercise 3c: the quartiles are 6 and 13.5, the range is 13.

2. 55 is the median. 30 is the lowest mark in the class and 80 is the highest mark. 45 is the lower quartile and 75 is the upper quartile. The range is 50.

3. The range is 18 cm. The mean is 174 cm. The median is 172 cm. The lower quartile is 168 cm and the upper quartile is 176 cm. The shortest student is 164 cm and the tallest student is 182 cm.

4. a) , c)

Group	Mean	Median	Mode	Lower quartile	Upper quartile	Range
A	16	16	15, 20	14	19	12
B	11.5	11	11	9.5	13.5	13
A and B	13.8	14	11	11	17	15

5. Answers may vary. For example:

  a) 32, 50, 50, 50, 70, 70, 70, 70, 74, 80, 80, 80, 91, 91, 92

  b)

```
3 | 2
4 |
5 | 000
6 |
7 | 00004
8 | 000
9 | 112
```

6. a) i) Phillies   **ii)** Phillies   **iii)** Phillies   **iv)** Phillies   **v)** Blue Jays

  b) Answers may vary. Yes

7. Answers may vary.

  a) The data are evenly distributed about the median.

  b) The data are unevenly distributed with more values around the lower end.

  c) Most of the data are between the lower and upper quartiles.

  d) The quartiles are close to the median and have very few values between them.

8. Answers may vary.

9. a) 50th, 25th, 75th   **b)** 22%

Linking Ideas: Mathematics and Technology
Unemployment Rates in Two Canadian Provinces, page 76

Answers may vary.

Mathematics File: The Poggendorf Effect, page 77

Answers may vary.

Samples and Populations
Working with Mathematics, page 80

1. Answers may vary.

  a) We have to consider students from all classes, and not only from our class.

  b) The choice of music varies with people of different age groups. A survey of the senior citizens will not include students, children, and middle-aged people.

  c) The people working in the Assembly Plant will be encouraged to buy the cars they produce. This sample will not cover students, senior citizens, and many other groups of people.

  d) My close friends are likely to have tastes similar to mine, and they would not be a random sample.

e) There will be many people of different groups not listening to the talk show, so the sample will not be random.

2. Answers may vary.
   a) A survey of a certain number of students in each class in school will give valid information on the average age of the students.
   b) A random sample covering all age groups in different provinces
   c) A survey at a parking lot in a mall or at a busy intersection
   d) A random sample of teenagers from different schools
   e) A random sample covering people of all age groups

3. Answers may vary.

4. Answers may vary.
   a) When a bulb has been checked, it cannot be sold or used.
   b) It would be impossible to survey the entire population of Canada.
   c) Food, when cooked in bulk, has the same ingredients so for its purity, a small sample is sufficient.
   d) Testing all ladders until they break will not leave any ladders to be sold.
   e) It is not possible to ask every shop manager how much he or she sells.
   f) It is not possible to check the blood sample of every person.

5. , 6. Answers may vary.

7. a) i) Canadians   ii) Telephone survey   iii) No
   b) i) Canadians   ii) Phone-in response   iii) No
   c) i) Canadians   ii) Personal interviews   iii) No
   d) i) Canadian teenagers ii) Interviews   iii) Yes

8. , 9. Answers may vary.

Linking Ideas: Mathematics and the Media
Sampling and TV Ratings, page 83

1. Because we cannot be sure exactly how many households watched the program

2. Approximately 0.015%

3. 20 668 200, 17 968 300, 17 409 700, 15 733 900, 15 082 200

4. 9.8 million   5. 3 000 000

6. All the measurements were not taken at the same time.

7. , 8. Answers may vary.

Misuses of Statistics
Working with Mathematics, page 86

1. Answers may vary.
   a) The graph suggests an increase but, for 6 out of the past 7 years, the numbers have been decreasing.
   b) The bars are not aligned horizontally and the unemployment rate appears to be greater than it is.

2. Answers may vary.
   a) After 5 days, most colds have gone, whether or not any drug was taken.
   b) The unemployed people may not be qualified for the advertised jobs.

3. Answers may vary.
   a) It does not say what percent of people who ski do not take lessons. There could be many more people who don't take lessons who have accidents, but the percent would be smaller.

b) This is not misleading.

c) We do not know whether the accidents occur because the drivers are young or because they are inexperienced. We need statistics on new drivers rather than young drivers to decide whether or not raising the age makes a difference.

d) We need to know what percent of drivers 1775 is, and what percent of cyclists 102 is, before we can say which is the safer mode of transport.

4. Answers may vary. Although fewer people under 25 are killed, there are many more people over 25 than under 25. We would need to calculate each number of deaths as a percent of its age group to find out which group is the better risk for insurance.

5. Graphs may vary.

6. , 7. Answers may vary.

8. Answers may vary. There are few accidents because there is little traffic on the road at this time, drivers reduce their speeds in fog, and very few drivers travel at 150 km/h.

9. , 10. , 11. Answers may vary.

Quest: How Many People in the Crowd?, page 88

Answers may vary.

Making Predictions
Working with Mathematics, page 93

1. a) .400   b) .389   c) .382   d) .382
   e) Answers may vary. It is better to use his average at the end of the season, because that is more current.

2. a: 48; e: 65; n: 33; s: 25

3. a) 1: 0.163; 2: 0.170; 3: 0.159; 4: 0.162; 5: 0.177; 6: 0.169
   b) Answers may vary. It does seem to be a fair die. Each number turns up approximately the same number of times.

4. 0.026   5. 621 students

6. O: 889; A: 700; B: 166; AB: 95

7. , 8. Answers may vary.

9. Answers may vary.
   c) The shortest cylinder is most likely to land on its end.

10. Answers may vary.

11. a) Education prepares us for tomorrow, but am I ready for today?
    b) With statistics you can fool most of the people most of the time, but not all of the people all of the time.

12. Answers may vary.

Probability
Working with Mathematics, page 97

1. a) $\frac{1}{50}$ b) $\frac{3}{25}$ c) $\frac{1}{25}$

2. a) $\frac{3}{8}$ b) $\frac{1}{4}$ c) $\frac{3}{8}$ d) $\frac{5}{8}$ e) $\frac{3}{4}$ f) $\frac{1}{4}$

3. a) i) Pink ball, yellow ball, orange ball   ii) Equally likely
   b) i) HH, HT, TH, TT   ii) Equally likely
   c) i) Purple marble, green marble, red marble
      ii) Not equally likely
   d) i) A, B, C, D, E, F, G, H   ii) Equally likely

4. a) $\frac{1}{4}$ b) $\frac{1}{2}$ c) 0

5. a) $\frac{15}{77}$ b) $\frac{3}{77}$ c) $\frac{21}{77}$ d) $\frac{32}{77}$

6. a) $\frac{9}{22}$ b) $\frac{13}{22}$ c) $\frac{4}{11}$

7. a) $\frac{6}{25}$ b) $\frac{12}{25}$ c) 0   d) $\frac{2}{25}$

8. a) $\frac{688}{4800}$ b) Greater   c) $\frac{688}{4800}$

9. a) i) 0.834 43   ii) 0.467 74   iii) 0.366 69
   b) $\frac{2220}{95\ 144}$
   c) Answers may vary. Older people pay premiums for a shorter time.

Mathematics File: Random Numbers, page 99

Answers may vary.

Quest: Sharing a Birthday, page 100

Answers may vary.

The Probability of Compound Events
Developing the Ideas, page 103

1. 2   2. 6   3. 12

5. a) $\frac{1}{12}$ b) $\frac{1}{4}$ c) $\frac{1}{3}$ d) $\frac{1}{4}$

Working with Mathematics, page 104

1. A compound event consists of two single events.

2. a) $\frac{1}{2}$ b) No   c) No

3. a) $\frac{5}{36}$ b) $\frac{1}{36}$ c) $\frac{1}{6}$ d) $\frac{1}{12}$ e) $\frac{31}{36}$

4. a) Final branches: GB; GG; BB; BG   b) $\frac{1}{4}$

5. a) Final branches: GGGG; GGGB; GGBG; GGBB; GBGG; GBGB; GBBG; GBBB; BGGG; BGGB; BGBG; BGBB; BBGG; BBGB; BBBG; BBBB
   b) $\frac{1}{16}$

6. a) $\frac{1}{6}$ b) $\frac{1}{6}$ c) $\frac{1}{9}$
   d) Answers may vary. The points which correspond to the same total lie on a straight line.

7. a) 0.25   b) 0.1875   c) 0.5625

Monte Carlo Methods
Working with Mathematics, page 107

1. Spin the arrow 10 times. Count how many times it lands on "correct." Record the number of times if it is 3 or more. Repeat the experiment many times. Divide the number of times that there were 3 or more by the number of experiments.

2. Answers may vary.
   a) The representation of one situation through the use of another situation
   b) The simulation is easier.
   c) Because the simulation imitates the problem

3. a) A coin
   b) A coin and a die, or a spinner divided into 12 equal parts
   c) A spinner divided into 4 equal parts
   d) A coin

4. Answers may vary.
   a) Toss 4 coins many times, and record if exactly 3H show.
   b) Toss 8 coins many times, and record if 5 or more H show.

5. Answers may vary. Toss 8 coins many times. Record if exactly

5H show. Divide the number of times exactly 5H showed by the number of times the 8 coins were tossed.

6. Answers may vary. Make a spinner with 3 equal sectors. Label one sector "correct." Spin the arrow 10 times. Record if it lands on "correct" 7 or more times. Repeat the experiment many times. Divide the number of recordings of 7 or more by the number of experiments.

7. Make a spinner with 6 equal sectors. Label one sector "defective." Spin the arrow 7 times. Record if it lands on "defective" 2 or more times. Repeat the experiment many times. Divide the number of recordings of 2 or more by the number of experiments.

8. Toss 5 coins many times. Record if 3H or more show. Divide the number of times 3H or more showed by the number of times the 5 coins were tossed.

9. Divide a spinner into regions whose areas are in the ratio $25:10:25$. That is, the sector angles are $150°$(green), $60°$(yellow), and $150°$(red). Spin the arrow 5 times. Record if it lands on green 3 or more times. Repeat the experiment many times. Divide the number of recordings of 3 or more by the number of experiments.

10. Approximately 0.5256

Mathematics File: Games of Chance, page 108

Answers may vary.

Review, page 109

1. , 2. Answers may vary.

3. From reference materials

4. Alberta: 6 million tonnes; Manitoba: 2.88 million tonnes; Saskatchewan: 13.68 million tonnes

5. a)

0	4567889
1	1222334467788
2	123

   b) 13, 13   c) 19; 8, 17

6. a) Mean   b) Mean

7. Explanations may vary.   8. 70

9. Answers may vary.   10. $27.00

11. , 12. , 13. Answers may vary.

14. Answers may vary. It could be that many more teenagers ski than any other age group. Similarly, it could be that very few people over the age of 50 ski.

15. Graphs may vary.

16. a) 0.121, 0.363, 0.388, 0.129
    b) i) About 36 times
    ii) Answers may vary. One hundred tosses are insufficient to draw a conclusion.

17. a) $\frac{1}{6}$ b) $\frac{1}{2}$ c) $\frac{1}{2}$ d) $\frac{1}{3}$ e) 1   f) 0

18. a) Final branches: TTTTT; FTTTT; TTTTF; FTTTF; TTTFT; FTTFT; TTTFF; FTTFF; TTFTT; FTFTT; TTFTF; FTFTF; TTFFT; FTFFT; TTFFF; FTFFF; TFTTT; FFTTT; TFTTF; FFTTF; TFTFT; FFTFT; TFTFF; FFTFF; TFFTT; FFFTT; TFFTF; FFFTF; TFFFT; FFFFT; TFFFF; FFFFF
    b) $\frac{1}{32}$

19. $\frac{5}{6}$

20. a) $\dfrac{25}{64}$ b) $\dfrac{5}{14}$

21. a) $\dfrac{9}{25}$ b) $\dfrac{16}{81}$ c) $\dfrac{9}{25}$

22. a) $\dfrac{1}{3}$ b) $\dfrac{1}{6}$ c) $\dfrac{33}{95}$

23. a) A spinner b) A spinner c) A coin

24. a) Toss 3 coins many times, and record if 3H show.
   b) Toss 2 coins many times, and record if 2H show.

25. Answers may vary.
   Toss 4 coins many times. Record if 2H and 2T show. Divide the number of times 2H and 2T showed by the number of times the 4 coins were tossed.

26. Use a spinner with 6 equal sectors. Label one sector "correct." Spin the arrow 8 times. Record if it lands on "correct" 2 or more times. Repeat the experiment many times. Divide the number of recordings of 2 or more by the number of experiments.

27. Use a spinner with 4 equal sectors. Label one sector "correct." Spin the arrow 10 times. Record if it lands on "correct" 6 or more times. Repeat the experiment many times. Divide the number of recordings of 6 or more by the number of experiments.

CHAPTER 3 APPLICATIONS OF INTEGERS AND RATIONAL NUMBERS

Start With What You Know, page 116

1. Answers and examples may vary.
   a) Integers that have 5 as a factor; they end in 5 or 0
   b) The product of an integer multiplied by itself
   c) An indicated quotient of two quantities
   d) Any of the numbers…-2, -1, 0, 1, 2…
   e) The value of 2^n where n is an integer
   f) Integers where each one is 1 more than (or 1 less than) the preceding integer
   g) A number whose only factors are itself and 1

2. 1, 2, 3, 5, 6, 10

3. 7, 56, 392; 2, 6, 12

4. 9, 3   5. 81

6. 8, $\dfrac{1}{8}$; 2, $\dfrac{1}{2}$

7. 90

8. Answers may vary.

Using Integers to Describe Change

Working with Mathematics, page 121

1. a) 72, -19, 893, -5662
   b) Answers may vary: a positive or negative natural number and zero

2. Answers may vary. When the number in the second box is greater (less) than the number in the third box, the number in the first box is positive (negative).

3. a) -4 b) $+3$ c) -7 d) -1 e) -1 f) -4

4. a) 7 b) 4 c) -6 d) 6 e) 7 f) -16

5. Answers may vary.

6. a) -2 b) -12 c) $+7$ d) -1 e) -3 f) $+12$

7. Answers may vary.

8. From left to right, the diagonals are consecutive integers. This is because $(+3) + (-2) = +1$. From right to left, the numbers in each diagonal decrease by 5. This is because $(-2) - (+3) = -5$.

-9	-6	-3	0	3
-7	-4	-1	2	5
-5	-2	1	4	7
-3	0	3	6	9
-1	2	5	8	11

9. a) -30 b) -21 c) $+20$ d) $+24$ e) -60 f) $+24$

10. Answers may vary.

11. a) The product is positive. b) The product is negative.

12. a) -6 b) 5 c) -3

13. , 14. Answers may vary.

15. a) British Columbia: $+7000$; Ontario: $+122\,000$; Nova Scotia: $+7000$; Prince Edward Island: $+1000$
    b) Yukon Territory: -3000; Alberta: $-32\,000$; Saskatchewan: -3000; Manitoba: -3000; Quebec: $-81\,000$; Newfoundland: $-15\,000$

16. a) Net change is zero.
    b) Answers may vary. For example, Prince Edward Island: from 1976–86, from 1981–91, and from 1991–92, the net change was 0.
    c) Zero

17. Yukon Territory: -2000; Northwest Territories: -9000; British Columbia: $+310\,000$; Alberta: $+112\,000$; Saskatchewan: $-87\,000$; Manitoba: $-88\,000$; Ontario: $+133\,000$; Quebec: $-292\,000$; New Brunswick: $-17\,000$; Nova Scotia: -4000; Prince Edward Island: 0; Newfoundland: $-54\,000$

18. 1000; 0; 1000; 0 Explanations may vary. Since this is how Canadians move within Canada, the net result for each line should be zero, but each number has been rounded, so when the numbers are added, the result is not always 0.

20. a) British Columbia
    b) Answers may vary. Economic prospects are best in this province, and it has the mildest climate.

21. a) Saskatchewan, Manitoba, Quebec, Newfoundland
    b) Answers may vary.

22. Answers may vary. There was an oil boom that didn't last.

23. Answers may vary.

24. a) $(+1)(+1)(+12)$; $(+1)(+2)(+6)$; $(+1)(+3)(+4)$; $(+2)(+2)(+3)$
    b) All of part a), plus $(+1)(-1)(-12)$; $(-1)(-1)(+12)$; $(+1)(-2)(-6)$; $(-1)(+2)(-6)$; $(-1)(-2)(+6)$; $(+1)(-3)(-4)$; $(-1)(+3)(-4)$; $(-1)(-3)(+4)$; $(+2)(-2)(-3)$; $(-2)(-2)(+3)$

Linking Ideas: Mathematics and Science

Atoms and Integers, page 123

1. i) a) 9 protons, 9 electrons b) 9 protons, 10 electrons, -1
   ii) a) 12 protons, 12 electrons b) 12 protons, 10 electrons, $+2$
   iii) a) 13 protons, 13 electrons b) 13 protons, 10 electrons, $+3$
   iv) a) 7 protons, 7 electrons b) 7 protons, 10 electrons, -3

Quest: Why Is the Product of Two Negative Numbers Positive?, page 124

Answers may vary.

Rational Numbers
Developing the Ideas, page 126

1. $\frac{-45}{100}, \frac{-11}{8}, \frac{-50}{1}, \frac{-1}{8}, \frac{0}{1}, \frac{192}{100}, \frac{1}{8}, \frac{29}{1}$

2. If we extended the number line we could show every number in the stock report on it.

Working with Mathematics, page 127

1. a) A: 1.5; B: −0.5; C: −1.5
   b) A: −1.75; B: −0.25; C: 0.5; D: −1.25
   c) A: 0.9; B: 0.3; C: −0.6; D: −0.1

2. a) $\frac{1}{4}$ b) $\frac{1}{4}$ c) $\frac{3}{2}$ d) $\frac{2}{3}$ e) $\frac{1}{2}$ f) $-\frac{1}{2}$

3. Explanations may vary.
   a) True   b) False   c) True   d) True

4. a) $-\frac{3}{5}, -\frac{2}{5}, -\frac{1}{5}$ b) $-\frac{1}{2}, \frac{1}{4}, \frac{5}{8}$ c) $-\frac{2}{9}, \frac{3}{7}, 1\frac{2}{5}$
   d) $-\frac{1}{2}, -\frac{1}{4}, \frac{1}{4}$ e) $-\frac{5}{6}, -\frac{1}{2}, \frac{2}{3}$ f) $-\frac{3}{2}, -\frac{5}{4}, \frac{1}{3}$

5. a) 0.3   b) −0.8$\overline{3}$ c) −2.4
   d) −0.375   e) −0.$\overline{4}$ f) 0.5$\overline{3}$

6. a) $-\frac{3}{4}$ b) $-\frac{5}{2}$ c) $\frac{2}{9}$ d) $-\frac{4}{9}$

7. a) $\frac{23}{4}, \frac{379}{8}, \frac{350}{1}, \frac{53}{8}, \frac{35}{1}, \frac{29}{4}, \frac{45}{8}, \frac{85}{1}$
   b) 5.75, 47.375, 350.0, 6.625, 35.0, 7.25, 5.625, 85.0

8. a) Since the remainders repeat, so will the digits in the quotient, because each is related to a remainder.
   b) With no remainder eventually, the decimal terminates. When the remainders repeat, there is a limit to what the remainder can be (for example, when dividing by 7, the remainders can only be 0, 1, 2, 3, 4, 5, 6) and hence continuing to divide will produce repeated remainders.
   c) Yes; it is called an irrational number.

Linking Ideas: Mathematics and History
The Introduction of Zero, page 129

1. a) 17   b) 4   c) 259   d) 23
   e) 0   f) 0   g) 0   h) Not defined

2. The 0 in 30 is a number that tells you how many ones there are. The zeros in 40 000 are numbers that tell you how many thousands, hundreds, tens, and ones there are.

Adding and Subtracting Rational Numbers
Developing the Ideas, page 130

1. Answers may vary. In each case the number in the units place is the same. The numbers on the left are integers; those on the right are rational numbers.

2. +1, +1.4; −4, −4.3; −7, −8.3

3. Answers may vary. In each case the number in the units place is the same. The numbers on the left are integers; those on the right are rational numbers.

4. +5, +5.6; −9, −9.9; −5, −5.3

Working with Mathematics, page 132

1. a) +1.0   b) −1.0   c) −1.0   d) +5.0   e) +1.0   f) +3.0

2. a) $-\frac{2}{5}$ b) −1   c) $-\frac{1}{4}$ d) $-\frac{1}{2}$ e) $\frac{7}{10}$ f) $\frac{1}{4}$

3. a) $55.40
   b) A cheque was written. The cheque was greater than the balance, and DR means overdrawn.
   c) $100 was deposited.

4. a) −0.7   b) −3.0   c) 3.7   d) $\frac{1}{2}$ e) $-\frac{7}{4}$ f) $-\frac{11}{10}$

5. a) 5.0   b) −1.7   c) −2.5   d) $\frac{3}{4}$ e) $-\frac{1}{6}$ f) $\frac{7}{4}$

6. a) 26.7 m − (−3.6 m) = 30.3 m
   b) 6.5°C − 8.0°C = −1.5°C
   c) $407.1 billion + $36.2 billion = $443.3 billion

7. a)

+5	−6	+2	+1
−4	+12	−8	0
+7	−6	−10	−9
+8	0	−16	−8

b)

−5.2	−8.9	+2.6	−11.5
−6.0	+3.3	+9.4	+6.7
+8.5	−5.7	+15.1	+17.9
−2.7	−11.3	+27.1	+13.1

8. a) Descriptions may vary. In each row, the numbers increase by 3. In each column, the numbers increase by 1.
   b) 11, 14, 17, 20, 23
   c) i) Row 3   ii) Row 2   iii) Row 1   iv) Row 3   v) Row 1   vi) Row 2

9. , 10. Answers may vary.

11. a) −6.0   b) −7.2   c) −1.6   d) −9.6   e) 6.8   f) −7.2

12. a) −1   b) $-\frac{1}{8}$ c) $\frac{1}{2}$ d) $-\frac{1}{4}$ e) $-\frac{28}{15}$ f) $-\frac{1}{6}$

13. a) $-\frac{5}{2}$ b) $-\frac{19}{14}$ c) $-\frac{7}{10}$ d) $\frac{5}{12}$ e) $\frac{37}{24}$ f) $-\frac{25}{18}$

14. a) $-\frac{1}{6}$ b) $-\frac{1}{4}$ c) $-\frac{3}{8}$ d) $\frac{1}{2}$ e) $\frac{11}{18}$ f) $-\frac{29}{24}$

15. −7°C

16. a) i) Answers may vary. For example, 6 : 15, 6 : 15, 6 : 25
   ii) There are several answers, which depend on the time you think elapsed between the people arriving.
   b) Answers may vary.

Mathematics File: Local Time Around the World, page 135

1. a) 3 a.m.   b) 2 a.m.   c) 10 a.m.   d) 6 p.m.

2. a) 7:30 a.m.   b) 3:30 a.m.   c) 6:30 p.m.   d) 7:30 p.m.

3. a) 12 noon   b) 7 a.m.   c) 5 p.m.   d) 1 a.m.

4. a) 8 p.m.   b) 3 p.m.   c) 4:30 p.m.   d) 2 p.m.
   e) 11 p.m.   f) 12 noon   g) 5 p.m.   h) 8 a.m. next day

5. a) Answers may vary. Bangkok, Washington; Beijing, Santiago; Dublin, Wellington; Beijing, Halifax; Jakarta, Ottawa; Jakarta, Washington; Bangkok, Ottawa; London, Wellington
   Answers may vary. The longitude lines that pass through each pair of cities lie on opposite ends of a diameter of Earth.
   b) i) Wellington and Vancouver   ii) 20 h
   iii) Answers may vary. They are both a long way from London, but in opposite directions.

Multiplying and Dividing Rational Numbers
Developing the Ideas, page 136

1. Answers may vary.
   a) The signs and the units digits are the same.
   b) The tenths digits are different.
2. $-6, -7, -7.5; -20, -21, -20.4; 10, 11, 11$
3. Answers may vary.
   a) In all cases except one, the denominators are the same. The signs are the same.
   b) The numerators are different.
4. $-2, -1.8, -2.1; -4, -3.5, -3.8; 2, 2.1, 1.5$

Working with Mathematics, page 138

1. a, c, e   2. c   3. a, e, f
4. a, b, d, e   5. -1.2 m/h
6. a) -8.6 b) $+4.8$ c) -2.1 d) $-\frac{1}{4}$ e) $-\frac{2}{9}$ f) $\frac{3}{4}$
7. a) -1.2 b) -24 c) 2.75 d) -4 e) $-\frac{3}{8}$ f) $\frac{2}{9}$
8. a) $(-12.4 \text{ m/min}) \times (2.5 \text{ min}) = -31$ m
   b) $(-10.5°C) \div (6 \text{h}) = -1.8°C/\text{h}$
   c) $(-2.5°C) \times (\frac{3000 \text{ m}}{500 \text{ m}}) = -15°C$
9. a) -8.4 b) -31 c) -2.5 d) -1.86 e) -43.2
   f) $+4$ g) -47 h) 14.4 i) $-17.\overline{3}$ j) -60.75
10. a) $\frac{6}{5}$ b) $-\frac{5}{6}$ c) $-\frac{5}{6}$ d) $-\frac{7}{15}$ e) $\frac{3}{10}$
    f) $\frac{3}{20}$ g) $\frac{2}{15}$ h) -6 i) $\frac{9}{16}$ j) $-\frac{21}{2}$
11. a) In A3: adds 1 to the number in A2
    In B3: adds 2 to the number in A3
    In C3: subtracts 2 from the number in A3
    In D3: multiplies the number in A3 by 2
    In E3: multiplies the number in A3 by -2
    b) Descriptions and explanations may vary.
    c) Descriptions and explanations may vary.
12. Answers may vary.

Order of Operations with Rational Numbers
Working with Mathematics, page 141

1. Descriptions may vary.
   a) $+10$ b) -10 c) -17 d) -9
   e) -10 f) -3 g) $-\frac{7}{4}$ h) $-\frac{1}{2}$
2. a) $+14$ b) $+15$ c) $+14$ d) -16
   e) -20 f) -28 g) 5 h) -8
3. a) -3 b) -16 c) $+80$ d) $+4$
   e) -4 f) -4 g) $\frac{1}{2}$ h) -5
4. a) $\frac{3}{8}$ b) $\frac{1}{8}$ c) $-\frac{3}{8}$ d) $-\frac{3}{16}$
   e) $\frac{2}{9}$ f) $\frac{1}{9}$ g) $-\frac{1}{54}$ h) $\frac{5}{18}$
5. a) $(5-3) \times 4 + 6$ b) $(5-3) \times (4+6)$ c) $5 - 3 \times (4+6)$
   d) $5 - (3 \times 4 + 6)$ e) $5 - (3 \times 4) + 6$
6. a) $1 - (3 \times 5 - 7)$ b) $2 \times (2 - 2 \times 2)$ c) $(5+5) \times (5+5)$
7. a) 0
   b) Answers may vary; for example, 4 different answers: $-\frac{1}{4}$, 0, $\frac{4}{9}$, $\frac{2}{3}$
   c) Yes, for example: $\frac{1}{36}$

Quest: Averaging Coordinates, page 142

This point is the midpoint of the line segment.

Slope of a Line Segment
Developing the Ideas, page 143

1. a) 1   b) 2   c) 1, 3, 2
2. a), b)

House	rise	run	$\frac{\text{rise}}{\text{run}}$
1	11	5	2.2
2	6	10	0.6
3	8	7	1.1

   c) The house with the steepest roof corresponds to the greatest value of $\frac{\text{rise}}{\text{run}}$.
   The house with the roof which is the least steep has the least value of $\frac{\text{rise}}{\text{run}}$.

Working with Mathematics, page 145

1. $\frac{1}{3}$
2. a) It has a zero slope.   b) Its slope is undefined.
3. a) Answers may vary. $A(0,0)$, $B(50,0)$, $C(250,150)$, $D(400,175)$, $E(600,350)$, $F(800,400)$
   b) AB: 0; BC: $\frac{3}{4}$; CD: $\frac{1}{6}$; DE: $\frac{7}{8}$; EF: $\frac{1}{4}$
   c) DE, AB
4. AB: -2; CD: $-\frac{1}{4}$; EF: 1; GH: 3; IJ: $\frac{2}{5}$
5. a) $\frac{4}{7}$ b) $\frac{1}{8}$ c) 0   d) $\frac{7}{9}$
   e) $-\frac{10}{11}$ f) $-\frac{8}{7}$ g) $\frac{12}{7}$ h) -1
6. b) i) Slopes are equal.   ii) Slopes are equal.
   c) Parallelogram (also rhombus)
7. Answers may vary. A vertical line does not have a slope. We say its slope is undefined.

Quest: Identifying Transformations, page 146

Answers may vary.

For the horizontal images: a rotation of 180°; reflection in a horizontal line; reflection in a vertical line; each word has been reflected in a vertical line through its centre; each letter has been reflected in a vertical line through its centre

For the vertical images: a reflection in a line at 45° to the horizontal; a rotation of 90° counterclockwise

Linking Ideas: Mathematics and Design
Scott Kim's Inversions, page 147

1. Answers may vary. A rotation of 180° in "Symmetry" and "Upside Down," a rotation of 120° and 240° in "Infinity," a reflection in "Mirror," a dilation in "Level"
2. Answers may vary. 6
3. a) "Symmetry," "Upside Down," "Infinity"   b) "Mirror"
4. a) "Mirror"   b) "Upside Down," "Symmetry"
5. Answers may vary.

Transformations and Mapping Rules

Working with Mathematics, page 150

1. Descriptions may vary.
   a) The trapezoid was reflected in the x-axis.
   b) The trapezoid was reflected in the y-axis.
   c) The trapezoid "stretched" in the x-direction.
   d) A rotation of 90° counterclockwise about the origin
   e) The trapezoid became a line segment of the line $x = 3$.
   f) The trapezoid became a line segment of the line $y = -2$.
   g) The trapezoid became the point $(-2, 4)$.
   h) The trapezoid was reflected in the line $y = x$.
   i) The trapezoid moved 3 units to the left and 2 units up.
   j) AD was unchanged, the trapezoid "stretched" in the positive x-direction.
   k) AB moved left, CD moved right, and the trapezoid changed shape.
   l) AD moved down, CB moved up, and the trapezoid changed shape.
   m) The trapezoid was enlarged.
   n) The trapezoid was reduced.
   o) The trapezoid was reflected in the x-axis and "stretched" in the y-direction.
   p) A rotation of 180° about the origin
   q) The trapezoid was rotated, then translated and reflected.
   r) The trapezoid was reflected in the line $x = 3$.
   s) The trapezoid seems to have been reflected, rotated, and enlarged.
   t) The trapezoid seems to have been rotated, translated, and enlarged.

2. Answers may vary.
   a) i) i   **ii)** a, b, h, r   **iii)** d, p   **iv)** m, n
   b) q, s, t   **c)** c, e, f, g, j, k, l, o

3. The vertices are translated and the sides of the triangle become curves.

4. a, b, d, h, i, p, q, r

Linking Ideas: Mathematics and Technology

Transformations and Grids, page 151

1. Answers may vary.
   Yellow: Rotation; Dark blue: Rotation; Purple: Rotation; Maroon: Translation; Orange: Reflection and translation; Green: Reflection; Light blue: Dilation

Mathematics File: Some Unusual Transformations, page 152

1. **a)** 4   **b)** 3   **c)** 6
   d) 5   **e)** 2   **f)** 1

2. When the mapping rule includes variables with exponents of 1, and no products of variables

3. Two different points on the original figure map onto the same point on the image.

Review, page 154

1. **a)** -8 **b)** $+3$ **c)** -8 **d)** $+3$
   e) -7 **f)** -10 **g)** -9 **h)** -52

2. From left to right, the numbers in each diagonal increase by 3. This is because $(-4) + (+7) = +3$. From right to left, the numbers in each diagonal increase by 11. This is because $(+7) - (-4) = +11$.

26	22	18	14	10
19	15	11	7	3
12	8	4	0	-4
5	1	-3	-7	-11
-2	-6	-10	-14	-18

3. **a)** -56 **b)** 54   **c)** 72   **d)** -42
   e) -4 **f)** 9   **g)** -27 **h)** -11

4. **a)** $1 + 3 + 5 + 7 = 4 \times 4$; $1 + 3 + 5 + 7 + 9 = 5 \times 5$; $1 + 3 + 5 + 7 + 9 + 11 = 6 \times 6$; the sum of each set of odd numbers is the square of half 1 plus the last number.
   b) $2 + 4 + 6 + 8 = 4 \times 5$; $2 + 4 + 6 + 8 + 10 = 5 \times 6$; $2 + 4 + 6 + 8 + 10 + 12 = 6 \times 7$; the sum of each set of even numbers is the product of half the last number and the next consecutive number.

5. **a)** $\frac{8}{6}$ **b)** $\frac{-7}{10}$ **c)** $\frac{12}{5}$ **d)** $\frac{-8}{28}$ **e)** $\frac{-27}{24}$ **f)** $\frac{52}{16}$

6. **a)** 0.625   **b)** $-0.\overline{4}$ **c)** $-0.\overline{72}$ **d)** $1.\overline{18}$

7. **a)** $-\frac{11}{12}$ **b)** $-\frac{9}{8}$ **c)** $-\frac{1}{12}$ **d)** 1   **e)** $-\frac{11}{14}$
   f) $-\frac{99}{10}$ **g)** -4.8 **h)** 39.5   **i)** -13.1 **j)** 0.5

8. **a)** 6   **b)** $-\frac{1}{12}$ **c)** 42   **d)** $-\frac{1}{2}$ **e)** $-\frac{21}{8}$ **f)** $\frac{20}{3}$
   g) -0.12 **h)** 0.9   **i)** -1.1 **j)** -0.65 **k)** 25.06   **l)** 12

9. $1.2\overline{4}$, $293.\overline{3}$, $2133.\overline{3}$

10. **a)** 11   **b)** -7 **c)** -17 **d)** 11
    e) $-\frac{1}{12}$ **f)** $\frac{19}{18}$ **g)** $\frac{11}{20}$

11. **a)** $9 - 4 \times (2 - 3)$ **b)** $3 \times (8 + 6 \div 2)$ **c)** $7 + 6 \times (6 - 7)$

12. AB: 0; CD: -4; EF: $\frac{4}{3}$; GH: -2; IJ: $\frac{1}{6}$; KL: $\frac{2}{5}$; MN: $-\frac{5}{3}$

13. **a)** AB: -1; BC: $\frac{9}{2}$; AC: $\frac{4}{7}$ **b)** RS: $\frac{1}{3}$; ST: $\frac{5}{2}$; RT: $-\frac{7}{5}$
    c) LM: $-\frac{5}{4}$; MN: 0; LN: undefined
    d) EF: -5; FG: 2; EG: 1

14. A: reflection; B: rotation; C: rotation; D: rotation; E: translation; F: reflection; G: reflection

16. **a)** Dilation   **b)** Translation   **c)** Reflection
    d) Reflection   **e)** Translation   **f)** Reflection

CHAPTER 4 POWERS AND ROOTS

Start With What You Know, page 160

1. 20 billion years, 10 billion years

2. 5 000 000 000, 694 000 000 000, 16 000 000 000

3. **a)** 100 000 000   **b)** 920 000 000
   c) 92 000 000 000   **d)** 100 000 000 000

4. b;
   Astronomy photo: 2.0×10^{10}, 1.0×10^{10}

Population photo: 5.0×10^9, 6.94×10^{11}, 2.15×10^3, 1.6×10^{10}

Rubik's photo: 1.5×10^1, 4.3×10^{19}

5. Trillion

Quest: Forming Expressions with 1, 4, 8, and 9, page 162

Expressions may vary.

Estimating with Large Numbers
Developing the Ideas, page 163

1. Estimates may vary.   2. Answers may vary.

3. a) Answers may vary. Most households and businesses have more telephones than telephone books.
   b) Estimates may vary.

4. , 5. , 6. Estimates may vary.

7. Answers may vary.

Page 164

1. a) Between 4 and 5   b) Yes

Page 165

2. Answers may vary.
   a) A standard business envelope is about 24 cm long.
   b) 2.88×10^9 cm, or 28 800 000 m
   c) This is almost three-quarters of Earth's circumference.
   d) Yes

Working with Mathematics, page 166

1. a) 320 500   b) 9 970 000 km^2 c) 350 km/h
   d) 104 000   e) 1 150 000 000   f) 26 000 000
   g) $680 000 000   h) 8890 km
   i) 807 m   j) 9 900 000

2. 2 million

3. , 4. , 5. , 6. Answers may vary.

7. Estimates may vary.

8. a) Answers may vary. 10 000 characters fill three to four pages in size 12 type.
   b) Answers may vary.

9. a) No
   b) 30 ha per minute is almost 16 million ha per year, which is much greater than the second rate. Explanations may vary.
   c) Answers may vary.

Using Powers to Express Large and Small Numbers
Developing the Ideas, page 169

1. 14 million metres — diameter of Earth; 1.4 billion metres — diameter of sun; 900 billion metres — diameter of the largest star; 90 thousand trillion metres: diameter of Crab Nebula; 10 millionths of a metre — diameter of a white blood cell; 10 billionths of a metre — diameter of a protein molecule; 100 trillionths of a metre — diameter of a carbon atom

Page 170

1. a) $10 \times 10 \times 10 = 1000$
   b) $10 \times 10 \times 10 \times 10 \times 10 \times 10 \times 10 = 10\ 000\ 000$
   c) 10   d) $2 \times 2 = 4$ e) $3 \times 3 \times 3 \times 3 = 81$
   f) $1.5 \times 1.5 \times 1.5 = 3.375$ g) $(-5) \times (-5) \times (-5) = -125$

h) $(-2) \times (-2) \times (-2) \times (-2) \times (-2) \times (-2) \times (-2) \times (-2)$
   $= 256$

2. a) 2^6 b) 7^9 c) $(-1)^5$

3. d and e
   It doesn't apply to powers with an exponent of zero, a negative exponent, or an exponent that is not a whole number.

4. Answers may vary. For every decrease of 1 in the exponent, the value of the power is one-tenth of the previous value. So, since $10^1 = 10$, 10^0 must be $\frac{1}{10}(10)$, or 1.

Page 171

5. a) $\frac{1}{10^3} = \frac{1}{1000}$, or 0.001   b) $\frac{1}{10} = 0.1$
   c) $\frac{1}{10^9} = \frac{1}{1\ 000\ 000\ 000}$, or 0.000 000 001
   d) $\frac{1}{2} = 0.5$ e) $\frac{1}{5^2} = \frac{1}{25}$, or 0.04
   f) $\frac{1}{2.5} = 0.4$ g) $\frac{1}{-2} = -0.5$
   h) $\frac{1}{(-1)^3} = \frac{1}{-1}$, or -1

6. a) 2^{-4} b) 3^{-5} c) 7^{-3}

Working with Mathematics, page 172

1. The reciprocal of a number is equal to 1 divided by the number.

2. a) 2^5 b) 3^4 c) $(-2)^4$ d) 2^{-3}

3. a) 2^1 b) 2^2 c) 2^3 d) 2^4
   e) 2^{-1} f) 2^{-2} g) 2^{-3} h) 2^{-4}

4. a) 100   b) 0.01   c) 100   d) 0.01   e) 64
   f) $\frac{1}{64}$, or 0.015 625   g) -64 h) $-\frac{1}{64}$, or -0.015 625
   i) 5   j) 1   k) 1   l) 0

5. b) Answers may vary. The largest power that can be displayed on many calculators is 2^{26}, or 67 108 864. The next power is displayed in scientific notation.
   c) The calculator displays an error message. The largest power many calculators can calculate is 2^{332}, or 8.749×10^{99}.

6. a) 25   b) 49   c) 13   d) 19   e) 16
   f) 18   g) 31   h) 17   i) 5   j) 80
   k) 1   l) 2   m) 1.5   n) 0.25   o) 0.25

7. a) $2^1 + 3^4 + 5^6 = 15\ 708$ b) $1^6 + 4^3 + 5^2 = 90$

8. a) 25   b) $\frac{1}{25} = 0.04$ c) 25
   d) $\frac{1}{25} = 0.04$ e) 32   f) $\frac{1}{32} = 0.031$ 25
   g) -32 h) $-\frac{1}{32} = -0.031$ 25

9. a) 2^4 b) 2^{-3} c) 3^3 d) 2^{-3} e) 3^2
   f) 2^{-3} g) 3^4 h) 4^{-3} i) 3^{25}

11. a) Saidah was correct. Explanations may vary.
    b) Answers may vary. 9^{841}

Mathematics File: How Big Is One Billion?, page 173

1. Estimates may vary.

2. a) 3600   b) 86 400   c) 31 536 000

3. Yes. It takes about 11.5 days to reach 1 million seconds.

4. Estimates may vary.

5. It takes almost 32 years to equal 1 billion seconds.

6. The number 1 000 000 would be $\frac{1}{1000}$ of the distance along the line, which is 0.1 mm from the left end.

7. No, the claim is not reasonable. To speak 7 billion words in

35 years, you would have to speak 200 000 000 words each year. Even if you spoke 24 hours a day, every day, this would be almost 381 words every minute, or over 6 words every second.

Quest: The National Debt Clock, page 174

$544 510 397 702

Multiplying and Dividing Powers
Developing the Ideas, page 176

1. a) $10 \times 10 \times 10$; $10 \times 10 \times 10 \times 10$
   b) $10 \times 10 \times 10 \times 10 \times 10 \times 10 \times 10$; 7
   c) 10^7

2. a) $10 \times 10 \times 10 \times 10 \times 10 \times 10 \times 10 \times 10$; 8
   b) 10^8

3. To multiply two powers of 10, keep the base and add the exponents. Yes, just keep applying the rule to each pair of powers in the product.

4. , 5. , 6. Yes. Examples may vary.

Page 177

7. a) $10 \times 10 \times 10 \times 10 \times 10 \times 10$; $10 \times 10 \times 10 \times 10$
   b) $\dfrac{10 \times 10 \times 10 \times 10 \times 10 \times 10}{10 \times 10 \times 10 \times 10} = 10 \times 10$; 2
   c) 10^2 **d)** 10^{-2}

8. a) $\dfrac{10 \times 10 \times 10 \times 10 \times 10 \times 10 \times 10}{10 \times 10 \times 10} = 10 \times 10 \times 10 \times 10$; 4
   b) 10^4 **c)** 10^{-4}

9. To divide two powers of 10, keep the base, and subtract the exponent of the divisor from the exponent of the dividend.

10. , 11. , 12. Yes. Examples may vary.

13. a) $(10 \times 10 \times 10 \times 10) \times (10 \times 10 \times 10 \times 10)$; 8
   b) 10^8 **c)** 10^8

14. a) $(10 \times 10 \times 10) \times (10 \times 10 \times 10) \times (10 \times 10 \times 10) \times (10 \times 10 \times 10) \times (10 \times 10 \times 10)$; 15
   b) 10^{15} **c)** 10^{15}

15. To determine a power of a power of 10, keep the base and multiply the exponents.

16. , 17. , 18. Yes. Examples may vary.

Page 178

1. Yes. Although the property is true for all exponents, from the way we have developed it, they must be positive integers.

2. Yes

Page 179

3. Yes. Although the property is true for all exponents, from the way we have developed it, they must be positive integers.

4. Yes

5. Because division by zero is not defined

6. Yes. Although the property is true for all exponents, from the way we have developed it, they must be positive integers.

7. Yes

Working with Mathematics, page 180

1. a) 100   **b)** 100   **c)** 10 000

2. Every "step" on the chart represents a ten-fold increase or decrease in size.

3. Answers may vary.

4. a) 10^5 **b)** 10^{13} **c)** 10^{16} **d)** 10^4
   e) 10^5 **f)** 10^{12} **g)** $(-4)^{17}$ **h)** 3^{11}
   i) 7.2^{12} **j)** $(-5)^{-2}$ **k)** 1.2^3 **l)** 9^8

5. a) i) one hundred thousand   **ii)** one hundred million
   iii) one hundred billion   **iv)** one thousand thousand
   v) one thousand million   **vi)** one thousand billion
   b) i) 1 000 000 000 000   **ii)** 1 000 000 000 000
   c) Eight thousand six hundred million billion
   d) Answers may vary.

6. a) 10^9 **b)** 10^9 **c)** 10^{10} **d)** 10^{14} **e)** 10^8
   f) 10^9 **g)** 10^8 **h)** 10^{15} **i)** 10^{11} **j)** 10^{15}

7. a) 10^7 **b)** 10^5 **c)** 10^7 **d)** 10^4 **e)** 10^2 **f)** 10^3

8. a) 10^{12} **b)** 10^6 **c)** 2^{25} **d)** $(-3.5)^8$

9. a) 3^5 **b)** 9^2 **c)** $(-8)^3$ **d)** $(-2)^7$
   e) 5^3 **f)** 2^6 **g)** 4^{-2} **h)** 7^2
   i) 11^7 **j)** 5.2^7 **k)** $(-3)^5$ **l)** 8.3^7

10. a) 10^4 **b)** 2^6 **c)** 3^5 **d)** $(-5)^6$ **e)** 6^8 **f)** $(-1)^4$

11. About 10^{22}

12. a) 15
   b) Answers may vary. Keep the numbers in the same places but make each entry a power with the same base.
   For example:

The magic product is 2^{15}.

13. 5^{2222}, 2^{5555}, 4^{3333}, 3^{4444}

Mathematics File: Powers of 2, page 182

1. a) 1 048 576   **b)** 2 097 152   **c)** 32
   d) 1 048 576   **e)** 262 144   **f)** 1 048 576

2. 16 777 216

3. a) Answers may vary. For positive exponents, the last digit follows a repeating pattern of 2, 6, 8, 4.
   For negative exponents, the last two digits are always 25 and the last three digits alternate between 125 and 625. The non-zero digits are the digits of the corresponding power of 5. For example, $2^{-5} = 0.031\ 25$ and $5^5 = 3125$.
   b) Explanations may vary.

4. a) 0.007 812 5   **b)** 1024   **c)** 1   **d)** 0.25
   e) 524 288   **f)** 0.000 000 953 674 316 406 25
   g) 0.000 976 562 5   **h)** 0.000 244 140 625

Linking Ideas: Mathematics and Technology
Half-life on a Spreadsheet, page 183

1. a) The formula in cell A5 divides the amount of iodine-131 by 2. The formula in cell B5 increases the number of days by 8.
   b) 50, 8

2. 11 days   **3.** 14 days

4. The computer displays negative powers of 2 in column C in descending order, beginning with 2^{-1} in row 6.

Scientific Notation

Developing the Ideas, page 185

1. Count the number of digits before the decimal point in the original number and subtract one. This number will be the exponent of 10. Examples may vary.

2. Count the number of digits after the decimal point up to and including the first non-zero digit. Multiply by -1. The result will be the exponent of 10. Examples may vary.

3. Answers may vary. All rational numbers can be written in scientific notation.

4. Answers may vary. It makes it easy to compare the numbers as well as to multiply or divide them.

Working with Mathematics, page 186

1. a) $1.3 \times 10^6\,^\circ$C b) 1.0×10^{-5} m
   c) 0.000 000 000 000 000 000 000 000 000 92 g
   d) 120 000 000 000 e) 4.5×10^9 years
   f) 5.0×10^{-9} cm g) 150 000 000 km^2

2. a) 1.0×10^{-9} g; 2.0×10^{-3} mm
   b) 8.2×10^9; 5.0×10^{-6} m

3. a) 1.6×10^{13} b) 1.6×10^{17} c) 1.6×10^{11}

4. a) 1.0585×10^{10} L
   b) Estimates may vary. There are about 13 million, or 1.3×10^7 registered vehicles in Canada. Using this number, the savings are about 814 L per vehicle per year.
   c) Answers may vary.

5. a) 4.3×10^3 b) 4.3×10^5 c) 4.3×10^{-3}
   d) 4.3×10^{-5} e) 3.75×10^4 f) 3.75×10^6
   g) 3.75×10^{-2} h) 3.75×10^{-7} i) -8.45×10^2
   j) 6.11×10^{-3} k) -9.86×10^{-5} l) 7.082×10^{-7}
   m) 1×10^3 n) -3.21×10^6 o) 1.0×10^{-4}
   p) -1.0×10^{-7}

6. a) 4.05×10^{13} km b) 4.0×10^{32} kg c) 7.02×10^8 km

7. 65 million; 13 million; 11 000; 5500; 2000; 800

8. a) 6.02×10^{23} b) About 3.06×10^{21}
   c) About 9.5×10^{22}

9. a) $1.670\,911 \times 10^{24}$ g b) About 1833

10. a) 9.4608×10^{15} m
    b) Each dimension would be about 10^{16} times as small as it is now. Thus, each exponent would be 16 less than on the current chart.

11. Each number would be 10^{10} times as great as it is now. Thus, each exponent would be 10 greater than on the current chart. For example, the height of a child would be 1×10^{10} Å.

Mathematics File: Naming Very Large and Very Small Numbers, page 188

1. a) Virgo Cluster b) Pollen grain c) Tarantula Nebula
   d) Proton e) Sun f) Bacterium
   g) Jupiter h) Virus i) Milky Way
   j) Uranium nucleus

2. a) 200 sextillion metres, 200 000 exametres, 2.0×10^{23} m, 2.0E23 m
   b) 100 millionths of a metre, 100 micrometres, 1.0×10^{-4} m, 1.0E–4 m
   c) 8 600 000 000 000 000 000 m, 8.6 exametres, 8.6×10^{18} m, 8.6E18 m
   d) 0.000 000 000 000 001 m, 1 femtometre, 1.0×10^{-15} m,

1.0E–10 m
   e) 1 400 000 000 m, 1.4 billion metres, 1.4×10^9 m, 1.4E9 m
   f) 0.000 001 m, 1 millionth of a metre, 1.0×10^{-6} m, 1.0E–6 m
   g) 140 000 000 m, 140 million metres, 140 megametres, 1.4E8 m
   h) 0.000 000 1 m, 100 billionths of a metre, 100 nanometres, 1.0E–7 m
   i) 660 000 000 000 000 000 000 m, 660 quintillion metres, 660 exametres, 6.6×10^{20} m
   j) 0.000 000 000 000 01 m, 10 quadrillionths of a metre, 10 femtometres, 1.0×10^{-14} m

3. Answers may vary.

4. Answers may vary. One might need numbers larger than 10^{26} to describe very large quantities, such as the number of grains of sand on Earth.

Linking Ideas: Mathematics and Science,
How Many Ants Are There?, page 189

1. 4×10^{-2} inches, 1.0×10^{-6}, 8.8×10^3 species, 1.0×10^{18} insects, 1×10^2, 1.0×10^{16}, 2.0×10^9 pounds, 1×10^1 percent

2. a) 5.3 billion b) Almost 2 000 000

3. The article estimates that 1 in every 100 insects is an ant and that there are a billion billion insects alive at any given moment. So, to estimate the number of ants, divide 1 billion billion by 100.

4. , 5. Answers may vary.

Estimating Square Roots
Developing the Ideas, page 190

1. 25 cm^2

2. a) 50 cm^2 b) No, its area would then be 100 cm^2.

3. Estimates may vary, about 7.1 cm.

4. Estimates may vary, about 8.7 cm and 10.0 cm.

Working with Mathematics, page 192

1. a) 3.6 b) 4.5 c) 9.2

2. No. 5^2 is 25, not 50. The square of a number increases more quickly than the number itself. You can estimate $\sqrt{50}$ by considering the closest perfect square which is greater than 50 and the closest perfect square which is less than 50 and choosing a number between their square roots.

3. a) ± 6 b) ± 10 c) ± 20 d) ± 1 e) $\pm \frac{1}{2}$ f) $\pm \frac{1}{3}$

4. Estimates may vary.
   a) 6.3 b) 9.8 c) 5.5 d) 8.1

5. Estimates for parts e and f may vary.
   a) 14 b) 44 c) 70 d) 48 e) 8.4 f) 3.7

6. a) i) 1.732 050 8 ii) 17.320 508 iii) 173.205 08
   iv) 1732.0508 v) 0.173 205 vi) 0.017 320 5
   b) As each number is multiplied (or divided) by 100, its square root is multiplied (or divided) by 10, since $\sqrt{100} = 10$.

7. a) ± 9 b) ± 8 c) ± 30 d) ± 11 e) ± 0.5 f) ± 0.1

8. Estimates may vary.
   a) 2.2 b) 3.5 c) 5.7 d) 8.3

9. Estimates may vary.
   a) 6.7 cm b) 7.3 cm c) 8.5 cm d) 9.3 cm

10. Estimates for parts c and f may vary.
   a) 5   **b)** 7   **c)** 2.6   **d)** 1   **e)** 12   **f)** 2.6

11. Answers may vary.

12. a) i) 1.414 213 6   **ii)** 4.472 136   **iii)** 14.142 136
   iv) 44.721 36   **v)** 141.421 36   **vi)** 447.2136
   b) In each case, the number whose square root you are finding
   is 10 times as great as the previous number. Thus, each
   answer you get is $\sqrt{10}$ times as great as the previous
   answer.

Linking Ideas: Number Concepts and Graphing
Graphing Squares and Square Roots, page 193

Group 1

Sample table

Number, x	Square of the number, x^2
0	0
0.25	0.0625
0.5	0.25
1	1
1.5	2.25
2	4

1. a) When x is between 0 and 1   **b)** When x is greater than 1
   c) Imagine a line through the origin at 45° to the positive x-
   axis. When x is between 0 and 1, the graph is below this
   line. When x is greater than 1, the graph is above this line.

Group 2

Sample table

Number, x	Square root of the number, $\sqrt{x}$
0	0
0.25	0.5
1	1
1.5	1.225
2	1.414
2.75	1.658
3	1.732
4	2

1. a) When x is greater than 1   **b)** When x is between 0 and 1
   c) Imagine a line through the origin at 45° to the positive x-
   axis. When x is between 0 and 1, the graph is above this
   line. When x is greater than 1, the graph is below this line.

Both groups

2. Answers may vary.
   If one group interchanged the columns in its table, the tables
   would match. The graphs have the same shape but are oriented
   differently. If you were to reflect one graph in the line at 45°
   to the positive x-axis, you would obtain the other graph.

The Pythagorean Theorem
Developing the Ideas, page 194

1. The areas are 9 cm^2, 16 cm^2, 25 cm^2, 36 cm^2, 49 cm^2,
   8 cm^2, 8 cm^2, 13 cm^2, and 20 cm^2.

4.

Area of square on one leg	Area of square on the other leg	Area of square on the hypotenuse
9	16	25
36	13	49
8	8	16
20	16	36

5. The area of the square on the hypotenuse is equal to the sum
   of the areas of the squares on the legs.

Working with Mathematics, page 196

1. Answers may vary. You could measure the angle with a
   protractor or compare it to an angle known to be right, such
   as the corner of a piece of paper.

2. a) 6.7   **b)** 8.1   **c)** 10.2   **d)** 14.4

3. 6.71 m   **4.** 12.65 m

5. a) Answers may vary.
   b) The squares with areas 8 cm^2, 9 cm^2, and 16 cm^2 form a
   triangle with an angle of about 87°.
   The squares with areas 8 cm^2, 13 cm^2, and 20 cm^2 form a
   triangle with an angle of about 88°.

Length of a Line Segment
Developing the Ideas, page 197

1. AE $\doteq$ 2.8 cm, HF $\doteq$ 3.6 cm, DG $\doteq$ 3.2 cm, IC $\doteq$ 5.4 cm

2. AB $\doteq$ 4.5 units

Working with Mathematics, page 198

1. Answers may vary. We cannot draw a right triangle if the line
   segment is horizontal or vertical. Also, if the points are not on
   lattice points you will have to estimate the lengths of the sides
   of the right triangle.

2. To one decimal place: AB $\doteq$ 3.0 units, CD $\doteq$ 5.7 units,
   EF $\doteq$ 6.7 units, GH $\doteq$ 7.1 units, IJ $\doteq$ 5.8 units

3. To one decimal place:
   a) 4.5 units   **b)** 2.8 units   **c)** 6.4 units   **d)** 2.5 units

4. a) PQ and RS are about 5.7 units long.
   PS and QR are about 2.8 units long.
   b) 16 square units   **c)** About 6.3 units

5. OA $\doteq$ 4.5 units, OB $\doteq$ 5.4 units, AB $\doteq$ 6.7 units

6. To one decimal place:
   a) 3.2 units   **b)** 4.2 units   **c)** 3.6 units   **d)** 6.5 units

7. To one decimal place: JK $\doteq$ 5.1 units, KL $\doteq$ 4.5 units,
   JL $\doteq$ 7.6 units

8. a) 12; A(0,5), B(3,4), C(4,3), D(5,0), E(4,−3), F(3,−4),
   G(0,−5), H(−3,−4), I(−4,−3), J(−5,0), K(−4,3),
   L(−3,4)
   b) 7; the vertices are as follows: KCEI, LBFH, ADGJ, KBEH,
   LCFI, BCHI, KLEF
   c) KCEI and LBFH have area 48 square units.
   ADGJ, KBEH, and LCFI have area 50 square units. BCHI
   and KLEF have area 14 square units.

Quest: Can You Make One Large Square from Two Small Ones?, page 199

Fold and cut each square along one of its diagonals. Then
arrange the pieces with the four right angles together to form a
large square.

If the side length of each small square is 1 cm, then its area is 1 cm^2; the area of the large square is 2 cm^2, and each side of the large square is $\sqrt{2}$ cm long.

Irrational Numbers

Developing the Ideas, page 200

1. a) 0.375　　b) 0.583 333...　　c) −1.4375
   d) −0.875　　e) 3.363 636...　　f) 0.535 353...
   g) 0.076 576 576 5...　　h) 3.142 857 1...

2. a) ii, iv, and vi are rational numbers.
   b) The others are not rational because they neither terminate nor repeat. Yes, they are numbers.

3. a) i) 4.999 999...　　ii) 17.020 202 02...　　iii) −8.512 732 73...
   b) $88\ 175.\overline{475}$, $-0.079\ 218\ 836\ 758\ 492\ 000\ \overline{783}\ 9$

Working with Mathematics, page 202

1. a) Rational　　　　　　　　b) Irrational
   c) No. 1.732 050 8 is a rational approximation of $\sqrt{3}$.

2. No, because C and d are not integers.

3. The phrase "appear to be" is used because a number which appears to repeat may eventually break from the pattern and conversely, a number which does not repeat may eventually begin to repeat.
   a) Rational　　b) Irrational　　c) Rational　　d) Irrational

4. a) Rational　　b) Rational　　c) Integer, rational
   d) Natural, integer, rational　　e) Natural, integer, rational
   f) Rational　　g) Natural, integer, rational　　h) Rational
   i) Rational　　j) Irrational　　k) Rational　　l) Rational

5. a, b, c, d, f, g, and i are all irrational.

6. a, b, and e are rational.

7. Answers may vary.

8. a) i) 2　　ii) 6　　iii) 120　　iv) 720　　v) 5040
   b) Answers may vary.

10. No, for example, the sum of $2 - \sqrt{3}$ and $\sqrt{3}$ is 2.

11. Answers may vary.

Review, page 204

1. Answers may vary.

2. a) 125　　b) 243　　c) $\frac{1}{125}$　　d) $\frac{1}{243}$　　e) −125
   f) −243　　g) $-\frac{1}{125}$　　h) $-\frac{1}{243}$　　i) 1

3. a) 52　　b) 100　　c) 80　　d) 1
   e) 39　　f) 50　　g) 0　　h) $\frac{13}{36}$

4. a) 5^4　　b) 8^{-3}　　c) 4^4　　d) 6^{-3}　　e) 9^2　　f) 2^{-6}

5. 5^5, or 3125

6. a) 10^{13}　　b) 7.3^8　　c) $(-12)^{14}$　　d) 8^5
   e) 9.4^7　　f) $(-3)^{13}$　　g) 3^4　　h) 6.25^5
   i) 8^7　　j) 2^{-6}　　k) 4^4　　l) $(-7)^4$

7. a) 4.17×10^4　　b) 4.17×10^9　　c) 4.17×10^{-4}
   d) 4.17×10^{-6}　　e) -2.1×10^6　　f) 3.1×10^{-6}
   g) 9.78×10^4　　h) -1.234×10^{-4}

8. a) 3.0×10^5 km/s　　b) $4.236\ 19 \times 10^8$　　c) 5.98×10^{24} kg
   d) 4.0×10^{-3} g　　e) 1.0×10^{-7} s

9. a) $3.056\ 91 \times 10^{79}$　　b) 80 digits

10. a) ±6　　b) ±20　　c) ±21　　d) ±16　　e) ±0.7　　f) ±0.1

11. Estimates may vary.

a) 4.2　　b) 5.9　　c) 9.2　　d) 10.2　　e) 12.2　　f) 14.5

12. Estimates may vary.
   a) 11　　b) 9.2　　c) 7　　d) 8.8
   e) 18　　f) 18　　g) 9.1　　h) 2.6

13. a) 22.2　　b) 17.9　　c) 8.5　　d) 10.2

14. No, the umbrella is longer than the diagonal.

15. AB: 3; CD: 4.1; EF: 4.1; GH: 6.4; IJ: 5; KL: 3.6

16. a) 9.9　　b) 8.9　　c) 9.4　　d) 9.2

17. Rational: a, d, f; irrational: b, c, e

18. a) Rational　　　　　　b) Rational
   c) Integer, rational　　　d) Natural, integer, rational
   e) Rational　　　　　　f) Rational
   g) Natural, integer, rational　　h) Irrational

19. Answers may vary.

CHAPTER 5 ALGEBRAIC OPERATIONS AND EQUATIONS

Start With What You Know, page 210

1. a) Multiply the number of wins by 2 and add the number of ties.
   b) Variables may differ. $2w + t$

2. a) 62　　b) 9　　c) 34

3. 163.0 cm, 166.0 cm　　　4. Tables and graphs may vary.

5. a) The formula in cell B4 multiplies the number in cell A4 by 3.34 and then adds 81.2. The formula in cell C4 multiplies the number in cell A4 by 3.27 and then adds 85.9. The formula in cell B5 multiplies the number in cell A5 by 3.34 and then adds 81.2. The formula in cell C5 multiplies the number in cell A5 by 3.27 and then adds 85.9.

6. Answers may vary.

The Concept of a Variable

Developing the Ideas, page 212

Number of green squares	Number of blue squares
2	6
4	8
6	10
8	12
10	14

1. a) 24　　　　　　b) 104

2. Add 4 to the number of green squares.

3. $s + 4$; an even number　　　4. 78

5. 96　　　6. See page 214.　　　7. 14 m, 17 m.

8. Widths and perimeters may vary.

Width (m)	Perimeter (m)
2	14
2.5	15
3	16
3.5	17
4	18
4.5	19

9. a) Add 10 m to twice the width.   **b)** $2w + 10$
    c) $2(w + 5)$ **d)** A positive rational number

10. 14.8 m   **11.** 1.5 m

12. a) See page 214.
    b) Find the width along the horizontal axis. From this point, move vertically until you meet the graph. Move horizontally until you meet the vertical axis. The point will be the perimeter.
    c) Find the perimeter along the vertical axis. From this point, move horizontally until you meet the graph. Move down until you meet the horizontal axis. This point will be the width.

13. It will be a vertical line.

Working with Mathematics, page 215

1. a) A symbol that represents numbers that can vary
    b) , **c)** Answers may vary.

2. a) Because we do not have an odd number of green squares
    b) Because it represents the width, a measurable distance

3. a) i) For the square — P: perimeter, s: side length, A: area
    ii) For the circle — C: circumference, r: radius, A: area
    iii) For the right triangle, the Pythagorean Theorem — c: hypotenuse, a, b: shorter sides
    b) π is not a variable; explanations may vary.

4. a) Yes   **b)** Yes; examples may vary.

5. b)

Number of cubes	Number of faces
1	5
2	8
3	11
4	14
5	17

    c) 14, 17   **d)** 32, 92
    e) Multiply the number of cubes by 3, then add 2.
    f) $3n + 2$ **g)** 50   **h)** 20   **i)** Answers may vary.

6. a) 10 m^2, 17.5 m^2
    b)

Width (m)	Area (m²)
2	10
2.5	12.5
3	15
3.5	17.5
4	20
4.5	22.5

    c) Multiply the width by 5.
    d) $5w$; positive rational number; between 0 and 5
    e) 6 m^2 **f)** 3 m
    g) i) Find the width along the horizontal axis. From this point, move vertically until you meet the graph. Move horizontally until you meet the vertical axis. This point will be the area.
    ii) Find the area along the vertical axis. From this point, move horizontally until you meet the graph. Move down until you meet the horizontal axis. This point will be the width.

7. b) Tables may vary.

Number in the UL corner	Sum of the numbers in the UR and LL corners
1	10
2	12
3	14
15	38
20	48
23	54

    c) Double the number and add 8.
    d) i) $2n + 8$ **ii)** Natural numbers between 1 and 23

8. Descriptions of patterns may vary.

a) 1:	**i)** 4 cm	**ii)** 4 cm	**iii)** 0 cm
2:	**i)** 8 cm	**ii)** 8 cm	**iii)** 4 cm
3:	**i)** 12 cm	**ii)** 12 cm	**iii)** 8 cm
4:	**i)** 16 cm	**ii)** 16 cm	**iii)** 12 cm

    b) i) 20 cm   **ii)** 20 cm   **iii)** 16 cm

c) 10th:	**i)** 40 cm	**ii)** 40 cm	**iii)** 36 cm
100th:	**i)** 400 cm	**ii)** 400 cm	**iii)** 396 cm

    d) i) Multiply the number by 4.   **ii)** Multiply the number by 4.
    iii) Multiply 4 by 1 less than the number.
    e) i) $4n$ **ii)** $4n$ **iii)** $4(n - 1)$
    f) 15 cm   **g)** 12 cm   **h)** No; explanations may vary.

9. a) $2s + 4$ **b)** $s + 10$

10. $1.50(2w + 10)$

11. a) $F = 2C + 30$ **b)** Answers may vary.

12. 10°C, 50°F

Quest: What If You Saved 1¢, Then 2¢, Then 3¢, Then 4¢, …?, page 218

1. $4.65; $50.50; $667.95   **2.** $\dfrac{n(n + 1)}{2}$

Linking Ideas: Arithmetic and Algebra
The Distributive Law, page 220

1. a) 50 m^2 **b)** Answers may vary.

2. Yes; rational numbers

Representing Variables and Expressions
Developing the Ideas, page 221

1. Variables may differ.
    a) $3x - 4$ **b)** $-2x + 5$

3. a) $2x + 8$ **b)** $6x - 3$ **c)** $12 - 6a$ **d)** $-4m + 6$

4. Answers may vary.

Working with Mathematics, page 224

1. a) Sometimes true   **b)** Sometimes true   **c)** Sometimes true

2. Yes, yes, explanations may vary.

3. Any pair of opposite tiles, such as a 1-tile and a flipped 1-tile.

4. a) $-4x + 3$ **b)** $2x - 7$

5. a) 17, −10   **b)** 4, −14   **c)** −18, 9   **d)** 0, −9

6. $3x + 2$, $2 + 3x$

7. a) $6 - 4x$ **b)** $-3z - 4$ **c)** $10 - 5a$ **d)** $6s - 3$

8. a) $12m + 21$ **b)** $-5x + 50$

c) $8a + 4b - 12$ d) $6x - 18y + 24z$

9. a) $7, -14$ b) $15, -13$ c) $-13, 22$ d) $-10, 11$

10. a) $6a + 3$ b) $6 - 2x$ c) $4 - 8t$ d) $-8 - 6x$

11. a) $24x + 54$ b) $-15c - 9$ c) $33 - 88z$ d) $20 - 70y$

12. a) $3x + 6y - 21$ b) $-2a + 10b - 4$
c) $-6m + 7n$ d) $36p + 4q - 36r$

13. a) $2.5n + 5$ b) $6.4 - 4.8r$ c) $\sqrt{2}x - 2$ d) $2\pi R - 2\pi r$

14. Answers may vary.

Mathematics File: Interpreting Number Properties Algebraically, page 225

1. Yes. Answers may vary.

2. a) Yes   b) Yes

3. No

Combining Like Terms
Developing the Ideas, page 227

1. a) $5x$ b) $-2n$ c) $-3a$

2. a) $6x + 4$ b) $2y - 1$ c) $-4a + 5$

3. a) $5x - 3$ b) $m + 5$ c) $2k - 3$

Working with Mathematics, page 229

1. Answers may vary.   2. a, d, f, g

3. $2x, 5x; 2x, -x; 2x, 4x; 5x, -x; 5x, 4x; -x, 4x; -3y, -y; 3, 5; 3, -1; 5, -1$

4. a) $3x$ b) $-2a$ c) $2k + 4$ d) $8x + 1$

5. a) $6x - 2; 22; -20$ b) $-x - 2; -6; 1$
c) $14x - 6; 50; -48$ d) $4 - x; 0; 7$

6. a) $10a - 3b$ b) $m - 5n$ c) $3x - 2y$ d) $-x - 12y + 5$

7. a) $6x + 2$ b) $3x + 2$ c) $-4x - 2$
d) $3a + 8$ e) $-x$ f) $8a - 8$

8. a) $x - 1; 6; -6; -1$ b) $-5x + 6; -29; 31; 6$
c) $2x - 8; 6; -18, -8$ d) $x - 3.2; 3.8, -8.2, -3.6$
e) $1.7x - 3.6; 8.3, -12.1, -3.6$

9. a) $-a + 2b + 4c$ b) $2x + 4y$
c) $6m - 3n$ d) $-a - 6b + 6c$

10. Answers may vary.

Mathematics File: Number Tricks, page 230

3. Change the last instruction to "Subtract the number you started with." Everyone will end up with 2 as an answer.

4. The steps can be written as follows: n; $n + 2$; $3n + 6$; $2n + 6$; $n + 3$; 3 You will always end up with 3.

Solving Equations Using Algebra Tiles
Developing the Ideas, page 232

1. -2 2. 2 3. 2 4. -5 5. 3 6. 2

Working with Mathematics, page 235

1. No; explanations may vary.   2. Answers may vary.

3. Answers may vary.

4. a) -3 b) 5 c) -5 d) -4

5. a) 2 b) -4 c) -2 d) 1

6. a) 5 b) -2 c) -3 d) 2 e) -5 f) 3

7. a) -6 b) -2 c) 2 d) -2 e) 3 f) 1

8. Answers may vary.

Solving Equations Algebraically
Working with Mathematics, page 238

1. Answers may vary.

2. a) 21 b) $\frac{3}{4}$ c) -2.5 d) $-\frac{2}{3}$

3. a) 4.9 b) 3.3 c) -11.4 d) 4.5

4. a) $\$58.50$ b) 310 km   c) Answers may vary.

5. a) 4 b) $\frac{20}{3}$ c) 0.6 d) -4.5 e) $-\frac{1}{2}$ f) 3

6. a) 7.2 b) $\frac{4}{3}$ c) $\frac{1}{3}$ d) -1.2 e) $\frac{5}{9}$ f) 0

7. a) The fixed cost; the cost that depends on the number of books printed
b) 222 c) 1333

8. a) The temperature that varies with depth; the temperature at Earth's surface
b) 3 km   c) 8 km

9. a) 90 m   b) 145 m

10. a) $d = \frac{1}{3}t$ b) 1.2 km   c) 24 s

11. , 12. Explanations and equations may vary.

Quest: How Do Builders Determine the Size of Steps in a Staircase?, page 240

Answers may vary.

Simplifying Equations Before Solving
Developing the Ideas, page 242

1. a) 5 b) 7 c) $-\frac{7}{3}$

2. Answers may vary.

3. a) 4 b) $\frac{19}{6}$ c) 2

4. Answers may vary.

5. a) 10 b) $-\frac{1}{3}$ c) 6

6. Answers may vary.

Working with Mathematics, page 244

1. , 2. Answers may vary.

3. a) 0.5 b) -1 c) 5 d) 1.8 e) $-\frac{5}{8}$ f) 2.4

4. a) About 7 min   b) About 15 min

5. a) -2 b) 4 c) -6 d) 7 e) -4
f) 4 g) $-\frac{4}{3}$ h) 1.5 i) 40

6. a) 9 b) 3 c) $-\frac{5}{6}$ d) -6 e) 0.5
f) -3 g) 5 h) 20 i) -0.5

7. a) 10 b) 24 c) $\frac{32}{3}$ d) 11.5 e) -24 f) 6

8. a) $-\frac{5}{3}$ b) 0.2 c) 0 d) 3.5 e) -0.5 f) -0.5

9. a) 2.0 b) -14.5 c) -4.9

10. a) 39 words/min   b) 5 c) 180

11. a) ± 3 b) ± 5 c) ± 10
d) $\pm\sqrt{2}$ e) 0 f) No solution

12. a) Subtract 30 and divide by 2. $C = \frac{F - 30}{2}$
b) $C = \frac{F - 32}{1.8}$

13. $50°$F, $10°$C

Quest: How Can You Design a Trundle Wheel?, page 246

Radius is approximately 15.9 cm.

Solving Problems in Different Ways
Developing the Ideas, page 248

15 dimes, 8 quarters

Working with Mathematics, page 250

1. Answers may vary.   **2.** 15 kg peanuts; 8 kg pecans

3. 15 h running; 8 h cycling   **4.** Answers may vary.

5. 54 nickels, 18 dimes   **6.** 482 g

7. 12.5 km   **8.** $10.90

Linking Ideas: Mathematics and Science
Keeping Ships Afloat, page 251

1. a) 135 922 330 L   **b)** 136 585 366 L

2. a) 153 005 465 L   **b)** 157 977 883 L

Solving Problems Using Equations
Working with Mathematics, page 255

1. Answers may vary.   **2.** 5¢

3. $250   **4.** $142.50   **5.** 24 cm, 48 cm

6. 228 cm   **7.** $13 000   **8.** 16 years

9. 13   **10.** $17   **11.** 10

12. a) 54   **b)** 104

13. a) Between 230 cm and 215 cm

    b) The length decreases by 1 cm.

Linking Ideas: Mathematics and Technology
Solving Problems with a Spreadsheet, page 257

1. a) Explanations may vary.   **c)** 15 dimes, 8 quarters

2. 21.5 m by 50.0 m

3. a) $10 625   **b)** $15 000

4. 43, 44, 45, 46

Solving Inequalities
Working with Mathematics, page 261

1. Explanations may vary.

2. a) $x > 1$ **b)** $x \le 2$ **c)** $x < -10$ **d)** $x \ge 8$

3. a) $x > -1$ **b)** $x \le 3$ **c)** $y \ge -5$
   d) $x < -4$ **e)** $a > -5$ **f)** $x \ge 2$

4. a) $x \ge 3$ **b)** $x < -2$ **c)** $c \le 2.75$
   d) $x < -4.5$ **e)** $m \le 2.5$ **f)** $y < 2.5$

5. a) $x > -5$ **b)** $x < -3$ **c)** $k \le -15$
   d) $t \le -1.5$ **e)** $x \ge 16$ **f)** $a \le -3$

6. Answers may vary.

Review, page 262

1. a)

Number of squares	Number of toothpicks
1	4
2	7
3	10

b) 13, 16, 31, 151, 301   **c)** Multiply by 3 and add 1.
d) $3s + 1$; a natural number   **e)** 106   **f)** 33

2. a) The sum is 4 times the number in the middle.
b) Multiply by 4.   **c)** $4n$; from 9 to 23

3. a) 50 m, 60 m   **b)** Tables may vary.

Length (m)	Perimeter (m)
15	50
20	60
25	70
30	80
35	90
40	100

c) Add the length to 10 m, and double the answer.
d) $2(10 + l)$; l is any rational number greater than 10.
e) 27 m

4. a) $4 - 3x$ **b)** $2x - 9$

5. a) 15, −5   **b)** −3, 27   **c)** 38, −22   **d)** −4, 36

6. a) $6x + 21$ **b)** $-20 - 15n$ **c)** $48s - 60$ **d)** $-8b + 6$

7. a) $5x + 2$ **b)** $-4m - 10$ **c)** $13a - 7b$
   d) $-5y + 5$ **e)** $-13t$ **f)** $-5m - 25n$

8. a) $7x$; 28, −21, −7   **b)** $12x + 6$; 54, −30, −6
   c) $-4x - 4$; −20, 8, 0   **d)** $7x - 22$; 6, −43, −29
   e) $-5x + 2$; −18, 17, 7   **f)** $-10x - 17$; −57, 13, −7

9. a) 2   **b)** 2   **c)** 3   **d)** −7   **e)** −3   **f)** 4

10. a) 5   **b)** −6   **c)** −9   **d)** −5   **e)** $\frac{1}{6}$ **f)** 2

11. a) i) 19.6 m/s   **ii)** 49 m/s   **iii)** 78.4 m/s
   b) i) 3 s   **ii)** 9 s   **iii)** 14 s
   c) 3.3 m/s, 8.2 m/s, 13.0 m/s; 18.0 s, 54.1 s, 84.2 s

12. a) 2.5   **b)** −2   **c)** 4   **d)** −15   **e)** 12   **f)** 180

13. 14 quarters, 17 dollars

14. 12, 13   **15.** Mercedes: 120 km/h; Jaguar: 144 km/h

16. 11 cm by 16 cm

17. a) $x > -4.5$ **b)** $y < 3$ **c)** $x \le 2$
   d) $a \ge 5$ **e)** $m > 4.\bar{3}$ **f)** $x < -0.75$

CHAPTER 6 RATIO, RATE, AND SIMILARITY
Start With What You Know, page 268

1. a) Estimates may vary. Current smokers: 30%; former smokers: 34%; never smoked: 36%
   b) 72%   **c)** 69%   **d)** 28 : 72   **e)** 31 : 69

2. a) $1.14   **b)** $0.70

3. a) 3 : 5, 4 : 5, 4 : 6, 5 : 7, 8 : 10, 11 : 14, 16 : 20, 20 : 24
   b) 3 : 5, 4 : 5, 2 : 3, 5 : 7, 4 : 5, 11 : 14, 4 : 5, 5 : 6
   c) 4 by 5, 8 by 10, 16 by 20

4. a) 163   **b)** 25%   **c)** 75%

5. Boneless sirloin steak

6. a) 4 : 3   **b)** 3 : 5   **c)** 4 : 5   **d)** 20 : 15 : 12

Applications of Percent
Working with Mathematics, page 272

1. Answers may vary. For every $1 on the bill, you give the waiter 15¢.

2. Explanations may vary.
   a) 750   **b)** 8   **c)** 10   **d)** 1.8

3. Estimates may vary.
 a) 33%   **b)** 50%   **c)** 50%
4. 150%
5. a) 32   **b)** 3   **c)** 11.52
   d) 4   **e)** 187.5   **f)** 9840
6. $3.92   **7.** 45.5%
8. a) 7.6%   **b)** 20%
9. $203.96   **10.** $1.52   **11.** 6.8%
12. 120   **13.** 7 354 000   **14.** 389
15. a) 8.5 cm by 5.7 cm   **b)** 12.1 cm by 8.1 cm
16. a) 134%   **b)** 75%   **c)** No, explanations may vary.
17. a) Answers may vary.   **b)** $1291.55
18. a) No   **b)** 93.75%

Applications of Ratio
Working with Mathematics, page 276

1. Explanations may vary.
 a) For every 205 children born, 100 are females and 105 are males.
 b) For 400 mL of gasoline, 10 mL of oil are needed.
 c) For every 11 cars sold, 7 are domestic and 4 are foreign.
 d) To make brass, for every 3 g of copper, we use 2 g of zinc.
 e) The width is greater than the height. For a width of 40 cm, the height is 30 cm.
2. a) Length : width = 3 : 1   **b)** Heads : tails = 1 : 1
 c) 1 cm : 1 km = 1 : 100 000 **d)** Hits : at bats = 400 : 1000
 e) Hours sleeping : hours awake = 1 : 2
3. a) $\frac{3}{5}$ **b)** $\frac{6}{4}$ **c)** $\frac{6}{5}$ **d)** $\frac{8}{3}$
4. a) 1 : 3   **b)** 2 : 1   **c)** 1 : 2   **d)** 5 : 3
5. a) 2 : 3   **b)** 4 : 3   **c)** 4 : 3
   d) 6 : 5   **e)** 21 : 20   **f)** 5 : 9
6. a) $\frac{37}{40}$ **b)** 92.5%   **c)** 462.5 g
7. No   **8.** About 0.4 mm
9. 187 : 313   **10.** Two
11. a) 191 707   **b)** 48.8%
12. 78 000 km^2 **13.** Approximately 3 000 000   **14.** 10 : 9 : 4
15. a) i) 32 km/h   **ii)** 64 km/h   **iii)** 96 km/h
   b) i) 48 km/h   **ii)** 32 km/h   **iii)** 64 km/h
16. a) 52 : 14   **b)** 10   **c)** 52 and 24

Quest: How Fast Can You Go?, page 278
You can go approximately 30 km/h.

Speed (km/h) =
$$\frac{6\pi(\text{diameter (cm)}) (\text{pedal gear teeth}) (\text{rate of pedalling (turns/min)})}{10\ 000\ (\text{wheel gear teeth})}$$

Some Special Ratios
Developing the Ideas, page 280

1. a) 27.43 m   **b)** 27.43 m
2. a) HF + FS, explanations may vary.
   b) Estimates may vary; for example, 40 m
3. a) , b) , c) 1.4
4. The length of a diagonal is approximately 1.4 times the length of a side.

5. 38.4 m

Page 281
Inscribed means that each vertex of the figure lies on the circumference of the circle.
The circumference of the circle is greater than the perimeter of the square.
The circumference of the circle is greater than the perimeter of the hexagon.
The circumference of the circle is greater than the perimeter of the octagon.
Answers may vary for the perimeter of the octagon, and the circumference of the circle.
The circumference is about 3 times the diameter.

Working with Mathematics, page 283

1. Explanations may vary.
 a) A closed figure bounded by straight-line segments
 b) Distance around a polygon
 c) Distance around a circle
 d) A chord passing through the centre of the circle
2. $d : l = 1.4 : 1; d = 1.4l$
3. Explanations may vary. Square the length of a side, double the answer, then take the square root.
4. Three times; $C \doteq 3D$ **5.** 81 cm
6. 12 700 km   **7.** 482
8. a) 48 mm   **b)** 42 cm   **c)** 40.8 m
9. 30.5 cm **10.** All paths have the same length.   **11.** 41 700 km

Linking Ideas: Mathematics and Technology
The Search for a Fraction that Approximates π, page 285
1. a) $\frac{355}{113}$ **b)** $\frac{256}{81}$
   c) i) All of them
     ii) None of them, the differences are all positive.

Mathematics File: $\frac{C}{D}$ is the Same for All Circles, page 286

1. The ratio of circumference to diameter for a circle
2. Pi has the same value for all circles.
3. a) If the ratio of the circumference to diameter was the same for all circles
   b) Answers may vary.

Applications of Rate
Developing the Ideas, page 288

1. Answers may vary. Cars use more gasoline when driving in the city.
2. Honda Accord; it has the higher value of litres per 100 km.
3. a) Lexus ES 300   **b)** Ford Crown Victoria
4. Honda Civic
5. Answers may vary.
 a) The larger the engine size, the greater the fuel consumption
 b) The greater the number of cylinders, the greater the fuel consumption
6. Answers may vary; for example, kilometres per hour

1. Answers may vary. A ratio compares two or more quantities with the same units. A rate compares two quantities with different units.

2. Answers may vary; for example, speed in kilometres per hour; heartbeat in beats per minute

3. A ratio

4. a) 32.5 L   b) 770 km

5. Richard   6. Gold

7. a) i) 1020   ii) 171 360
   b) i) About 59 min   ii) About 4 days 2 h

8. 40

9. a) 47.25¢/100 g, 43.62¢/100 g   b) 525-g box

10. About 16   11. About 15 s   12. $539.58

13. a) 39.8¢/100 mL; 25.2¢/100 mL; the 950-mL size
    b) The 950-mL size

14. Answers may vary.   15. $2378

16. 2 L : 86¢; 1 L : 62¢   17. 45.5 h

Linking Ideas: Mathematics and Science
Food for a Healthy Heart, page 293

1. a) 8.6 g   b) About 327 kJ

2. a) 660 kJ   b) About 49.5%   c) No

3. 5.0%

4. a) No   b) Answers may vary.

5. Multiply the mass of fat in grams by 38 and divide by the total energy in kilojoules. Multiply by 100%.

6. , 7. Answers may vary.

Solving Proportions
Working with Mathematics, page 296

1. a) $\dfrac{\text{Mass of blue whale}}{\text{Mass of African elephant}} = \dfrac{\text{Mass of person}}{\text{Mass of chicken}}$

   b) $\dfrac{\text{Population of China}}{\text{Population of Canada}} = \dfrac{\text{Population of Canada}}{\text{Population of Calgary}}$

2. Answers may vary.   3. 4 by 6

4. a) 75%   b) 75%

5. 1.5 times   6. 7%

7. a) i) 400 cm^2 ii) 25%
   b) i) 300 cm^2 ii) 25%
   c) The percents are the same.

8. a) i) 7.6 m by 4.0 m   ii) 6.5 m by 3.6 m   iii) 5.8 m by 3.5 m
   b) Yes

9. a) 2.6   b) 12   c) 16   d) 21

10. a) 27   b) 0.625   c) 3.9375   d) 5.1

11. 8.2 g   12. 616.0 t

13. a) 7.2 m
    b) Answers may vary. The sun's rays hit the trees at the same angle.

14. About 28 700 000   15. Answers may vary.

16. Proofs may vary.

Quest: How Can You Estimate the Number of Fish in a Lake?, page 298

The number of fish in the lake was approximately 600.

Linking Ideas: Mathematics and Geography
Remote Sensing, page 301

1. About 60 km   2. About 120 km   3. About 35 200 km^2

4. a) Answers may vary.   b) Yes

5. Answers may vary.

6. Answers may vary. About 45 700 km

7. a) About 27 400 km/h   b) 658 000 km
   c) i) 3.6   ii) 14.4   iii) 100.8   iv) 432

8. About 11 min 23 s

9. a) About 16 days 4 h 20 min from now
   b) About 4 h 20 min from now
   c) West

10. a) 216
    b) Answers may vary. No, scans cannot be taken at night or when there is cloud cover.

Similar Figures
Developing the Ideas, page 302

1. 1.5 cm, 2.6 cm, 0.6; 1.5 cm, 5.2 cm, 0.3; 3.0 cm, 5.2 cm, 0.6

2. The first and third logos have the same height-to-width ratio.

3. , 4.

Rectangle	Length (cm)	Width (cm)	$\dfrac{\text{Length}}{\text{Width}}$
A	4.5	1.0	4.5
B	3.0	1.0	3.0
C	2.5	2.5	1.0
D	2.0	1.5	1.$\overline{3}$
E	4.5	1.5	3.0
F	5.0	2.0	2.5

5. B, E   6. B, E

Working with Mathematics, page 304

1. Answers may vary. Measure their lengths and widths. If the length-to-width ratios are equal, the rectangles are similar.

2. Answers may vary. Measure the lengths of their sides. If corresponding sides are in the same ratio, then the triangles are similar.

3. Answers may vary. Two figures are similar if they have the same shape.

4. No. Explanations may vary; for example, they do not have the same shape.

5. Yes. Explanations may vary; for example, corresponding sides are in the same ratio.

6. a) 4 : 2; 6 : 3   b) Yes   c) 1.5
   d) Yes. Explanations may vary; all circles are similar to each other.

7. a) $\dfrac{\text{FD}}{\text{DE}}$ b) $\dfrac{\text{DE}}{\text{EF}}$ c) $\dfrac{\text{ED}}{\text{DF}}$

8. a) 7   b) 4.2   c) 7.5

9. C; it has the same length-to-width ratio.

10. a) 2 : 1   b) 2 : 1   c) 3.7 cm   d) 1.8 cm
    e) 11.5 cm^2, 6.8 cm^2 f) 59%

11. 1.2 cm, 2.4 cm, 1.9 cm, 3.8 cm; yes

12. a) kp b) k^2A

Quest: Is a Laser Gun Better For Catching Speeders Than a Radar Gun?, page 306

At 200 m, the radar beam is about 21 m wide while the laser beam is 60 cm wide. The laser gun is better because it has only one car in its field of vision at this range.

Linking Ideas: Mathematics and Technology
Constructing Similar Figures, page 308

1. a) 12 square units   b) 48 square units
2. a) 2 : 1   b) 2 : 1   c) 2 : 1
3. 4 : 1   5. 2 : 5
6. A : B : C : D : E = 2 : 4 : 1 : 3 : 5   7. Answers may vary.

Enlargements and Reductions
Developing the Ideas, page 309

3. The diagonals of similar rectangles lie on the same line.
4. a) 4 by 5 and 16 by 20; 4 by 6 and 8 by 12
   b) 4 by 6 and 8 by 12
   c) 3 by 4, 4 by 5, 5 by 7, 11 by 14, 16 by 20, 20 by 24

Working with Mathematics, page 312

1. Explanations may vary.
   a) A similar figure that is larger than the original figure
   b) A similar figure that is smaller than the original figure
   c) The quotient of corresponding lengths on two similar figures
   d) A drawing that is similar to another, but is larger or smaller
   e) A scale factor written as a ratio with two terms
2. a) Reduction
   b) If the scale factor is greater than 1, the drawing is an enlargement. If the scale factor is less than 1, the drawing is a reduction.
3. a) 2   b) 0.2   c) $1.\overline{6}$ d) 0.4   e) 8   f) 0.6
4. a) 2 : 1   b) 3 : 2   c) 1 : 2   d) 1 : 4   e) 5 : 2   f) 5 : 1
5. Answers may vary.
6. a) 1.3   b) The length-to-width ratios are the same.
7. a) 13.5 cm   b) 10.5 cm
8. a) Enlargement   b) 1.4   c) 140%
9. Answers may vary.
   a) Pencil   b) Paper clip   c) Table top
   d) Floor plan of house
10. a) 2   b) 10   c) 0.125   d) 0.01
11. 0.000 03   12. 0.0015
13. a) 1.3 cm, 2.9 cm, 3.4 cm, 3.9 cm, 4.3 cm, 4.9 cm
    b) i) Pyramid: 147 m   ii) 1: 11 300
    c) 486 m
    d) 328 m, 384 m, 441 m, 534 m
    e) Answers may vary.
14. a) 4   b) 16   c) $k^2 : 1$

Linking Ideas: Mathematics and Science
Fast Food, Safe Food, page 314

1. a) 1000 mL   b) 1 : 10 000
2. 1.47×10^6
3. a) 1.47×10^5 b) Yes

Review, page 315

1. a) 10   b) 9   c) 35   d) 2.4
2. a) 11 : 9   b) 3 : 55   c) 100 : 3
3. About 1 mm
4. a) i) 3.0   ii) 0.9
   b) About 7290 km/h
5. 4-cm drain; twice as fast
6. a) About 26 L   b) About 1180 km
7. a) 5.5   b) 14.4   c) $\frac{20}{7}$ d) 10.8   e) 26   f) 0.3
8. a) 9   b) 10   c) 15
9. a) , b) Rectangles may vary.
   c) Their length : width ratios must be equal.
10. a) 20 cm, 48 cm, 52 cm   b) 3.75 cm, 9 cm, 9.75 cm

CHAPTER 7 MEASUREMENT

Start With What You Know, page 320

1. 21 m^2 2. 3 m^2 3. 420 L or 470 L   4. 17.5 m
5. Answers may vary.
   a) The distance between two points
   b) A measure of the surface covered by a figure
   c) A measure of the space filled by a solid
6. a) Area of a rectangle, area of a square, volume of a rectangular prism, circumference of a circle, perimeter of a rectangle, perimeter of a square, area of a circle, volume of a cube, circumference of a circle, area of a triangle, area of a parallelogram, perimeter of a rectangle
   b) Summaries may vary.

Linking Ideas: Mathematics and Technology
Designing a Lawn Sprinkler System, page 322

3. a) 4 m^2 b) π m^2 c) 0.858 m^2 d) 21.5%   e) No
4. No   5. Answers may vary.   6. Answers may vary.

Total Surface Area of a Cylinder
Developing the Ideas, page 323

1. a) It is a rectangle.
   b) Answers may vary. The area is the product of length and width. The curved surface area can be considered as a rectangle.
2. The product of π and the radius squared
3. , 4. Answers may vary.
5. $A = 2\pi rh + 2\pi r^2$

Working with Mathematics, page 325

1. The second cylinder
2. a) About 132 cm^2; about 176 cm^2 b) 3 : 4
3. a) 3.18 cm   b) About 464 cm^2
4. $\frac{3\pi x^2}{2}$
5. a) 240.5 cm^2 b) 34.2 cm^2 c) 308.9 cm^2
6. About 60 243 cm^2
7. a) About 595 cm^2 b) About 1098 cm^2 c) About 560 cm^2

8. a) Surface area increases in each case, but it is not doubled, or tripled, or multiplied by a factor n.

b) Surface area increases in each case. It is more than doubled, more than tripled, and multiplied by a factor greater than n.

c) Surface area is multiplied by 4, multiplied by 9, and multiplied by a factor n^2.

9. a) The area of the base of the cylinder; the area of the curved surface; the sum of the areas of two circles and the curved surface area

Mathematics File: What Shapes Make Cardboard Cylinders?, page 327

1. a) Parallelogram   **c)** Answers may vary.

2. c) 3.8 cm, 12.0 cm; 5.4 cm, 8.5 cm

3. The parallelogram is a rhombus.

Quest: How Can You Fill a Can Exactly Half Full without Measuring?, page 328

Answers may vary.

Volumes of a Cylinder and a Cone
Developing the Ideas, page 330

1. Answers may vary.

2. a) Fill the can with the cubes and then count the cubes.
b) Answers may vary.

3. a) The volume is the product of the base area and the height.
b) Answers may vary.
c) The answers will differ because the cubes do not completely fill the can.

4. a) $V = \pi r^2 h$

Page 331

2. a) 3

3. a) The volume of the cone is one-third the volume of the cylinder.
b) Cylinder: $V = \pi r^2 h$; cone: $V = \frac{1}{3}\pi r^2 h$

Working with Mathematics, page 334

1. a) About 785 cm^3; 262 cm^3 **b)** About 78.5%; 26.2%

2. a) 157.1 cm^3 **b)** 62.8 cm^3

3. 1062 cm^3; answers may vary.

4. a) Volume is doubled; tripled.
b) Volume is quadrupled; multiplied by 9.
c) Volume is multiplied by 8; multiplied by 27.

5. a) 50 kg   **b)** 225 kg   **c)** 112.5 kg

6. a) About 1.12 m^3 **b)** Answers may vary.

7. a) About 35 000 mm^3 **b)** About 0.2 mm

8. 6.0 cm, 5.3 cm, 199.5 cm^3; 4.0 cm, 6.9 cm, 116.1 cm^3; 2.0 cm, 7.7 cm, 32.4 cm^3

9. a) 250 cm^3 **b)** 251 cm^3 **c)** 250 cm^3 **d)** 250 cm^3
The volumes are approximately equal.

10. a) 0.9 m   **b)** 3.1 m^3 **11.** 20.6 m^3

12. a) 325 117 cm^3; about 325 L   **b)** 28 149 cm^2

13. a) 52.4 cm^3 **b)** 20.9 cm^3

14. a) About 14 260 m^3 **b)** About 510

15. Answers may vary.

16. Same amount of milk in water as water in milk

Quest: Which Cylinder Has the Greater Volume?, page 336

The cylinder with the short side as the height has the greater volume.

Linking Ideas: Mathematics and Technology
Designing Package Sizes, page 338

1. Divides the base diameter by 2; divides the volume by π and by the square of the radius; multiplies π by the square of the radius; multiplies π by 2, by the radius, and by the height; adds twice the area of the base to the area of the label

2. Answers may vary.

3. a) Answers may vary.   **b)** Height equals diameter.

4. Yes

Surface Area and Volume of a Sphere
Developing the Ideas, page 341

1. Answers may vary.   **2.** Areas are equal.

3. The ratio is π.   **4.** $A = \pi d^2$

Page 342

1. The volume of the water is equal to the volume of the ball.

2. $\frac{2}{3}$

3. The volume of the sphere is $\frac{2}{3}$ the volume of the cylinder.

4. $V = 2\pi r^3$; $V = \frac{4}{3}\pi r^3$

Working with Mathematics, page 343

1. Answers may vary.

2. Sphere   **3.** 3.804×10^7 km^2, 2.207×10^{10} km^3

4. a) 9   **b)** 27

5. Surface area: multiplied by a factor of 4, a factor of 9; volume: multiplied by a factor of 8, a factor of 27

6. It is double.

7. a) 172.0 cm^2, 212.2 cm^3 **b)** 58.1 cm^2, 41.6 cm^3
c) 43.0 cm^2, 26.5 cm^3 **d)** 1372.3 cm^2, 4780.1 cm^3

8. 314.2 cm^2, 523.6 cm^3 **9.** πx^2 cm^2, $\frac{\pi x^3}{6}$ cm^3

10. a) 12 cm   **b)** 1790 cm^2 **c)** 7124 cm^3

11. Answers may vary.

12. a) $A = \pi d^2$, $V = \frac{\pi d^3}{6}$ **b)** $A = \frac{C^2}{\pi}$, $V = \frac{C^3}{6\pi^2}$

13. a) It doubles the radius, which gives the edge of the cube; it cubes the edge of the cube; it multiplies the cube of the radius by π and by $\frac{4}{3}$.
b) C4 – D4
c) The statement is reasonable. The length of the radius does not affect the answer.

14. a) 2.5 cm   **b)** $\sqrt{2}\,r$

Linking Ideas: Measurement and Graphing
Total Surface Areas and Volumes of Cylinders with the Same Radius, page 345

Answers may vary.

Quest: How Do Sled Dogs Keep Warm?, page 346

Answers may vary.

Surface Area of a Cone
Developing the Ideas, page 349

1. The surface area of the cone is $\frac{3}{4}$ the area of the circle.
2. Answers may vary.

Working with Mathematics, page 351

1. Answers may vary. The line from the vertex to the centre of the base is perpendicular to the base.
2. The cone with radius greater than height has the greater total surface area.
3. a) About 113 cm^2, 75 cm^2 b) 3 : 2
4. 37.7 cm^2, 25.1 cm^2, 12.6 cm^2
5. a) 7.5 cm   b) 29.0 cm   c) About 707 cm^2
6. a) 204 cm^2 b) 102.4 m^2 c) 3383.6 cm^2 d) 287.1 cm^2
7. a) 53.4 m^2 b) 3393 cm^2 c) 24 429 cm^2 d) 151.2 cm^2
8. a) $\pi r \sqrt{r^2 + h^2}$ b) $\pi r \sqrt{r^2 + h^2} + \pi r^2$
9. $\frac{\pi x^2}{4}(\sqrt{5} + 1)$

Linking Ideas: Mathematics and Science
Measuring a Molecule, page 352

Answers may vary.

Volume of a Rectangular Pyramid
Developing the Ideas, page 355

1. The volume of the pyramid is one-third the volume of the prism.

Working with Mathematics, page 357

1. The formulas are the same: one-third base area times height.
2. The volumes are the same.
3. a) 4, 4, 6   b) 5, 5, 8   c) 6, 6, 10   d) 7, 7, 12
4. The numbers of faces and vertices equal 1 + the number of sides in the base. The number of edges is twice the number of sides in the base.
5. 4500 cm^3
6. a) Doubled; tripled   b) Doubled; tripled
   c) Quadrupled; multiplied by 9
   d) Multiplied by 8; multiplied by 27
7. a) About 9023 m^3 b) Answers may vary.
8. a) 2 592 100 m^3 b) 1.127 m^3 c) 6.348 × 10^6 t
   d) Answers may vary. The pyramid has weathered and its height has decreased.
9. a) About 2.2 times   b) Answers may vary.
10. Answers may vary. 8.0 cm^3

Review, page 359

1. a) 2494 m^3, 1063 m^2 b) 2788 cm^3, 1230 cm^2
   c) 3666 cm^3, 1339 cm^2 d) 2219 cm^3, 1101 cm^2
   e) 139 500 cm^3, 17 868 cm^2
2. a) 4.77 cm, 7.96 cm   b) About 1643 cm^2, 1898 cm^2
   c) About 3581 cm^3, 5968 cm^3

3. 7.5 m^3
4. a) 1810 cm^2, 7238 cm^3 b) 50.3 cm^2, 33.5 cm^3
   c) 133 cm^2, 144 cm^3
5. 6.05 × 10^{12} km^2, 1.40 × 10^{18} km^3
6. 2714 cm^2, 10 857 cm^3; 1810 cm^2, 7238 cm^3
7. 471 m^3 8. 16 753 cm^3
9. a) 4.7 m^3 b) 3800 cm^3 c) 52.8 cm^3 d) 22 341 cm^3
10. 5772 cm^3

CHAPTER 8 POLYNOMIALS

Start With What You Know, page 364

1. a) 301.7 cm^2, 401.3 cm^3; 337.8 cm^2, 475.2 cm^3; 490.0 cm^2, 786.7 cm^3
   b) 10.0 cm, 528 cm^3
   c) Doubling the height does not double the surface area. Doubling the height does double the volume. Explanations may vary.
2. a) 282.7 cm^2, 339.3 cm^3; 329.0 cm^2, 435.8 cm^3; 534.0 cm^2, 942.5 cm^3
   b) Doubling the radius does not double the surface area. Doubling the radius multiplies the volume by a factor of 4.
3. a) i) 6
   ii) 1 × 1 × 24; 1 × 2 × 12; 1 × 3 × 8; 1 × 4 × 6; 2 × 2 × 6; 2 × 3 × 4
   b) i) 9
   ii) 1 × 1 × 48; 1 × 2 × 24; 1 × 3 × 16; 1 × 4 × 12; 1 × 6 × 8; 2 × 2 × 12; 2 × 3 × 8; 2 × 4 × 6; 3 × 4 × 4

The Concept of a Polynomial
Working with Mathematics, page 369

1. $37 Can, $37 U.S.
2. Explanations may vary. The bills may have different values, but the currency is the same, so we can add the money.
3. Reasons may vary. a, b, c, e
4. Reasons may vary.
   a) Binomial   b) Monomial   c) Binomial   d) Monomial
   e) Trinomial   f) Monomial   g) Trinomial   h) Binomial
5. a) $3x^2 + 4x + 3$ b) $4x^2 + 6x - 3$ c) $x^2 - 5x + 4$
6. a) Binomial   b) Monomial
8. b, c, e, f
9. a) $2x + 4$ b) $8x$ c) $2x + 8$
10. a) $2x$ b) $4x^2$ c) $4x$
12. a) $6x + 2$, $3x$ b) $6x$, $2x^2$ c) $2x + 12$, $6x$
13. Answers may vary. For example:
   a) $\frac{1}{x}$ b) $y^2 + 3$ c) x^3
14. a) $4x + 6$ b) $4x + 14$ c) $4x + 6$
15. a) $4s^2$
   b) i) $4s^2$ ii) s^2 iii) $3s^2$
16. a) $2\pi x$ b) $2\pi x$ c) $\frac{\pi x^2}{4}$, πx^2 d) $\frac{\pi x^2}{4}$

Linking Ideas: Mathematics and Technology

The Search for a Polynomial to Generate Prime Numbers, page 371

1. Yes

3. b) 1681   **c)** No

5. Answers may vary.

6. a) $1681 = 41^2$
  b) Answers may vary. N = 81 generates $1763 = 41 \times 43$

7. Answers may vary. For example:
  a) 7   **b)** 17   **c)** 42

Adding and Subtracting Polynomials

Developing the Ideas, page 372

1. a) $3x^2 + 5x + 2$ **b)** $4x^2 - 3x + 1$ **c)** $-4x^2 - 8x - 5$ **d)** 0

2. Answers may vary.
  a) If we ignore the signs, the terms are the same.
  b) The like terms have opposite signs.

3. a) $-3x^2 + 2x + 1$ **b)** $2x^2 + 2$

Working with Mathematics, page 374

1. a) $-3x^2 - 7$ **b)** $-2x^2 + 5x - 3$ **c)** $4n^2 - 3n + 5$

2. 0

3. The polynomial 0 is equal to its opposite.

4. a) $-3x^2 + 2x + 1$ **b)** $3x^2 - 2x - 1$
  c) The opposite of the opposite of a polynomial is the original polynomial.
  d) Yes, explanations may vary. Each term has its sign reversed twice, so it returns to its original value.

5. a) Flip the tiles.   **b)** Change the sign of every term.

6. a) $(3x^2 + 5) + (-2x^2 - 1)$ **b)** $(x^2 + 2x) + (x + 1)$
  c) $(x^2 + 3x - 2) + (x^2 + x - 1)$

7. Explanations may vary. The tiles that produce 0-pairs are opposites and add to zero.

8. Explanations may vary.
  a) The first terms have the same sign.
  b) The first terms have different exponents.
  c) The last terms have the same sign.
  d) The last terms are different.

9. a) $4x^2 - 2x + 7$ **b)** $2x^2 - 2x + 1$
  c) $-m^2 + 5m - 6$ **d)** $-3m^2 + 5m + 6$

10. a) $-5x^2 + x - 6$ **i)** -10 **ii)** -28
  b) $x^2 - 3x + 10$ **i)** 8   **ii)** 20

11. a) $x^2, 2x; x^2 + 2x$ **b)** $x^2, x^2, 3x; 2x^2 + 3x$
  c) $2x, x^2, 3x, 6; x^2 + 5x + 6$

12. a) $-4x^2 - 2x + 10$ **b)** $x^2 - 4x + 15$
  c) $x^3 - 10x^2 + 2x + 8$ **d)** $8x - 7$

13. a) $2x^2 + 3x + 7$ **b)** $4m^2 - 6m + 11$
  c) $3a^2 - a^3 + 6$ **d)** $-9x^2 + 5x - 12$

14. a) $5x^2 - 15x + 3$ **i)** 53   **ii)** 3
  b) $2b^3 + b^2 - 7b - 5$ **i)** -3 **ii)** 37

15. a) i) $x - 7$ **ii)** $x + 7$ **iii)** $3x - 3, 3x, 3x + 3$ **iv)** $9x$
  b) Divide the sum by 9.

16. a) $25 - 10x - 7x^2$ **b)** 28.25

Quest: A Magic Birthday Card, page 376

Explanations may vary.

Multiplying and Dividing Monomials

Working with Mathematics, page 380

1. a) $3, x, x$ **b)** $4, x, x, x$ **c)** $-x, x$
  d) $2, x, x, x, x, x$ **e)** $-\frac{1}{2}, a, a, a, a$ **f)** $3, 3, x, x, y$
  g) $-2, 3, a, a, b, b$ **h)** $5, m, m, n, n, n$

2. a) $12x^5$ **b)** $-2x^8$ **c)** $\frac{1}{4}a^6$ **d)** $-30a^3$

3. a) $\frac{5}{2}m^2$ **b)** $-\frac{5}{2}x^3$ **c)** $-5x^4$

4. Answers may vary. There are many possible answers. For example:
  a) $x, 3x^5$ **b)** $(-5b), b^2$ **c)** $(-3), 2x$
  d) $4x^3, 2x$ **e)** $3x^4, 2x$ **f)** $x, 4x$

5. a) $-x^5$ **b)** $6p^5$ **c)** $-12y^4$
  d) $6a^3b^3$ **e)** $36x^4y^2$ **f)** $-4x^2y^6$

6. a) πr^3 **b)** x^3

7. a) $5x^2$ **b)** $-3y$ **c)** $-5a$
  d) $3bn$ **e)** $5m^3a^2$ **f)** $3y^3$

8. a) $3r$ **b)** $1.5x$

9. a) $21m^9$ **b)** $8x^5$ **c)** $56a^{14}$ **d)** $-10b^7$
  e) $-18x^8$ **f)** $48p^6$ **g)** $\frac{2}{5}y^{11}$ **h)** $\frac{3}{16}s^8$

10. a) $-7a^5$ **b)** $-4s^2$ **c)** $4c^6$
  d) $5x^6$ **e)** $6y^2$ **f)** $7m^8$

11. a) $(3x)(3x)(3x)$ **b)** $27x^3$ **c)** $42x^9$

Multiplying a Polynomial by a Monomial

Working with Mathematics, page 383

1. a) $x(x + 2)$ **b)** $2x(x + 2)$ **c)** $x(2x + 1)$

2. Answers may vary.

3. a) $x^2 + x$ **b)** $3x^2 + 2x$
  c) $2x^2 + 2x + 6$ **d)** $2x^2 + 4x$

4. a) $5x^3 - 6x$ **b)** $2x + 6x^2$ **c)** $-3b^4 + 3b^3$
  d) $6a^2 + 2a$ **e)** $-4m^3 + 4m^2$ **f)** $x^2 - x^5$

5. a) 1652   **b)** $14x^2 + 21x + 42, 1652$
  c) Answers may vary.

6. a) $10x^2 + 15x$ **b)** $15c - 6c^2$ **c)** $-8n^2 + 4n$
  d) $-14y^3 + 35y^2$ **e)** $12a^3 - 8a^2$ **f)** $6x^2 + 10x^4$
  g) $15s^3 - 10s^2 - 35s$ **h)** $6p - 9p^2 - 3p^3$
  i) $-21a^3 + 14a^2 + 28a$

7. a) $6x^2 - 3x$ **b)** $6x^2 + 3x$ **c)** $-6x^2 - 8x$ **d)** $12x^3 + 8x^2$

8. a) $\frac{3}{4}x$ **b)** $\frac{3}{4}(x + 4)$ **c)** $\frac{3}{4}x^2 + 6x + 12$
  d) $6x + 12$ **e)** 243 square units, 363 square units

Linking Ideas: Mathematics and Science

Recursive Processes and Growth of Populations, page 384

1. a) Yes   **b)** Yes   **c)** No

2. a) Numbers approach 2   **b)** Numbers approach 1.5

3. a) Numbers approach 2   **b)** Numbers approach 1.5
  d) Numbers approach: $1.\overline{3}, 1.25, 1.2, 1.1\overline{6}$; in each case, the numerator of the number in the column is the denominator of the seed, and the denominator of the number in the column is 1 less than the numerator.

4. d) Answers may vary.   **5.** Answers may vary.

Factoring Polynomials
Working with Mathematics, page 391

1. a) x b) $3b$ c) $5y$ d) $3x$ e) $2x$ f) $2y$

2. a) $2(x + 1)$ b) $3(x + 3)$ c) $2(2x + 5)$ d) $3(x + 5)$

3. a) $x(x + 2)$ b) $2x(x + 2)$ c) $3(x + 3)$ d) $4x(x + 2)$

4. a) $8(2x + 5)$ b) $3(5n - 8)$ c) $2a(-a - 3)$
   d) $6n(3n - 2)$ e) $a(a^2 + 9a + 3)$ f) $3x(x + 3)$

5. a) $5(2x + 3)$ b) $3(2x - 3)$ c) $5(3x + 5)$
   d) $2x(x - 2)$ e) $4x(x - 4)$ f) $3y^2(y + 3)$
   g) $2(x^2 + 2x + 4)$ h) $3x(4x^2 - 3x + 2)$

6. a) $a(a^2 - 9a + 3)$ b) $3(-9x^2 - 3x + 1)$
   c) $x(5x^2 + 3x - 1)$ d) $a(9a^2 + 7a + 18)$
   e) $8d(-1 - 3d - d^2)$ f) $17k(1 - 5k - 3k^2)$

7. $A = 2\pi r(h + r)$

8. a) $2(x - 3)$ b) $2(x^2 - 3x + 2)$ c) $2(x^2 + 3)$ d) $2(x^2 - 3)$
   In parts b, c, and d, the tiles are in equal rows, rather than
   rectangles. In each case, the rows have equal areas.

9. $A = Ch + \dfrac{C^2}{2\pi}$

Dividing a Polynomial by a Monomial
Working with Mathematics, page 393

1. a) $\dfrac{5}{2}$ b) $\dfrac{3mn}{2}$ c) $-2y^2$

2. a) $3m^2 - 2$ b) $\dfrac{5}{2}x^2 - 5$ c) $3 - y^2$ d) $-3a + 1$

3. a) $3(x^2 - 4x + 2)$ b) $-x^2 + 4x - 2$

4. a) Divide each term by -3, or factor the numerator then divide
   it by the denominator.
   b) Answers may vary.

5. a) $2a + 1$ b) $4y - 1$ c) $3x^2 - 1$ d) $2a + 5$
   e) $6x - 1$ f) $5 - 2m$ g) $-3 + n$ h) $3x^2 - x + 5$

6. a) $x - 2$ b) $x - 2$ c) $6 - 7a$
   d) $-4n - 1$ e) $-4y^2 + y$ f) $-8b^2 - 2b$

7. a) $3 - x$ b) $1 + 3c - 2c^2$ c) $x^2 - 3x + 2$
   d) $4 + a - a^2$ e) $3x^2 - 6x + 1$ f) $-3a^2 - a + 2$

8. $2x(x + 2l)$

Multiplying Two Binomials
Developing the Ideas, page 394

1. a) $x^2 + 3x + 2$ b) $2x^2 + 7x + 3$

Working with Mathematics, page 396

1. a) $(x + 3)(x + 4)$ b) $x^2 + 7x + 12$

2. a) $(x + 2)(x + 5)$ b) $x^2 + 2x + 5x + 10$

3. a) 1 b) 12 c) -10 d) -6

4. a) i) $(x + 2)(x + 2)$ ii) $x^2 + 4x + 4$
   b) i) $(x + 2)(x + 3)$ ii) $x^2 + 5x + 6$
   c) i) $(2x + 3)(x + 1)$ ii) $2x^2 + 5x + 3$
   d) i) $(x + 1)(x + 5)$ ii) $x^2 + 6x + 5$

5. a) i) $(x + 3)(x + 5)$ ii) $x^2 + 3x + 5x + 15$
   b) i) $(a + 2)(a + 4)$ ii) $a^2 + 2a + 4a + 8$
   c) i) $(n + 1)(n + 7)$ ii) $n^2 + 1n + 7n + 7$

6. a) $x^2 + 7x + 12$ b) $n^2 + 8n + 12$
   c) $a^2 + 8a + 15$ d) $n^2 + 10n + 9$

7. a) $t^2 - 5t + 4$ b) $x^2 + 3x - 10$ c) $n^2 - n - 12$
   d) $a^2 - 2a - 48$ e) $x^2 + 2x - 63$ f) $x^2 + 7x - 60$

8. a) i) $x - 8$, $x - 6$, $x + 6$, $x + 8$
   ii) $x^2 - 16x + 64$, $x^2 - 12x + 36$, $x^2 + 12x + 36$,
   $x^2 + 16x + 64$
   iii) $4x^2 + 200$
   b) Subtract 200, then divide by 4. Take the square root of the
   quotient.

9. a) $4a^2 + 4a + 1$ b) $9n^2 + 6n + 1$ c) $x^2 - 12x + 36$
   d) $a^2 - 6a + 9$ e) $4y^2 - 20y + 25$ f) $9b^2 + 30b + 25$

10. Answers may vary. The middle term is twice the product of
    the square roots of the first and third terms.

11. a) $x^2 - 9$ b) $4a^2 - 1$ c) $64n^2 - 9$
    d) $16a^2 - 9$ e) $9x^2 - 4$ f) $25x^2 - 1$

12. Answers may vary. The middle terms add to zero.

13. a) $12x^2 - 36x + 15$ b) $9b^2 - 4$ c) $20a^2 - 31a - 7$
    d) $8a^2 + 65a + 8$ e) $4a^2 - 12a + 9$ f) $6a^2 - a - 12$

14. a) $3x^2 - x - 2$ b) $2a^2 - 11a + 15$ c) $4n^2 + 13n - 35$
    d) $6x^2 + 13x - 15$ e) $36x^2 - 9x - 1$ f) $10n^2 - 12n + 2$

15. a) $14c^2 - 3c - 5$ b) $18x^2 - 2$ c) $3x^2 + 5x - 2$
    d) $6a^2 - 13a - 5$ e) $40y^2 - 23y + 3$ f) $8x^2 + 2x - 21$

16. a) $x^2 - x - 2$ b) $2x^2 - 5x - 3$ c) $4x^2 - 14x + 12$
    d) $-2x^2 - 7x - 3$ e) $9x^2 - 1$ f) $x^2 + 8x + 16$

Quest: A Student's Letter, page 398

Explanations may vary.

Special Products of Binomials
Developing the Ideas, page 400
Using Manipulatives

1. c) A square   d) Yes   e) $x^2 + 6x + 9$

2. $x^2 + 8x + 16$

Through an Activity

1. a) $x^2 + 2x + 1$ b) $x^2 + 4x + 4$
   c) $x^2 + 6x + 9$ d) $x^2 + 8x + 16$

2. Descriptions may vary. The coefficient of the second term
   (x term) is double the second term in the binomial. The
   coefficient of the third term (constant term) is the square of
   the second term in the binomial.

Page 401

1. a) $x^2 - 1$ b) $x^2 - 4$ c) $x^2 - 9$ d) $x^2 - 16$

2. Descriptions may vary. There are no x terms.

Working with Mathematics, page 402

1. Answers may vary.

2. Explanations may vary.

3. a) $x^2 + 8x + 16$ b) $x^2 - 6x + 9$
   c) $4y^2 + 24y + 36$ d) $49 - 42x + 9x^2$

4. a) $x^2 - 25$ b) $16 - y^2$ c) $1 - 4m^2$ d) $4x^2 - 9$

5. a) $x^2 + 2x + 1$ b) $x^2 - 4x + 4$ c) $x^2 - 10x + 25$
   d) $x^2 + 10x + 25$ e) $4x^2 + 4x + 1$ f) $4x^2 - 4x + 1$
   g) $1 - 4x + 4x^2$ h) $9x^2 + 12x + 4$

6. a) $x^2 - 2x + 1$ b) $4b^2 + 4b + 1$
   c) $9p^2 + 12p + 4$ d) $16m^2 - 24mn + 9n^2$

7. a) 1681   b) 4624   c) 9801

8. a) 399   b) 896   c) 2475

9. a) Numbers may vary.

b) It is twice the sum of the squares of the numbers.

c) It is four times the product of the numbers.

d) Yes **e)** Proofs may vary.

Quest: A Shortcut for Squaring Numbers Ending in 5, page 403

Add 1 to the tens digit. Multiply this number by the tens digit and write 25 after this number.

Factoring Trinomials

Developing the Ideas, page 404

1. $x^2 + 7x + 10$

2. b) $x + 5$ **c)** $x + 2$ **d)** $(x + 5)(x + 2)$

3. Answers may vary.   **4.** $x + 2$, $x + 5$

5. a) $(x + 4)(x + 1)$ **b)** $(x + 4)(x + 2)$ **c)** $(x + 2)(x + 2)$

Working with Mathematics, page 406

1. a) -1, -14; 1, 14; -2, -7; 2, 7
b) -2, -7 **c)** $(x - 2)(x - 7)$

2. No, explanations may vary. For example, $(x - 4)(x + 4)$, a difference of squares, is a binomial, $x^2 - 16$

3. a) i) $x^2 + 6x + 5$ **iii)** $(x + 5)(x + 1)$
b) i) $x^2 + 6x + 8$ **iii)** $(x + 2)(x + 4)$
c) i) $x^2 + 8x + 7$ **iii)** $(x + 7)(x + 1)$
d) i) $x^2 + 8x + 12$ **iii)** $(x + 2)(x + 6)$

4. a) $(x + 1)(x + 1)$ **b)** $(x + 2)(x + 1)$
c) $(x + 3)(x + 1)$ **d)** $(x + 4)(x + 1)$

5. a) The coefficient of the middle term is 1 more than the constant term.
b) One side of each rectangle has exactly 1 x-tile.
c) $x^2 + 6x + 5$, $x^2 + 7x + 6$, $x^2 + 8x + 7$

6. a) $(x + 5)(x + 1)$ **b)** $(a + 6)(a + 2)$ **c)** $(m + 3)(m + 3)$
d) $(x - 2)(x + 1)$ **e)** $(x - 3)(x - 2)$ **f)** $(p + 4)(p - 2)$

7. a) $(x - 4)(x - 2)$ **b)** $(x + 3)(x + 6)$ **c)** $(a - 9)(a - 2)$
d) $(m + 7)(m + 4)$ **e)** $(n - 5)(n - 5)$ **f)** $(n - 10)(n - 3)$
g) $(p + 8)(p + 8)$ **h)** $(y - 7)(y - 6)$
i) $(x + 7)(x + 8)$ **j)** $(x - 14)(x + 4)$

8. a) $(x + 2)(x + 3)$ **b)** $(a + 3)(a + 4)$
c) $(x + 3)(x + 5)$ **d)** $(n + 2)(n + 7)$

9. a) $(r - 2)(r - 7)$ **b)** $(a - 10)(a + 2)$ **c)** $(n - 4)(n - 4)$
d) $(m - 4)(m - 5)$ **e)** $(k - 3)(k - 5)$ **f)** $(x + 6)(x + 4)$
g) $(a - 5)(a + 3)$ **h)** $(m + 4)(m + 5)$
i) $(n - 7)(n + 2)$ **j)** $(a + 14)(a - 1)$

10. a) $(x - 1)(x - 1)$ **b)** $(x - 4)(x + 1)$ **c)** $(x + 3)(x - 2)$
d) $(x - 3)(x - 3)$ **e)** $(x - 7)(x + 1)$ **f)** $(x - 2)(x - 8)$

Factoring a Difference of Squares
Working with Mathematics, page 408

1. a) $(x - 2)(x + 2)$ **b)** $(x - 5)(x + 5)$ **c)** $(a - 4)(a + 4)$
d) $(x - 1)(x + 1)$ **e)** $(a - 10)(a + 10)$ **f)** $(b - 8)(b + 8)$

2. a) 39   **b)** 159   **c)** 360   **d)** 800

4. a) $(5 - x)(5 + x)$ **b)** $(3 - x)(3 + x)$
c) $(9 - x)(9 + x)$ **d)** $(7 + x)(7 - x)$

5. a) i) $x - 8$, $x - 6$, $x + 8$, $x + 6$
ii) $x^2 - 16x + 64$, $x^2 - 12x + 36$, $x^2 + 16x + 64$, $x^2 + 12x + 36$
iii) $32x$, $24x$

---

b) For the numbers in the upper left and lower right, divide by 32; for the numbers in the upper right and lower left, divide by 24.

6. a) $(2a - 2)(2a + 2)$ **b)** $(6 - n)(6 + n)$
c) $(y - 7)(y + 7)$ **d)** $(3a - 2)(3a + 2)$
e) $(5x - 3)(5x + 3)$ **f)** $(4s + 1)(4s - 1)$

7. a) $(6 - 10n)(6 + 10n)$ **b)** $(10x - 11)(10x + 11)$
c) $(12p - 7)(12p + 7)$ **d)** $(7a - 1)(7a + 1)$
e) $(2 - 6x)(2 + 6x)$ **f)** $(3 - 8m)(3 + 8m)$

8. a) $2(x - 3)(x + 3)$ **b)** $3(n^2 + 10)$ **c)** $a(a - 7)(a + 7)$

9. a) $\pi R^2 - \pi r^2$ **b)** $\pi(R + r)(R - r)$

10. a) $(x - 1)(x + 1)$ **b)** $(2x - 3)(2x + 3)$
c) $(3x - 2)(3x + 2)$

Review, page 409

2. a) $4x + 8$, $x^2 + 4x$ **b)** $6x + 8$, $2x^2 + 5x + 3$
c) $6x + 12$, $2x^2 + 11x + 5$

3. a) $6x^2 + y^2$ **b)** $12x - 1$ **c)** $14a^2 - 2a - 10$
d) $6x - 4$ **e)** $6x^2 - 6x$ **f)** $x^2 + 9x - 2$

4. a) $6x$ **i)** 12   **ii)** -18
b) $3x^2 - 2x + 12$ **i)** 20   **ii)** 45

5. a) $-200n^4$ **b)** $140c^5$ **c)** $85x^5$ **d)** $-140n^4$

6. a) $9y^2$ **b)** $\frac{3}{5}n^2$ **c)** -5 **d)** $\frac{3}{2}c^3$ **e)** $6x^3$ **f)** $-4y$

7. a) $15c - 6c^2$ **b)** $-8n^2 + 4n$
c) $-14y^3 + 35y$ **d)** $18k - 6k^2 + 6k^3$
e) $15s^3 - 10s^2 - 35s$ **f)** $6p^2 - 9p^3 - 3p^4$

8. a) $5(y - 2)$ **b)** $6(2a + 3)$ **c)** $3(-x^2 + 2x - 4)$
d) $2(a^2 - 5a + 1)$ **e)** $w(4 - 3w - 7w^2)$ **f)** $2y(4y^2 - 2y + 1)$

9. a) $x - 2$ **b)** $x - 2$ **c)** $6 - 7a$
d) $-4n - 1$ **e)** $-4 + y$ **f)** $-8b^2 - 2b$

10. a) $5x^2 - 13x - 6$ **b)** $4a^2 + 8a + 3$ **c)** $16n^2 - 14n + 3$
d) $16a^2 + 24a + 9$ **e)** $12x^2 - 17x + 6$ **f)** $30x^2 - 14x - 4$

11. a) $n^2 - 14n + 49$ **b)** $c^2 + 8c + 16$ **c)** $x^2 - 2x + 1$
d) $9x^2 - 4$ **e)** $16x^2 - 9$ **f)** $9 - 25x^2$

12. a) $(x + 2)(x + 8)$ **b)** $(a + 6)(a - 2)$ **c)** $(x - 5)(x - 5)$
d) $(c - 7)(c + 5)$ **e)** $(x - 4)(x + 3)$ **f)** $(a + 6)(a - 5)$

13. a) $(a - 7)(a + 7)$ **b)** $(m - 8)(m + 8)$
c) $(h + 12)(h - 12)$ **d)** $(9y - 7)(9y + 7)$
e) $(4a - 9)(4a + 9)$ **f)** $(8x + 11)(8x - 11)$

CHAPTER 9 TWO-DIMENSIONAL GEOMETRY

Start With What You Know, page 414

1. Answers may vary; see glossary.

2. a) 4 m   **b)** 2.5 cm   **c)** 10^2 m   **d)** 70 m

3. 51.4 m   **4.** 8.0 m

Mathematics File: Angles and Intersecting Lines, page 416

1. a) The angles opposite each other are equal.
b) Explanations may vary.

2. The bisectors are perpendicular to each other.

3. Examples may vary.

Sum of the Angles in a Triangle

Developing the Ideas, page 418

1. a) The vertices meet at one point and form a straight angle.
b) The sum of the angles in the triangle was 180°.

2. The sum of the angles in any triangle is 180°.

3. Answers may vary.

Working with Mathematics, page 419

1. a) 80°   **b)** 20°   **c)** 125°   **d)** 60°
e) 135°   **f)** 100°   **g)** 145°   **h)** 95°

2. a) 81°, acute, scalene   **b)** 35°, acute, scalene
c) 114°, obtuse, scalene   **d)** 90°, right, scalene

3. a) 25°   **b)** 80°   **c)** 48°, 96°   **d)** 125°

4. Questions may vary.

5. a) Acute, scalene   **b)** Obtuse, scalene   **c)** Right, isosceles

6. a) 8
b) 5 triangles are right, 2 are obtuse, and 1 is acute. 4 triangles are scalene, 4 are isosceles, and none is equilateral

7. 6; a figure can be drawn with 4 line segments that contains one triangle of each type.

8. a) Yes, for example, a right triangle has 2 acute angles.
b) Yes, for example, an equilateral triangle has 3 acute angles.
c) No. Two right angles have a sum of 180°, so the third angle would measure 0°.
d) No. Two obtuse angles have a sum greater than 180°, which is not possible in a triangle.
e) No. A straight angle has a measure of 180°, so the other 2 angles would both measure 0°.
f) No. A right angle and an obtuse angle have a sum greater than 180°, which is not possible in a triangle.

9. a) Subtract from 90° to find the measure of the third angle. Tables may vary depending on the angles chosen.
b) The plotted points appear to lie along a straight line that slopes down to the right with slope −1. As the measure of the angle on the horizontal axis increases, the measure of the angle on the vertical axis decreases by the same amount.

10. a) The sum of the angles in a quadrilateral is 360°.
b) A pentagon can be divided into 3 triangles; the sum of its angles is 540°. A hexagon can be divided into 4 triangles; the sum of its angles is 720°.
c) The number of triangles a polygon can be divided into is 2 less than the number of sides in the polygon. Each triangle will have an angle sum of 180°.
d) $180° (n - 2)$

Mathematics File: A Property of a Right Triangle, page 421

1. The creases are perpendicular.

2. a) The point where the creases meet is the same distance from the three vertices.

3. The midpoint of the hypotenuse of a right triangle is equidistant from the vertices of the triangle.

4. a) The midpoint of the hypotenuse is the centre of the circle, and the hypotenuse is the diameter of the circle. The centre of a circle is the same distance from each point on the circle and we showed by paper folding that the midpoint of the hypotenuse is equidistant from the vertices.

Linking Ideas: Mathematics and Technology

Investigating Properties of Angles in Triangles, page 422

1. a) Increases by 10°   **b)** Increases by 5°   **c)** Decreases by 5°

2. For every 20° increase in the measure of ∠A in the table, there is a 10° increase in the measure of ∠D. The graph slopes up to the right, with slope 0.5.

3. Because the sum of the angles in a triangle is 180° and the measures of the other 2 angles in △DBC are half of the measures of the other 2 angles in △ABC

4. $\angle D = 90 + \frac{1}{2}\angle A$

Angles and Parallel Lines

Developing the Ideas, page 424

1. a) The corresponding angles have equal measure.

2. a) The alternate angles have equal measure.

Working with Mathematics, page 426

1. a) 4 and 6, 3 and 5
b) 1 and 5, 4 and 8, 2 and 6, 3 and 7

2. Examples may vary.   **3.** Answers may vary.

4. a) 75°   **b)** 120°   **c)** 55°, 60°   **d)** 50°, 53°, 103°

5. ∠ABC = 40°, ∠ACB = 76°, ∠BAC = 64°

6. a) 110°   **b)** 63°, 117°   **c)** 74°, 106°
d) 35°   **e)** 58°, 122°, 58°, 122°   **f)** 75°, 55°

7. Questions may vary.   **8.** No. Diagrams may vary.

9. No, not in the same plane. Diagrams may vary.

10. a) Three lines can also intersect in 1 or 3 points.
b) The greatest number of points in which four lines can intersect is 6, the least is 0. There are also examples of four lines intersecting in 1, 3, 4, and 5 points, but not in 2 points.
c) The greatest number of points in which five lines can intersect is 10; for 6 lines, the greatest number of points is 15.
d) The greatest number of points in which n lines can intersect is $\frac{n(n-1)}{2}$.

Mathematics File: Extending the Pythagorean Theorem, page 428

1. a) The area of the figure on the hypotenuse is equal to the sum of the areas of the figures on the other 2 sides.
b) As described in part a, the Pythagorean Theorem also holds for similar figures other than squares.

2. The Extended Pythagorean Theorem applies to each of these cases; explanations may vary.

3. a) 30°–60°–90° triangle: $\frac{\sqrt{3}}{2}x^2 \doteq 0.866x^2$;
circle: $\frac{\pi}{4}x^2 \doteq 0.785x^2$;
equilateral triangle: $\frac{\sqrt{3}}{4}x^2 \doteq 0.433x^2$
b) Rectangles with length twice the width: $0.5x^2$; triangles with height half the base: $0.25x^2$; semicircles: $\frac{\pi}{8}x^2 \doteq 0.393x^2$; quarter circles: $\frac{\pi}{4}x^2 \doteq 0.785x^2$
c) They are all x^2 multiplied by a constant. Since the Pythagorean Theorem gives you an expression for x^2, multiplying this expression by the constant gives an expression for the figure you used.

Linking Ideas: Mathematics and Design

The Triangle in Engineering and Architecture, page 430

1. The cube with crossbeams feels solid beneath your palm while the other cube shifts as your palm moves.

2. Tests may vary. The cube with crossbeams will support much more weight than the other cube.

3. Answers may vary.

Isosceles and Equilateral Triangles

Developing the Ideas, page 431

1. a) Isosceles
   b) Two sides have equal length. The angles opposite the equal sides are equal.

2. Yes   3. Answers may vary.

Working with Mathematics, page 433

1. a) 70°   b) 75°   c) 60°   d) 136°
   e) 50°   f) 120°   g) 108°, 144° h) 30°, 90°

2. a) 25°   b) 103°   c) 100°, 40°
   d) 54°, 126° e) 38°, 142° f) 50°, 80°

3. There are 2 triangles which satisfy these conditions. Their angles are 45°, 45°, 90° and 36°, 72°, 72°.

4. 30°, 120° or 75°, 75°   5. 40°, 70°, 70° or 50°, 50°, 80°

6. a) Yes, an isosceles right triangle will have angles 45°, 45°, 90°.
   b) Yes, for example, a triangle with angles 120°, 30°, 30° is isosceles and obtuse.
   c) Yes, for example, a triangle with angles 70°, 70°, 40° is isosceles and acute.
   d) No. If a triangle is scalene it has no equal sides and therefore cannot be isosceles.

7. a) 35°, 32.5°, 20°, 15°, 7.5°
   b) Divide by 2.   c) $y = \frac{x}{2}$
   d) When $x = 90°$, $y = 45°$ e) When $x = 0°$, $y = 0°$

Quest: Calculating Angles in House Construction, page 435

The carpenter must cut the boards for the peak of the roof at an angle of 26°, and the boards for the baseline at an angle of 58°.

Linking Ideas: Algebra and Geometry

Patterns in the Angles in Isosceles Triangles, page 436

Group 1

1. The points appear to lie along a straight line sloping down to the right. For every 5° increase or decrease in the measure of one of the equal angles, there is a corresponding 10° decrease or increase in the measure of the third angle.

2. a) $y = 180° - 2x$
   b) x must be between 0° and 90°, y will be between 180° and 0°.

Group 2

1. There are two groups of points. The points in each group appear to lie on lines sloping down to the right, but with different slopes. The lines meet at (60°, 60°). The more steeply sloped line represents the case when the third angle is the largest, the other line represents the case when the equal

angles are the largest.

2. When the third angle is largest:
   a) $y = 180° - 2x$
   b) x must be between 0° and 60°, y will be between 180° and 60°.

   When the equal angles are largest:
   a) $y = \frac{180° - x}{2}$
   b) x must be between 0° and 60°, y will be between 90° and 60°.

Properties of Chords in Circles

Developing the Ideas, page 437

Activity 1

1. The perpendicular bisector passes through the centre of the circle.

2. Yes

Activity 2

1. ∠OMC and ∠OMD both measure 90°.   2. Yes

Activity 3

1. NE and NF have equal lengths.   2. Yes

Working with Mathematics, page 439

1. Yes, the properties apply to diameters. However, the perpendicular distance from the centre to the diameter is 0.

2. a) 8   b) 5   c) 13.4
   d) 5.3   e) 2.2   f) 6

3. a) 9.3   b) 4   c) 3.3   d) 6.1

4. a) 3.0 cm   b) 8.0 cm   c) 8.9 cm   d) 2.2 cm

5. a) $y = 2\sqrt{25 - x^2}$
   b) x must be between 0 cm and 5 cm. The corresponding values of y are 10 cm and 0 cm.

6. a) 10.4 cm   b) 46.8 cm²   c) About 41%

Quest: Locating the Centre of a Circle, page 440

The point of impact is about 7.2 cm from the shoreline. On the tracing, this represents about 216 km.

Properties of Angles in Circles

Developing the Ideas, page 442

Activity 1

3. ∠C = 90°   4. ∠C always has measure 90°.   5. Yes

Activity 2

1. The corner of the cardboard traces a semicircle.

2. The corner of the cardboard is a 90° angle. The tacks represent the diameter.

Activity 3

3. Answers may vary.

4. When F is on the same side of the chord, the angle measure does not change. If F is on the opposite side of the chord, its angle measure is 180° minus the angle measure of F on the other side of the chord.

5. Yes

Activity 4

1. The corner of the cardboard traces an arc of a circle.

2. The corner of the cardboard represents ∠F. The tacks represent a chord.

Activity 5

4. The measure of ∠O is twice the measure of ∠J.

5. The results are the same.   6. Yes

Activity 6

3. ∠A + ∠C = 180°, ∠B + ∠D = 180°   4. Yes

Working with Mathematics, page 446

1. a) 60°   b) 90°   c) 64°
   d) 50°   e) 35°, 25°   f) 38°, 90°

2. 80°

3. a) 55°, 110°   b) 90°, 90°   c) 65°, 65°
   d) 70°, 80°   e) 90°, 105°   f) 115°, 100°

4. a) 90°, 90°   b) 60°, 60°   c) 110°, 20°   d) 50°, 70°

5. i) a) Multiply x by 2.   b) $y = 2x$
      c) x must be between 0° and 90°, y will be between 0° and 180°.
   ii) a) Subtract x from 90°.   b) $y = 90 - x$
      c) x must be between 0° and 90°, y will be between 90° and 0°.
   iii) a) Subtract x from 180°.   b) $y = 180 - x$
      c) x must be between 0° and 180°, y will be between 180° and 0°.

6. Use Property 1. Draw a right angle with its endpoints on the circle. Join the endpoints to form a diameter.

7. , 8. Explanations may vary.

Linking Ideas: Mathematics and Technology
Investigating Properties of Angles in a Circle, page 448

Answers may vary.

Quest: Saving Wood by Growing Square Trees, page 450

The area of the square is about 64% of the area of the circle.

Review, page 452

1. a) 135°   b) 80°   c) 77°   d) 110°   e) 25°
   f) 130°, 50°, 130°   g) 58°, 128°, 128°   h) 105°
   i) 30°, 80°, 80°   j) 35°   k) 40°   l) 90°, 60°

2. a) 13.6   b) 21.8   c) 19.0   d) 15.0

3. a) 9.8 cm   b) 9.2 cm   c) 8.0 cm   d) 6.0 cm

4. a) 48°, 96°   b) 40°   c) 30°, 50°
   d) 110°, 30°   e) 95°, 65°   f) 130°, 115°

CHAPTER 10 FUNCTIONS

Start With What You Know, page 458

1. a) In 1982 the price increased by 13¢.   b) About 76%

2. a) 1915, 1931, 1943, 1954, 1968, 1971, 1972, 1988, 1989, 1990, 1991, 1993

b) To one decimal place, the percent increases were: 50%, 50%, 33.3%, 25%, 20%, 16.7%, 14.3%, 2.8%, 2.7%, 2.6%, 2.6%, 2.4%

3. a) 1926   b) 33.3%

4. a) A postal rate remains unchanged for a few months or even years before the next increase.

   b) The gaps occur on the dates the rates changed since the rate changes from one rate to another without taking any values between the two.

5. Yes, explanations may vary.

6. Answers may vary. This is based on the rate in 1994.
   a) 43¢
   b)

Number of letters, n	Postage cost, C dollars
1	0.43
2	0.86
3	1.29
4	1.72
5	2.15
6	2.58
7	3.01
8	3.44
9	3.87
10	4.30

7. a) A rate compares two quantities with different units.
   b) Answers may vary.

8. AB: −2, CD: 0, EF: −0.75, GH: $0.\bar{3}$, IJ: undefined, KL: −0.25

9. a) $\frac{4}{7}$ b) −0.125   c) 0   d) Undefined

What Is a Function?
Developing the Ideas, page 461

Tables may vary, depending on the input numbers chosen.

Rule 1:   c) All numbers can be used.   d) $y = x + 3$
Rule 2:   c) All numbers can be used.   d) $y = 3x$
Rule 3:   c) All numbers can be used.   d) $y = 2x + 3$
Rule 4:   c) All numbers can be used.   d) $y = 10 - x$
Rule 5:   c) No negative numbers can be used.   d) $y = \sqrt{x}$

Working with Mathematics, page 463

1. Yes. For every date along the horizontal axis there is one postal rate.

2. a) False. A table often shows only a selection of input values.
   b) False. A graph may be a set of points, as in *Example 1*.

3. a) Yes. If you input a number and press one of these keys you will get one number out.
   b) Yes. You cannot use negative input values for $y = \sqrt{x}$, and you cannot use 0 as an input for $y = \frac{1}{x}$.

4. a) Each graph involves a relation in which the output number is four times the input number.
   b) In the first graph, all numbers can be used as input values; in the second, only whole numbers can be used; in the third, all numbers can be used as inputs, but for input values that are not whole numbers the output is determined by rounding to the next whole number and then multiplying by 4.

5. a) Tables may vary, depending on the input numbers chosen.
   c) i) , ii) All numbers can be used as inputs.
      iii) Negative numbers cannot be used as inputs.

7. b) Answers may vary. The graphs are all straight lines with slope 2, but each crosses the x-axis and y-axis at different points.

8. Experimental results may vary.

10. b) Answers may vary. The graphs all have the same shape and orientation.

11. a) iii   **b)** i   **c)** ii   **d)** iv

12. b) Answers may vary. While p decreases as the time increases, q increases.

13. Experimental results may vary.

14. a) i) There would be twice as many points plotted since points would be shown for half-hour values of h, such as $(0.5, 2.75)$ and $(1.5, 8.25)$.
ii) There would be four times as many points plotted since points would be shown for quarter-hour values of h, such as $(0.25, 1.37)$, $(0.5, 2.75)$, and $(0.75, 4.13)$.
b) To draw the graph as a straight line, employees would have to be paid for every second they worked. However, in practice, an employer or employee may draw a straight-line graph because it is faster than drawing a series of points and will still provide the desired information.

Quest: Is the Fuel Gauge in a Car Accurate?, page 466

Answers may vary.

Mathematics File: Does 64 = 65?, page 468

1. The slope of each line segment on the first graph is 0.5 On the second graph, the slopes are AB: 3, BC: 1, AD: 1, BD: 0.5.

2. Answers may vary.   **3.** Answers may vary.

4. Along a straight line, the line segments have the same slope. Along a line which is not straight, line segments have different slopes.

5. The diagonal in the second diagram is not a straight line. To check, calculate the slope of the segment along the triangle and along the trapezoid. One has slope 0.375, the other has slope 0.4.

Linear Functions
Developing the Ideas, page 469

1. a) The equation would be $a = p$.
b) The graph would still be a straight line and pass through the origin, but it would have a steeper slope.
c) 1

2. a) The equation would be $a = 0.5p$.
b) The graph would still be a straight line and pass through the origin, but it would have a less steep slope.
c) 0.5

Working with Mathematics, page 471

1. a

2. Examples of linear functions on pages 460 to 464 may vary. Not all the functions on these pages are linear. For example, on page 460, $y = x^2$ is not linear.

3. a)

Age, n years	Allowance, a dollars
6	0.75
7	1.50
8	2.25
9	3.00
10	3.75
11	4.50
12	5.25
13	6.00
14	6.75
15	7.50
16	8.25

b) $a = 0.75(n - 5)$

4. b) 13 exposures —$9.53; 25 exposures —$13.73; 37 exposures —$17.93

c)

NUMBER OF EXPOSURES	COST
9	$8.13
10	$8.48
11	$8.83
21	$12.33
22	$12.68
23	$13.03
33	$16.53
34	$16.88
35	$17.23

d) The slope of the line is 0.35. This represents the additional cost to print each exposure, beyond the flat rate to develop the film.

5. b) The cooking time needed per kilogram
c) The slope would be less steep for large values of m.
d) The slope would be steeper.
e) The labels on the horizontal axis are the only parts of the graph that would change.

6. a) The coordinates are: $(500, 80)$, $(750, 120)$, $(1000, 160)$, $(1250, 200)$
b) $\frac{4}{25}$, or 0.16   **c)** 9600 ft
d) 500 s, or 8 min 20 s   **e)** $h = 0.16d$

7. b) $\frac{32}{500}$, or 0.064   **c)** 480 ft   **d)** Answers may vary.

8. b) i) This adds 1 to the number of exposures.
ii) This adds 35¢ to the cost because this is the charge for each exposure.
iii) This calculates the mean cost for each exposure by dividing the cost by the number of exposures.
c) The mean cost per exposure decreases as the number of exposures increases. When the number of exposures is large, the flat fee of $4.98 for developing the film is divided among a greater number of exposures.
e) The function is not linear because the mean cost per exposure is not constant.

The Equation of a Line
Developing the Ideas, page 473

2. a) When $x = 0$, $y = 4$; this is the y-coordinate of the point where the line crosses the y-axis.
b) When $y = 0$, $x = 4$; this is the x-coordinate of the point

where the line crosses the x-axis.

3. a) When the input number increases by 1, the output number decreases by 1.

b) You can observe this change by comparing pairs of input and output numbers in the table, or by calculating that the slope of the line in the graph is -1.

Working with Mathematics, page 476

1. You need a minimum of 2 points to graph a straight line. Plotting 1 or 2 more points is a good way to verify that the line is correct.

2. a) You want to find the coordinates of the point where the line crosses the x-axis. Since $y = 0$ for all points on the x-axis, you know the y-coordinate will be 0.

b) You want to find the coordinates of the point where the line crosses the y-axis. Since $x = 0$ for all points on the y-axis, you know the x-coordinate will be 0.

3. a) A line that is parallel to the x-axis has a y-intercept, but no x-intercept, and has slope 0. A line that is parallel to the y-axis has an x-intercept, but no y-intercept, and has an undefined slope.

b) No. Each type of line described in part a has only one intercept. All other lines have both an x-intercept and a y-intercept.

c) $y = 3$ d) $x = 3$

4. a) x-intercept: 3, y-intercept: 4, slope: $-\frac{4}{3}$

b) x-intercept: 6, y-intercept: -3, slope: 0.5

c) x-intercept: -2, no y-intercept, slope is undefined

d) x-intercept: -2, y-intercept: 4, slope: 2

e) No x-intercept, y-intercept: 3, slope: 0

f) x-intercept: 2.5, y-intercept: 2.5, slope: -1

5. Tables may vary depending on the input numbers chosen.

6. Tables may vary depending on the input numbers chosen.

7. a) i) The top pattern contains a line with the equation $x + y = 4$.

ii) $x - y = 4$, $x + y = -4$, $x - y = -4$, $x - y = 8$, $x + y = -8$, $x - y = -8$, $x + y = 8$, $x + y = 0$, $x - y = 0$

b) $x + y = 3$, $x + y = 9$, $x + y = -3$, $x + y = -9$, $x - y = 3$, $x - y = -3$, $x - y = -9$, $x - y = 9$

8. a) x-intercept: 10, y-intercept: 2

b) x-intercept: 3, y-intercept: -4

c) x-intercept: $-\frac{4}{3}$, y-intercept: $-\frac{2}{3}$

d) x-intercept: 6, y-intercept: 4.5

e) x-intercept: -4; y-intercept: 7

f) x-intercept: 3, y-intercept: -6

9. Tables may vary, depending on the input numbers chosen.

10. a) $\frac{1}{3}$ b) 3   c) $\frac{2}{3}$ d) $-\frac{4}{5}$ e) $-\frac{2}{3}$ f) $\frac{1}{2}$

11. a) The equation is $F = 1.8C + 32$. The F-intercept is 32 and the C-intercept is $-\frac{32}{1.8}$, or approximately -17.8.

b) The Fahrenheit temperature equivalent to 0°C and the Celsius temperature equivalent to 0°F

12. There are 2 squares which can be drawn. The fourth side of one of these is contained in the line $x - y = -2$. The fourth side of the other is contained in the line $x - y = 6$. Explanations may vary.

13. a) Tables may vary, depending on the input numbers chosen.

b) This rule does not define a function since for each input number there are 2 output numbers. For example, for an input of 2 the outputs are -2 and 6.

Mathematics File: Intersecting Lines, page 478

1. a) The distances which complete the table are: 50, 100, 150, 200, 250, 300, 350, 400

2. a) The distances which complete the table are: 300, 240, 180, 120, 60, 0

3. About $(3.3, 165)$; the cars meet after about 3 h and 18 min. When they meet they are about 165 km from Vancouver.

4. The cars meet on Highway 5 about 16 km east of Hope.

5. The cars would be about 190 km from Vancouver when they meet.

6. The cars would be about 154 km from Vancouver when they meet.

7. a) i) $(1, 3)$ v) $(2, 0)$

b) The coordinates that are estimated may vary.

ii) $(1.7, 1.7)$ iii) $(1, -3)$

iv) $(-2, 1.5)$ vi) $(3.5, 3.5)$

8. The coordinates that are estimated may vary.

a) $(4, -1)$ b) $(1, 3)$ c) $(3, 1)$

d) $(4.5, -2)$ e) $(2.5, 1.5)$ f) $(2.4, 3.6)$

Finding Relationships in Data
Developing the Ideas, page 480

1. Answers may vary. Three possible rules are: $y = x + 1$, $y = x^2 - 1$, and $x + y = 5$

2. No, as you can see from exercise 1, several rules can be determined for one pair.

3. Yes, $y = 2x - 1$

Working with Mathematics, page 481

1. Answers may vary. Three possible rules are: $y = 2x$, $y = x^2$, and $y = 3x - 2$

2. a) $y = 2x$ b) $y = 10x + 1$

3. a) $y = 3x$ b) $y = -0.5x$

4. i) a)

x	y
-3	7.5
-1.5	6
2.5	2
6	-1.5

b) $y = 4.5 - x$

c) Calculated table entries may vary. The corresponding points should lie on the graph.

ii) a)

x	y
-4	13
-2	1
1	-2
3	6

b) $y = x^2 - 3$

c) Calculated table entries may vary. The corresponding points should lie on the graph.

5. a) $y = x + 2$ b) $y = 2x + 1$ c) $y = -3 - x$

d) $y = x(x + 1)$ e) $y = x^3$ f) $y = \frac{12}{x}$

6. a)

x	y
1	2
2	4
3	6
4	8
5	10
6	24

b) For input numbers of 1, 2, 3, 4, and 5, the results are the same. But when $x = 6$, the results are different.

c) No

Quest: Predicting Long Jump Records, page 482

Answers may vary, about 1995.

Linking Ideas: Mathematics and Technology

Finding a Rule, page 484

1. c) $y = 3x - 2$

Review, page 485

1. a) Tables may vary.

c) iii) No negative numbers can be input.

d) i) $y = 2x - 1$ **ii)** $y = 8 - x^2$ **iii)** $y = 3 + \sqrt{x}$

2. Descriptions may vary.

a) Square a number and subtract 3.

b) Subtract 3 from a number and square the result.

c) Square a number and add 3.

d) Add 3 to a number and square the result.

3. a) $60, $100, $180   **b)** 19 km, 25 km, 43 km

4. x-intercept is last. l_1: -2, 6, 3; l_2: $\frac{3}{4}$, 2, -3; l_3: 0, 5, none; l_4: $\frac{1}{2}$, -2, 4; l_5: $-\frac{1}{2}$, 1, 2

5. y-intercept is first.

a) -3, 4, $\frac{3}{4}$ **b)** -5, 2, $\frac{5}{2}$ **c)** 2, -4, $\frac{1}{2}$ **d)** 4, -2, 2

6. Tables may vary.

7. a) $y = -2x$ **b)** $y = 3x - 1$

8. a)

Row	Sum of the numbers
1	1
2	-1
3	2
4	-2
5	3
6	-3
7	4
8	-4
9	5
10	-5

b) -50, 51

c) i) $-\frac{n}{2}$ **ii)** $\frac{n+1}{2}$

Explanations may vary.

acute angle: an angle measuring less than 90°

acute triangle: a triangle with three acute angles

additive inverses: a number and its opposite; the sum of additive inverses is 0; for example, $+3 + (-3) = 0$

alternate angles: angles that are between two lines and are on opposite sides of a transversal that cuts the two lines
angles 1 and 3 are alternate angles
angles 2 and 4 are alternate angles

angle: the figure formed by two rays from the same end point

angle bisector: the line that divides an angle into two equal angles

approximation: a number close to the exact value of an expression; the symbol $\doteq$ means "is approximately equal to"

arc: a segment of a circle
AB is an arc of the circle, centre O

area: the number of square units needed to cover a region

average: a single number that represents a set of numbers; see *mean, median,* and *mode*

bar graph: a graph that displays data by using horizontal or vertical bars whose lengths are proportional to the numbers they represent; see page 64

bar notation: the use of a horizontal bar over decimal digits to indicate that they repeat; for example, $1.\overline{3}$ means 1.333 333 …

bias: an emphasis on characteristics that are not typical of the entire population

binomial: a polynomial with two terms; for example, $3x - 8$

binomial square: a binomial multiplied by itself

bisector: a line that divides a line segment in two equal parts
the broken line is a bisector of AB

box-and-whisker plot: a diagram in which data are plotted horizontally and values between the upper and lower quartiles are enclosed in a box; see page 72

broken-line graph: a graph that displays data by using points joined by line segments; see page 468

capacity: the amount a container can hold

chord: a line segment with its end points on a circle

circle: the set of points in a plane that are a given distance from a fixed point (the centre)

circle graph: a diagram that uses parts of a circle to display data; see page 56

circumference: the distance around a circle, and sometimes the circle itself

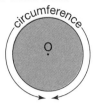

coefficient: the numerical factor of a term; for example, in the terms $3x$ and $3x^2$, the coefficient is 3

commission: a fee or payment given to a sales person, usually a specified percent of the person's sales

common denominator: a number that is a multiple of each of the given denominators; for example, 12 is a common denominator for the fractions $\frac{1}{3}$, $\frac{5}{4}$, $\frac{7}{12}$

common factor: a number that is a factor of each of the given numbers; for example, 3 is a common factor of 15, 9, and 21

compound event: a combination of two or more events

compound interest: see *interest*; if the interest due is added to the principal and thereafter earns interest, the interest earned is compound interest

cone: a solid formed by a region and all line segments joining points on the boundary of the region to a point not in the region

congruent: figures that have the same size and shape, but not necessarily the same orientation

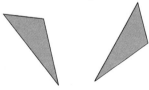

consecutive numbers: integers that come one after the other without any integers missing; for example, 34, 35, 36 are consecutive numbers, so are -2, -1, 0, and 1

constant term: a number

Consumer Price Index: the change in the costs of goods and services, based on their costs on a set date

continuous-line graph: a graph that shows the value of one variable corresponding to the value of another variable, for all values over a given interval; see page 462

coordinates: the numbers in an ordered pair that locate a point in the plane

corresponding angles: angles that are on the same side of a transversal that cuts two lines and on the same side of each line
angles 1 and 3 are corresponding angles
angles 2 and 4 are corresponding angles
angles 5 and 7 are corresponding angles
angles 6 and 8 are corresponding angles

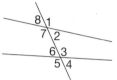

cyclic quadrilateral: a four-sided figure with its vertices on a circle

cylinder: a solid with two parallel, congruent, circular bases

data: facts or information

database: facts or information supplied by computer software

denominator: the term below the line in a fraction

density: the mass of a unit volume of a substance

diagonal: a line segment that joins two vertices of a figure, but is not a side

diameter: the distance across a circle, measured through the centre and a chord that passes through the centre of the circle

digit: any of the symbols used to write numerals; for example, in the base-ten system the digits are 0, 1, 2, 3, 4, 5, 6, 7, 8, and 9

dilation: a transformation in which the image is the same shape as the object, but is enlarged or reduced in size

Distributive Law: the property stating that a product can be written as a sum or difference of two products; for example, for all real numbers a, b, and c:

$$a(b + c) = ab + ac \text{ and } a(b - c) = ab - ac$$

double-bar graph: a bar graph that shows two sets of data; see page 63

equation: a statement that two expressions are equal

equilateral triangle: a triangle with three equal sides

even number: an integer that has 2 as a factor; for example, 2, 4, −6

event: any set of outcomes of an experiment

exponent: a symbol that is placed to the right of and above another symbol

expression: a meaningful combination of symbols

extremes: the highest and lowest values in a set of numbers

factor: to factor means to write as a product
to factor a given integer means to write it as a product of integers, the integers in the product are the factors of the given integer
to factor a polynomial with integral coefficients usually means to write it as a product of polynomials with integral coefficients

factorial: the product of a sequence of consecutive natural numbers starting with 1; a factorial is indicated by the symbol !; n factorial is $1 \times 2 \times 3 \times 4 \times ... \times n = n!$

formula: a rule that is expressed as an equation

fraction: an indicated quotient of two quantities

frequency: the number of times a particular number occurs in a set of data

function: a rule that gives a single output number for every valid input number

grouping property of addition (and multiplication): when three or more terms are added (or multiplied), the operations can be performed in any order

hectare: a unit of area that is equal to 10 000 m^2

hexagon: a six-sided polygon

histogram: a graph that uses bars, where each bar represents a range of values, and the data are continuous; see page 56

hypotenuse: the side that is opposite the right angle in a right triangle

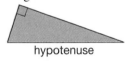
hypotenuse

identity for addition: a number that can be added to any number without changing the number; 0 is the identity for addition of real numbers

identity for multiplication: a number that can be multiplied by any number without changing the number; 1 is the identity for multiplication of real numbers

image: the figure that results from a transformation

inequality: a statement that one quantity is greater than (or less than) another quantity

inscribed angle: an angle that has its vertex on the circumference of a circle and has chords for arms
∠C is an inscribed angle
∠C is subtended by arc AB

integers: the set of numbers... −3, −2, −1, 0, +1, +2, +3,...

interest: money that is paid for the use of money, usually according to a predetermined percent

intersecting lines: lines that meet or cross; lines that have one point in common

interval: a regular distance or space between values

inverse: see *additive inverses* and *multiplicative inverses*

irrational number: a number that cannot be written in the form $\frac{m}{n}$ where m and n are integers ($n \neq 0$)

isometry: a transformation that preserves length; for example, a translation

isosceles acute triangle: a triangle with two equal sides and all angles less than 90°

isosceles obtuse triangle: a triangle with two equal sides and one angle greater than 90°

isosceles right triangle: a triangle with two equal sides and a 90° angle

isosceles triangle: a triangle with two equal sides

lattice point: on a coordinate grid, a point at the intersection of two grid lines

legs: the sides of a right triangle that form the right angle

light-year: a unit for measuring astronomical distances; one light-year is the distance light travels in one year

like terms: terms that have the same variables; for example, $4x$ and $-3x$ are like terms

line of best fit: the line that passes as close as possible to a set of plotted points

line segment: the part of a line between two points on the line

line symmetry: a figure that maps onto itself when it is reflected in a line is said to have line symmetry; for example, line l is the line of symmetry for figure ABCD

linear function: a function that can be represented by a straight-line graph

magic square: an array of numbers in which the sum of the numbers in any row, column, or diagonal is always the same; see page 24

magic sum: the sum of the numbers in a row, column, or diagonal of a magic square

mapping: a correspondence of points or figures under a transformation or rule

mapping rule: it describes a transformation on a coordinate grid

mass: the amount of matter in an object

mean: the sum of a set of numbers divided by the number of numbers in the set

measure of central tendency: a single value that represents a set of data; see *mean, median,* and *mode*

median: the middle number when data are arranged in numerical order

median of a triangle: the line from one vertex to the midpoint of the opposite side

midpoint: the point that divides a line segment into two equal parts

mode: the number that occurs most often in a set of numbers

monomial: a polynomial with one term; for example, 14 and $5x^2$ are each a monomial

Monte Carlo method: the procedure of performing an experiment whose outcomes have the same probability as the outcomes in another experiment that is more difficult to perform

multiple: the product of a given number and a natural number; for example, some multiples of 8 are 8, 16, 24,...

multiplicative inverses: a number and its reciprocal; the product of multiplicative inverses is 1; for example, $3 \times \frac{1}{3} = 1$

natural numbers: the set of numbers 1, 2, 3, 4, 5,...

negative number: a number less than 0

numeracy: the ability to read, understand, and use numbers

numerator: the term above the line in a fraction

obtuse angle: an angle greater than 90° and less than 180°

obtuse triangle: a triangle with one angle greater than 90°

octagon: an eight-sided polygon

odd number: an integer that does not have 2 as a factor; for example, 1, 3, −7

operation: a mathematical process or action such as addition, subtraction, multiplication, or division

opposite angles: the equal angles that are formed by two intersecting lines

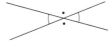

opposite number: a number whose sum with a given number is 0; for example, 3 and −3 are opposites

opposites: two numbers whose sum is zero; each number is the opposite of the other

opposites principle: when two equal expressions are multiplied by −1, the results will be equal

order of operations: the rules that are followed when simplifying or evaluating an expression

order property of addition (and multiplication): two terms that are added (or multiplied) can be added (or multiplied) in any order

outcome: a possible result of an experiment or a possible answer to a survey question

parallel lines: lines in the same plane that do not intersect

parallelogram: a quadrilateral with both pairs of opposite sides parallel

pentagon: a five-sided polygon

per capita: for each person

percent: the numerator of a fraction with a denominator of 100

percentiles: hundredths of the data when they are arranged in order

perfect square: a number that is the square of a whole number; a polynomial that is the square of another polynomial

perimeter: the distance around a closed figure

perpendicular: intersecting at right angles

perpendicular bisector: the line that is perpendicular to a line segment and divides it in two equal parts
the broken line is the perpendicular bisector of AB

pi (π): the ratio of the circumference of a circle to its diameter; $\pi \doteq 3.1416$

pictograph: a graph in which a symbol represents a certain amount, and repetitions of the symbol illustrate the data

plane geometry: the study of two-dimensional figures; that is, figures drawn or visualized on a plane

point of intersection: a point that lies on two or more figures

polygon: a closed figure that consists of line segments and their end points

polynomial: a mathematical expression with one or more terms, in which the exponents are whole numbers and the coefficients are real numbers

population: the set of all things or people being considered

population density: the average number of people per square kilometre of land

positive number: a number greater than 0

power: an expression of the form a^n, where a is called the base and n is called the exponent; it represents a product of equal factors; for example, $4 \times 4 \times 4$ can be expressed as 4^3

prime number: a whole number with exactly two factors, itself and 1; for example, 3, 5, 7, 11, 29, 31, and 43

prism: a solid that has two congruent and parallel faces (the *bases*), and other faces that are parallelograms

probability: if the outcomes of an experiment are equally likely, then the probability of an event is the ratio of the number of outcomes favourable to the event to the total number of outcomes

proportion: a statement that two ratios are equal

pyramid: a solid that has one face that is a polygon (the *base*), and other faces that are triangles with a common vertex

Pythagorean Theorem: for any right triangle, the area of the square on the hypotenuse is equal to the sum of the areas of the squares on the other two sides

quadrant: one of the four regions into which coordinate axes divide a plane

quadrilateral: a four-sided polygon

quartiles: quarters of the data when they are arranged in order

radius (plural, **radii**): the distance from the centre of a circle to any point on the circumference, or a line segment joining the centre of a circle to any point on the circumference

random numbers: a set of single-digit numbers that are generated such that each number has an equal chance of occurring each time

random sample: a sampling in which all members of the population have an equal chance of being selected

range: the difference between the highest and lowest values (the *extremes*) in a set of data

rate: a certain quantity or amount of one thing considered in relation to a unit of another thing

ratio: a comparison of two or more quantities with the same unit

rational number: a number that can be written in the form $\frac{m}{n}$ where m and n are integers ($n \neq 0$)

real numbers: the set of rational numbers and the set of irrational numbers; that is, all numbers that can be expressed as decimals

reciprocals: two numbers whose product is 1; for example, $\frac{3}{4}$ and $\frac{4}{3}$ are reciprocals, 2 and $\frac{1}{2}$ are reciprocals

rectangle: a quadrilateral that has four right angles

rectangular prism: a prism that has rectangular faces

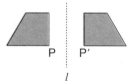

rectangular pyramid: a pyramid with a rectangular base

reflection: a transformation that maps every point P onto an image point P′ such that P and P′ are equidistant from line l, and line PP′ is perpendicular to line l

reflex angle: an angle between 180° and 360°

regular hexagon: a polygon that has six equal sides and six equal angles

regular octagon: a polygon that has eight equal sides and eight equal angles

regular polygon: a polygon that has all sides equal and all angles equal

relative frequency: of an outcome of an experiment is the ratio of the number of times the outcome occurred to the number of times the experiment was conducted

rhombus: a parallelogram with four equal sides

right angle: a 90° angle

right circular cone: a cone in which a line segment from the centre of the circular base to the vertex is perpendicular to the base

right triangle: a triangle that has one right angle

rise: the difference in elevation of two points; the difference between the *y*-coordinates of two points

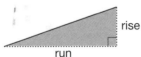

rotation: a transformation in which the points of a figure are turned about a fixed point

rotational symmetry: a figure that maps onto itself in less than one full turn is said to have rotational symmetry; for example, a square has rotational symmetry about its centre O

run: the difference between the *x*-coordinates of two points

sample/sampling: a representative portion of a population

scale: the ratio of the distance between two points on a map, model, or diagram to the distance between the actual locations; the numbers on the axes of a graph

scale factor: the ratio of corresponding lengths on two similar figures

scalene triangle: a triangle with no two sides equal

scientific notation: a number expressed as the product of a number greater than −10 and less than −1 or greater than 1 and less than 10, and a power of 10; for example, 4700 is written as 4.7×10^3

semicircle: half a circle

sharing principle: when two equal expressions are divided by the same number, the results will be equal

similar figures: they have the same shape, but not necessarily the same size

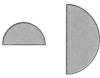

slope: the steepness of a line or line segment; the ratio of the rise of a line or line segment to its run

sphere: the set of all points in space that are a given distance from a fixed point, the centre

spherical geometry: a study of figures drawn or visualized on the surface of a sphere

spherical triangle: a triangle drawn or visualized on the surface of a sphere

spreadsheet: a computer-generated arrangement of data in rows and columns

square: a quadrilateral with equal sides and equal angles

square of a binomial: the product of a binomial multiplied by itself

square of a number: the product of a number multiplied by itself; for example, 25 is the square of 5

square root: a number which, when multiplied by itself, results in a given number; for example, 5 and −5 are the square roots of 25

statistics: the branch of mathematics that deals with the collection, organization, and interpretation of data

stem-and-leaf diagram: a way to represent data; for two-digit values, the tens digits are shown as the stem and the ones digits as the leaves; see page 62

straight angle: an angle measuring 180°

symmetrical: possessing symmetry; see *line symmetry* and *rotational symmetry*

term: of a fraction is the numerator or the denominator of the fraction
when an expression is written as the sum of several quantities, each quantity is called a term of the expression

tessellation: a tiling pattern

tetrahedron: a solid with four triangular faces

transformation: a mapping of the points of a figure that results in a change in position, shape, size, or appearance of the figure; for example, translations, rotations, reflections, and dilations are transformations

translation: a transformation that moves a point or a figure in a straight line to another position in the same plane

transversal: a line crossing two or more lines

trapezoid: a quadrilateral that has only one pair of parallel sides

tree diagram: a branching diagram used to show all possible outcomes of an experiment; see page 102

triangular number: a natural number that can be represented by arranging objects in a triangle; for example, 1, 3, 6, 10, 15,...

10

trinomial: a polynomial with three terms; for example, $3x^2 + 6x + 9$

unit fraction: a fraction that has a numerator of 1

unlike terms: terms that have different variables, or the same variable but different exponents; for example, $3x$, $-4y$ and $3x^2$, $-3x$

variable: a letter or symbol representing a quantity that can vary

vertex (plural, **vertices**): the corner of a figure or a solid

volume: the amount of space occupied by an object

whole number: the set of numbers 0, 1, 2, 3,...

x-axis: the horizontal number line on a coordinate grid

x-intercept: the x-coordinate of the point where a line or curve crosses the x-axis

y-axis: the vertical number line on a coordinate grid

y-intercept: the y-coordinate of the point where a line or curve crosses the y-axis

zero principle: the sum of opposites is zero

Monte Carlo methods, 105
Muller, Kurt, 289
Multiple, 116
Multiplicative inverse, 225

Nanometre, 188
National debt clock, 174
Natural numbers, 200, 202
Neutron, 123
Nielsen ratings, 82, 83
Nonillion, 188
Non-repeating decimal, 200, 202, 282
Novemdecillion, 188
Nucleus, 123
Number line, 126
Number properties, 225

Obtuse angle, 414, 419
Octagon, 282
Octillion, 188
Octodecillion, 188
Odometer, 246, 466
One-tile, 221, 366
Opposite angles, 416, 455
Opposite polynomials, 372
Opposite tiles, 221, 222, 226, 372
Opposites principle, 232
Order of operations, 140
Order properties, 225
Outcome(s), 90
    equally-likely, 95
Output number, 460

Parallel lines, 414, 424, 455
Parallelogram, 414
Pascal, Blaise, 108
Pedal gears, 278, 316
Pei, I.M., 415
Pentagon, 420
People meter, 82
Percent, 39–41, 270–273
Percentiles, 75
Perfect square, 116, 191

Perimeter
    of a rectangle, 321
    of a square, 321
Periodic table, 123
Perpendicular bisector
    of a chord, 437
Perpendicular lines, 414
Petametre, 188
Pi (π), 282, 284, 286
Picometre, 188
Placeholder, 129, 184
Plane geometry, 453
Poggendorf effect, 77
Polygon, 420
Polynomial(s), 366–409
    definition, 367
    in ascending powers, 375
    opposite, 372
Population, 78
Population density, 275, 291
Population growth, 384–387
Powers, 116, 170, 171
    dividing, 177–179
    multiplying, 176, 178
    of 2, 182
    powers of powers, 177, 179
    with the same base, 178
Prime number, 116, 371
Probability, 95
Proportions, 294–299, 349
Proton, 123, 187
Pythagoras, 194
Pythagorean Theorem, 194, 195, 197, 283, 348, 349, 354, 428, 429, 438

Quadrilateral, 145, 420
Quadrillion, 188
Quartile, 72
Quattuordecillion, 188
Quindecillion, 188
Quintillion, 188

Radar gun, 306, 307
Radical sign, 191
Rand, Mary, 482

Random numbers, 29, 92, 99
Random sample, 79
Range, 72
Rate, 36–38, 42, 43, 287–291
Ratio, 32, 33, 274–277
Rational numbers, 126, 200, 202, 214
    adding, 130
    dividing, 136
    multiplying, 136
    order of operations, 140
    subtracting, 130
Reaction time distance, 66, 277
Real numbers, 201, 203
Reciprocal, 117, 137, 171, 172
Rectangle, 414
Rectangular prism, 354, 357
    volume of, 356
Rectangular pyramid
    edges, 354, 357
    faces, 354, 357
    net of, 358
    slant height of face of, 354
    vertices, 354, 357
    volume of, 354–358
Recursive process, 384–387
Reductions, 309–313
Reed, Nigel, 327
Reflection, 146, 147
Relative frequency, 90, 102
Remote sensing, 300, 301
Repeating decimal, 127, 200, 201
Rhombus, 414
Right circular cone, 351
Right triangle, 194, 414
    a property of, 421
Rise, 143
Riser height, 241
Robertson, Leslie, 415
Roberval, 101
Rosendahl, Heidemarie, 482
Rotation, 146, 147
Rotational symmetry, 147
Rubik, Erno, 161
Rubik's cube, 161
Run, 143

PHOTO CREDITS AND ACKNOWLEDGMENTS

The publisher wishes to thank the following sources for photographs, illustrations, articles, and other materials used in this book. Care has been taken to determine and locate ownership of copyright material used in this text. We will gladly receive information enabling us to rectify any errors or omissions in credits.

p. 25 Canapress Photo Service/ p. 25 "New Math Gives Superstar Albums Sales Advantage" reprinted with permission — the Toronto Star Syndicate/ p. 30 Jack Zehrt/Masterfile (photo manipulation by Jun Park)/ p. 31 Pronk&Associates/ p. 32 David Michael Allen/ p. 34 Reproduced by permission of Dale Seymour Publications./ p. 35 Tony Stone Images/ p. 36 "Costs of foreign mail" reprinted with permission — the Toronto Star Syndicate/ p. 36 David Michael Allen/ p. 37 (left) Glen Allison/Tony Stone Images/ p. 38 "Taco Bell Food Chain Celebrates Opening of 4,000th Location" — The Canadian Press/ p. 38 Pronk&Associates/ p. 39 (top) James Balog/Tony Stone Images/ p. 39 (centre) Canapress Photo Service/ p. 39 (bottom) © Glenn Christianson/Tony Stone Images/ p. 40 "Estimated Percents of Households Using Selected Products" — Globe & Mail/ p. 41 "Canadian Content in NHL" reprinted with permission — the Toronto Star Syndicate/ p. 41 David Michael Allen/ p. 42 (left) Pronk&Associates/ p. 42 (right) Tony Stone Images/ p. 42 (girl) Pronk&Associates/ p. 44 (top) Canapress Photo Service/ p. 45 Canapress Photo Service/ p. 47 "Papers Shrink Pages" John Partridge/Globe & Mail/ p. 48 (left) Pronk&Associates/ p. 48 (right) David Michael Allen/ p. 49 "Milking the Rules to the Smallest Drop" Alan Freeman/Globe & Mail/ p. 52 (top) Courtesy of Trevor Poczynek/ p. 52 (bottom) David Michael Allen (photo manipulation by Jun Park)/ p. 53 "Pennies From Hell: Businesses Starting to Keep the Change" copyright © 1993 by *The New York Times Company*. Reprinted by permission./ p. 53 David Michael Allen/ p. 56 John Foster/Masterfile/ p. 56 (inset) Earth Scenes © E.R. Degginger/ p. 57 (top) Norman Piluke/Tony Stone Images/ p. 57 (bottom) David Michael Allen/ p. 58 Pronk&Associates/ p. 59 David Michael Allen/ p. 59 Used by permission of Statistics Canada/ p. 61 Landslides/ p. 62 David Michael Allen/ p. 63 Pronk&Associates/ p. 64 Lori Adamski Peek/Tony Stone Images/ p. 67 David Michael Allen/ p. 69 Terry Vine/Tony Stone Images (photo manipulation by Jun Park)/ p. 70 Tony Stone Images/ p. 74 (top) Canapress Photo Service/ p. 74 (bottom) © Allsport USA/Rick Stewart/ p. 84 Hi & Lois reprinted with special permission of King Features Syndicate/ p. 85 Used by permission of Ann Landers and Creators Syndicate/ p. 86 "Winter Resort Industry Takes Off" and "Tilting Chart Makes Dividend Growth Look Better" reprinted from *200% of Nothing* by A.K. Dewdney. Copyright © 1993 by A.K. Dewdney. Reprinted by permission of John Wiley & Sons, Inc./ p. 87 The Bettmann Archive/ p. 88 (top & bottom) David Michael Allen/ p. 88 (centre) Canapress Photo Service/ p. 90 David Michael Allen/ p. 93 David Michael Allen/ p. 95 Shoe cartoon reprinted by permission: *Tribune Media Services* / p. 97 David Michael Allen/ p. 99 David Michael Allen/ p. 100 David Michael Allen/ p. 101 (top) © Fred Lyon, Photo Researchers/ p. 102 David Michael Allen/ p. 103 David Michael Allen (photo manipulation by Jun Park)/ p. 106 David Michael Allen/ p. 108 (top) David Michael Allen/ p. 111 David Michael Allen/ p. 112 "Have large feet, will travel south" courtesy of Joan Hardwick/ p. 113 David Michael Allen/ p. 116 (right) Robert Morfey/Tony Stone Images/ p. 116 (bottom right) Robert Morfey/Tony Stone Images/ p. 116 (bottom left) Canapress Photo Service/ p. 117 (top) Dirk Wales/ p. 117 (bottom right) Pronk&Associates/ p. 118 (top left) Daryl Benson/Masterfile/ p. 118 (top right) Mike McCabe/Tony Stone Images/ p. 118 (bottom left) Robert Galbraith/Canapress Photo Service/ p. 118 (bottom right) Cosmo Condina/Tony Stone Images/ p. 119 (top) Barry Rowland/Tony Stone Images/ p. 119 (bottom) Barrett & MacKay/Masterfile/ p. 124 David Michael Allen/ p. 126 Pronk&Associates/ p. 128 *The Guinness Book of Numbers* by Adrian Room. Copyright © Guinness Publishing Limited 1989./ p. 128 (top) David Sutherland/Tony Stone Images/ p. 128 (left) © Will & Deni McIntyre, Photo Researchers/ p. 128 (bottom right) David Hiser/Tony Stone Images/ p. 132 © 1993 Dave G. Houser/ p. 133 Copyright, James H. Karales/Peter Arnold, Inc./ p. 135 Pronk&Associates/ p. 137 David Michael Allen/ p. 138 Earth Scenes © Breck P. Kent/ p. 143 L.J. Lozano/ p. 144 (left) © 1994 S. McVicker/ p. 144 (centre) © Allsport USA/Pascal Rondeau, 1989/ p. 144 (right) Richard Mann/ p. 147 From: INVERSIONS by Scott Kim. Copyright © 1989 by Scott Kim. Reprinted with permission of W.H. Freeman and Company./ p. 154 Pronk&Associates/ p. 156 Reprinted with permission from *Canadian Geographic* / p. 156 (left) Bill Brooks/Masterfile/ p. 156 (right) Roy Ooms/Masterfile/ p. 160 (top) © 1990 Roger Ressmeyer — Starlight/ p. 160 (bottom left & right) Courtesy of Paul Ehrlich, Dept. of Biological Science, Stanford University/ p. 160 (inset top left) Courtesy of Jacqueline Hewitt/ p. 160 (inset top right) Courtesy of John Tonry/ p. 161 (right) Pronk&Associates/ p. 161 (left) Reuters/Bettmann/ p. 163 David Michael Allen/ p. 164 (top) Canada Post Corporation/ p. 166 Animals Animals © Donna Aitkenhead/ p. 167 Jacques Jangoux/Tony Stone Images/ p. 173 (left) *The Toronto Star* /T. Bock/ p. 173 (right) David Michael Allen (photo manipulation by Jun Park)/ p. 174 (left) Reuters/Bettmann/ p. 174 (right) David Michael Allen (photo manipulation by Jun Park)/ p. 177 Paul Eckoff/ p. 180 Ken Biggs/Tony Stone Images/ p. 181 Courtesy of NASA/Finley Holiday/ p. 183 Reuters/Bettmann/ p. 184 K. Iwasaki/Masterfile/ p. 185 © 1993 Roger Ressmeyer — Starlight/ p. 187 "The Year 1991 in Science" by Bob Berman. Copyright © 1992 *Discover Magazine*./ p. 189 "Empire of the Ants" by E.O. Wilson. Copyright © 1990 *Discover Magazine*./ p. 190 Sherman Hines/Masterfile/ p. 194 David Michael Allen/ p. 195 (top) L.J. Lozano/ p. 195 (bottom) © Moredum Animal Health Ltd./Science Photo Library/Photo Researchers/ p. 198 Pronk&Associates/ p. 199 David Michael Allen/ p. 203 David Michael Allen/ p. 204 (right) © Jonathan Watts/Science Photo Library/Photo Researchers/ p. 204 (left) Peter Cade/Tony Stone Images/ p. 206 NASA/ p. 207 (top) K. Iwasaki/Masterfile/ p. 207 (centre & bottom) Courtesy of NASA/Finley Holiday/ p. 211 (left) © Fred Sharp/SHARP IMAGES/ p. 211 (right) Pronk&Associates/ p. 212 Pronk&Associates/ p. 218 David Michael Allen/ p. 220 David Michael Allen/ p. 229 Pronk&Associates/ p. 231 David Michael Allen/ p. 235 Pronk&Associates/ p. 237 Photos courtesy of Tourism Regina/ p. 238–239 Pete Turner/The Image Bank Canada (photo manipulation by Jun Park)/ p. 240 Pronk&Associates/ p. 240 (stairs) special thanks to Linear Wood Products Inc./ p. 245 Pronk&Associates/ p. 246 (top left) Pronk&Associates/ p. 246 (centre, bottom left, right) David Michael Allen/ p. 247 Pronk&Associates/ p. 248 David Michael Allen/ p. 249 David Michael Allen/ p. 250 © Telegraph Colour Library/V.C.L./Masterfile/ p. 251 Don Landwehrle/The Image Bank Canada/ p. 252 Pronk&Associates/ p. 254 (right) Bill Ivy/ p. 254 (left) *The Hamilton Spectator* / p. 258 (top) Lynn M. Stone/The Image Bank Canada/ p. 258 (bottom) Pronk&Associates/ p. 259 (top) A. de Cruz/Masterfile/ p. 259 (bottom) David Michael Allen/ p. 261 Pronk&Associates/ p. 264 David Michael Allen/ p. 265 David Michael Allen/ p. 268 Pronk&Associates/ p. 269 (top) John Edwards/Tony Stone Images/ p. 269 (bottom) David Michael Allen/ p. 270 (bottom) Canapress Photo Service/ p. 270 (top) Pronk&Associates/ p. 272 (right) Copyright, Henry Groskinsky/Peter Arnold, Inc./ p. 272 (left) Copyright, Clyde

H. Smith/Peter Arnold, Inc./p.**273** Don Smetzer/Tony Stone Images/ p.**274** Jeffrey Aaronson/Network Aspen/p.**275** Copyright, Vic Cox/Peter Arnold, Inc./p.**276** Science Photo Library/p.**277** David Michael Allen/ p.**278** David Michael Allen (photo manipulation by Jun Park)/p.**279** Dennis O'Clair/Tony Stone Images/p.**280** Walter Schmid/Tony Stone Images/p.**281–282** Pronk&Associates/p.**283** David Michael Allen/p.**284** (top) David Michael Allen/p.**286** Alan Porter/Focused Images/p.**286** Reprinted by permission: *Tribune Media Services*/p.**288** Photos: Ford of Canada/p.**290** David Michael Allen/p.**291** Air Canada/p.**292** (top) David Michael Allen/p.**294** L.J. Lozano/p.**295** Copyright, Vic Cox/Peter Arnold, Inc./p.**297** Pronk&Associates/p.**298** (left) Courtesy of Lesley Barnes/p.**298** (top right) Barrett & MacKay/Ivy Images/p.**298** (bottom right) Animals Animals © W. Gregory Brown/p.**299** Barrett & MacKay/Ivy Images/p.**300** Courtesy of *Advanced Satellite Productions Inc.*, Vancouver, Canada/p.**306** (top) Courtesy of Kustom Signals, Inc./ p.**306** (bottom) Courtesy of Tribar Industries Inc./p.**309** David Woodfall/Tony Stone Images/p.**310** (top) Canadian Museum of Civilization/ p.**310** (bottom) Penny Tweedie/Tony Stone Images/p.**312** Copyright, Kevin Schafer/Peter Arnold, Inc./p.**313** © David Young-Wolff/Tony Stone Images/p.**314** (left) © G.W. Willis, MD/Biological Photo Service/p.**314** (right) © USDA/Science Source/Photo Researchers/ p.**315** David Scharf Photography/p.**317** Lotus Engineering/p.**323** (left) Pronk&Associates/p.**323** (right) David Michael Allen/p.**324** Dennis O'Clair/Tony Stone Images/p.**325** (top & bottom) Pronk&Associates/ p.**325** (centre) Abitibi Price/p.**326** Copyright, David Smiley/Peter Arnold, Inc./p.**327** David Michael Allen/p.**328–329** Pronk&Associates (photo manipulation by Jun Park)/p.**330** (left) Pronk&Associates/p.**330** (right) David Michael Allen/p.**331** Pronk&Associates/p.**332** © 1984 Ron Sherman Photography/p.**334** David Michael Allen/p.**335** Charlie Waite/Tony Stone Images/p.**336–337** Pronk&Associates (photo manipulation by Jun Park)/p.**340** (top) © 1980 U.S.G.S., Flagstaff, Arizona — Starlight/p.**340** (bottom) Pronk&Associates/p.**341** Pronk&Associates/ p.**343** © 1994 M.C. Escher/Cordon Art — Baarn — Holland. All rights reserved./p.**344** Copyright, Matt Meadows/Peter Arnold, Inc./p.**345** David Michael Allen/p.**346** Nicholas DeVore/Tony Stone Images/ p.**346** (inset) © Gerard Vandystadt, Photo Researchers/p.**347** Animals Animals © Jack Wilburn/p.**348** Pronk&Associates/p.**350** Copyright, 1985, Werner H. Muller/Peter Arnold, Inc./p.**350** (inset) David Michael Allen/p.**351** Pronk&Associates/p.**352** Pronk&Associates/p.**353** Pronk&Associates/p.**354** (top right) Jean-Marc Truchet/Tony Stone Images/p.**354** (top left) David Sutherland/ Tony Stone Images/p.**354** (bottom) Pronk&Associates/p.**355** Pronk&Associates/p.**356** Cosmo Condina/Tony Stone Images/p.**357** Jean-Marc Truchet/Tony Stone Images/ p.**358** © John Sutton/Photo Search Ltd./p.**360** (right) © 1990 Roger Ressmeyer — Starlight/p.**360** (left) Pronk&Associates (photo manipulation by Jun Park)/p.**361** Pronk&Associates (photo manipulation by Jun Park)/p.**364** David Michael Allen/p.**365** David Michael Allen/ p.**366** David Michael Allen/p.**375** (top) David E. Myers/Tony Stone Images/p.**376** Pronk&Associates/p.**376** Courtesy of Recycled Paper Greetings/p.**384** Copyright, Ed Reschke/Peter Arnold, Inc./p.**385** (top) Copyright, Ed Reschke/Peter Arnold, Inc./p.**385** (bottom) © John M. Burnley, Photo Researchers/p.**386** & **387** Copyright, Ed Reschke/Peter Arnold, Inc./p.**389** Albert Klein/p.**393** Michael Salas/The Image Bank Canada/p.**397** (top) Johan Elzenga/Tony Stone Images/p.**397** (bottom) Pronk&Associates/p.**398** Pronk&Associates/p.**399** David Michael Allen/p.**410** (top) Courtesy of Marsha Falco/p.**410** (bottom) David Michael Allen/p.**411** David Michael Allen/p.**414** (top) Skidmore, Owings & Merrill/p.**414** (bottom) Kunio Owaki/Masterfile/p.**415** (top left)

Phil Huber/Black Star/p.**415** (bottom left) Leslie E. Robertson & Associates/p.**415** (top right) Aliza Auerbach/p.**415** (bottom right) J.A. Kraulis/Masterfile/p.**416** Pronk&Associates/p.**417** Pronk&Associates/ p.**421** (top left & bottom) Pronk&Associates/p.**421** (top right) David Michael Allen/p.**422** & **423** The Geometer's Sketchpad, Key Curriculum Press, P.O. Box 2304, Berkeley, CA 94702, 1-800-338-7638/ p.**423** L.J. Lozano/p.**424** Pronk&Associates/p.**427** David Michael Allen/ p.**430** (centre & bottom) Pronk&Associates/p.**430** (top) Courtesy of SCIENCE WORLD British Columbia/p.**431** Pronk&Associates/p.**434** Pronk&Associates/p.**435** Bob Alexander/p.**437** Pronk&Associates/p.**441** Reprinted with permission from *Satellite Images: Photographs of Canada from Space* by Brian Banks, Camden House Publishing. Photo by Canada Centre for Remote Sensing./p.**442** Pronk&Associates/ p.**443** Pronk&Associates/p.**447** Mike Dobel/Masterfile/p.**448** The Geometer's Sketchpad, Key Curriculum Press, P.O. Box 2304, Berkeley, CA 94702, 1-800-338-7638/p.**450** Perry Zavitz (photo manipulation by Jun Park)/p.**450** The Globe & Mail/p.**451** Pronk&Associates/ p.**453** (top & centre) Pronk&Associates/p.**454** Pronk&Associates/p.**458** (left) National Archives of Canada/p.**458–459** David Michael Allen (photo manipulation by Jun Park)/p.**461** Nick Boothman/Masterfile/ p.**462** Courtesy of NASA/Finley Holiday/p.**464** David Michael Allen/ p.**466** L.J. Lozano/p.**467** Pronk&Associates/p.**469** Pronk&Associates/ p.**472** Pronk&Associates/p.**478** Photo courtesy of General Motors/ p.**480** David Michael Allen/p.**482** (left) © 1988 Allsport USA/Gray Mortimore/p.**482** (right) © 1993 Allsport USA/Gray Mortimore/p.**483** © 1990 Allsport USA/Gray Mortimore/p.**484** Pronk&Associates/p.**486** L.J. Lozano

Digital photo retouching and manipulation by Jun Park.

ILLUSTRATIONS

Steve Attoe, **46**, **50**, **68**, **78–79**, **105**, **112**, **131**, **139**, **171**, **176**, **177** (top), **182**, **187**, **191**, **349**, **370**, **402**
Michel Garneau, **117** (bottom left)
Don Gauthier, **47**
Bob Hambly, **22–23**
Stephen Harris, **155**, **157**, **292** (bottom)
Michael Herman, **24**, **38**, **98**, **170**, **213**, **216** (top left), **220** (top left), **316**, **320**, **321**, **322**, **375** (bottom)
Heather Holbrook, **160** (bottom left)
Bernadette Lau, **189**
Margo Davies Leclair/Visual Sense Illustration, **152–153**
Jack McMaster, **210** (left)
Ted Nasmith, **228**, **311**, **361** (right), **455**, **465**
Martha Newbigging, **27**, **29**, **37** (right), **44** (bottom), **82–83**, **140**, **162**, **164** (bottom), **165**, **168–169**, **188**, **210** (top right), **230**, **231** (left), **269** (centre), **305**, **365** (bottom), **475**, **487**
Jun Park, **232**, **296**, **338–339**
Pronk&Associates, **248–249**, **313** (top)
Margo Stahl, **129**, **179**
Tracy Walker, **72**

Technical art (Answers section) by Margo Davies Leclair/Visual Sense Illustration.